TRITIUM AND ITS COMPOUNDS

TRITIUM
and its Compounds

E. Anthony Evans

B.Sc. Ph.D.(Lond.), A.R.C.S., D.I.C., A.R.I.C.

Principal Scientific Officer, Organic Dept., U.K.A.E.A.,
Radiochemical Centre, Amersham

D. VAN NOSTRAND COMPANY, INC.

PRINCETON, NEW JERSEY

TORONTO   LONDON

NEW YORK

©
Butterworth & Co. (Publishers) Ltd.
1966

Printed in Great Britain by
Spottiswoode, Ballantyne & Co. Ltd., London and Colchester

FOREWORD

Tritium is an exceptionally interesting nuclide, partly because it is an isotope of hydrogen and duplicates the highly diversified chemistry of that element, and partly because of its unique nuclear properties. Until quite recently the difficulty of measurement restricted its use as a tracer to a few laboratories having the necessary expertise. Modern instrumentation for beta liquid scintillation counting has changed all that, and tritium is rapidly assuming its rightful place as a tracer isotope of major importance.

The low cost, low toxicity, high specific activity, excellent autoradiographic properties and comparative ease of labelling procedures are the obvious reasons for the extensive use of tritium as a tracer. These properties make it certain that this use will continue on an increasing scale for some time to come, an appropriate continuation of the historical tracer work with deuterium initiated by Schoenheimer and Rittenberg. There are, inevitably, some related disadvantages which may lead the unwary user astray. The uncertain stability of a hydrogen isotope in a molecule, and the too familiar instability of highly radioactive organic compounds, are the most obvious.

In this book Dr. E. A. Evans has set out to help anyone interested in tritium, by providing a thorough and extensive survey of published work, made more useful by his critical and well-informed discussions, and by information obtained in the course of his own work at the Radiochemical Centre. Dr. Evans is unusually well qualified to write such a survey. He has acquired his knowledge and opinions in a hard school, producing tritium-labelled compounds for discerning and critical research users. It is moreover an appropriate time for a book on this subject to appear. The body of present knowledge is large enough and sufficiently well established to warrant a thorough review, and it is also growing so rapidly (and attracting so many new workers into the field) that there is a need for a fairly comprehensive primary source for reference.

Dr. Evans has met this need well. I am confident that many readers will, as I have done, derive pleasure and instruction from reading this book, and will find it a useful work of reference for many aspects of knowledge of tritium and its compounds.

JOHN R. CATCH
1965

v

CONTENTS

CONTENTS

ACKNOWLEDGEMENTS

It is with much pleasure that I record grateful thanks to my colleague Dr. John R. Catch for his many helpful suggestions, guidance and encouragement which has made the task of writing this book less difficult than it might have been.

The labours of writing a book may be lightened considerably by the courtesy and willingness of librarians and I thank Mr. B. J. Wilson and Staff of the Radiochemical Centre Library for their unfailing assistance and for carrying out the important but rather laborious task of reference checking.

I thank also other colleagues for their collaboration, and Dr. R. H. Herz and Mr. J. A. G. Clifton (Technical Advisory Department, Kodak Limited, Harrow, Middlesex) for helpful discussions concerning autoradiography.

Publication of this book is sponsored by the United Kingdom Atomic Energy Authority whose support is gratefully acknowledged, and in particular that of Dr. W. P. Grove, Director, Radiochemical Centre.

E. A. E.

INTRODUCTION

Following the discovery of deuterium[1] in ordinary hydrogen and in samples of water concentrated by electrolysis[2,3], it was natural that efforts should be made to discover other isotopes of hydrogen. Two schools vigorously engaged themselves in this problem, one in the United States of America at Princeton University and the other at Cambridge University in Great Britain. The American team looked for hydrogen of mass three in natural sources while the British team studied isotopes produced artificially by nuclear reactions. In March 1934 the Cambridge team led by Rutherford published[4] definite evidence for the existence of a hydrogen isotope of mass three. This was produced by the bombardment of a deuterium target with fast deuterons. The following month Lozier, Smith and Bleakney at Princeton[5] reported finding positive evidence for the existence of hydrogen-3 in natural sources. Both teams thought that the newly discovered hydrogen isotope, called tritium, was stable[6,7]. Earlier spectroscopic investigations[8,9] had failed to provide evidence for the existence of tritium and the detection of tritium in water by the magneto-optic method reported by Latimer and Young[10,11], is now generally regarded as doubtful.

It was several years later in 1938 that observations of the formation of an excited helium-3 in the disintegration of deuterium by accelerated deuterons led Bonner to suggest[12] that tritium may spontaneously disintegrate into helium-3 with the emission of an electron. In September 1939, at the outbreak of World War II, Alvarez and Cornog working at the University of California Radiation Laboratory demonstrated that tritium produced by Rutherford's method was definitely radioactive and had a long half-life[13]. A number of reviews were subsequently published describing this fascinating and exciting work in the search for tritium[14-18].

In the next 15 to 20 years tritium came into use as a radioactive tracer isotope, gradually displacing the stable isotope deuterium. Progress was slow mainly due to the difficulty of measurement, arising from the low energy of the β-particles. There was often some reluctance to work with a radioactive material which is difficult to detect, and deuterium was preferred from this point of view. In 1956 Wilzbach[19] discovered a simple method for labelling compounds

with tritium; this stimulated a new interest in using tritium compounds as tracers, although the method of labelling subsequently
proved less useful than had been hoped. The value of tritium and its
compounds was rapidly recognized and their use was quickly accelerated by new techniques for their measurement[20], particularly
liquid scintillation methods.[21] From 1957 onwards the growth in the
use of tritium and compounds labelled with tritium has been quite
phenomenal and the isotope is proving invaluable in many fields of
study.

This book has been written primarily to guide and encourage the
research worker to examine the many opportunities which tritium
offers as a radioactive tracer. It is not intended as a practical book,
in that readers are referred to original papers for experimental details.
Instead an attempt has been made to illustrate the fundamental
principles of working with tritium rather than to provide a fully
comprehensive review of all aspects of tritium work.

The book is divided into six chapters, the first of which is devoted
to the physical properties and the natural and artificial production of
the isotope. Some of the very many uses of tritium and the great
variety of compounds labelled with tritium are described in Chapter
2. One of the most important aspects of any work with radioisotopes is
safety and Chapter 3 deals with the methods for the safe handling of
tritium and its compounds. A very wide variety of compounds have
been labelled with tritium, ranging from simple molecules such as
water or methane to the more complex organic compounds, for
example vitamin-B_{12}. In Chapter 4 the various methods available for
the preparation of tritium compounds are briefly described. The
measurement of radioactivity and the analysis of labelled compounds
has interested physicists and chemists alike ever since radioactivity
was discovered by Becquerel[22] in 1896. Refinements to existing
methods and new techniques are constantly being published. The
measurement of tritium activity by beta liquid scintillation counting
has proved to be most generally useful; this and other methods are
described in Chapter 5 and the inclusion of a bibliography of tritium
measurement in this chapter will (it is hoped) be most useful to the
reader and perhaps especially to those intending to start work with
tritium compounds. To the user of radioactive tracer compounds,
properties which are peculiar to such compounds are of especial
interest. Such properties include decomposition by self-irradiation,
isotope effects and the stability of the label under the various environments it may encounter. Every isotope has its own set of peculiar
properties and tritium is no exception to this rule, as readers will dis-

cover in Chapter 6. A short note on the nomenclature of tritium compounds is included in this last chapter.

Throughout the book readers will find that most emphasis is placed on tritiated organic compounds, for it is in the use of these labelled compounds in the fields of organic chemistry and biochemistry that the greatest advances have been made. Inorganic tritiated compounds on the other hand are only slowly finding uses, whereas in organic chemistry and biochemistry tracer work using first deuterium and nitrogen-15 and more especially carbon-14 was already well established before 1950[23, 24].

REFERENCES

[1] Urey, H. C., Brickwedde, F. G. and Murphy, G. M. *Phys. Rev.* 39 (1932) 164, 864 (Abstract)

[2] Washburn, E. W. and Urey, H. C. *Proc. natn. Acad. Sci. U.S.A.* 18 (1932) 496

[3] Kendall, J. and Crittenden, E. D. *Proc. natn. Acad. Sci. U.S.A.* 9 (1923) 75

[4] Oliphant, M. L. E., Harteck, P. and Rutherford, E. *Proc. R. Soc.* 144A (1934) 692

[5] Lozier, W. W., Smith, P. T. and Bleakney, W. *Phys. Rev.* 45 (1934) 655

[6] Bleakney, W., Harnwell, G. P., Lozier, W. W., Smith, P. T. and Smyth, H. D. *Phys. Rev.* 46 (1934) 81

[7] Oliphant, M. L. E., Kempton, A. E. and Rutherford, E. *Proc. R. Soc.* 150A (1935) 241

[8] Lewis, G. N. and Spedding, F. H. *Phys. Rev.* 43 (1933) 964

[9] Bleakney, W. and Gould, A. J. *Phys. Rev.* 45 (1934) 281

[10] Latimer, W. M. and Young, H. A. *Phys. Rev.* 44 (1933) 690

[11] Allison, F. *Phys. Rev.* 30 (1927) 66

[12] Bonner, T. W. *Phys. Rev.* 53 (1938) 711

[13] Alvarez, L. W. and Cornog, R. *Phys. Rev.* 56 (1939) 613

[14] Eidinoff, M. L. *J. chem. Educ.* 25 (1948) 31

[15] Rutherford, E. *Nature, Lond.* 140 (1937) 303

[16] Aivazov, B. V. and Neiman, M. B. *Usp. fiz. Nauk* 36 (1948) 145

[17] Chernyaev, V. I. *Usp. fiz. Nauk* 21 (1939) 466

[18] Baskinski, A. *Wiad. chem.* 2 (1948) 127

[19] Wilzbach, K. E. *Chem. Engng News* 34 (1956) 4616

[20] Glascock, R. F. *Isotopic Gas Analysis for Biochemists* 1954. New York; Academic Press

[21] Rosenthal, D. J. and Anger, H. O. *Univ. Calif. Radiat. Lab. Rep.* UCRL–2320 (1953)

[22] Becquerel, H. *C. r. hebd. Séanc. Acad. Sci., Paris* 122 (1896) 420, 501

[23] Catch, J. R. *Carbon-14 Compounds* 1961. London; Butterworths

[24] Calvin, M., Heidelberger, C., Reid, J. C., Tolbert, B. M. and Yankwich, P. F. *Isotopic Carbon* 1949. New York; Wiley

CHAPTER 1

PHYSICAL PROPERTIES AND PRODUCTION

There are now three well-known isotopes of hydrogen namely:

^{1}H, hydrogen or protium (stable)
^{2}H, deuterium or 'heavy hydrogen' (stable)
^{3}H, tritium (radioactive)

The existence of two other hydrogen isotopes of mass four and five has recently been reported[1,2]. Argan, Bendiscioli, Piazzoli and colleagues at the Frascati Laboratories in Italy[3,4] reported the discovery of hydrogen-4 which is very unstable and quickly breaks down to tritium and a neutron (1.1):

$$\gamma + {}^4\text{He} \rightarrow [{}^4\text{H}] \rightarrow {}^3\text{H} + {}^1_0\text{n} \quad \cdots \cdots \quad (1.1)$$

The probable instability of a hydrogen isotope of mass four was predicted by Breit and McIntosh[5] in 1951.

Nefkens in the United States of America, working at Purdue University, Indiana, reported[2,6] the discovery of a hydrogen isotope of mass five. The isotope is like tritium a β-emitter but it has a very short half-life (10^{-1} sec). The energy of the β-radiation is much higher than that of tritium and the maximum energy is greater than 15 MeV.

Because of their very short life both of these newly discovered hydrogen isotopes are unlikely to be of much value as radioactive tracers.

Physical and Radioactive Properties

Tritium is an isotope emitting low-energy pure β-radiation; there are several values reported in the literature for the average energy of the tritium β-particles[7-11]. A value of 5,700 eV is generally accepted[12].

Determination of the maximum energy of the tritium β-particles has also been the subject of numerous publications and a summary of a number of reported values is given in Table 1.1.

The present accepted value for this maximum beta energy is 18·5 keV for use in physical calculations. The decay energy per millicurie

1

of tritium per day amounts to 1.82×10^{16} eV, although the percentage of the beta radiation with energy above 17 keV is only 0·05.

TABLE 1.1

Energy keV	9.5 ± 2	14·5	15 ± 3		11 ± 1	16.9 ± 0.3	17
References	13	8	14		17	18	19
Energy keV	18·6	11 ± 2	18	18·9	18·6	17·9	17·5–19·4
References	20	15, 16	21	22	23	24	25

Half-life—Determination of the decay constant and the half-life have also attracted much attention and a number of reported values for the half-life of tritium are recorded in Table 1.2.

The best values for the half-life have been determined by measuring the accumulation of helium-3 which is produced by the natural decay of tritium (1.2):

$$^3H \rightarrow \ ^3He + \beta^- \qquad \text{. . . .} \quad (1.2)$$

TABLE 1.2

Half-life years	Method of determination	References
31 ± 8	Tritium decay in unit time	26
10.7 ± 2	Ion current measurements	27
12.1 ± 0.5	Helium accumulation	29
12.46 ± 0.2	Helium accumulation	9, 10
12.262 ± 0.004	Helium accumulation	28
$12.41 \pm \left\{ \begin{matrix} 0.15 \\ 0.25 \end{matrix} \right\}$	Absolute calculation	30
12.58 ± 0.18	Decay curve determined calorimetrically	11

The present value accepted as the most accurate for the half-life of tritium is 12·26 years with the radioactive decay constant λ of 1.791×10^{-9} sec^{-1}.

The energy of the tritium β-particles being rather low the penetrating range in matter is consequently also very low reaching a maximum of about 6 mm in air and a mean range of 0·5 mm[31]. The radiation is stopped by about 6 μ (6×10^{-4} cm) of material of unit density, such as water[32]. As the particle range is inversely proportional to the density of the medium, the range of the tritium β-particles in photographic emulsion (density around 3·5) is reduced to only 1 μ. This makes tritium an ideal isotope for use in high-resolution autoradiographic applications which are described in detail in Chapters 2 and 5.

2

Like hydrogen and deuterium, tritium molecules can exist in two forms, namely the ortho- and para-states. Tritium at room temperature is predominantly ortho and is converted into the para-state by adsorption on charcoal at liquid neon or liquid helium temperatures[34]. One interesting feature is the conversion half-time for ortho- to the para-state in the adsorbed and solid state has been observed to be much faster (about 24 times) than the similar conversion of hydrogen molecules[34].

A few calculated[33] physical properties of tritium are recorded in Table 1.3.

TABLE 1.3

Critical temperature	$43.7° K$
Critical pressure	20.8 atm
Critical volume	53.7 cm³/mole
Heat of vaporization	316 cal/mole
Molecular volume	18.6 cm³/mole
Triple-point volume of liquid	21.9 cm³/mole
Triple-point volume of solid	19.24 cm³/mole
Triple-point pressure	0.248 atm
Inversion temperature	$87° K$

The density of liquid tritium over the temperature range $20.6° K$ to $29° K$ has been reported by Grilly[35].

Natural Occurrence

Tritium arises in nature both by natural and artificial processes. Natural tritium was first detected in the atmospheric hydrogen by Faltings and Harteck[36] and was later shown to be present in rainwater by Libby and his collaborators[37].

Prior to the testing of thermonuclear weapons in 1954, the amount of this natural tritium on the earth was calculated to be about 900 g[38] which in terms of radioactivity is approximately 9 million curies. This tritium is the result of nuclear reactions induced by cosmic radiation in the upper atmosphere, where fast neutrons, protons and deuterons collide with molecules to produce tritium. Examples of such reactions are given in the equations (1.3) to (1.5):

$$^{14}_{7}N + ^{1}_{0}n \rightarrow ^{3}_{1}H + ^{12}_{6}C \qquad \ldots \ldots (1.3)$$

$$^{14}_{7}N + ^{1}_{1}H \rightarrow ^{3}_{1}H + \text{fragments} \qquad \ldots \ldots (1.4)$$

$$^{2}_{1}H + ^{2}_{1}H \rightarrow ^{3}_{1}H + ^{1}_{1}H \qquad \ldots \ldots (1.5)$$

The energetic tritium atoms (tritons) produced in these reactions are incorporated into water molecules, by exchange or oxidation (1·6), and the tritium falls onto the earth's surface as rain-water.

$$_{1}^{3}\text{H} \quad \xrightarrow[\text{exchange}]{\text{oxidation}} \quad \begin{array}{l} _{1}^{3}\text{H}_{2}\text{O} \\ _{1}^{3}\text{H}_{1}^{1}\text{HO} \quad + \quad _{1}^{1}\text{H} \end{array}$$

$$\ldots \ldots (1.6)$$

Rutherford missed finding tritium in natural water during the search for hydrogen-3 because, not realizing that tritium was a radioactive isotope, he examined his electrolytically enriched samples with a mass spectrometer which was not sufficiently sensitive to detect the very small amount of tritium present. Subsequent re-examination of Rutherford's sample by Libby at the University of Chicago proved the sample radioactive, due to the presence of natural tritium.

Evaporation neutron spectra and fast neutron spectra have been used to calculate the mean rate of production of tritium in the atmosphere by cosmic radiation [39]. A value of $0·12$ tritium atoms $cm^{-2}sec^{-1}$ is reported whereas the production of tritium in stars is $0·24$ atoms $cm^{-2}sec^{-1}$.

In samples of rain-water taken before March 1954, the tritium originated very largely from cosmic radiation. Since this time, which marks the beginning of thermonuclear-weapon testing, a very large quantity of tritium has been injected into the atmosphere. This has resulted in a sharp rise in the tritium content of rain-water from a level of $0·5$ to 5 'tritium units' [37, 40] to values as high as 500 tritium units [41]. (1 Tritium unit, denoted 1 T.U., equals a ratio of 1 tritium atom to 10^{18} atoms of hydrogen. In terms of actual radioactivity 1 T.U. is about $3·3 \times 10^{-9}$ $\mu c/ml$. of water, or approximately $7d.p.m./l$.)

An unforeseen consequence of nuclear-weapon testing has been to provide geophysicists with experimental evidence on the movement of water in the atmosphere and in the oceans [42-50]. The tritium content of meteorites has also been of interest and provides further valuable information relating to atmospheric tritium [51-54, 58, 59].

The presence of significant amounts of tritium in atmospheric methane [55, 57] is attributed to thermonuclear-weapon testing [56, 57], rather than to natural processes.

Artificial Production

There are many nuclear reactions which can be used to produce tritium artificially. Historically the first such reaction to be recognized was the $D(d,n)^3H$ reaction which is also accompanied by the reaction $D(d,n)^3He$. The bombardment of certain other elements with deuterium, for example boron, copper[60] or fluorine[61], also give rise to tritium. In the cyclotron tritium can readily be produced by the bombardment of a beryllium target with deuterons[62] reaction 1.7:

$$^9Be + {}^2H \rightarrow {}^8Be + {}^3H \qquad . \quad . \quad . \quad . \quad (1.7)$$

In 1935 experiments with the Wilson cloud-chamber showed that collisions between neutrons and lithium led to the nuclear reaction 1.8:

$$^6Li + {}_0^1n \rightarrow {}^4He + {}^3H \qquad . \quad . \quad . \quad . \quad (1.8)$$

The helium and tritium atoms are ejected in opposite directions with ranges of 20 and 65 mm respectively in air at atmospheric pressure[63, 64]. These early experiments formed the basis for the method now adopted for the production of tritium.

On the large scale tritium is prepared in a reactor by the irradiation of enriched lithium-6, usually in the form of an alloy with magnesium[65, 66] or aluminium[67]. As a result of the n, α reaction which occurs, tritium is produced, of which some escapes and some is retained as the metal tritide. Treatment of the alloy with acid then liberates the tritium. The helium-3 which is the natural decay product of tritium also undergoes a nuclear reaction 1.9 and is converted into tritium and hydrogen[68, 69].

$$^3He + {}_0^1n \rightarrow {}^3H + {}^1H \qquad . \quad . \quad . \quad . \quad (1.9)$$

The separation and concentration of the tritium may be accomplished by thermal diffusion and helium-3 removed by the differential adsorption of the gases on charcoal at liquid nitrogen temperatures ($-196°$ C)[70]. A recently described process[71] produces tritium by the neutron irradiation of lithium fluoride at $450°$ C *in vacuo*. The tritium is recovered from the gaseous products by passage through a palladium barrier.

Because of the military importance of tritium, details for large-scale production of this isotope have not been published.

Tritium can be obtained isotopically pure and is conveniently stored by adsorption on pyrophoric uranium[72] from which it can be liberated by heating the uranium to temperatures in excess of $400°$ C.

Reactor-irradiated samples of natural lithium fluoride have been suggested as convenient sources of small (millicurie) amounts of tritium for tracer use[74]. The irradiated lithium fluoride is heated for 15 min at its melting point ($870°$ C) to liberate the tritium. However, for most practical purposes tritium gas is usually obtained

5

commercially in glass 'break-seal' type ampoules which avoids any need for heating.

The Weight of 1 c of Tritium and the Maximum attainable Specific Activity

The availability of isotopically pure tritium provides raw material for the production of tritium compounds at very high specific activities. The maximum attainable specific activity and the weight of 1 c of tritium are derived by a simple calculation as follows:

For a simple radioactive decay process

$$-\frac{\mathrm{d}N}{\mathrm{d}t} = \lambda N$$

where λ is the radioactive decay constant and $\mathrm{d}N/\mathrm{d}t$ is the rate of disintegration when N active atoms are present. If T is the half-life of the radioactive nuclide, then

$$\lambda = \frac{0\cdot693}{T}$$

hence

$$-\frac{\mathrm{d}N}{\mathrm{d}t} = \frac{0\cdot693}{T}N$$

By definition, one millicurie is the amount of radioactive material producing $3\cdot7 \times 10^7$ disintegrations/sec. For tritium $T = 12\cdot26$ years thus

$$3\cdot7 \times 10^7 = \frac{0\cdot693\ N}{12\cdot26 \times 365 \times 24 \times 3,600}$$

where N is now the number of tritium atoms equivalent to 1 mc

$$N = \frac{3\cdot7 \times 10^7 \times 12\cdot26 \times 365 \times 24 \times 3,600}{0\cdot693}$$

$$= 2\cdot07 \times 10^{16}\ \text{atoms/mc}$$

The number of atoms per gram-atom (Avogadro's number) is

$$6\cdot02 \times 10^{23}$$

hence the weight of tritium equivalent to 1 c

$$= \frac{2\cdot07 \times 10^{16} \times 3 \times 10^3}{6\cdot02 \times 10^{20}}$$

$$= 0\cdot103\ \text{mg}$$

A millimole of tritium will thus have an activity

$$= \frac{6 \times 1}{0\cdot103}$$

$$= 58\cdot25\ \text{c}$$

6

In any hydrogen-containing compound therefore, the replacement of one hydrogen atom with a tritium atom will result in the compound having a specific activity of $29 \cdot 12$ c/mM. Using tritium of 100 per cent isotopic purity it is possible to prepare many compounds at a very high specific activity and methods for doing this are described in Chapter 4.

To conclude this chapter a comparison of some of the properties cf tritium with other pure β-emitting isotopes is shown[73] in Table 1.4.

TABLE 1.4

Isotope	Mass	Maximum β-energy MeV	Half-life	Production process
TRITIUM	3	0·018	12·26 years	$^6\text{Li}(n, \alpha)^3\text{H}$
Ruthenium	106	0·039	1 year	$\text{U}(n,f) \rightarrow {}^{106}\text{Ru}$
Nickel	63	0·067	125 years	$^{62}\text{Ni}(n, \gamma)^{63}\text{Ni}$
Carbon	14	0·159	5,760 years	$^{14}\text{N}(n, p)^{14}\text{C}$
Sulphur	35	0·167	87·2 days	$^{35}\text{Cl}(n, p)^{35}\text{S}$; $^{34}\text{S}(n, \gamma)^{35}\text{S}$
Promethium	147	0·22	2·6 years	$\text{U}(n,f) \rightarrow {}^{147}\text{Pm}$
				$^{146}\text{Nd}(n,\gamma)^{147}\text{Nd} \xrightarrow[11 \cdot 1 \text{ days}]{\beta} {}^{147}\text{Pm}$
Calcium	45	0·25	165 days	$^{44}\text{Ca}(n, \gamma)^{45}\text{Ca}$
Phosphorus	33	0·25	25 days	$^{33}\text{S}(n, p)^{33}\text{P}$
Rubidium	87	0·275	5×10^{10} years	Natural abundance 27·85%
Technetium	99	0·29	$2 \cdot 12 \times 10^5$ years	$\text{U}(n,f) \rightarrow {}^{99}\text{Tc}$
				$^{98}\text{Mo}(n, \gamma)^{99}\text{Mo} \xrightarrow[67 \text{ h}]{\beta} {}^{99}\text{Tc}$
Erbium	169	0·34	9·4 days	$^{168}\text{Er}(n, \gamma)^{169}\text{Er}$
Tin	121	0·38	28 h	$^{120}\text{Sn}(n, \gamma)^{121}\text{Sn}$
Tungsten	185	0·43	73 days	$^{184}\text{W}(n, \gamma)^{185}\text{W}$
Strontium	90	0·54	28 years	$\text{U}(n,f) \rightarrow {}^{90}\text{Sr}$
Chlorine	36	0·714	$3 \cdot 03 \times 10^5$ years	$^{35}\text{Cl}(n, \gamma)^{36}\text{Cl}$
Thallium	204	0·77	3·9 years	$^{203}\text{Tl}(n, \gamma)^{204}\text{Tl}$
Praseodymium	143	0·93	13·8 days	$^{142}\text{Ce}(n, \gamma)^{143}\text{Ce} \xrightarrow[33 \text{ h}]{\beta} {}^{143}\text{Pr}$
Phosphorus	32	1·71	14·3 days	$^{31}\text{P}(n, \gamma)^{32}\text{P}$; $^{32}\text{S}(n, p)^{32}\text{P}$
Scandium	49	2·0	37 min	$^{48}\text{Ca}(n, \gamma)^{49}\text{Ca} \xrightarrow[8 \cdot 8 \text{ min}]{\beta} {}^{49}\text{Sc}$
Yttrium	90	2·25	64·2 h	$^{89}\text{Y}(n, \gamma)^{90}\text{Y}$

REFERENCES

[1] New Scient. 17 (1963) 587
[2] New Scient. 17 (1963) 534
[3] Argan, P. E., Bendiscioli, G., Piazzoli, A., Bisi, V., Ferrero, M. I. and Piragino, G. CNEN notiziario 8 (12) (1962) 85 (Short Press Note)
[4] Argan, P. E. and Piazzoli, A. Physics Lett. 4(1963) 350
[5] Breit, G. and McIntosh, J. S. Phys. Rev. 83 (1951) 1245
[6] Nefkens, B. M. K. Phys. Rev. Lett. 10 (1963) 55
[7] Alvarez, L. and Cornog, R. Phys. Rev. 57 (1940) 248 (Abstract)

REFERENCES

[8] Nielsen, C. E. *Phys. Rev.* 60 (1941) 160 (Abstract)

[9] Jenks, G. H., Ghormley, J. A. and Sweeton, F. H. *Phys. Rev.* 75 (1949) 701

[10] Jenks, G. H., Sweeton, F. H. and Ghormley, J. A. *Phys. Rev.* 80 (1950) 990

[11] Popov, M. M., Gargarinskii, I. V., Senin, M. D., Mikhalenko, I. P. and Morozov, I. M. *Soviet J. atom. Energy* 4 (1958) 393

[12] Pillinger, W. L., Hentges, J. J. and Blair, J. A. *Phys. Rev.* 121 (1961) 232

[13] Brown, S. C. *Phys. Rev.* 59 (1941) 954

[14] O'Neal, R. D. *Phys. Rev.* 60 (1941) 359

[15] Watts, R. J. and Williams, D. *Phys. Rev.* 70 (1946) 640

[16] Konopinski, E. J. *Phys. Rev.* 72 (1947) 518

[17] Byatt, W. J., Rogers, F. T. and Waltner, A. *Phys. Rev.* 74 (1948) 699

[18] Curran, S. C., Angus, J. and Cockcroft, A. L. *Nature, Lond.* 162 (1948) 302

[19] Byatt, W. J., Rogers, F. T. and Waltner, A. *Phys. Rev.* 75 (1949) 909

[20] Curran, S. C., Angus, J. and Cockcroft, A. L. *Phys. Rev.* 76 (1949) 853

[21] Graves, E. R. and Mayer, D. I. *Phys. Rev.* 76 (1949) 183 (Abstract)

[22] Hanna, G. C. and Pontecorvo, B. *Phys. Rev.* 75 (1949) 983

[23] Slack, L., Owen, G. E. and Primakoff, H. *Phys. Rev.* 75 (1949) 1448

[24] Voikhanski, M. E., Dzhelepov, B. S. and Sliv, L. A. *Dokl. Akad. Nauk SSSR* 66 (1949) 829

[25] Hollander, J. M., Perlman, I. and Seaborg, G. T. *Rev. mod. Phys.* 25 (1953) 469

[26] O'Neal, R. D. and Goldhaber, M. *Phys. Rev.* 58 (1940) 574

[27] Goldblatt, M., Robinson, E. S. and Spence, R. W. *Phys. Rev.* 72 (1947) 973

[28] Jones, W. M. *Phys. Rev.* 100 (1955) 124

[29] Novick, A. *Phys. Rev.* 72 (1947) 972

[30] Jones, W. M. *Phys. Rev.* 83 (1951) 537

[31] Libby, W. F. *Analyt. Chem.* 19 (1947) 2

[32] Glendenin, L. E. *Nucleonics* 2 (1) (1948) 12

[33] Hammel, E. F. *J. Chem. Phys.* 18 (1950) 228

[34] Albers, E. W., Harteck, P. and Reeves, R. R. *Z. Naturf.* 18a (1963) 197; *J. Am. chem. Soc.* 86 (1964) 204

[35] Grilly, E. R. *J. Am. chem. Soc.* 73 (1951) 5307

[36] Faltings, V. and Harteck, P., *Z. Naturf.* 5a (1950) 438

[37] Grosse, A. V., Johnston, W. H., Wolfgang, R. L. and Libby, W. F. *Science, N.Y.* 113 (1951) 1

[38] Libby, W. F. *Scient. Am.* 190 (4) (1954) 38

[39] Lujanas, V. *Liet. TSR mokslu Akad. Darb. Ser. B.* 1 (32) (1963) 21

[40] Kaufmann, S. and Libby, W. F. *Phys. Rev.* 93 (1954) 1337

[41] Begemann, F. *Proc. 2nd. Int. Conf. peaceful Uses atom. Energy*, Geneva, 18 (1958) 545

[42] Libby, W. F. *Proc. Symp. Tritium phys. Biol. Sci., I.A.E.A.*, Vienna 1 (1962) 5

[43] Libby, W. F. *J. geophys. Res.* 68 (1963) 4485

[44] Israel, G., Roether, W. and Schumann, G. Conf–55–1. *Symp. Trace Gases Natural Artificial Radioactivity Atmosphere*, Utrecht, Aug. 1962; *J. geophys. Res.* 68 (1963) 3771

[45] Bainbridge, A. E. and O'Brien, B. J. *Proc. Symp. Tritium phys. Biol. Sci.,* I.A.E.A., Vienna 1 (1962) 33

[46] Bainbridge, A. E., Suess, H. E., Friedman, I. *Nature, Lond.* 192 (1961) 648

[47] Gat, J. R., Karfunkel, U. and Nir, A. *Proc. Symp. Tritium phys. Biol. Sci.* I.A.E.A., Vienna 1 (1962) 41

[48] Taylor, C. B. *Nature, Lond.* 201 (1964) 146

[49] Shen, S. P., Korff, S. A. and Neuberg, H. A. C. *Nature, Lond.* 199 (1963) 60

[50] Giletti, B. J. and Kulp, J. L. *Science, N.Y.* 129 (1959) 901

[51] Tilles, D. *Nature, Lond.* 200 (1963) 563

[52] Dubost, H. and Lefort, M. *Nature, Lond.* 200 (1963) 566

[53] Charalambus, St. and Goebel, K. *Geochim. cosmochim. Acta* 26 (1962) 659

[54] Fireman, E. L. *Proc. Symp. Tritium phys. Biol. Sci.* I.A.E.A., Vienna 1 (1962) 69

[55] Bishop, K. F., Delafield, H. J., Eggleton, A. E. J., Peabody, C. O. and Taylor, B. T. *Proc. Symp. Tritium phys. Biol. Sci.* I.A.E.A., Vienna 1 (1962) 55

[56] Begemann, F. *AED-Conf.* (1962) 142–16

[57] Wolfgang, R. *Nature, Lond.* 192 (1961) 1279

[58] Tamers, M. A. *Nature, Lond.* 197 (1963) 276

[59] Bainbridge, A. E. Suess, H. E. and Wanke, H. *Geochim. cosmochim. Acta* 26 (1962) 471

[60] Kundu, D. N. and Pool, M. L. *Phys. Rev.* 71 (1947) 140 (Abstract)

[61] Krishnan, R. S. *Nature, Lond.* 148 (1941) 407

[62] O'Neal, R. D. and Goldhaber, M. *Phys. Rev.* 57 (1940) 1086 (Abstract)

[63] Budnizki, D. Z., Kurtschatow, I. W. and Latyshev, G. D. *Phys. Z. SowjUn.* 71 (1935) 474

[64] Chadwick, J. and Goldhaber, M. *Proc. Camb. phil. Soc. biol. Sci.* 31 (1935) 612

[65] Arrol, W. J., Wilson, E. J., Evans, C., Chadwick, J. and Eakins, J. *Radioisotope Conference*, vol. II, p. 59, 1954. London; Butterworths

[66] Massey, B. J. *Oak Ridge Natn. Lab. Rep.* ORNL–2238 (1957)

[67] Abraham, B. M. *U.S. Patent 3,100,184* (6th Aug. 1963)

[68] Coon, J. H. and Nobles, R. A. *Phys. Rev.* 75 (1949) 1358

[69] King, L. D. P. and Goldstein, L. *Phys. Rev.* 75 (1949) 1366

[70] Robinson, E. S., Briesmeister, A. C., McInteer, B. B. and Potter, R. M. *Radioisotopes Phys. Sci. and Ind.*, I.A.E.A., Vienna 2 (1962) 431

[71] Jenks, G. H., Shapiro, E. M., Elliott, N. and Cannon, C. V. *U.S. Patent, 3,079,317* (26th Feb. 1963)

[72] Wilson, E. J. *Vacuum* 4 (1954) 303

[73] Radiochemical Centre. *The Radiochemical Manual. Part I: Physical Data* 1962. Amersham; Radiochemical Centre

[74] Cohen, H. and Diethorn, W. S. *Int. J. Appl. Radiat. Isotopes* 15 (1964) 553

CHAPTER 2

THE USES OF TRITIUM AND ITS COMPOUNDS

The use of tritium in thermonuclear weapons and the consequent large-scale production have made tritium readily available in very large quantities for peaceful purposes. The United States Atomic Energy Commission made one million curies available in 1959 for peaceful applications of the isotope[1].

Tritium has certain unique advantages. It is one of the least expensive radioisotopes and this makes large-scale tracer experiments possible. For small-scale laboratory use, being a hydrogen isotope and weak β-emitter, it often makes the radioactive labelling of materials easier and quicker than it would otherwise be. The half-life of 12·26 years is conveniently long, although short enough to reduce concern about production and the use of rather large quantities. The extremely high specific activities (compared for example with carbon-14) and the excellent autoradiographic properties, due to the weakness of the β-radiation, makes tritium irreplaceable in much biological tracer work.

A complete review of all the uses of tritium and its compounds, especially the many examples of applications in biology, would be outside the scope of this book. Examples in this chapter have been chosen to illustrate the various aspects of tritium uses.

The scheme shown (*Figure 2.1*) represents a 'family tree' for the uses of tritium and its compounds which is adopted as a basis for classification.

(A) PHYSICAL USES

Major physical applications of tritium include the preparation of tritium targets and light sources. Tritium is of course the 'raw' material for the preparation of hundreds of tritium compounds which themselves have numerous applications.

(A1) Tritium Targets

When tritium is bombarded with accelerated deuterons a nuclear reaction occurs (2.1) with the emission of neutrons having an energy of about 14 MeV and the formation of helium-4[2].

(A) PHYSICAL USES

$$\text{{}^3_1H + {}^2_1H \rightarrow {}^4_2He + {}^1_0n} \qquad \ldots \ldots \quad (2.1)$$

Development of neutron activation analysis[3-5] has promoted the value of tritium targets for the easy production of energetic neutrons by the $^3H(d,n)^4He$ reaction.

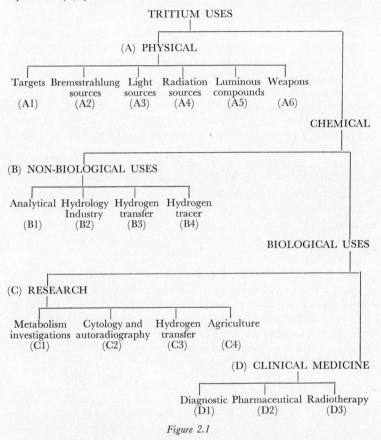

Figure 2.1

The targets are commonly prepared by the adsorption of pure tritium on titanium or zirconium metal[6], although the rare earth metals neodymium and praseodymium have also been used[7]. By virtue of the difference in atomic weight between titanium and zirconium, it is possible to adsorb about twice as much tritium on a titanium target as on a zirconium target of equal weight. A typical zirconium target for example, of total weight 7 mg will adsorb about

1 ml of tritium which, at the maximum specific activity corresponds to 2·6 c. The targets may vary from a few millicuries to several curies and a number of good reviews describe both their preparation and uses in more detail[8-10].

The distribution of tritium in the titanium or zirconium may be determined radiographically[11,11a] and information on the behaviour of zirconium targets saturated with tritium, under various temperature conditions has also been published[12]. For the heavier targets platinum or tungsten is used as the backing metal instead of the more usual copper[13].

Although used primarily as neutron sources[13a], tritium targets also find application as detectors in gas–liquid chromatography[14,14a] and tritium adsorbed on titanium sources of 10–20 c can be used as static eliminators. One such use is in coil-winding machines in which tissue paper is used as insulator[15].

Ionization current in air is proportional to the pressure of the air for values between 10^{-3} and 50 torr (1 Torr = 1 atm/760 = 1333·22368 dyn/cm^2 = 1·0 mm Hg) and varies from 10^{-12} to 10^{-8} A. Use is made of this in the adaptation of tritium sources to devices for measuring vacuum[16].

(A2) Bremsstrahlung sources

Another application of tritium sources makes use of the Bremsstrahlung radiation from such targets. The demand for sources emitting low-energy radiation is increasing rapidly with the expansion in the use of radioactive sources of electromagnetic radiation in x-ray fluoroscopy and the extension of thickness gauging to very thin materials[17]. In another application the absorption of the Bremsstrahlung radiation from a tritium–titanium source has been employed for the estimation of sulphur in oil[18,19].

(A3) Light Sources

Tritium gas in the presence of activated zinc sulphide emits a greenish light, and this can be used as a light source[20, 21], for example on 'Exit' signs in dark rooms. However, the isotope in the gaseous form presents a potential health hazard, if the source is damaged or leakage of tritium occurs; it is now more favourably used for this purpose in the form of an organic compound (see tritiated luminous compounds page 13).

(A4) Radiation sources

Tritiated water can be used with advantage as an 'internal' radiation source to overcome the problem of the appearance of the electron spin resonance spectrum of glass (or quartz) tubes containing samples which have been irradiated by high-energy radiation, such as cobalt-60 γ-radiation [22]. Tritiated tryptophan and dimethyl diethyl tin have also been used for similar investigations [23].

Tritiated water also offers perhaps the best *in situ* 'uniform' source for studying the effects of β-radiation on various materials in aqueous solution [23a].

(A5) Luminous compounds

When a tritium compound is intimately mixed with a copper-activated zinc sulphide, the tritium β-radiation impinging on the zinc sulphide crystals is dissipated as light energy and a greenish light is emitted.

Tritiated luminous compounds are now becoming important for the manufacture of luminous paint, which is to some extent replacing the radium-based paints. Radium, being a bone seeker, is a highly toxic radioisotope and its use in the manufacture of luminous paint is regarded as radiologically undesirable [24, 25]. In some parts of the world its use for this purpose is now illegal.

Owing to the short range of the tritium β-particles it is necessary for the tritiated compound to be in close proximity with the zinc sulphide phosphor and to remain so in the paint mixture, to obtain maximum light efficiency. It is also necessary to have the tritium compound at very high specific activity so that the chemical absorption of the light emitted is minimal.

Compounds studied to date include acids, alcohols and paraffins of long chain length [26] such as tritiated palmitic and stearic acids and tritiated octadecanol. However, best results have been obtained with tritiated polymers, polymethylmethacrylate [27], polyesters and polyurethanes [28], a polymer of maleic acid and hexamethylenediol cross-linked with hexamethylene di-isocyanate [29], and tritiated nylon [30]. The polymer must not leak or exchange tritium when immersed in water [31] and rapid immersion tests have been developed [32].

The β-emitting isotope promethium-147 offers some competition to the use of tritium in luminous paint [33, 34].

(A6) Weapons

There is virtually no published information on the use of tritium in thermonuclear weapons.

CHEMICAL USES

The chemical uses of tritium and tritium compounds have been divided into two groups, non-biological and biological. In both these groups the isotope has two main functions; as a tracer for hydrogen and as a tracer for carbon structures. Of these, little need be said in general about the first, except that quantitative results need to be carefully interpreted because of the large isotope effects which can occur (see Chapter 6).

In its second function of use, tritium is something of a makeshift for a carbon isotope, but it has (as already mentioned) unique advantages in specific activity and autoradiographic precision. However, all uses for tracing carbon depend upon knowledge of the integrity of the carbon–hydrogen bond during the experiment, and here a word of caution cannot be expressed too strongly. Systematic knowledge of the behaviour of carbon–tritium bonds is still very incomplete even under purely chemical conditions to say nothing of biological experiments. An attempt is made to review the present state of knowledge in Chapter 6, but for the present it is often wise to obtain direct evidence in the actual experiment, using a double-labelling technique in two or more positions or with two isotopes.

(B) NON-BIOLOGICAL USES OF TRITIUM

Some of the applications described under this heading may be indirectly used for, or associated with, biological investigations.

(B1) Analytical applications

The limited use [35, 36] which has been made of labelled compounds as analytical reagents is somewhat disappointing and there is undoubtedly much more to be done in this field. The peculiar advantages and relatively modest requirements have yet to be widely recognized. There are a number of analytical applications of tritium and its compounds which are worthy of comment.

Hydrogen in metals—Tracer analytical applications of tritium gas include a study of the adsorption of hydrogen and the hydrogenation of ethylene on a nickel catalyst [37] and the determination of the adsorption of hydrogen in metals [38]. For example, a value as low as two parts per million of hydrogen in sodium metal has been determined by isotope dilution with tritium [39].

Determination of 'active hydrogen'—The number of chemically active hydrogen atoms in a compound may be determined by hydrogen isotope exchange with tritiated isopropyl alcohol-(*hydroxyl*-T) [40].

14

(B) NON-BIOLOGICAL USES OF TRITIUM

$$R \cdot H + Me_2CH \cdot OT \rightarrow R \cdot T + Me_2CH \cdot OH \quad . \quad . \quad . \quad . \quad (2.2)$$

The organic compound is treated with an excess of isopropyl alcohol labelled with tritium in the hydroxyl group. Tritium in this position instantaneously exchanges with similarly situated 'active' hydrogen atoms in the compound as shown in equation (2.2). After distillation of the alcohol from the compound, the specific activity of the compound is measured. From the specific activity of the isopropyl alcohol used and the compound labelled, the number of 'active' hydrogen positions in the molecule may be calculated.

The method is obviously unsuitable for volatile compounds which cannot be easily separated from the radioactive alcohol. One could of course overcome this difficulty by reversing the technique and using a tritiated solid or high-boiling compound such as cholesterol-3-*hydroxyl*-T or hexadecanol-*hydroxyl*-T, as the reagent.

A disadvantage of this method is that small impurities in the compound to be analysed, may contain 'active' hydrogen positions, for example water or alcohol of crystallization, which could give very misleading results.

Table 2.1 records some results which were obtained by Eastham and Raaen [40] using isopropyl alcohol-*hydroxyl*-T as the reagent.

TABLE 2.1

Compound	Relative specific activities mc/mM		No. of 'active' hydrogen atoms
	Compound	Reagent	
Cholesterol	30·7	30·3	1
Aniline hydrochloride	77·7	30·3	3
p-Aminobenzoic acid	82·6	30·3	3
Malonic acid	114·4	59·9	2
Benzamide	61·6	30·3	2
Benzoic acid	26·9	30·3	1

The low values recorded for the specific activity of benzoic and *p*-aminobenzoic acids may well have been due to esterification; the resulting esters would be non-radioactive. The low value of the activity of the aniline hydrochloride could be due to loss of tritiated hydrogen chloride on distillation of the solvent.

Lithium aluminium tritide has also been used for 'active' hydrogen determination, but in a more conventional manner [41, 42, 100, 144].

Amino acid estimation—1-Fluoro-2,4-dinitrobenzene reacts with amino acids to give the 2,4-dinitrophenyl derivative (2.3):

$$NO_2-\langle\bigcirc\rangle-F \quad + \quad H_2N\cdot CH\cdot R \quad \longrightarrow \quad NO_2-\langle\bigcirc\rangle-NH\cdot CH\cdot R$$

with NO_2 and $COOH$ groups

$$\cdots \cdots (2.3)$$

By using tritiated 1-fluoro-2,4-dinitrobenzene the estimation of amino acids and N-terminal groups in as little as 1 μg of protein can be achieved [43, 44]. The accuracy of this method is at least as good as that obtained by non-isotopic methods.

Double isotope derivative analysis—Trace amounts of organic compounds in biological samples are often difficult to determine quantitatively by conventional analytical procedures. A powerful new analytical tool, the double isotope derivative method, has been introduced for the analysis of a number of groups of compounds. The principles of the method are illustrated by the following examples.

Steroid analysis. The selective determination of steroids in biological fluids has been handicapped by the lack of specific and sensitive analytical procedures. For example, biological assays are limited by the variation inherent in animal responses and chemical methods are very tedious requiring extensive purification processes. During such purification the amounts of steroid finally recovered may be too small for accurate estimation. Tritiated acetic anhydride is now used quite extensively for the routine determination of microgramme quantities of steroids [45-50].

Conventional isotope dilution methods [36, 52] are frequently not applicable to the determination of certain steroids in biological material, because the small dilution of the active material makes the error of the determination too great. For this reason the double isotope derivative analysis technique is preferred, which involves the use of both tritiated and carbon-14-labelled acetic anhydride. This can follow two general procedures depending on the availability of the labelled reagents.

(1) In the first, a known amount of carbon-14-labelled steroid identical with the steroid to be determined, is added to the sample. This acts as an 'internal standard' to check the efficiency of the recovery process. The steroid is then isolated by extraction with an organic solvent and purified by chromatography. If, at this stage, the purified steroid can be determined by conventional analysis (such as ultra-violet absorption spectra, or fluorescence), measurement of the radioactivity will correct for losses in purification, so that the quantity in the original (unlabelled) sample may be calculated.

(B) NON-BIOLOGICAL USES OF TRITIUM

If conventional analysis is not possible, the second isotope is used, the steroid mixture or the purified product being acetylated with tritium-labelled acetic anhydride of known specific activity. After purification of the acetate, determination of the tritium 'acetyl' activity (together with a knowledge of the number of acetylatable hydroxyl groups in the steroid molecule) will give the quantity of steroid, while the carbon-14 measurement (as before) corrects the analysis for losses incurred during the purification.

Exactly the same procedure may be used, with a 'reference steroid' labelled with tritium[53] and using acetic anhydride labelled with carbon-14.

(2) The second, a rather different procedure, can be adopted for the determination of a steroid in an unknown mixture of steroids; the isolated steroid mixture is acetylated with tritiated acetic anhydride and the carbon-14-labelled steroid acetate corresponding to the steroid whose determination is required, is added in a known amount. The mixture is then extensively purified until a constant T:C-14 ratio is obtained. Knowing the specific activity of the tritiated acetic anhydride and the amount of carbon-14 steroid acetate added, the amount of steroid can be calculated in the original mixture from the equation (2.4)[45]:

$$A = \frac{(m-cr)\,C}{Sc} \times \frac{M}{1,000} \qquad \cdot \quad \cdot \quad \cdot \quad \cdot \quad (2.4)$$

where A = number of microgrammes of steroid in sample extracted
   m = disintegrations per minute (d.p.m.) for carbon-14 and tritium after subtracting the background (voltage V)
   c = d.p.m. for carbon-14 minus background only (voltage V')
   r = ratio of d.p.m. for carbon-14 at V volts to d.p.m. for tritium at V' volts
   C = d.p.m. of carbon-14 tracer added (voltage V')
   S = specific activity of steroid acetate d.p.m. of tritium per millimicromole (voltage V)
   M = molecular weight of steroid
   V = 1,150 V and $V' = 700$ V.

(The exact values selected for V and V' will depend of course on the instrument used for the radioactive measurements.)

The accuracy of the method is dependent upon the completeness of the acetylation of the steroid. Dominguez, Seeley and Gorski[54a] have investigated the relative reactivity of the various acetylatable hydroxy groups in the steroid molecule. The order of reactivity is

17

found to be 3-phenolic-OH > 21β-OH > 3β-OH > 6β-OH > 21α-OH > 20β-OH > 16α-OH > sec-17β-OH > sec-17α-OH. (Ring numbering of steroids—see page 169.) The ease of this acetylation thus does vary depending on the steroid, but it can obviously be checked using known amounts of steroid.

Here again the order of use of the isotopes may be reversed. This procedure has the advantage of revealing acetylatable steroids other than the specific one sought. A review of methods for the microchemical identification of steroids from biological media, using labelled steroids, is given by Berliner[54]; an article particularly useful for beginners in this field.

The double isotope derivative method has been extensively used for the determination of urinary aldosterone[55]. An efficient analysis can be done with 5 to 30 ml of human urine or 2 to 3 ml of dog adrenal vein plasma. Quantities of 0·01 μg of aldosterone can be estimated accurately[47].

Methylation with tritiated dimethyl sulphate has been used for the determination of oestrogens in avian plasma by the double isotope derivative technique[52a].

For the double isotope derivative analysis of plasma steroids which cannot be acetylated (or methylated), for example progesterone, a suitable tritium-labelled derivative has been prepared by reduction of the keto groups with sodium borotritide[51, 51a].

The double isotope derivative method can of course be readily applied to compounds other than steroids. Another example of this kind using acetic anhydride labelled with tritium, is in the determination of thyroxine levels in human plasma[56].

S-*Adenosylmethionine*. In mammals, methionine is the major source of

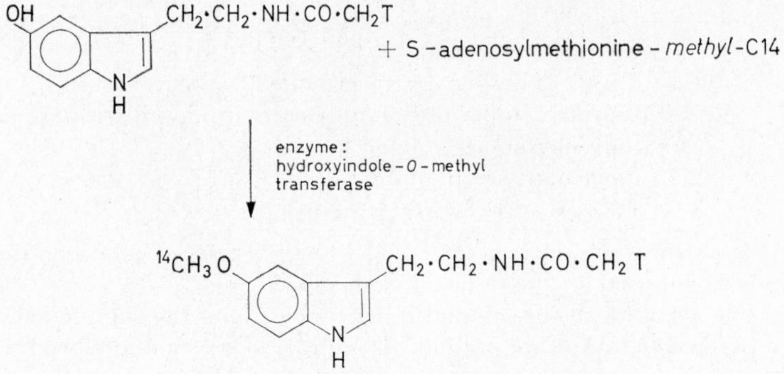

$$OH \quad CH_2 \cdot CH_2 \cdot NH \cdot CO \cdot CH_2T$$

\+ S –adenosylmethionine – *methyl*–C14

enzyme:
hydroxyindole – *O* – methyl
transferase

$$^{14}CH_3O \quad CH_2 \cdot CH_2 \cdot NH \cdot CO \cdot CH_2 T$$

Melatonin –*methoxy* – C14 – *acetyl* –T

. . . . (2.5)

methyl groups and a slightly more complex example of double isotope analysis is the determination of tissue levels of S-adenosylmethionine. A known amount of S-adenosylmethionine-*methyl*-C14 is added to the tissue extract. The specific activity of the diluted S-adenosyl-methionine-C14 is then determined by enzymic formation of melatonin-(*methoxy*-C14)(*acetyl*-T) from N-acetylserotonin labelled with tritium in the acetyl group (2.5)[57].

Analysis of fermentation liquors. Use of the double isotope derivative procedure has been made to determine gibberellins in fermentation liquors[58]. In this case the crude gibberellins are treated with tritiated water, whereby the hydrogen atom of the carboxyl group becomes labelled by exchange (2.6)

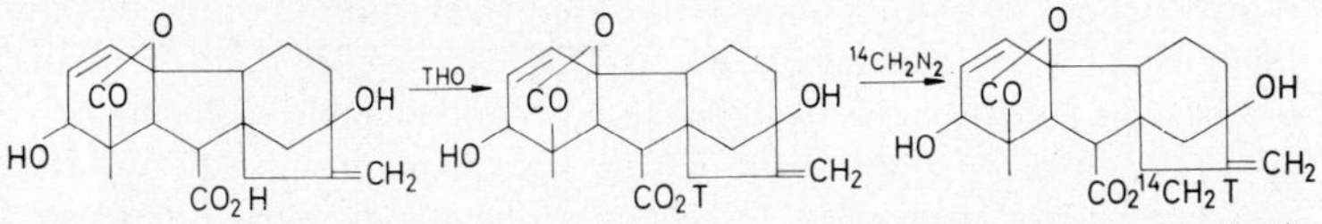

$$\cdots \quad (2.6)$$

and the reaction mixture is then treated with diazomethane labelled with carbon-14 of known specific activity. The gibberellin esters are purified by paper chromatography and the tritium and carbon-14 activity in the derivative measured. The weight of gibberellin in the original sample can be calculated as previously described (*vide supra*). Note that tritiated diazomethane cannot be used for such determinations because of the possible lability of the tritium (see Chapter 6).

The double isotope derivative dilution technique has also been used for the determination of microgramme amounts of pesticides (such as 'DDT' and dieldrin)[58a] which are likely to be present in food products, as a result of the widespread use of pesticides in agriculture.

Radiation chemistry—The radiation chemistry of organic and other compounds can often be studied more effectively by using compounds labelled with radioisotopes. This greatly helps in the detection and identification of the radiolysis products. For example, the γ-irradiation of tritiated toluene labelled in the methyl hydrogens produced tritiated methane and tritiated xylenes[59]. From these results and from the determination of tritium in the products, it can be inferred that the methane is formed exclusively from the methyl group of the toluene. The xylenes are formed by the attack of methyl radicals on the toluene. Oxidation of the recovered toluene also provides information on the transfer of tritium from the methyl group into the benzene ring during the irradiation.

The tritium content of the methane, produced by radiolysis of tritiated acetic acid, indicated that it was formed almost exclusively from the acetic acid by a radical process in which the intermediate methyl radical abstracted hydrogen from the methyl group of the acetic acid[60].

Miscellaneous—Other analytical applications of tritium compounds worthy of mention are the use of tritiated (and carbon-14) labelled nucleosides in the quantitative analysis of nucleotide kinases[61] and the use of tritium compounds in radiometric titrations, for example the estimation of copper with tritiated anthranilic acid[62].

One of the first analytical uses of tritiated water was the determination of the solubility of water in benzene[63] and the method has since been extended for the determination of the solubility of water in other hydrocarbons[64, 65] and organic halides[65]. Tritiated water has also been used for the estimation of traces of water in oils[66, 67] or varnish films[68] and for diffusion studies in agar gel and water[69]. The dielectric properties of anodized tantalum films are affected by water and tritiated water has been used to determine the residual water in such films[70].

Water-free iodine is required for the preparation of anhydrous iodides. Tritiated water has been used for the determination of the water content of iodine after vacuum drying with molecular sieves[71].

Tritiated nickel and iron hydroxides have been employed for measurements on diffusion in solids[72].

(B2) Tritium in Hydrology and Industry

The most abundant chemical compound on the earth is water and the behaviour and movement of water is of considerable importance and interest both in agriculture and industry.

For studying such effects, tritium with its 12·26 year half-life is the nearest approach to the ideal isotope. In spite of much research no other tracers for water have been found satisfactory[73, 74]. Other radioisotopes[75] such as sulphur-35 and phosphorus-32 fail as tracers for water under natural conditions because of their adsorption or exchange with the sulphur or phosphorus in rocks and soil, whereas actual loss of tritium by conversion into an insoluble form through hydrogen ion exchange, is most unlikely.

As mentioned in Chapter 1, tritium is produced in nature as a result of nuclear reactions in the atmosphere brought about by cosmic radiation. This tritium exchanges with the water vapour and falls on the earth as rain. The tritium activity then decays exponentially with time and by measuring the tritium content of stored water, the age of a given water sample can be calculated. The 'true' age of vintage wines may be determined by this technique[76-78], in much the same manner as carbon-14 has been used for carbon 'dating'.

In recent years, as the result of thermonuclear explosions, the tritium content of rainfall has risen. By analysing rain-water from various parts of the world valuable information on the age of different 'water bodies' and the rate at which they are replenished can be obtained[79-81]. A thermonuclear explosion may thus be regarded as a rather 'super' tracer experiment in hydrology.

The International Atomic Energy Agency, Vienna, with the co-operation of the World Meteorological Organization is collecting monthly samples from over 100 stations throughout the world. After concentration by electrolysis, the tritium content of each sample is measured[82].

Tritium is used as a tracer for investigating the distribution of ground water in oil fields[73]. A knowledge of the dynamics of ground water is of considerable interest in connection with the problems of maintaining pressure in the reservoir rock by water drive. The method consists of pumping tritiated water into a borehole and then determining its concentration as it emerges from the reservoir rock in a working well. Here again, electrolytic enrichment[83-85] of the water samples is normally necessary prior to tritium measurement, as in all experiments in hydrology the tritiated water inevitably becomes diluted enormously, beyond even the great sensitivity of the simple tracer dilution. Although the requisite pre-enrichment of tritium in hydrological samples, prior to measurement, is normally done by electrolysis, alternative procedures using low-temperature solid-gas chromatography have been explored by several workers[85a, 85b]. The main disadvantage of this method of enrichment is the necessity to convert fairly large volumes (litres) of water into hydrogen (tritium) gas and without isotopic fractionation.

It is also of interest to note that tritium gas and tritiated gases such as methane or ethane can be used for studying the movement and concentration of natural gases in oil fields[86, 87]. About 1 curie per million cubic feet of gas is required.

Other examples of the use of tritiated water in hydrology include the tracing of springs, river courses and lakes[88]; studying canal-water seepage[89] or loss of water from reservoirs. In the form of ice it can be used for following the movement of glaciers[90, 91] and the direction of water flow.

Tritium tracers have also found application in the motor-gasoline industry. Long-term storage of gasoline results in the formation of gums which present problems in fuel handling. These gums form deposits in induction systems and cause clogging of filters and carburettor jets of internal-combustion engines. The use of tritium compounds has enabled the principal gum-forming compounds (olefines, aromatic compounds, organo-sulphur and nitrogen compounds, and oxygen) to be identified. Conventional analytical methods proved unsuccessful in identifying these compounds[92].

In the electronics industry, the use of tritium for stabilizing the breakdown voltage in thermionic valves and other discharge apparatus, depends upon the ability of tritium gas to 'contaminate' counting tubes[93].

(B3) Hydrogen Transfer Reactions

Tritium can be used advantageously as a tracer for any reactions which involve the migration or exchange of protons. Reactions which involve the migration of hydrogen (or tritium) from one molecule to another are termed intermolecular hydrogen transfer reactions. If the migration takes place within the same molecule the process is described as an intramolecular transfer.

One of the simplest hydrogen transfer reactions is the disproportionation of cyclohexene to benzene and cyclohexane under mild conditions, which has been known for many years[94, 95], (2.7)

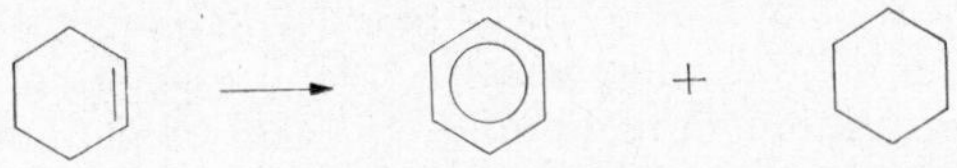

$$\text{cyclohexene} \longrightarrow \text{benzene} + \text{cyclohexane}$$

$$. \quad . \quad . \quad . \quad (2.7)$$

It is known that in the presence of platinum or palladium catalysts hydrogen can be transferred from cyclohexene to many organic compounds[96]. For example, heating cyclohexene, palladium and 2,4-dinitrobenzene under reflux produces *m*-nitraniline (2.8).

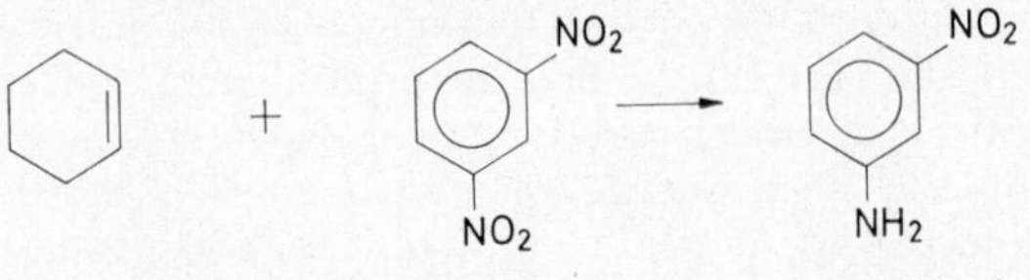

$$\text{cyclohexene} + \underset{NO_2}{\overset{NO_2}{\bigcirc}} \longrightarrow \underset{NH_2}{\overset{NO_2}{\bigcirc}}$$

$$. \quad . \quad . \quad . \quad (2.8)$$

The mechanism of these intermolecular hydrogen transfer reactions can be conveniently studied by placing tritium atoms in particular positions within the molecule. Such studies are liable to isotope effects which are discussed in Chapter 6.

Transfer of tritium from a tritiated solvent to another compound in the presence of a catalyst is of course frequently used for the preparation of tritium-labelled compounds. Although these are strictly hydrogen transfer reactions, they are more usually termed isotope 'exchange' reactions, and relatively little is known about their mechanism.

A simple example of an intramolecular hydrogen transfer is the decarboxylation of a pyrimidine carboxylic acid. If the carboxyl group hydrogen atom is replaced by tritium and the tritiated compound decarboxylated, the resulting pyrimidine retains the tritium atom in a non-labile position (2.9). This also serves to prove that the migrating hydrogen atom is the one attached to the carboxyl group.

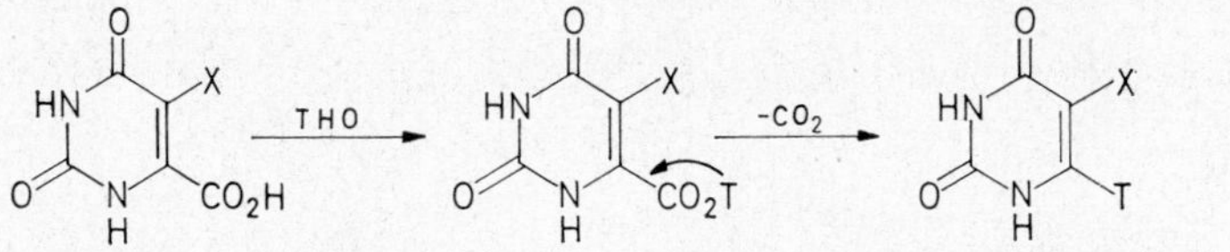

$$\cdots \quad (2.9)$$

An example of this type of reaction is the conversion of 5-bromo-orotic acid-(*carboxyl*-T) (X = Br in (2.9)) to 5-bromouracil-6-T [97]. There are of course many similar reactions described in the literature [98] and frequent use is made of this type of reaction for converting a 'labile' tritium atom into a stable position in a molecule, as readers will observe in Chapter 4.

Using deuterium it has been shown [99] that migration of hydrogen atoms occurs from the amino group into the ortho- and para-positions when aniline hydrochloride is heated to 150° C. The reaction is reversible but with deuterium favouring the ring.

Experiments at the Radiochemical Centre [30] have confirmed that hydrogen (tritium) transfer occurs from the amino group exclusively into the ortho- and para-positions (2.10).

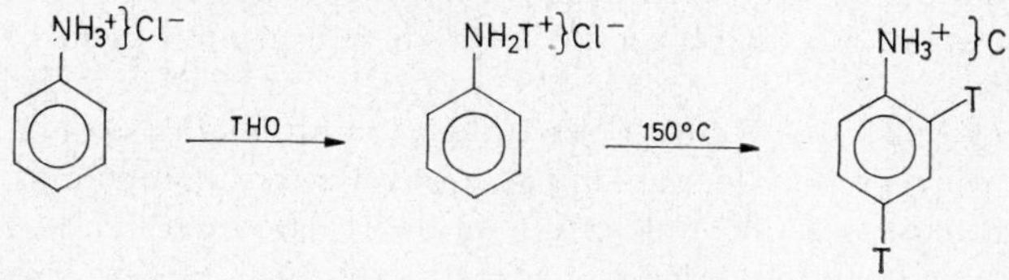

$$\cdots \quad (2.10)$$

It was observed however, that during the initial exchange of the aniline hydrochloride with tritiated water at room temperature some exchange into the meta-positions took place, under the acidic conditions of the reaction. On heating very rapid transfer of the amino-tritium into the ortho- and para-positions occurred and conversion of the product into the tribromo-derivative gave tribromoaniline which had the same specific activity as the tribromo-derivative prepared from the unrearranged compound, confirming that no rearrangement into the meta-positions occurs under these conditions (2.11).

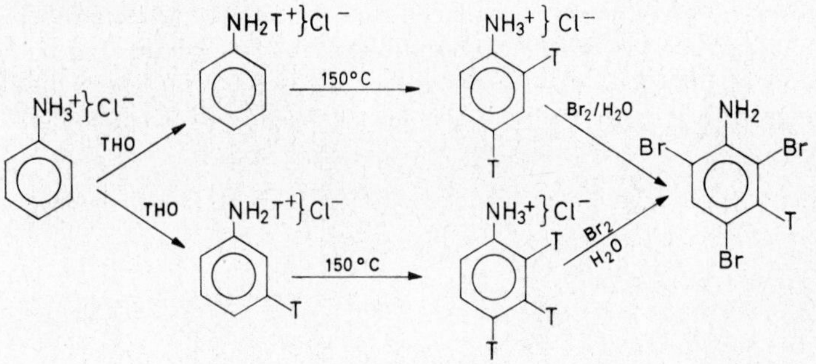

. . . . (2.11)

(B4) Tritium as a Hydrogen Tracer

Increasing use is being made of tritium as a tracer for hydrogen in the study of reaction mechanisms and kinetics. The aromatic series is particularly attractive for study with tritium as many aromatic compounds readily undergo substitution reactions, whereby the tritium atoms in the molecule can be located and their distribution determined.

Extensive use of detritiation of numerous aromatic compounds labelled with tritium, notably by Eaborn and his colleagues[101-107,107a] (and others[108,108a-c].) has permitted the determination of 'aromatic reactivity' of various systems. The rates of tritiation of heteroaromatic compounds has been employed by Katritzky and Ridgewell[109] for studying the mechanism of electrophilic substitution in such compounds.

Hydrogen isotope effects (see Chapter 6) although usually a nuisance (when present) for most applications of tritium compounds, have proved most valuable in determining the reaction mechanism of the replacement and transfer of hydrogen atoms[110,111]. An excellent account of hydrogen isotope effects in aromatic substitution reactions is given by Zollinger[112].

Tritium and deuterium isotopes are frequently used in the study of reaction kinetics and readers are referred to reviews on this subject[113].

24

Mechanism of the ninhydrin oxidation of α-amino acids—Two different mechanisms for the ninhydrin oxidation of α-amino acids have been proposed[114].

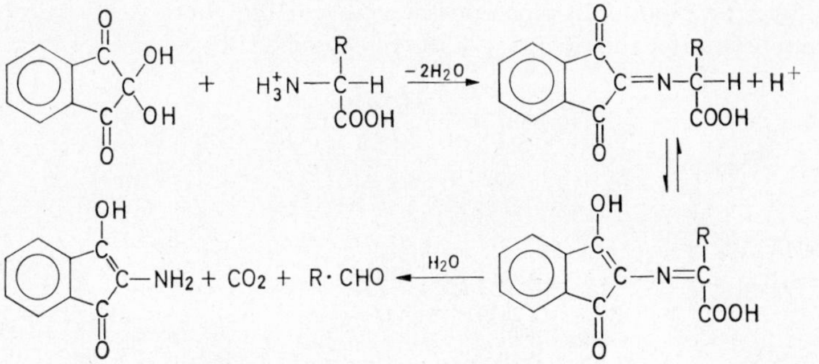

. . . . (2.12)

In the reaction (2.12) a tritiated amino acid labelled in the α-hydrogen position would lose its tritium from this position in the tautomeric reaction. However, experiments have shown[114,115] that the ninhydrin oxidation of amino acids labelled in the α-position do not lose their tritium and the resulting aldehydes have the same specific activity as the amino acid. The alternative reaction mechanism (2.13) has therefore been proposed[114].

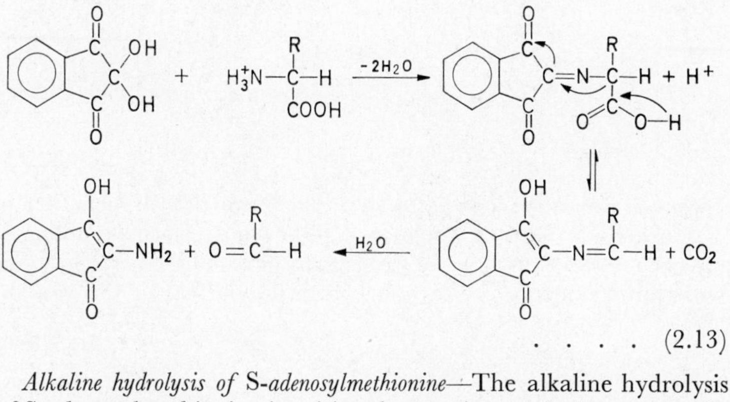

. . . . (2.13)

Alkaline hydrolysis of S-*adenosylmethionine*—The alkaline hydrolysis of S-adenosylmethionine in tritiated water is a typical example of a reaction for which the mechanism has been established by the use of a tritiated solvent[116].

When S-adenosyl-L-methionine is hydrolysed in alkaline tritiated water, transitory desaturation of the ribose moiety and re-hydration

25

occur. This is indicated by the uptake of tritium into the carbo-hydrate part of the molecule. There is at the same time some splitting of the glycoside bond. The resulting product is S-pentosyl-methio-nine; the methionine moiety is racemized but there is no tritium activity in the adenine part of the molecule (2.14).

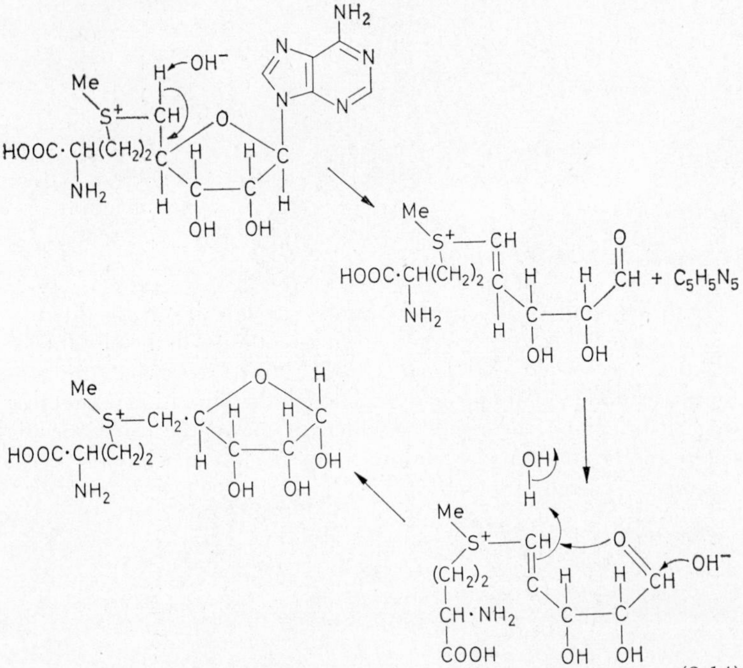

$$\dots \dots (2.14)$$

Quinone dehydrogenation of steroids—Chemical dehydrogenation of 3-keto-steroids with 2,3-dichloro-5,6-dicyano-1,4-benzoquinone[117] has been shown to involve the hydrogen atoms in the 1 and 2 positions with the introduction of a carbon–carbon double bond in this position (2.15).

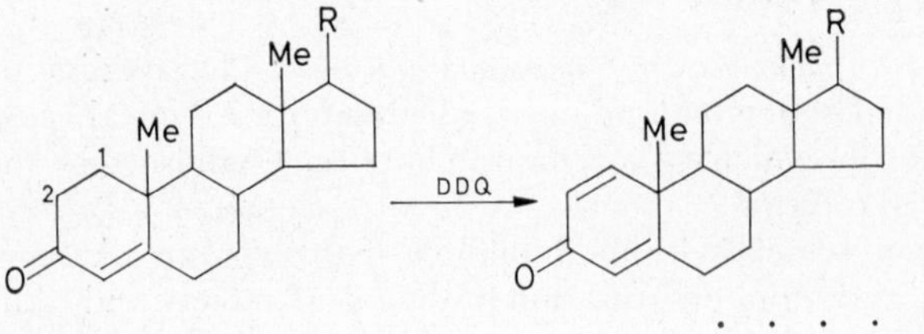

$$\dots \dots (2.15)$$

By labelling the steroid with tritium in the 1-position the stereo-specificity of the dehydrogenation reaction has been determined and shown to involve predominantly the 1α hydrogen atom[118].

These are just three examples selected from the numerous problems of chemical reaction mechanism in which tritium has proved a valuable tracer for hydrogen. Some of the others include the pinacol–pinacolone rearrangement[119], the kinetics and mechanism of the formation of sugar osazones[120], Hofmann degradation of quaternary ammonium bases[121], the ionization rates of weak acids[122] and studies on the mechanism of the Cannizzaro reaction[123].

From the selected examples illustrated, the reader can no doubt appreciate the value of tritium and its important role as a tracer for hydrogen in non-biological systems. Deuterium has of course been used for many investigations, but these have often to be carried out at high deuterium isotopic abundance, because of the difficulty in the detection of this stable isotope.

The real advantage of tritium is its relative ease of detection and it can consequently be used at very low isotopic abundance for mechanistic investigations. At these low specific activities, radiation-induced side reactions and isotope effects seem not to have complicated the use of tritium as a tracer, but the cautious experimentalist will bear the possibility in mind.

BIOLOGICAL USES OF TRITIUM

Uses of tritium in biological investigations can be divided into two major groups:

    (C)   biological research
    (D)   clinical medicine

At present, by far the greatest use of tritium and its compounds is in biological research with a very limited use in clinical medicine.

(C) BIOLOGICAL RESEARCH

(C1) Metabolic and Biosynthetic Pathways

In biology as in hydrology, tritiated water occupies a rather special position; it is invaluable as a tracer compound from the ease with which its tritium atoms can be exchanged with other hydrogen atoms and the sensitivity of measurement.

More than half of the human body consists of water and the determination of the exact percentage of total body water has interested many scientists, from the possibility that variations may be of pathological importance.

The first *in vivo* determination of total body water using tritium was

27

made in 1947[124]. Although it takes about one hour for the tritiated water to be distributed throughout the body, a half-time of only 3·6 msec has been found for the rate of diffusion of water into the red blood cell[125].

Values recorded for the total body water of man are mostly around 60 per cent[126,127], slightly lower values (58 per cent) being found for women[127]. There is no evidence to suggest that tritiated water is concentrated in any particular part of the body, although this had been suspected from experiments with deuterium[128]; the results were not confirmed with tritium[129].

An interesting application of tritiated water is the whole-body 'labelling' of mice with tritium to study the effects of external irradiation, which are followed by changes in the tritium content of organs and tissue[130].

A further discussion of the metabolism and biological half-life of tritiated water is presented in Chapter 3.

Studies of metabolism (using tritium compounds as auxiliary tracers for carbon)—In this, the major use of tritium compounds, everything depends on the integrity of the chemical bond linking the tritium atom to a carbon atom. It is not always easy to answer the crucial question 'how stable is the tritium label under the conditions of the experiment?' and a large portion of Chapter 6 is devoted to this important subject, on which present knowledge is certainly very incomplete.

One of the great difficulties in using tritium compounds for metabolic or biosynthetic investigations is this question of the stability of the tritium label under biological conditions. Even chemically tested stable tritium may become labile under biological conditions due to enzymic reactions at specific positions in the molecule (2.16).

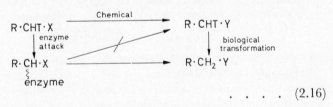

$$. . . . (2.16)$$

This may result in the loss of tritium by exchange but the carbon skeleton remains essentially the same. Even if tritium in the substrate is biologically stable, the metabolic products may have their tritium in biologically unstable positions.

One should always be aware of the limitations of tritium compounds used in this respect, but broadly speaking hydrogen atoms are less likely to be detached in synthetic processes than in degradation; tritium is therefore rather more likely to give a valid result when studying biosynthesis rather than mapping catabolic pathways.

Two other requisites for a tracer analysis of the turnover of labelled compounds are that:

(1) the radioactivity of the label is low enough not to cause radiation damage
(2) the amount of substance is small enough to avoid disturbing normal metabolism. Although there may be 'pools' of compounds (endogenous synthesis), addition of a compound at the wrong phase of a metabolic process may upset the normal pattern.

In spite of the potential disadvantages of tritium compounds for metabolic studies, these two requisites are by and large satisfied, and here tritium also has certain distinct advantages:

(a) the relatively low toxicity of tritium from a radiological point of view, permits the use in humans of larger amounts of radioactivity than is the case of other isotopes, such as carbon-14 its nearest analogue.

(b) the second (perhaps the main) advantage, is the very high specific activities which can be achieved with tritium compounds, so that valid tracer experiments are possible even with compounds whose normal physiological concentrations are extremely low.

Position of the tritium label—Compounds 'generally' or 'randomly' labelled with tritium can sometimes be effectively used when the incorporation of a molecule occurs essentially in the intact state; of thymidine into DNA for example[131], or an amino acid into protein[132]. Compounds can on occasion be used, even when the pattern of labelling is not known[133].

For studies of metabolic degradation reactions, however, specific labelling is often essential for conclusive results. The importance of the specificity of tritium labelling is more fully dealt with in Chapter 5.

Tritium in any organic form is likely sooner or later in the course of a biological experiment to pass through the chemical form of water. This is important in respect of the probable toxicity of that chemical form, and also because the tritium is likely to be re-converted from water to other organic forms. Some discussion of the metabolism of tritium compounds is therefore appropriate here; the reader is also referred to other relevant sections such as those on biological hydrogen transfer reactions (page 44), isotope effects in biological reactions (Chapter 6) and the biological half-life of tritium compounds (Chapter 3).

Nucleosides—The *in vivo* and *in vitro* metabolism of tritiated

29

nucleosides is of particular importance owing to their rapid uptake into cells, and the consequential significance in the toxicity of these compounds (see Chapter 3).

The metabolism of tritiated thymidine in humans for example, gives rise to tritiated water, tritium-labelled deoxyribosenucleic acid (DNA), β-aminoisobutyric acid (a known metabolite of thymine[134]) and other unidentified tritiated compounds[135] (2.17).

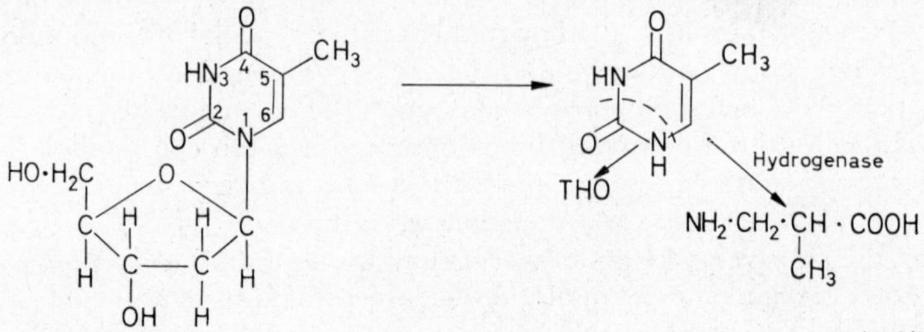

$$. \quad . \quad . \quad . \quad (2.17)$$

During catabolism, the carbon atom at position 2 is oxidized to carbon dioxide, as shown by experiments with carbon-14[136].

Plasma clearance of tritiated thymidine commences in the first circulation time and becomes exponential following apparent equilibrium with total body water. This rapid plasma clearance is associated with the incorporation of the tritiated thymidine into the newly formed DNA of the proliferating cells as early as one minute following injection.

In the bone marrow the labelling of the proliferating cells is complete 10 min after injection and the label appears to remain there during the life span of these cells, which can be up to several days[137], diluted only in successive mitoses[134]. The utilization of thymidine for *in vitro* DNA synthesis in human leukaemic blood and normal dog bone marrow suspensions is restricted to the first 20 min of incubation. Only a small fraction of the DNA-thymidine of labelled cells is derived from tritiated thymidine[138].

Quite small amounts of unlabelled thymidine, thymidylic acid and the related deoxyuridines can effect a partial 'blocking action' by competition and depress the effective labelling of the cells by tritiated thymidine[138,139]. When using labelled thymidine it should be remembered that it is not merely the specific activity as administered which is important, but the actual specific activity *in situ*, allowing for dilution with endogenous unlabelled thymidine or competitive compounds.

The incorporation of tritiated thymidine into the various organs of the mouse is described by Pelc[140].

β-Ureidoisobutyric acid and β-aminoisobutyric acid have also been shown to be the principal products of the *in vitro* catabolism of thymidine by normal and leukaemic human leukocytes[141] and in various plant tissues (buds of *Lilium longiflorum* and root tips of *Vicia faba*)[142].

Although much work is described on the use of other nucleosides such as cytidine, uridine and guanosine, for cytological labelling (see page 41), little is published concerning the metabolism of these compounds.

Proteins and amino acids—Most investigations with tritiated amino acids have been concerned with their incorporation into cellular protein and little information appears to be published on their actual catabolism. Almost the same state of affairs applies to the metabolism of tritiated proteins (or synthetic peptides) where tritium has advantages over other possible labels such as ^{131}I-iodinated proteins.

The biological fate of a peptide or protein labelled with iodine on the tyrosyl residues or 'generally' with tritium, may be determined in biological systems only if the protein molecule remains undamaged and the radioactive label does not alter the biological function or biological activity of the protein. Unfortunately there are no simple, reliable methods for preparing tritiated proteins at high specific activity (see page 156).

It is very difficult to determine the radiochemical purity of macromolecular structures, such as proteins, to establish beyond all reasonable doubt the integrity of the label[143], and caution must be exercised when interpreting the results of investigations with them, particularly if they are labelled by the Wilzbach or similar tritium gas-exposure methods. It is known, for example, that exposure of tritiated L-amino acids to tritium gas causes some degree of racemization[30] but it has not been established whether racemization occurs in peptides labelled with tritium in this manner.

An illustrative example[145] in the study of peptide metabolism is the biological fate in female rats of the octapeptide angiotensin II (L-aspartyl-L-arginyl-L-valyl-L-tyrosyl-L-isoleucyl(or L-valyl)-L-histidyl-L-prolyl-L-phenylalanine), labelled with tritium by a modified Wilzbach technique. In Table 2.2 is shown a comparison of the distribution of radioactivity in the various organs immediately after infusion and 30 min later.

The biological half-life of the compound in the circulation is very short (less than 15 min) but is similar to other peptides such as vasopressin, oxytocin and bradykinin[146]. It is however quite different from the value of 10 h obtained when ^{131}I-labelled angiotensin is used[147].

TABLE 2.2

Organ	End of infusion		30 min after end of infusion	
	Radioactivity cts min^{-1}g^{-1} or ml^{-1}	Electrophoretic mobility	Radioactivity cts min^{-1}g^{-1} or ml^{-1}	Electrophoretic mobility
Heart	15×10^3		15×10^3	
Lung	20×10^3		18×10^3	9·7
Kidney	127×10^3	14·8	227×10^3	8·8 and 12·3
Adrenal	143×10^3	16·0	77×10^3	
Liver	13×10^3		18×10^3	
Spleen	16×10^3		15×10^3	
Brain	5×10^3		69×10^3	12·0
Blood	36×10^3	16·0	8×10^3	8·9 and 15·8
Urine	$4·5 \times 10^3$	11·2 and 15·2	342×10^3	12·1
Uterus	128×10^3	15·5	$5·6 \times 10^3$	21·0
Aorta	$11·5 \times 10^3$	15·5	$19·3 \times 10^3$	
Skeletal muscle	$8·8 \times 10^3$	15·5	10×10^3	
Angiotensin II		15·5		15·6

Albumin labelled with ^{131}I has been used in recent years for the study of protein absorption and *in vitro* investigations have demonstrated that the radioactive iodine label remains bound to the protein or to protein residues during digestion[148]. However, the iodine label can become detached from the protein in the lumen of the gut[149], and *in vivo* use is unsatisfactory. Triitiated albumin, again labelled by the Wilzbach method, has been used for intestinal absorption studies in normal subjects and in patients suffering from intestinal diseases. The biological half-life was 5 days compared with a half-life of 20 days for the ^{131}I-labelled protein[150], showing the unsuitability of the tritium-labelled protein for turnover studies.

The *in vivo* behaviour of iodine-labelled protein has been verified (in rabbits) with carbon-14 labelling[151]. The short biological half-life of the albumin and smaller polypeptides labelled with tritium, casts some doubt on the stability of the tritium introduced into proteins by the Wilzbach method. At present it would seem more reliable to label proteins *in situ* with tritiated amino acids for studying their metabolism[152–154]. As pointed out by Barbour and Bartter[155], to obtain meaningful results when studying biological half-life and degradation rate (i.e. turnover), it is essential to use a biologically pure labelled compound (see also page 156).

Steroids—Steroids are widely distributed in the human (or animal) body but only the adrenal cortex, the gonads and the placenta secrete steroid hormones. Basically there are four distinct aspects of steroid metabolism involving compounds which are:

1. secreted by the glands,
2. present only in the glands,
3. circulating in the peripheral blood and plasma,
4. urinary excretion products.

Tritium and other tracers have been freely used in the study of all these aspects of steroid metabolism. This is probably because there was already a firm (although recent) foundation of knowledge acquired by classical methods of analysis, much of it concerned with steroid metabolism in both normal and pathological states[156].

Tracers have provided direct evidence on metabolic changes, and indirect assistance from their use in refined methods of analysis (page 16). Table 2.3 lists some of the many examples where tritiated steroids have proved useful in metabolic investigations.

TABLE 2.3

Steroid	Position of tritium label	Biological system	References
Aldosterone	1α, 2α	Human	158
Aldosterone	1α, 2α	Rat	159
Aldosterone	7α	Human	160–162
Δ⁴-Androstene-3,17-dione	General	Guinea pig	163
Δ⁴-Androstene-3,17-dione	7α	Human corpus luteum (*in vitro*)	164
Δ⁴-Androstene-3,17-dione	7α	Rat	165
Δ⁴-Androstene-11β-ol-3,17-dione	1α, 2α	Cerebral cortex (*in vitro*)	166
Δ⁵-Androstene-3β,17β-diol	17α	Human adrenal and placental tissue (*in vitro*)	167
Δ⁵-Androstene-3β,17β-diol	17α	Human (leukaemic)	168
Androstene glucuronide	General	Human	169
Cholesterol	General	Rat	170, 171
Cholesterol	General	Rabbit	172
Cholesterol	General	Human	173, 174
Cholesterol	General	Guinea pig	175
Cholesterol	7β	Cockroach	176
Cholesterol	7α	Baboon	177
Cholesterol	7α	Rat liver (*in vitro*)	178
Cholesterol	7α and 7β	Rat	157
Cholesterol	6α	Rat and pig	179
Cholesterol	4β	Guinea pig	180
Corticosterone	1α,2α	Mouse	181
Corticosterone	1α,2α	Cerebral cortex (*in vitro*)	166
Cortisol	1α,2α	Sheep	183
Dehydroepiandrosterone	7α	Human	184, 185
Dehydroepiandrosterone	7α	Human adrenal carcinoma (*in vitro*)	186

TABLE 2.3 *continued*

Steroid	Position of tritium label	Biological system	References
Dehydroepiandrosterone	7α	Adrenal carcinoma (*in vitro*)	187
Dehydroepiandrosterone	7α	Cat	293
Digitoxin	General	Human	188, 189
Digitoxin	General	Rat	190
Digoxin	General	Human	191
Digoxin	General	Rat	190
$3\beta,17$-Dihydroxy-Δ^5-pregnene-20-one	7α	Human (with adrenal carcinoma)	192
β-Glycyrrhetic acid (triterpene)	General	Rat	193
Norethindrone (17α-ethynyl-19-nortesto-sterone)	General	Human	194
Norethynodrel (17α-ethynyl-oestra-5(10)-ene-3-one-17β-ol)	General	Human	194
Norethynodrel	General	Rabbit	195
Oestradiol	6,7	Human	196
Oestradiol	17	Human	197
Oestradiol	General	Rat	182
Oestrone	16	Rat intestine (*in vitro*)	198
Ouabain	General	Rat, sheep, human	190, 199
Δ^5-Pregnenolone	7α	Dog	200, 200a
Δ^5-Pregnenolone	7α	Human adrenal tissue (*in vitro*)	201, 201a
Δ^5-Pregnenolone	16	Bovine ovarian tissue (*in vitro*)	202
Progesterone	16	Human	203, 204
Progesterone	7α	Rat (pregnant)	205
Progesterone	7α	Guinea pig adrenals (*in vitro*)	206
Progesterone	7α	Stein Leventhal ovaries (*in vitro*)	207
β-Sitosterol	General	Fly	208
β-Sitosterol	General	Guinea pig	209
Testosterone	$1\alpha, 2\alpha$	Human	210
Testosterone	17α	Human	218
Triamcinolone (7α-fluoro-11β,16α,17α,21-tetrahydroxypregna-1,4-diene-3,20-dione)	General	Human	211

For some investigations not only the position of the labelled atom is important but also its stereochemical conformation, and one specific use of tritium is the study of the stereospecificity of the biological hydroxylation of steroids. For example, Bergstrom *et al.*[157] showed that the *in vivo* conversion of cholesterol-4-C14-7α-T to cholic acid in the rat, resulted in at least 93 per cent loss of the tritium from the 7-position (2.18). However, when cholesterol-4-C14-7β-T was used the tritium label was retained in the cholic acid.

By using cholesterol-6α-T Samuelsson[179] has shown that reduction of the 5,6-double bond during the metabolic conversion to bile acids, involves the 5 and 6β-positions.

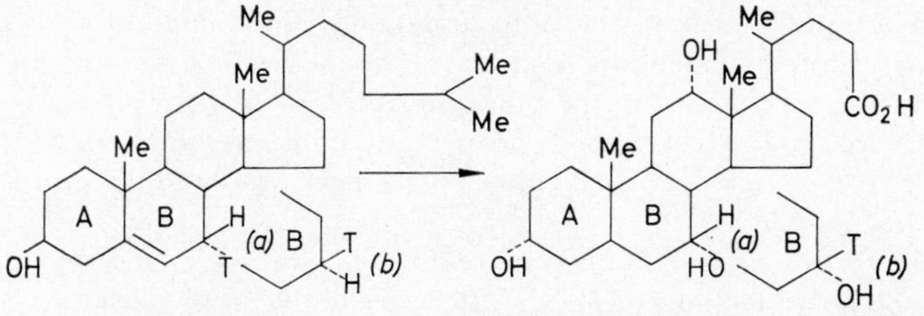

Cholesterol-7-T
(a) alpha-T
(b) beta-T

3, 7, 12-Trihydroxycholanic acid
(cholic acid)
(a) unlabelled
(b) labelled

. . . . (2.18)

Tritium labelling of androgens in the 1α and 1β-positions have helped to clarify some controversial results [212] concerning the mechanism of their *in vivo* conversion into oestrogens [213].

For *in vivo* and *in vitro* experiments with labelled steroids it is often necessary to use double labelling, usually with tritium and carbon-14. This is necessary because of the possible loss of tritium under the biological conditions, such as those described above.

Miscellaneous—Two examples of the metabolism of tritiated compounds selected from the many publications are:
Folic acid (2.19; R = H) a compound of importance which has some diagnostic use for identifying haematological and other disorders.

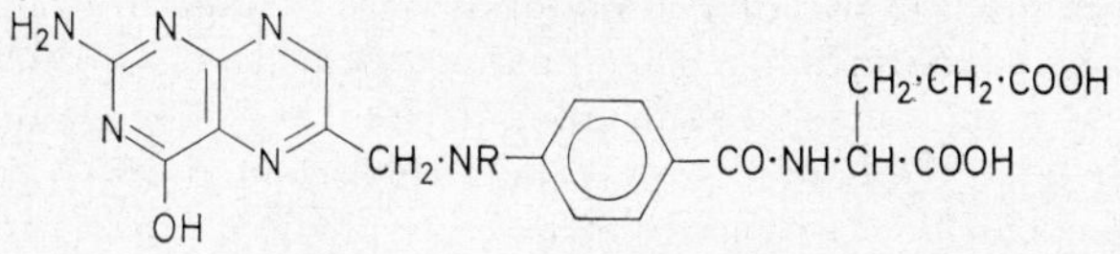

. . . . (2.19)

The study of normal patients and patients with, for example megaloblastic anaemia, idiopathic steatorrhea or tropical sprue, can readily be carried out by balance studies of the intake of folic acid compared with the excretion rate in urine and faeces[214-217, 219]. Most of the tritium in the urine is accounted for as folic acid or its analogues, and appears during the first 12 h after the administered dose. The avidity with which this bulky molecule is removed from the plasma by the tissue cells is quite remarkable; 90 to 95 per cent of the administered radioactivity is removed in 3 min and 60 per cent in one circulation time[217].

The uptake of folic acid and analogous compounds by cells is a specific process depending on the structure of the pteridine and on the substituents attached to the pteridine ring[220]. A slight alteration in the molecular structure, as for example in methotrexate (2.19; R = Me), a much reduced (about 10 times) rate of entry into cells occurs[221].

Metabolic products of tritiated folic acid which are excreted in the urine and which have been identified are folinic acid, pteridines and p-aminobenzoylglutamic acid. Methotrexate labelled with tritium is metabolized slowly, mainly to two unidentified conversion products[221], which had not been observed in earlier investigations[222]. *Adrenaline* (2.20; R' = H; R = Me) and its analogous compounds noradrenaline (2.20; R = R' = H) and metanephrine (2.20; R = Me; R' = Me) are compounds of interest in studying mental disturbances.

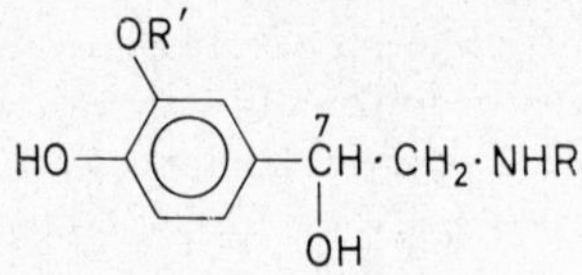

$$\text{HO} - \underset{}{\bigcirc} - \overset{OR'}{\underset{OH}{\overset{7}{\text{CH}}}} \cdot \text{CH}_2 \cdot \text{NHR}$$

. . . . (2.20)

The use of these compounds labelled with tritium in the 7-position has helped to elucidate the metabolic products of the catecholamines[223]. After the intravenous infusion of adrenaline-7-T into man, a number of tritiated compounds were isolated from the urine which included unchanged adrenaline, catechols, 3,4-dihydroxymandelic acid (almost equal amounts free and conjugated), and O-methylated compounds, metanephrine, 3-methoxy-4-hydroxymandelic acid and 4-hydroxy-3-methoxy-phenylglycol. The major metabolite is 3-methoxy-4-hydroxymandelic acid and demonstrates that the 3-O-methylation pathway is the major one for the metabolism of circulating adrenaline in man[224]. The biological half-life for tritiated adrenaline is only 6 h.

It is hoped that this brief review, although necessarily selective and rather superficial, will interest readers who may be new to such applications of tritium compounds.

A list of tritiated compounds (again necessarily selective) is given

(C) BIOLOGICAL RESEARCH

TABLE 2.4
In Vivo Uses of Selected Tritium Compounds

Compound	Position of tritium label	Biological system	References
DL-Adrenaline	7	Human	224
DL-Adrenaline	7	Rat	226, 227
Angiotensin II	General	Rat	145
Bilirubin	General	Rat	228, 229
Cytidine		Mouse	230
Deoxyribonucleic acid	General	Mouse	232
Deoxyribonucleic acid	General	Rat	233
Diethylstilboestrol	General	Rat	234
Dihydromorphine	5,8	Mouse	231
Dihydrostreptomycin		Mouse	235
2,3-Dimethoxy-5-methyl-1,4-benzoquinone	General	Rat	236
Endoxan(Cyclophosphamide)	General	Human	237, 238
DL-α-Fluoro-β-alanine	General	Rat	238a
Folic acid	General	Human	214, 217, 220
Genistein (4′,5,7-trihydroxyiso-flavone)	General	Hen	239
Glycerol	2	Dog	241
Glyceryl tristearate	Stearate-9,10	Human	240
Hexoestrol		Human	380
Insulin	General	Rat	242, 243
Kynurenine	General	Rat	244
Leucine		Dog	154
Linoleic acid	9,10,12,13	Chick	246
Luminous paint (tritiated polymer)	General	Rat	138
Metanephrine	7	Rabbit	248
Methanol	Methyl	Rat	252
Methotrexate	General	Human	221
Myleran	General	Human	249
Noradrenaline	7	Guinea pig	250
Noradrenaline	7	Cat	358
Noradrenaline	7	Human	225
Pentaborane	General	Rat	251
DL-Phenylalanine	General	Rat	253
DL-Proline	4,5	Rat	230
Prostaglandin E_1	5,6	Rat	247
Sodium acetate		Human	171
Sodium formate		Rat	254
Tetanus toxin	General	Mouse	257
Tetracycline	7	Mouse	235
Tetracycline	7	Rat	256
Tetrasodium 2-methyl-1,4-naphthaquinol diphosphate (Synkavit)	5,6,7	Human	255
β-Thienylalanine	Alanine-β-T	Rat	264
Thymidine		Hedgehog	258
Thymidine	Methyl-T	Human	135, 259
Thymidine		Mouse	260, 261
Thymidine		Human (leukaemic)	262

37

TABLE 2.4 (*continued*)

Compound	Position of tritium label	Biological system	References
Thymidine	General	Rat	263
L-Tyrosine		Mouse	230
Tritiated water		Human	129, 268, 269
Tritiated water		Mouse	270, 271
Tritiated water		Cattle	267
Tritium gas		Human and mouse	265, 266
Vasopressin	General	Rat and dog	274, 275
Vinblastine	General	Rat	245
Vitamin-D$_2$	General	Rat	273
Vitamin-D$_3$	General	Rat	272, 273
Vitamin-D$_3$	1	Rat	276

TABLE 2.5

In Vitro Uses of Selected Tritium Compounds

Compound	Position of tritium label	Biological system	References
Bacitracin	Ornithine-T(G)	*Bacillus licheniformis*	277
Biotin	General	*Propionibacterium shermanii*	278
Cytidine		*Acetabularia Mediterranea*	279
Glucose	1,2 and 6	Rat mammary gland	280
Isoleucine	General	Ox pancreas	283
Leucine	4,5	Ox pancreas	281
Leucine	4,5	Hen's oviduct	282
5-Methylcytosine	6	*Acetabularia Mediterranea*	279
Myleran	General	*Chlamydomonas eugametes*	284
Noradrenaline	7	Canine heart	285
Palmitic acid		Adipose tissue	286
Sodium acetate		Rat mammary gland	280
Thymidine	Methyl-T	Human leukaemic blood	138
Thymidine	Methyl-T	Human leukaemic leukocytes	141
Thymidine		Percutaneous liver biopsy specimens	288
Thymidine		Ehrlich and Landschutz ascites cells	289
Thyronine		Kidney and muscle	290
Thyroxine		Kidney and muscle	290
L-Tyrosine		Sheep thyroid slices	291
Uridine	General	*Bacillus megaterium*	292

in Table 2.4 (*in vivo* uses) and Table 2.5 (*in vitro* uses), with references, for those who would like to study this subject further.

Biosynthetic Pathways

Tritium compounds, again used principally as tracers for carbon structures, are proving very important aids in the elucidation of pathways in biosynthesis. A few selected examples are very briefly described which have been chosen from the wide range of publications.

Alkaloids—Viridicatin an alkaloid first isolated from the mycelium of *penicillium viridicatum* [294] was found to contain tritium when anthranilic acid labelled in the phenyl ring with tritium was added to the growth-medium of *penicillium viridicatum*, whereas no labelling resulted when anthranilic acid–*carboxyl*-C14 was used as a precursor. These observations have been interpreted as evidence for a reaction such as (2.21) in which the carboxyl group of the anthranilic acid is lost [295].

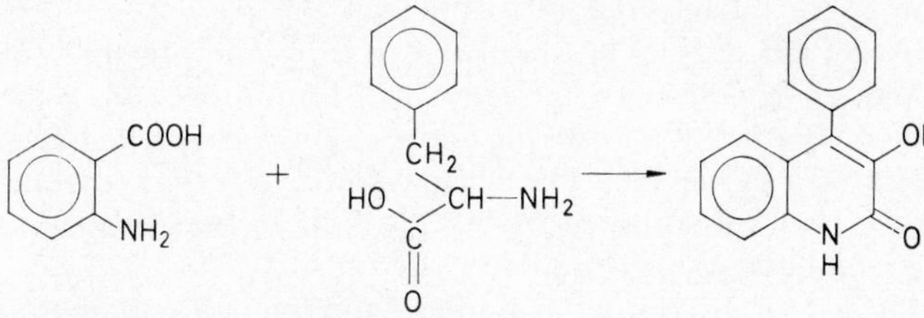

$$\cdots \cdots (2.21)$$

Morphine—A third and long-sought synthesis of the morphine alkaloids has been demonstrated by double isotope experiments [296]. The substituted benzylisoquinoline labelled with tritium and carbon-14 in the specific positions shown (2.22) was fed to *Papaver somniferum* plants. Labelled morphine was obtained with all the carbon-14 activity associated with the N-methyl group and the same ratio of carbon-14 to tritium as in the precursor. This led the authors to propose the reaction (2.22) for this conversion.

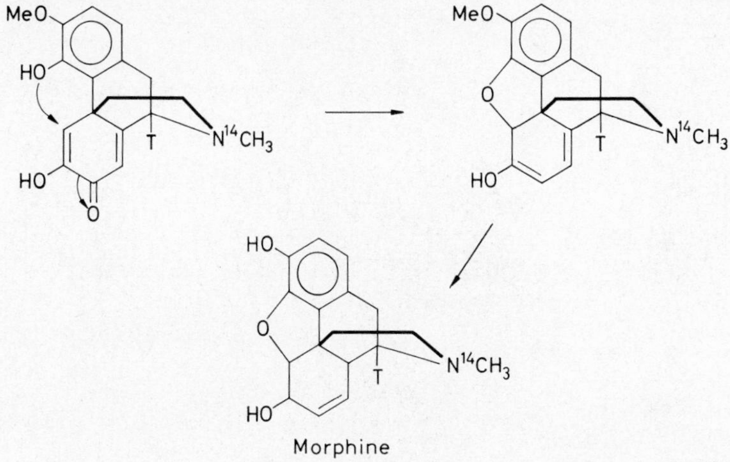

Morphine

$$\cdots \cdots (2.22)$$

39

Amaryllidaceae alkaloids—The isolation of tritiated lycorine from protocatechuic aldehyde and caffeic acid, both labelled with tritium, provided the first direct evidence that cinnamic acid and hydroxylated cinnamic acids are important intermediates in alkaloid biosynthesis and established the cinnamic acid pathway for the amaryllidaceae alkaloids[379].

Another example in the alkaloid field is the use of tritiated (and carbon-14) nicotinic acids which are precursors of the pyridine ring of nicotine in the tobacco plant[297, 298].

Ecdysone—Cholesterol has been shown to be the precursor of the insect metamorphosis hormone ecdysone. Tritium-labelled ecdysone was obtained after 36 h following an injection of tritiated cholesterol into *Calliphora* larvae[299]. The chemical structure of ecdysone has recently been established[300, 300a] as $2\beta,3\beta,14\alpha,22\beta_F,25$-pentahydroxy-$5\beta$-cholest-7-en-6-one.

Penicillin—An interesting example of the use of a tritiated amino

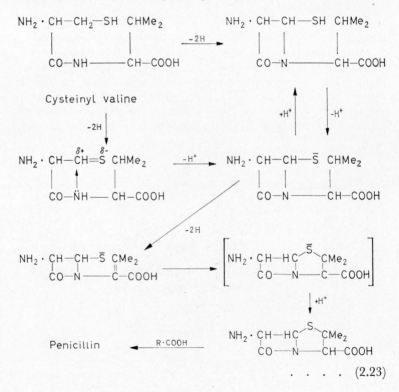

$$\cdots\cdots (2.23)$$

acid is in the mechanism of the formation of the thiazolidine-β-lactam rings from specifically labelled cystines. Both α and β-tritiated cystine give rise to labelled penicillin in *Penicillin chrysogenum*[301]. The biosynthetic pathway is outlined in (2.23)

Degradation of the penicillin showed all the radioactivity to be present in the penicillic aldehyde moiety corresponding to positions 5 and 6 (2.24).

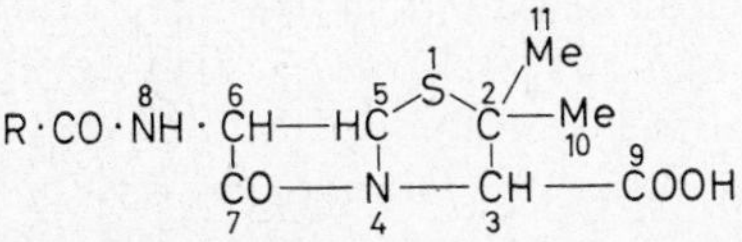

$$R \cdot CO \cdot NH \cdot \underset{8}{} \underset{6}{CH} - \underset{5}{HC} \overset{1}{\underset{}{S}} \overset{2}{\underset{}{C}} - Me \quad \begin{array}{c} \overset{11}{Me} \\ \end{array}$$

$$\ldots \ldots (2.24)$$

Further degradation of the labelled penicillin showed that most of the radioactivity derived from α-tritiated cystine is located at position 6 which is what would be expected for intact incorporation of cystine.

Gliotoxin—Another example of the use of a tritiated amino acid, this time generally labelled, is the incorporation of phenylalanine-T(G) into gliotoxin (2.25) which provided evidence that all nine carbon atoms are incorporated[302].

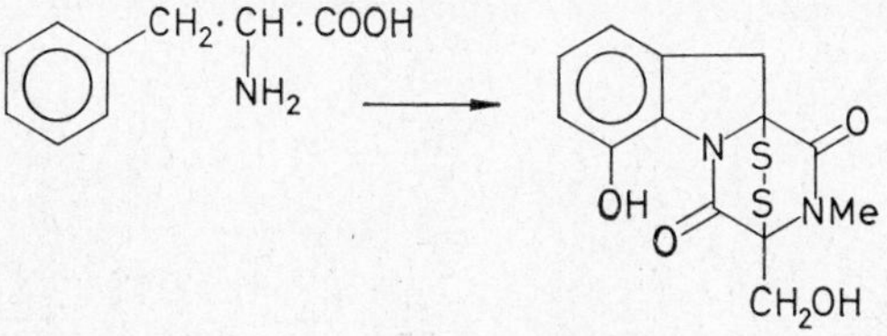

$$\ldots \ldots (2.25)$$

(C2) Cytological Applications and Autoradiography

Many of the results from the use of tritium compounds, particularly in cytological investigations (or to use the current term 'Molecular Biology'), depend upon autoradiographic examination of the specimens. The technique of autoradiography with tritium compounds has for the first time made it possible to study the dynamics of cell proliferation and of chemical processes occurring not only in the whole cell but also within single chromosomes and chromatids. Fuller details of the techniques employed in autoradiography are given in Chapter 5.

The very low energy and low penetrating power of the tritium β-radiation permits precise localization on autoradiographs (to within less than 1 μ) of the atom that disintegrates. This is a unique property of tritium[303]; other radioisotopes such as phosphorus-32[304] or even sulphur-35 and carbon-14[305] cannot give such fine resolution.

These very sharply defined autoradiographs have made tritium of prime importance in detailed cytological investigations and for the localization of compounds in various organs and tissues. In fact it has been said[306] that the introduction of high-resolution autoradiography with tritium compounds is 'probably the most dramatic achievement with radioisotopes in the past few years'. The very large number of publications, and the wealth of information which have flowed into various journals over the past few years and which continue to do so at an increasing pace, would certainly support this statement.

Most attention has so far been focused on the use of tritiated nucleotides and nucleosides for labelling deoxyribosenucleic acid (DNA) and ribosenucleic acid (RNA), the essential constituents of all living cells. Although it was shown in 1951 that the 2'-deoxyribonucleoside thymidine (2.26a) is a specific precursor of DNA[307], it was not until 1957 that the tritiated material was first prepared[308, 309] and subsequently shown to be of immense value as a radioactive tracer. For example, the experiments carried out by Taylor, Woods and Hughes at Columbia University (U.S.A.)[309] in 1957 demonstrated for the first time the mechanism of chromosome duplication, as originally

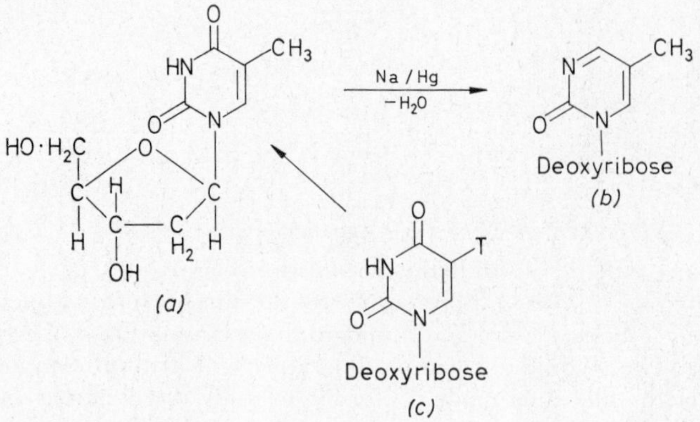

$$\dots \dots (2.26)$$

proposed by Watson and Crick[309a] (Cambridge University) in 1953. It is interesting to note that a slight alteration in the structure of thymidine by (say) converting it into the corresponding pyrimid-2-one (2.26b) is sufficient to completely prevent its incorporation into

DNA. This was demonstrated by Laland and Serck-Hanssen using tritiated 5-methyl-pyrimid-2-one-2'-deoxyriboside[381].

Generally labelled tritiated uridine and cytidine are used for labelling RNA[310-316], but these compounds are not specific for RNA as they also label DNA. However, by using uridine specifically labelled with tritium in the 5-position (2.26c) the tritium label in this position should be lost during any biochemical transformation into thymidine, i.e. into DNA, and the labelled compound should therefore serve as a specific precursor of RNA. Hayhoe and Quaglino[382] have shown that uridine-5-T can be used as a specific precursor of RNA from experiments using *in vitro* cultures of human leucocytes.

The actual mechanisms which regulate and trigger cell division are still unknown although knowledge of the various stages in the cell cycle has been substantially increased particularly with the aid of tritiated compounds.

The cell cycle time is the time required for a cell to complete the generation cycle $G_1 + S + G_2 + M$ where G_1 is the pre-synthetic period, S is the period of DNA synthesis, G_2 is the post-synthetic period and M is the time spent in mitosis. Synthesis of DNA normally occurs during the S period only, while RNA and protein is synthesized during G_1, G_2 and the S periods. During the actual mitotic division no DNA, very little protein and sometimes no RNA is produced[324a]. Oehlert[324b] reviews the cell cycle times for various types of cells. In general, for mammalian cells, increase in the cell cycle time corresponds to a lengthening of the G_1 period, whereas S and $G_2 + M$ periods have been found to vary relatively little[324c, 324d], having values in the region 6 to 10 h and 1 to 5 h respectively. The duration of mitosis is of great importance in evaluating the growth rate in proliferating somatic tissues[324e]; tumour cells usually have a longer replication and S period than normal cells[324f].

Tritiated thymidine is of course widely used for labelling cells synthesizing DNA, i.e. cells in S phase, but simultaneous marking of cells in two different segments of the cell cycle is often required. Van't Hof and Ying[324g] used unlabelled colchicine to mark the cells in metaphase by spindle disruption or inhibition; in conjunction with tritiated thymidine this method can be used to identify cells in two different segments. Another method is the double-labelling technique of Wimber and Quastler[324h] using tritiated and carbon-14-labelled thymidine[324m], which marks two stages of cell populations which are in S phase. The double-labelling technique has been used for studying (for example) cell population kinetics of osteogenic tissue[324i].

Highly differentiated cells (non-dividing cells) such as osteoblasts for example, can take up tritiated thymidine which is suggested to indicate a renewal of DNA connected with cellular function and not with mitosis [324j].

Numerous efforts have been made to induce transformations with exogenous (labelled) DNA in mice, rats, rabbits, ducks and fowls but with little success. Yoon and Sabo [324k] propose that this failure is due to the extremely low probability of incorporating the donor DNA marker into the recipient cells.

Tritiated myleran has been used for the determination of the size of DNA molecules in cells [324l].

Another essential constituent of cells is protein and tritiated amino acids are frequently used for labelling cellular protein [317–320].

Mathematical procedures for computing cellular proliferation kinetics are described by Dawson and Field [321] and by Rigas [322].

To attempt a complete review of the rapid progress which has been made in this field of investigation using tritium compounds, could in itself constitute a separate book. Readers are therefore referred to existing reviews by Baserga and Kisieleski [323, 324, 324a] and by Lima-de-Faria [325, 326] for further reading of this, perhaps the most fascinating application of tritium-labelled compounds.

(C3) Biological Hydrogen Transfer Reactions

Many examples of hydrogen transfer reactions are known in biology and biochemistry, although the mechanisms of only a few are completely understood. Isotopic studies using deuterium and, more recently tritium are helping to complete the understanding of some of the processes involved.

Biological hydrogen transfer reactions differ from ordinary chemical hydrogen transfer in that the hydrogen atoms which are transferred either intermolecularly or intramolecularly to the product are the same hydrogen atoms which are removed from the donor. In electron transfer they will not in general be the same, since they are derived from the hydrogen ions of the solution. The early work with deuterium which finally provided proof that biological oxidations catalysed by dehydrogenases and similar enzymes take place by this direct transfer of hydrogen atoms, is summarized by Vennesland [327].

In biological systems there are two co-enzymes which are of prime importance in hydrogen transfer processes; these are the pyridine nucleotides, nicotinamide adenine dinucleotide (NAD$^+$), also known as diphosphopyridine nucleotide (DPN$^+$), and its 3′-phosphoric acid derivative (NADP$^+$) or triphosphopyridine nucleotide (TPN$^+$)

(2.27). These compounds with their reduced forms (NADH, NADPH or DPNH and TPNH) are co-enzymes in a very large number of enzymic oxidations and reductions.

The mode of reduction of these co-enzymes was established in 1955 [328]. When NAD^+ and $NADP^+$ are converted into their reduced

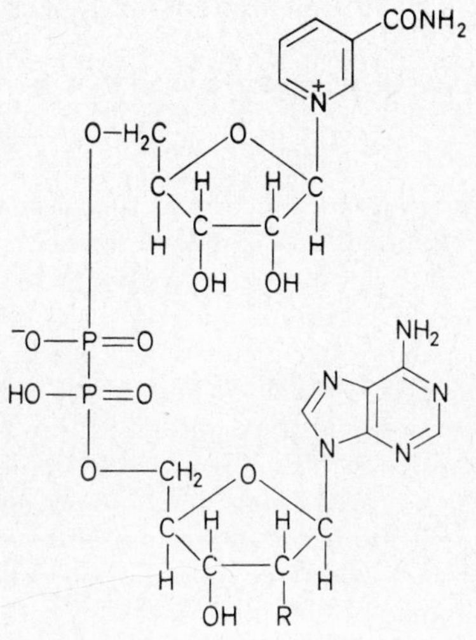

$$R = -OH \text{ (NAD)}; \quad R = -OPO_3H_2 \text{ (NADP)}$$

$$\ldots \ldots (2.27)$$

forms NADH or NADPH respectively, 1,4-reduction of the nicotin-amide ring occurs so that when re-oxidation occurs, a hydrogen atom in the 4-position is transferred from the molecule (2.28).

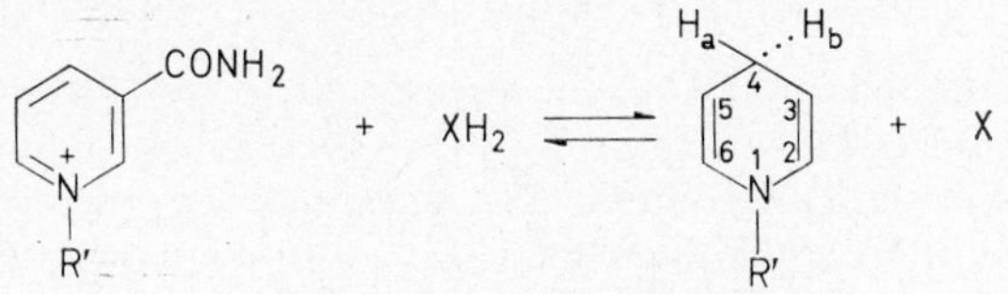

X = oxidized form of the substrate

$$\ldots \ldots (2.28)$$

NADH and NADPH both exist in alpha and beta forms. In biological systems the NAD^+ acts as the hydrogen acceptor and the NADPH as the donor. The overall reaction is (2.29)

$$NADPH + NAD^+ = NADP^+ + NADH \quad \ldots \ldots (2.29)$$

Some groups of compounds can serve as co-enzymes for carrying hydrogen alternately between the pyridine nucleotides. A classical example is that of 3α-hydroxy steroid dehydrogenase which in rat liver mediates the hydrogen transfer between the 3α-hydroxy steroids and the 3-ketosteroids [329], where the dehydrogenase doubles as a transferase to give the net result as in equation (2.30).

$$3\alpha\text{-hydroxy steroid} + NAD \rightleftharpoons 3\text{-ketosteroid} + NADH$$
$$3\text{-ketosteroid} + NADPH \rightleftharpoons 3\alpha\text{-hydroxy steroid} + NADP$$

$$. \quad . \quad . \quad . \quad (2.30)$$

Further basic information concerning the mechanism of hydrogen transfer can be obtained from standard textbooks on enzymes [330].

The enzyme-catalysed transfer of hydrogen to and from the nicotinamide ring of the pyridine nucleotides is known to be stereospecific [331] for a particular enzyme which operates with only one of the two available positions (H_a or H_b) on the reduced C-4 position. Enzymes are therefore classified into A-type which transfer H_a or B-type which transfer H_b [331]. The absolute configuration of the two atoms H_a and H_b has been determined by Cornforth et al. [332].

By substituting tritium (or deuterium) for one of the hydrogen atoms at position 4, valuable information relating to hydrogen transfer processes may be obtained and this is one of the few examples of the use of tritium as a tracer for hydrogen in biological systems. Although deuterium has the advantage of high accuracy with no radiation effects, tritium has the advantage of a more rapid estimation of the isotope. At the specific activities normally used for this type of investigation (about 1 mc/mM for the co-enzymes) no abnormal effects due to radiation have been reported. The preparation of the tritiated pyrimidine nucleotides is discussed in Chapter 4.

Some examples of the use of the tritiated nucleotides include:

1. An examination of the stereospecificity of dehydrogenase reactions [333].
2. Use of NADPH-T to demonstrate the transfer of hydrogen from the 6-position of the pteridine ring of 5,10-methylene tetrahydrofolate to thymidylate, during the biosynthesis of the latter in Streptococcus faecalis R [334].
3. The beta-position of the NADPH-T was shown to be involved during the biosynthesis of squalene from farnesyl pyrophosphate [335] and subsequent conversion into cholesterol in rat liver [336].
4. There are numerous examples [337–339, 341] in fatty acid biosynthesis: for example, the tritium atom from the 1-position of glucose is

46

efficiently transferred to the fatty acids by lactating rat mammary-gland preparations, in the presence of NADP[340].

5. The relationship between the loss of tritium from a pyridine nucleotide and time, and between the integral change of specific activity of the pyridine nucleotide and time, has been shown to follow a normal decay law[340].

An example of another type of hydrogen transfer system investigated is the glutamate isomerase reaction. An attempt to find the source of the hydrogen atom which is transferred between the β-carbon of glutamate and the methyl carbon of β-methyl aspartate by studying the glutamate isomerase reaction in tritiated or deuterated water, proved that a free proton is not involved in the reaction[342].

(C4) Tritium in Agriculture

Apart from the use of tritiated water for soil-irrigation studies which was mentioned earlier in the chapter (page 20), very little specific use has been made of tritium-labelled compounds in agriculture. Conferences have been devoted entirely to the use of radio-isotopes in agriculture[343] without having one example involving the use of tritium. One earlier reported investigation involves a study of the metabolism of hexoestrol (used in cattle fattening) in cattle after feeding with a diet containing tritiated hexoestrol[344].

A little work has been done on studying the effects of compounds on fruit ripening. For example, ethylene is known to hasten the post-harvest maturation of certain fruits[344a]. By using tritiated ethylene and mature green *Avocado* fruit, the amount of ethylene metabolized by the fruit during the ripening process can be determined. In fact this is very small and at concentrations of 250 and 2,000 p.p.m. only 0·015 and 0·042 per cent respectively are incorporated[345, 346].

D-Xylose-5-T was isolated from ripe strawberries after feeding with myo-inositol-2-T. The xylose-T was degraded to ethanol-1-T with retention of configuration at carbon-5. The same absolute configuration for the xylose and alcohol was admirably demonstrated

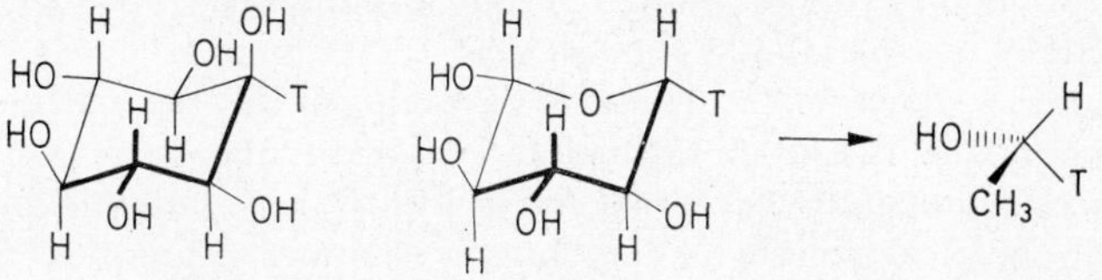

. . . . (2.31)

by using the ethanol-1-T as substrate for yeast alcohol dehydrogenase and NAD⁺, which yielded tritiated NADH and unlabelled acetaldehyde (2.31)[347].

Host–parasite relationships may be studied with the help of tritiated compounds. Tritiated uridine is incorporated into the cytoplasm of vegetable hyphae and of the plectenchyma layer of *Elytroderma deformans hysterothecia* growing within the needles of *Ponderosa* pine[348]. Tritium compounds used in this way provide valuable information on the fungal life cycles and on the location of hyphae within the host tissues. Three species of mistletoe growing on *Nerium oleander* are known to extract cardiac glycosides selectively from the host plant[349]. The use of (tritium) labelled compounds could make the analysis of such transfers easier.

The use of tritium compounds in helping to elucidate biosynthetic pathways in plants has already been discussed and one can forsee an extension of this use to investigations of plant diseases[350]. Other possible future investigations may involve the location and metabolism of insecticides such as D.D.T., malathion or dieldrin under natural conditions, or the effect of plant-growth hormones on cell-turnover.

(D) CLINICAL MEDICINE

The uses of tritium in clinical medicine can be divided into three major groups

    D1. Diagnostic medicine
    D2. Pharmaceutical research
    D3. Experimental radiotherapy

(D1) Diagnostic Medicine

Tritium gas can be used in the measurement of lung ventilation volumes and kinetics of respiration, to provide information on patients with respiratory diseases[351].

One of the few examples in the diagnostic use of tritium compounds is the study of tritiated folic acid retention for the routine diagnosis of megaloblastic anaemia[214–217, 219, 220]. The study of intestinal absorption of tritiated human serum albumin has also been reported[150].

There is however little use of tritium (or indeed carbon-14) compounds in diagnostic medicine, even experimentally. Current research is hopefully exploring the wealth of new radionuclides in simple chemical forms with emphasis on scanning techniques[352, 353]; it tends to avoid the problem, which is admittedly much more difficult, of turning known biochemistry to practical diagnostic use. When this development comes, as it surely must, tritium will often be the tracer of choice, if only because of its chemical versatility and low toxicity.

(D2) *Pharmaceutical Research*

The criteria for the acceptance of new drugs for pharmacological use in humans have become more stringent in the past three years. Before any drug can be accepted and used clinically some knowledge of its metabolism (especially its distribution, turnover and excretion) is commonly required by national licensing authorities.

Information as to whether a drug is metabolized slowly or rapidly in man can also, for example, furnish a rational basis for establishing dosage schedules needed for its initial clinical evaluation.

Such detailed information on new (and old-established) drugs is usually best obtained by tracer experiments. It is indeed fair to observe that research laboratories which have taken up tracer methods in the first place to help meet licensing requirements have quickly come to recognize their value in the development of new and improved drugs. The pharmacologist is no longer satisfied to know only the ultimate effects of a drug; he wishes to know in increasing detail every step in its action. Radioactive-labelled compounds, particularly those labelled with carbon-14 or tritium, as Professor Paoletti has observed [354], will play an ever-increasing role in pharmacological research.

The use of tritium-labelled drugs would seem to provide a valuable and inexpensive method for investigating these basic requirements. Commercial secrecy and patent regulations often prevent publication of information and may largely account for what seems to be a meagre use of tritium (and carbon-14) compounds for drug evaluation. The uncertainty of the stability of the tritium label under biological conditions may also account for their lack of use, but of course this would not apply to carbon-14 compounds where the stability of the label is known.

The stability of tritium compounds under chemical and biological conditions is discussed in Chapter 6 with a view to clarifying some mistaken conceptions concerning the stability of tritium compounds generally.

Some tritiated drugs which have been studied include tetracycline (2.32) [235], dihydrostreptomycin (2.33) [235], oleandomycin [355] and the tranquillizer 'Atarax' (2.34) [355]. In the case of tetracycline for example, the highest concentrations of the antibiotic 30 min after administration is in the liver, and the excretion via the bile is indicated by the high concentration in the gall bladder. Tetracycline is accumulated in all lymphoid tissues but the concentration in the blood is lower than in most other tissues, in contrast to other antibiotics.

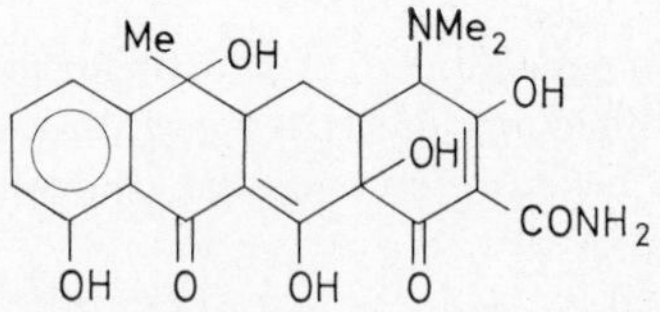

Tetracycline

. . . . (2.32)

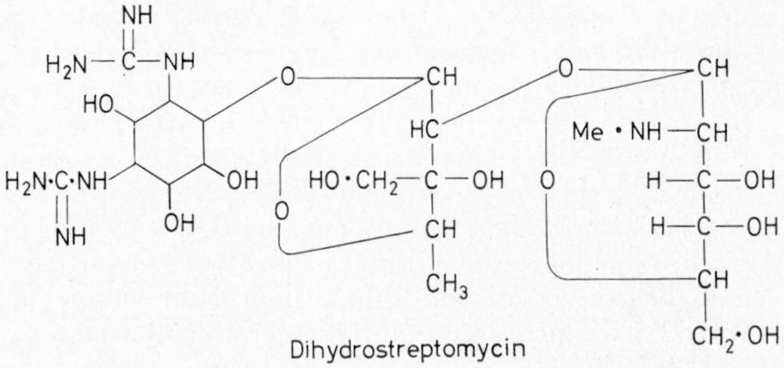

Dihydrostreptomycin

. . . . (2.33)

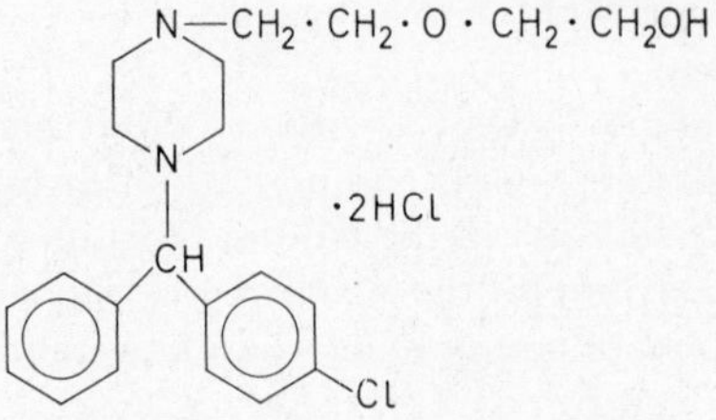

Atarax

. . . . (2.34)

Another indirect approach to the investigation of the action of drugs, is to study the effect of the drug on the metabolism of a (tritium) labelled compound of known metabolic behaviour. An example is the effect of cocaine on the metabolism of tritiated noradrenaline. Results show that cocaine (and reserpine) markedly reduces the uptake of circulatory noradrenaline into certain tissues (adrenal gland, heart, spleen and liver), presumably by interfering with the binding of the hormones[356]. This has the effect of raising the amount of circulating catecholamine and causes super-sensitivity of the sympathetically innervated organs.

Similar studies have been carried out by following changes in the metabolism of tritiated noradrenaline (norepinephrine) by tolbut-amide (1-butyl-3-tolylsulphonyl urea), a drug widely used in the treatment of diabetes[357].

There is now an ever-increasing use made of this approach to drug research[358-368] in addition to the use of tritiated drugs and more examples are given in Table 2.6.

The refinements of investigations which are possible with tracers have caused increasing attention to be given to the *precise* localization of drugs in tissues, and the changes in concentration with time. Many studies of this kind were presented in publications at the International Conference, Chicago 1964[287] (publication forthcoming[458]). The observations suggest that comparatively gross studies of concentrations in whole organs, and without attention to changes in concentration with time, may be very misleading.

Tritiated nucleosides are frequently used for labelling DNA and RNA to investigate the effects of cytotoxic drugs such as 5-fluorour-acil[359, 361, 367, 386], or of antibiotics, for example actinomycin-D[362, 383], puromycin[368, 384], or mitomycin[385], or simply the effects of γ or x-irradiation. Other examples are shown in Table 2.6.

TABLE 2.6

Use of Tritiated Compounds for Studying 'Drug' and Radiation Effects

Labelled compound	Biological system	Investigation	References
DL-norAdrenaline-7-T	Intact rat brain	Effect of imipramine and related cpd.	387
DL-norAdrenaline-7-T	Cat, cerebral cortex, heart and spleen	Effect of reserpine and ouabain	225
Carbaminoyl choline chloride-(*methyl*-T) (Carbachol)	Rat brain slices	Effect of d-tubocurarine	388
Cytidine-T	Mouse epidermal cells	Action of carcinogenic hydrocarbons	389
Cytidine-T	Rat central nervous system	Effect of radiation on RNA synthesis	390
Cytidine-T	Rat	Effect of oestradiol on RNA synthesis	391
Decamethonium-N-*methyl*-T dichloride	Rat	Effect of d-tubocurarine	391a

TABLE 2.6 (*continued*)

Labelled compound	Biological system	Investigation	References
Leucine-T	Rat	Effect of oestradiol on protein synthesis	391
L-Phenylalanine-2,3-T	Rat and mouse	Effect of ionizing radiation on protein synthesis	425
Pregnenolone-7α-T Progesterone-7α-T	Rat adrenal slices	Effect of adrenocorticotrophic hormone and adenosine cyclic 3′,5′-monophosphate on (tritiated) cortisol formation	392
Thymidine-T	Regenerating rat liver tissue	Effect of cortisone and adrenocorticotrophic hormone	393
Thymidine-T	Suspension of human cells	Effect of puromycin and chloramphenicol	394
Thymidine-T	Human leukocyte cells *in vitro*	Effect of β-mercaptoethanol and other sulphhydryl compounds	395
Thymidine	Mouse cells	Effect of endoxan (cyclophosphamide)	396 397
Thymidine-T	Rat tumour cells	Effect of 3′-methyldiaminoazobenzene	324f
Thymidine-T	Mouse adrenal cells	Effect of carbon tetrachloride stress	398
Thymidine-T	Vaccinia-infected mouse fibroblasts	Effect of cold shock	399
Thymidine-T	Rat submaxillary gland	Effect of isoproterenol hydrochloride 1(3,4-dihydroxyphenyl-alanine)2-isopropylaminoethanol HCl	400
Thymidine-T	Rat testis, intestine, adrenal gland	Effect of 9,10-dimethylbenzanthracene	401
Thymidine-T	Rat	Effect of pyridoxine deficiency on nucleic acid metabolism	402
Thymidine-T	Chinese hamster cells	Effect of radiation	403, 404
Thymidine-T	Mouse	Effect of radiation	405, 406
Thymidine-T	Rat	Effect of radiation	407
Thymidine-T	Rat nerve cells	Effect of x-irradiation on DNA synthesis	409
Thymidine-T	Mouse lung cells	Effect of x-irradiation on urethane-stimulated cell proliferation	410
Thymidine-T	HeLa cells	Effect of x-irradiation	411
Thymidine-T	D98S cells (from human bone marrow)	Combined effects of 5-bromodeoxyuridine and u.v.-light	412
Thymidine-T	Ehrlich ascites tumour cells	Effect of x-irradiation	413, 414

(D) CLINICAL MEDICINE

TABLE 2.6 (continued)

Labelled compound	Biological system	Investigation	References
Thymidine-T	Injured cells of lens epithelium	Effect of x-irradiation	415
Thymidine-T	Grasshopper neuro-blast chromosomes	Effect of x-irradiation	416
Thymidine-T ⎫ Thymine-T ⎬ Thymidine-T ⎭	E. coli (chromo-somes)	Effect of x-irradiation	417
	Drosophila melanogaster	Effect of radiation	418
Thymidine-T	Murine spinal cord cells	Effects of radiation	422
Tritiated water	Rat	Effect of radiation	419
Tritiated water	Rat	Effect of α-p-chloro-phenoxyisobutyryl ethyl ester on cholesterol biosyn-thesis	420
Uracil-T	E. coli	Ethylenediamine sen-sitization of cells to actinomycin	421
Uridine-T	Salivary gland chromosomes of Chironomus tentans	Effects of actinomycin and puromycin	423
Uridine-T	Ehrlich ascites cells in the mouse peritoneal cavities	Effect of colchicine, vinblastine and vin-cristine on RNA synthesis	424
DL-Valine-T(G)	Vicia faba chromo-somes	Effects of radiation	408

In all such investigations tritium-labelled compounds and high-resolution autoradiography offer, of course, the highest possible degree of tissue localization.

To conclude this section perhaps the most important points to emphasize are, the necessity of using radiochemically pure labelled drugs, the possibility of isotope effects particularly using tritium compounds, the biological stability or instability of the tritium label and finally the possible effects of radiation on the system.

(D3) Experimental Radiotherapy

The basic principles in the treatment of cancer by radiotherapy are 'old-established'[369] but it has long been sought to apply Ehrlich's idea of the 'magic bullet' to radiotherapy, by developing radioactive chemical compounds which will be selectively taken up by the tumour cells in sufficient quantity to destroy them without intolerable irradiation of surrounding normal tissue.

Tritium is in many ways peculiarly suitable for such a compound. The maximum range in tissue of unit density is only 6 μ and the mean

53

range 0·9 μ, which makes the radiation very localized. A concentration of 1 mc/g delivers a dose of 293 rads/day, and the high maximum specific activity of 29 c/matom of tritium makes therapeutic doses attainable without demanding too much in the way of selective uptake. Its half-life is convenient and its chemical character permits of synthesis into a very wide range of compounds.

Professor J. S. Mitchell and his colleagues at Cambridge University have worked systematically for many years on this subject[255, 370-376], concentrating their attention finally on the salts of 2-methyl-1,4-naphthaquinol diphosphate (2.35).

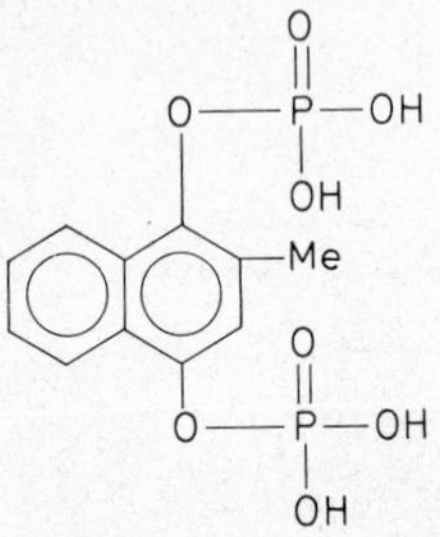

. . . . (2.35)

This compound can be labelled with tritium to a very high specific activity (3 tritium atoms per molecule) by the halogen–tritium exchange of suitable halogenated intermediates[374, 378].

An encouraging differential uptake into tumour cells has been demonstrated and has had some success in the treatment of spontaneous tumours in animals[376]. Clinical trials are now in progress[375a, 375b] but are being complicated by the instability and erratic behaviour of the labelled compound at high specific activities[375].

One cannot help but feeling that there must also be other compounds which might be examined but a great deal of intensive work may be required to find them.

Concluding Remarks

These examples of the uses of tritium and its compounds make it quite evident that many more are awaiting development. Some readers may wonder why tritium does not displace carbon-14 as a tracer. Although tritium is much cheaper than carbon-14 there is no question of tritium compounds being generally substituted for those of carbon-14, since each isotope has its own peculiar properties and they must be regarded as being complementary to one another.

For metabolite studies, until the stability of the tritium label under biological conditions is ascertained, only carbon-14-labelled compounds can be used with confidence. The future development of tritium compounds and their uses depends on a thorough understanding of the behaviour of such compounds under the various environments and this aspect is dealt with in Chapter 6.

For further reading articles may be selected from the bibliography pertaining to applications of tritium compounds (page 68).

REFERENCES AND BIBLIOGRAPHY

[1] U.S.A.E.C. Press Release B–62, 27th April, 1959

[2] Lefevre, H. W. *Diss. Abstr.* 22 (1962) 4380

[3] Holtzman, R. B. *Argonne Natn. Lab. Radiol. Phys. Div. Semi-annual Rep.* ANL–6474 (July–Dec. 1961), 42

[4] Coleman, R. F. *Analyst, Lond.* 86 (1961) 39

[5] Steim, J. M. *Diss. Abstr.* 23 (10) (1963) 3632

[6] Rochlin, R. S. *Rev. scient. Instrum.* 23 (1952) 100

[7] Redstone, R. and Rowland, M. C. *Nature, Lond.* 201 (1964) 1115

[8] Olive, G., Cameron, J. F. and Clayton, C. G. *A.E.R.E. Harwell Rep.* AERE–R 3920 (1962)

[9] Scott, V. D. and Owen, L. W. *Brit. J. appl. Phys.* 10 (1959) 91

[10] Adelson, H. E., Bostick, H. A., Moyer, B. J. and Waddell, C. N. *Rev. scient. Instrum.* 31 (1960) 1

[11] Brook, B., Zavyalov, A. and Kapirin, G. *Proc. 2nd Int. Conf. peaceful Uses atom. Energy,* Geneva 19 (1958) 219

[11a] Cupp, C. R. and Flubacher, P. J. *J. nucl. Mater.* 6 (1962) 213

[12] Petrov, V. I. and Oparin, E. M. *Priborý Tekh. Éksp.* 5 (1962) 38

[13] McCormick, R. D. and McCormack, J. D. *Gen. elect., Hanford Works Rep.* HW–67797 (1960)

[13a] Klassen, N. V. and Baerg, A. P. *Can. J. Chem.* 42 (1964) 2684

[14] Condon, R. D. *Analyt. Chem.* 31 (1959) 1717

[14a] Shoemake, G. R., Fenimore and Zlatkis, A. *J. Gas Chromatog.* 3 (8) (1965) 285

[15] Reasbeck, P. *Proc. Conf. Radioisotopes phys. Sci. Ind.,* I.A.E.A., Vienna 2 (1962) 157

[16] Blanc, D. and Dagnac, R. *Vide* 18 (1963) 322 (NSA. 17 (1963) 32325)

[17] Cameron, J. F., Rhodes, J. R. and Berry, P. F. *A.E.R.E. Harwell, Rep.* AERE–R 3086 (1963)

[18] Enomoto, S., Watanabe, M., Furuta, T. and Mori, C. *Radio-Isotopes, Tokyo* 10 (1961) 112

[19] Kannuna, M. M., Cameron, J. F. *Int. J. appl. Radiat. Isotopes* 2 (1957) 76

[20] *Nucleonics* 11 (8) (1953) 73; *Rev. scient. Instrum.* 24 (1953) 564

[21] *Tracerlog* 69 (1955) 3

[22] Kroh, J., Green, B. C. and Spinks, J. W. T. *Nature, Lond.* 189 (1961) 655

[23] Damerau, W., Lassmann, G., Thom, H.-G. *Z. phys. Chem.* 223 (1963) 99

[23a] Nias, A. H. W. and Lajtha, G. *Nature, Lond.* 208 (1965) 400

[24] Eikodd, A., Reistad, A., Storruste, A. and Synnes, J. *Physics Med. Biol.* 6 (1961) 25

[25] McCarthy, R. and Mejdahl, V. *Physics Med. Biol.* 8 (1963) 279

[26] Shapiro, E. (Tracerlab. Inc.), *U.S. Patent 2,749,251* (5th June, 1956)

[27] Fischer, E. and Kaltenhauser, A. (Trilux-Lenze, K.-G) *Ger. Patent 1,113,752* (14th Sept. 1961)

[28] Heller, A. and Anbar, M. *Israel Atom. Energy Comm. Rep.* IA–735, Part II, 1962

[29] Gamma Ges. für Praktische Radiologie Harthann and Futterknecht and Westo G.m.b.H., Fabrik für Chemisch-Technische Erzeugnisse, *Brit. Patent 874,791* (10th Aug. 1961)

[30] Radiochemical Centre (Unpublished results)

[31] Dane, J. *Atom. Energy Law J.* 4 (1) (1962)

[32] Graul, E. H., Futterknecht, R. and Hundeshagen, H. *Atompraxis* 8 (1962) 175

[33] Wahl, R. *Ind. Lackier-Betrieb* 30 (1962) 187, 228

[34] Veit, W. *Kerntechnik* 5 (1963) 221

[35] Reynolds, S. A. and Leddicotte, G. W. *Nucleonics* 21 (8) (1963) 128

[36] Renault, H. *Bull. Soc. chim. Fr.* (4) (1963) 657

[37] Takeuchi, T. and Asano, T. *Z. phys. Chem. Frankf. Ausg.* 36 (1963) 118

[38] Evans, C. and Herrington, J. *Proc. Conf. Radioisotopes Phys. Sci. Ind.*, I.A.E.A., Vienna 2 (1962) 309

[39] Evans, C. and Herrington, J. *Analyt. Chem.* 35 (1963) 1907

[40] Eastham, J. F. and Raaen, V. F. *Analyt. Chem.* 31 (1959) 555

[41] Chleck, D. J. and Ziegler, C. A. *Nucleonics* 17 (9) (1959) 130

[42] Chleck, D. J., Brousaides, F. J., Sullivan, W. and Ziegler, C. A. *Int. J. appl. Radiat. Isotopes* 7 (1960) 182

[43] Whitehead, J. K. *Biochem. J.* 80 (1961) 35P

[44] Beale, D. and Whitehead, J. K. *Proc. Symp. Tritium phys. Biol. Sci.*, I.A.E.A., Vienna 1 (1962) 179

[45] Peterson, R. E. *Atomlight* (24) (1962) 2

[46] Peterson, R. E. *Adv. Tracer Methodol.* 1 (1961) 265

[47] Kliman, B. and Peterson, R. E. *J. biol. Chem.* 235 (1960) 1639

[48] Avivi, P., Simpson, S. A., Tait, J. F. and Whitehead, J. K. *Radioisotope Conference*, Oxford 1 (1954) 313

[49] Demey, E. *Bull. Soc. Chim. biol.* 41 (1959) 795

[50] Ködding, R., Lamprecht, W., Wolff, H. P., Karl, J. and Koczorek, K. R. *Z. analyt. Chem.* 181 (1961) 574

[51] Woolever, C. A. and Goldfien, A. *Int. J. appl. Radiat. Isotopes* 14 (1963) 163

[51a] Woolever, C. A. *Proc. 2nd Int. Congr. Endocrinology*, London, August 1964. Int. Congress Series No. 83. Excepta Medica Foundation, London 1965, page 287

[52] Rosenblum, C. *Analyt. Chem.* 29 (1957) 1740

[52a] O'Grady, J. E. and Heald, P. J. *Nature, Lond.* 205 (1965) 390

[53] Barlow, J. J. *Analyt. Biochem.* 6 (1963) 435

[54] Berliner, D. L. *Atomlight* (31) (1963) 1

[54a] Dominguez, O. V., Seely, J. R. and Gorski, J. *Analyt. Chem.* 35 (1963) 1243

[55] Kliman, B. and Peterson, R. E. *Fedn. Proc. Fedn. Am. Socs exp. Biol.* 17 (1958) 255 (Abstract only)

[56] Whitehead, J. K. and Beale, D. *Clinica chim. Acta* 4 (1959) 710

[57] Baldessarini, R. J. and Kopin, I. J. *Analyt. Biochem.* 6 (1963) 289

[58] Baumgartner, W. E., Lazer, L. and Dalziel, A. *Adv. Tracer Methodol.* 1 (1962) 257

REFERENCES AND BIBLIOGRAPHY

[58a] Bogner, R. L., Domek, N. S., Eleftheriou, S. and Ross, J. J. *Nuclear Science and Engineering Corp. U.S.A. Rep.* NSEC–85 (15th May, 1963)

[59] Wilzbach, K. E. *Proc. Conf. Radioisotopes Phys. Sci. Ind.*, I.A.E.A., Vienna 3 (1962) 463

[60] Burr, J. G. *J. Phys. Chem.*, Ithaca 61 (1957) 1481

[61] Furlong, N. B. *Analyt. Biochem.* 5 (1963) 515

[62] Aylward, G. H., Garnett, J. L., Hayes, J. W. and Law, S. W. *J. inorg. nucl. Chem.* 16 (1961) 350; idem *Chemy. Ind.* (20) (1960) 560

[63] Joris, G. G. and Taylor, H. S. *J. chem. Phys.* 16 (1948) 45

[64] Caddock, B. D. and Davies, P. L. *J. Inst. Petrol* 46 (1960) 391

[65] Jones, J. R. and Monk, C. B. *J. chem. Soc.* (1963) 2633

[66] Cameron, J. F., Boyce, I. S. and Glaister, R. M. *Brit. J. appl. Phys.* 10 (1959) 463

[67] Kitahara, K. and Tanaka,Y. *J. pharm. Soc. Japan* 83 (1963) 559

[68] Calkins, G. D., Pobereskin, M., Young, V. E. and Nowacki, L. J. *Nucleonics* 13 (2) (1955) 76

[69] Nakayama, F. S. and Jackson, R. D. *J. phys. Chem.*, Ithaca 67 (1963) 932

[70] Krembs, G. M. *J. electrochem. Soc.* 110 (1963) 938

[71] Reid, A. F. and Mills, R. *J. inorg. nucl. Chem.* 26 (1964) 892

[72] Wyttenbach, A. *Helv. chim. Acta* 44 (1961) 418

[73] Alekseev, F. A., Soifer, V. N., Filonov, V. A. and Finkel'Shtein, Ia. B. *Soviet J. atom. Energy* 4 (1958) 396

[74] Kaufmann, W. J. and Orlob, G. T. *Trans. Am. geophys. Un.* 37 (1956) 297

[75] Merritt, W. F. *Hlth Phys.* 8 (1962) 185

[76] Pro, M. J. and Etienne, A. D. *J. Ass. off. agric. Chem.* 42 (1959) 386

[77] Pro, M. J., Martin, W. L. and Etienne, A. D. *U.S. Treasury Dept. Internal Revenue Service Rep.* TID–13828 (1961)

[78] Kaufman, S. and Libby, W. F. *Phys. Rev.* 93 (1954) 1337

[79] Von Buttlar, H. and Wendt, I. *Proc. 2nd Int. Conf. peaceful Uses Atom. Energy*, Geneva 18 (1958) 591

[80] Libby, W. F. *J. geophys. Res.* 68 (1963) 4485

[81] Carlston, C. W. *Science, N.Y.* 143 (1964) 804

[82] *Int. atom. Energy Ag. Bull.* 5 (3) (1963) 11

[83] Von Buttlar, H., Vielstich, W. and Barth, H. *Ber. Bunsenges. phys. Chem.* 67 (8) (1963) 650

[84] Ostlund, H. G. and Werner, E. *Proc. Symp. Tritium Phys. Biol. Sci.*, I.A.E.A., Vienna 1 (1962) 95

[85] Bockris, J. O'M., Srinivasan, S. and Devanathan, M. A. V. *J. electroanal. Chem.* 6 (1963) 205

[85a] Borowitz, J. L. and Gat, J. R. *Int. J. appl. Radiat. Isotopes* 15 (1964) 401

[85b] Crespi, M. B. A. and Perschke, H. *Int. J. appl. Radiat. Isotopes* 15 (1964) 569

[86] Carr, D. R. *Adv. Tracer Methodol.* 1 (1962) 263

[87] Welge, H. J. *Oil Gas J.* 77 (1955) 54

[88] Frederick, B. J. *Int. J. appl. Radiat. Isotopes* 14 (1963) 401

[89] Kaufman, W. J. and Todd, D. K. *Proc. Symp. Tritium Phys. Biol. Sci.*, I.A.E.A., Vienna 1 (1962) 83

[90] Giletti, B. J. and Kulp, J. L. *Science, N.Y.* 129 (1959) 901

[91] Schumacher, E., Hughes, B., Oeschger, H., Mühlemann, C. and Renaud, A. *AED-Conf.* 62–142–18 (Presented at the *Symp. Trace Gases and Natural Artificial Radioactivity in the Atmosphere*, Utrecht, Aug. 1962)

92 Whisman, M. L., Eccleston, B. H., Schwartz, F. G., Allbright, C. S. and Ward, C. C. *Trans. Am. nucl. Soc.* 3 (1960) 202

93 Arrol, W. J. and Jefferson, S. *Brit. Patent 738,182* (12th Oct. 1955)

94 Böeseken, J. *Recl. Trav. chim. Pays-Bas Belg.* 37 (1918) 255

95 Zelinsky, N. D. and Pawlow, G. S. *Ber. dt. chem. Ges.* 66 (1933) 1420

96 Linstead, R. P., Braude, E. A., Mitchell, P. W. D., Wooldridge, K. R. H. and Jackman, L. M. *Nature, Lond.* 169 (1952) 100

97 Moravek, J. and Filip, J. *Colln Czech. chem. Commun, Engl. Edn,* 25 (1960) 2697

98 Lindauer, M. W. and Smith, H. A. *J. org. Chem.* 27 (1962) 2245

99 Okazaki, N. and Okumura, A. *Bull. chem. Soc. Japan* 34 (1961) 989

100 Chleck, D., Brousaides, F. J. and Ziegler, C. A. *Int. J. appl. Radiat. Isotopes* 15 (1964) 627

101 Eaborn, C. and Taylor, R. *J. chem. Soc.* (1960) 3301

102 Eaborn, C. and Taylor, R. *J. chem. Soc.* (1961) 247, 1012

103 Eaborn, C. and Taylor, R. *J. chem. Soc.* (1961) 2388

104 Baker, R., Eaborn, C. and Taylor, R. *J. chem. Soc.* (1961) 4927

105 Baker, R. and Eaborn, C. *J. chem. Soc.* (1961) 5077

106 Baker, R., Eaborn, C. and Sperry, J. A. *J. chem. Soc.* (1962) 2382

107 Baker, R., Bott, R. W. and Eaborn, C. *J. chem. Soc.* (1963) 2136

107a Bancroft, K. C. C., Bott, R. W. and Eaborn, C. *Chemy. Ind.* (1964) 1951

108 Kresge, A. J. and Chiang, Y., *J. Am. chem. Soc.* 83 (1961) 2877

108a Blatchly, J. M. and Taylor, R. *J. chem. Soc.* (1964) 4641

108b Schulze, J. and Long, F. A. *J. Am. chem. Soc.* 86 (1964) 331

108c Thomas, R. J. and Long, F. A. *J. Am. chem. Soc.* 86 (1964) 4770

109 Katritzky, A. R. and Ridgewell, B. J. *J. chem. Soc.* (1963) 3753

110 Yakushin, F. S. *Usp. Khim.* 31 (1962) 241

111 Eastham, J. F., Bloomer, J. L. and Hudson, F. M. *Tetrahedron* 18 (1962) 653

112 Zollinger, H. *Advances in Physical Organic Chemistry* Ed. V. Gold, Vol. 2, page 163, 1964. London and New York; Academic Press

113 Brown, L. M. *Natn. Bur. Stand.,* NBS-4712 (July, 1956) and NBS-4877 (Nov. 1956)

114 Kay, J. G. and Rowland, F. S. *J. org. Chem.* 24 (1959) 1800

115 Crawhall, J. C. and Smyth, D. G. *Biochem. J.* 69 (1958) 280

116 Schlenk, F. and Dainko, J. L. *Biochem. biophys. Res. Commun.* 8 (1962) 24

117 Muller, G., Martel, J. and Huynh, C. *Bull. Soc. chim. Fr.* (1961) 2000

118 Gut, M. and Hayano, M. *Atomlight* (23) (1962) 1

119 Duncan, J. F. and Lynn, K. R. *Aust. J. Chem.* 10 (1957) 1

120 Simon, H., Keil, K.-D. and Weygand, F. *Chem. Ber.* 95 (1962) 17

121 Weygand, F., Daniel, H. and Simon, H. *Chem. Ber.* 91 (1958) 1691; *Justus Liebigs Annln Chem.* 654 (1962) 111

122 Hofmann, J. E., Muller, R. J. and Schriesheim, A. *J. Am. chem. Soc.* 85 (1963) 3002

123 Powell, A. L., Swain, C. G. and Morgan, C. R. *Proc. Symp. Tritium Phys. Biol. Sci.,* I.A.E.A. Vienna 1 (1962) 153

124 Pace, N., Kline, L., Schachman, H. K. and Harfenist, M. *J. biol. Chem.* 168 (1947) 459

125 Solomon, A. K., Sidel, V. W. and Paganelli, C. V. *Proc. 1st Natn. Biophys. Conf.* Eds. H. Quastler and H. J. Morowitz, New Haven, Yale University Press (1959) p. 322 (Abstract only)

[126] Prentice, T. C., Sin, W., Berlin, N. I., Hyde, G. M., Parsons, R. J., Sviner, E. E. and Lawrence, J. H. *J. clin. Invest.* 31 (1952) 412

[127] Fallot, P., Aeberhardt, A. and Masson, J. *Int. J. appl. Radiat. Isotopes* 1 (1957) 237

[128] Taggart, N. and Hytten, F. E. *Nature, Lond.* 184 (1959) 457

[129] Coppen, A. J. and Gibbons, J. L. *Nature, Lond.* 186 (1960) 724

[130] Zuppinger, A., Poretti, G., Schwarz, K., Zaoralek, P. and Aebi, H. *Radiologia clin.* 32 (1963) 402

[131] Albach, R. A. *J. Protozool.* 10 (Suppl.) (1963) 7

[132] Warshawsky, H., Leblond, C. P. and Droz, B. *J. Cell Biol.* 16 (1963) 1

[133] Byers, T. J., Platt, D. B. and Goldstein, L. *J. Cell Biol.* 19 (1963) 453

[134] Fink, K., Cline, R. E., Henderson, R. B. and Fink, R. M. *J. biol. Chem.* 221 (1956) 425

[135] Rubini, J. R., Cronkite, E. P., Bond, V. P. and Fliedner, T. M. *J. clin. Invest.* 39 (1960) 909

[136] Kriss, J. P., Shaw, R. K., Loevinger, R. and Edmunds, N. *Nature, Lond.* 202 (1964) 1021

[137] Cronkite, E. P., Fliedner, T. M., Killmann, S. A. and Rubini, J. R. *Proc. Symp. Tritium Phys. Biol. Sci.* I.A.E.A., Vienna 2 (1962) 189

[138] Rubini, J. R., Keller, S., Eisentraut, A. and Cronkite, E. P. *Proc. Symp. Tritium phys. Biol. Sci.* I.A.E.A., Vienna 2 (1962) 247

[139] Bootsma, D., Budke, L. and Vos, O. *Expl Cell Res.* 33 (1964) 301

[140] Pelc, S. R. *Nature, Lond.* 193 (1962) 793

[141] Marsh, J. C. and Perry, S. *J. clin. Invest.* 43 (1964) 267

[142] Takats, S. T. and Smellie, R. M. S. *J. Cell Biol.* 17 (1963) 59

[143] Baeyens, W., Zamorani, G. and Ledoux, L. *Proc. Conf. Methods of Preparing and Storing Marked Molecules.* European Atomic Energy Community, Euratom, EUR 1625e (May 1964) p. 1191

[144] Seaman, W. and Stewart, D. *Int. J. appl. Radiat. Isotopes* 15 (1964) 565

[145] Khairallah, P. A., Page, I. H., Bumpus, F. S. and Smeby, R. R. *Science, N.Y.* 138 (1962) 523

[146] Du Vigneaud, V., Schneider, C. H., Stouffer, J. E., Murti, V. V. S., Aroskar, J. P. and Winestock, G. *J. Am. chem. Soc.* 84 (1962) 409

[146a] Fong, C. T. O., Silver, L., Christman, D. R. and Schwartz, I. L. *Proc. natn. Acad. Sci. U.S.A.* 46 (1960) 1273

[147] Mendlowitz, M., Wolf, R. L., Gitlow, S. E. and Naftchi, N. *Circulation* 25 (1962) 231

[148] Parkins, R. A., Dimitriadou, A. and Booth, C. C. *Clin. Sci.* 19 (1960) 595

[149] Jeejeebhoy, K. N. A Study of Albumin Metabolism in Gastrointestinal Disease *Ph.D. Thesis*, University of London, 1963

[150] Jeejeebhoy, K. N., Stewart, J. H., Evans, E. A. and Booth, C. C. *Gut* 5 (1964) 346

[151] Cohen, S., Holloway, R. C., Matthews, C. and McFarlane, A. S. *Biochem. J.* 62 (1956) 143

[152] Schultze, B. and Maurer, W. *Proc. Symp. Tritium Phys. Biol. Sci.*, I.A.E.A., Vienna 2 (1962) 229

[153] Gavosto, F. *Proc. Symp. Tritium Phys. Biol. Sci.* I.A.E.A., Vienna 2 (1962) 237

[154] Sachs, H. *J. Neurochem.* 10 (1963) 299

[155] Barbour, B. H. and Bartter, F. C. *J. clin. Endocr. Metab.* 23 (1963) 313

[156] Pincus, G. and Vollmer, E. P. (Eds.) *Biological Activities of Steroids in Relation to Cancer* 1960. New York and London; Academic Press

[157] Bergstrom, S., Linstredt, S., Samuelson, B., Corey, E. J. and Gregoriou, G. A. *J. Am. chem. Soc.* 80 (1958) 2337
[158] Pasqualini, J. R. and Jayle, M.-F. *Nature, Lond.* 198 (1963) 1095
[159] McCaa, C. S., Sulya, L. L., Read, V. H. and Bomer, D. L., *Physiologist, Wash.* 6 (1963) 230
[160] Kliman, B. *Atomlight* (32) (1963) 1; *Adv. Tracer Methodol.* 2 (1965) 213
[161] Flood, C., Layne, D. S., Ramcharan, S., Rossipal, E., Tait, J. F. and Tait, S. A. S. *Acta endocr. Copenh.* 36 (1961) 237
[162] Ulick, S., Kusch, K. and August, J. T. *J. Am. chem. Soc.* 83 (1961) 4482
[163] Thomas, G. H., Forchielli, E. and Brown-Grant, K. *Nature, Lond.* 202 (1964) 260
[164] Huang, W. Y. and Pearlman, W. H. *J. biol. Chem.* 238 (1963) 1308
[165] Pearlman, W. H. and Pearlman, M. R. J. *J. biol. Chem.* 236 (1961) 1321
[166] Grosser, B. I. and Bliss, E. L. *Fedn. Proc. Fedn Am. Socs exp. Biol.* 22 (2, Pt. 1) (1963) 271 (Abs.)
[167] Baulieu, E-E., Wallace, E. and Lieberman, S. *J. biol. Chem.* 238 (1963) 1316
[168] Baulieu, E-E. and Robel, P. *Steroids* 2 (1963) 111
[169] Süteri, P. K. and Lieberman, S. *Biochemistry, N.Y.* 2 (1963) 1171
[170] Chevallier, F. *Proc. Symp. Tritium Phys. Biol. Sci.*, I.A.E.A., Vienna 2 (1962) 413
[171] Hellman, L., Rosenfield, R. S., Fukushima, D. K., Bradlow, H. L., Gallagher, T. F., Gould, R. G. and Leroy, G. V. *Int. Conf. peaceful Uses Atom. Energy*, United Nations, New York, Geneva 12 (1956) 532
[172] Biggs, M. W. and Kritchevsky, D. *Circulation* 4 (1951) 34
[173] Biggs, M. W. *Int. Conf. peaceful Uses Atom. Energy*, United Nations, New York, Geneva 12 (1956) 526
[174] Plotz, E. J. Argonne Cancer Research Hospital, *Semi-annual Rep.* ACRH–4 (Sept. 1955) 30
[175] Werbin, H., Chaikoff, I. L. and Jones, E. E. *J. biol. Chem.* 234 (1959) 282
[176] Clayton, R. B. and Edwards, A. M. *J. biol. Chem.* 238 (1963) 1966
[177] Shapiro, I. L., Werthessen, N. T. and Kritchevsky, D. *Fedn Proc. Fedn Am. Socs exp. Biol.* 22 (2, Pt. 1) (1963) 590
[178] Goodman, D. S., Deykin, D., Shiratori, T. *J. biol. Chem.* 239 (1964) 1335
[179] Samuelsson, B. *J. Biol. Chem.* 234 (1959) 2852
[180] Werbin, H. and Chaikoff, I. L. *Biochim. biophys. Acta* 82 (1964) 581
[181] Stevens, W. and Berliner, D. L. *Radiat. Res.* 20 (1963) 510
[182] Jancik, I.-H., Graul, E. H. and Geipel, K. *Atompraxis* 10 (1964) 324
[183] Paterson, J. Y. F. *Biochem. J.* 86 (1963) 1P; *J. Endocr.* 28 (1964) 183
[184] MacDonald, P. C. and Gonzales, O. *J. clin. Endocr. Metab.* 23 (1963) 665
[185] Vandewiele, R. L., MacDonald, P. C., Bolte, E. and Lieberman, S. *J. clin. Endocr. Metab.* 22 (1962) 1207
[186] Wallace, E. Z. and Lieberman, S. *J. clin. Endocr. Metab.* 23 (1963) 90
[187] Cohn, G. L., Mulrow, P. J. and Dunne, V. C. *J. clin. Endocr. Metab.* 23 (1963) 671
[188] Okita, G. T. *J. Am. Geriat. Soc.* 5 (1957) 163
[189] Spratt, J. L., Okita, G. T. and Geiling, E. M. K. *Int. J. appl. Radiat. Isotopes* 2 (1957) 167
[190] Dutta, S. *Fedn Proc. Fedn Am. Socs exp. Biol.* 23 (2, Pt. 1) (1964) 122
[191] Doherty, J. E., Perkins, W. A. and Mitchell, G. K. *Archs intern. Med.* 108 (1961) 531

[192] Fukushima, D. K., Bradlow, H. L., Hellman, L. and Gallagher, T. F. *J. clin. Endocr. Metab.* 23 (1963) 266

[193] Parke, D. V., Pollock, S., Williams, R. T. *J. Pharm. Pharmac.* 15 (1963) 500

[194] Layne, D. S., Golab, T., Arai, K. and Pincus, G. *Biochem. Pharmac.* 12 (1963) 905

[195] Arai, K., Golab, T., Layne, D. S., Pincus, G. *Endocrinology* 71 (1962) 639

[196] Malinow, M. R., Moguilevsky, J. A., Lema, B. and Burr, G. E. *J. clin. Endocr. Metab.* 23 (1963) 306

[197] Fishman, J., Bradlow, H. L., Zumoff, B., Hellman, L. and Gallagher, T. F. *Acta endocr., Copenh.* 37 (1961) 57

[198] Smith, F. R., Tapley, D. F., Ross, J. E. *Biochim. biophys. Acta* 69 (1963) 68

[199] Dutta, S. *Diss. Abstr.* 24 (1963) 326

[200] Depaoli, J. and Eik-Nes, K. B. *Biochim. biophys. Acta* 78 (1963) 457

[200a] Aakyaag, A. and Eik-Nes, K. B. *Biochim. biophys Acta* 86 (1964) 380

[201] Weliky, I. and Engel, L. L. *J. biol. Chem.* 238 (1963) 1302

[201a] Killinger, D. W. and Solomon, S. *J. clin. Endocr. Metab.* 25 (1965) 290

[202] Miller, W. R. and Turner, C. W. *Steroids* 2 (1963) 657

[203] Pearlman, W. H. *Biochem. J.* 65 (1957) 7P

[204] Harkness, R. A. and Fotherby, K. *Biochem. J.* 88 (1963) 308

[205] Lawson, D. E. M. and Pearlman, W. H. *Fedn. Proc. Fedn Am. Soc. exp Biol.* 22 (2, Pt. 1) (1963) 469 (Abstract)

[206] Billiar, R. B. and Eik-Nes, K. B. *Fedn Proc. Fedn Am. Socs exp. Biol.* 23 (2, Pt. 1) (1964) 250 (Abstract)

[207] Kase, N., Kowal, J. and Soffer, L. J. *Acta Endocr.* 44 (1963) 8

[208] Kaplanis, J. N., Monroe, R. E., Robbins, W. E. and Louloudes, S. J. *Ann. ent. Soc. Am.* 56 (1963) 198

[209] Werbin, H., Chaikoff, I. L. and Jones, E. E. *J. biol. Chem.* 235 (1960) 1629

[210] Horton, R., Rosner, J. M. and Forsham, P. H. *Proc. Soc. exp. Biol. Med.* 114 (1963) 400

[211] Florini, J. R. and Buyske, D. A. *J. Biol. Chem.* 236 (1961) 247

[212] Axelrod, L. R. and Goldzieher, J. W. *J. clin. Endocr. Metab.* 22 (1962) 537

[213] Morato, T., Raab, K., Brodie, H. J., Hayano, M. and Dorfman, R. I. *J. Am. chem. Soc.* 84 (1962) 3764

[214] Anderson. B., Belcher, E. H., Chanarin, I. and Mollin, D. L. *Br. J. Haemat.* 6 (1960) 439

[215] Sheehy, T. W., Santini, R., Guerra, R., Angel, R. and Plough, I. C. *J. Lab. clin. Med.* 61 (1963) 650

[216] Klipstein, F. A. *Blood* 21 (1963) 626

[217] Johns, D. G., Sperti, S. and Burgen, A. S. V. *J. clin. Invest.* 40 (1961) 1684

[218] Baulieu, E-E. and Mauvais-Jarvis, P. *J. biol. Chem.* 239 (1964) 1569

[219] Johns, D. G. *J. clin. Invest.* 42 (1963) 945

[220] Johns, D. G. and Plenderleith, I. H. *Bioch. Pharmac.* 12 (1963) 1071

[221] Johns, D. G., Hollingsworth, J. W., Cashmore, A. R., Plenderleith, I. H. and Bertino, J. R. *J. clin. Invest.* 43 (1964) 621

[222] Henderson, E. S. and Denham, C. *Proc. Am. Ass. Cancer Res.* 4 (1963) 27

[223] Kopin, I. J. *Atomlight* (27) (1963) 1; *Adv. Tracer Methodol.* 2 (1965) 237 Plenum Press, N.Y.

[224] La Brosse, E. H., Axelrod, J., Kopin, I. J. and Kety, S. S. *Proc. Symp. Tritium Phys. Biol. Sci.* I.A.E.A., Vienna 2 (1962) 407

[225] Fecher, R., Chanley, J. D., Rosenblatt, S. *Analyt. Biochem.* 9 (1964) 54

226 Hertting, G. and La Brosse, E. H. *J. biol. Chem.* 237 (1962) 2291
227 Kopin, I. J., Axelrod, J. and Gordon, E. *J. Biol. Chem.* 236 (1961) 2109
228 Grodsky, G. M., Carbone, J. V., Fanska, R. and Peng, C. T. *Am. J. Physiol.* 203 (1962) 532
229 Grodsky, G. M., Contopoulos, A. N., Fanska, R. and Carbone, J. V. *Am. J. Physiol.* 204 (1963) 837
230 Maurer, W. and Primbsch, E. *Expl Cell Res.* 33 (1–2) (1964) 8
231 Hug, C. C. and Mellett, L. B. *Univ. Mich. med. Bull.* 29 (1963) 165
232 Tsumita, T. and Iwanaga, M. *Nature, Lond.* 198 (1963) 1088
233 Popovic, A., Becarevic, A., Kanazir, D., Stosic, N. and Pantic, V. *Nature, Lond.* 198 (1963) 165
234 Gawienowski, A. M., Knoche, H. W. and Moser, H. C. *Biochim. biophys. Acta* 65 (1962) 150
235 André, T. *Acta Radiol.* 142 (Suppl.) (1956)
236 Gloor, U. and Wiss, O. *Archs Biochem. Biophys.* 83 (1959) 216
237 Graul, E. H., Hundeshagen, H. and Steiner, B. *Atompraxis* 7 (1961) 449
238 Bolt, W., Ritzel, F., Toussaint, R. and Nahrmann, H. *Arzneimittel-Forsch.* 11 (2a) (1961) 170
238a Winnick, T., Winnick, R. E. and Bergman, E. D. *Biochim. biopyhs. Acta* 69 (1963) 48
239 Cayen, M. N., Carter, A. L. and Common, R. H. *Biochim. biophys. Acta* 86 (1964) 56
240 Lubran, M. and Corsini, G. *Minerva nucl.* 4 (1960) 130
241 Havel, R. J. and Carson, C. A. *Life Sci.* No. 9 (1963) 651
242 Holt, C. V., Voelker, J. J., Holt, L. V. *Biochim. biophys. Acta* 38 (1960) 88
243 Holt, C. V., Nolte, I. and Holt, L. V. *Proc. 2nd Int. Conf. peaceful Uses Atom. Energy*, Geneva 25 (1958) 230
244 Remy, J., Meunier, J. and Aeberhardt, A. CEA–2155 (1962)
245 Beer, C. T., Wilson, M. L. and Bell, J. *Can. Jnl. Physiol. & Pharmacol.* 42 (1964) 1
246 Sgoutas, D. S. *Diss. Abstr.* 24 (1964) 3963
247 Samuelsson, B. *J. biol. Chem.* 239 (1964) 4091
248 Potter, W. De., Bacq, Z. M., Criel, G., Schaepdryver, A. F. De. and Renson, J. *Biochem. Pharmac.* 12 (1963) 661
249 Vodopick, H. A., Hamilton, H. E., Jackson, H. B., Peng, C. T. and Sheets, R. F. *J. clin. Invest.* 42 (1963) 989
250 Smith, A., Fabrykant, M., Gitlow, S. and Wortis, S. B. *Nature, Lond.* 193 (1962) 577
251 Reed, D. J., Dost, F. N. and Wang, C. H. *Fedn Proc. Fedn Am. Socs exp. Biol.* 22 (2) (1963) 541
252 Verly, W. G., Rachele, J. R., Du Vigneaud, V., Eidinoff, M. L. and Knoll, J. E. *J. Am. chem. Soc.* 74 (1952) 5941
253 Gurin, S. and Delluva, A. M. *J. biol. Chem.* 170 (1947) 545
254 Rachele, J. R., Kuchinskas, E. J., Knoll, J. E. and Eidinoff, M. L. *Archs Biochem. Biophys.* 81 (1959) 55
255 Mitchell, J. S., King, E. A., Marrian, D. H. and Chipperfield, B. *Acta Radiologica (New Series)* 1 (5) (1963) 321
256 Pamukcu, F. S., Gerstein, J., Palma, R. and Gray, S. J. *Proc. Soc. exp. Biol. Med.* 113 (1963) 575
257 Speirs, R. S. *Proc. Symp. Tritium Phys. Biol. Sci.*, I.A.E.A., Vienna 2 (1962) 419

REFERENCES AND BIBLIOGRAPHY

[258] Saetersdal, T. A. S. *Årbok Univ. Bergen* (1963) 3

[259] Lipkin, M., Bell, B. and Sherlock, P. *J. clin. Invest.* 42 (1963) 767

[260] Brenner, R. M. *Am. J. Anat.* 112 (1963) 81

[261] Greulich, R. C., Cameron, I. L. and Thrasher, J. D. *Proc. natn. Acad. Sci. U.S.A.* 47 (1961) 743

[262] Gavosto, F., Pileri, A., Pegoraro, L. and Momigliano, A. *Nature, Lond.* 200 (1963) 807

[263] Gerber, G., Gerber, G. and Altman, K. I. *Nature, Lond.* 187 (1960) 956; *J. biol. Chem.* 235 (1960) 1433

[264] Samal, B. A., Frazier, L. E., Monto, G., Slesers, A., Hruban, Z. and Wissler, R. W. *Proc. Soc. exp. Biol. Med.* 112 (1963) 442

[265] Pinson, E. A. and Anderson, E. C. *U.S.A.E.C, Rep.*, AECU–937 (Classified); Pinson, E.A. *Univ. Calif. Rep.* LA–1218 (March, 1951)

[266] Trujillo, T. T., Anderson, E. C. and Langham, W. H. *Univ. Calif. Rep.* LA–1986 (Dec. 1955)

[267] Black, A. L., Baker, N. F., Bartley, J. C., Chapman, T. E. and Phillips, R. W. *Science, N.Y.* 144 (1964) 876

[268] Fallot, P. and Aeberhardt, A. *Proc. Int. Conf. peaceful Uses Atom. Energy*, Geneva 10 (1955) 453

[269] Gatt, S. and Berman, E. R. *J. Neurochem.* 10 (1963) 73

[270] Thompson, R. C. *G.E.C. Rep.* Hanford Works HW–20092 (1951)

[271] Thompson, R. C. *J. biol. Chem.* 200 (1953) 731

[272] Schachter, D., Finkelstein, J. D., Kowarski, S. *J. clin. Invest.* 43 (1964) 787

[273] Norman, A. W. and Deluca, H. F. *Biochemistry* 2 (1963) 1160

[274] Towbin, E. J. and Ferrell, C. B. *Physiologist, Wash.* 6 (1963) 288

[275] Towbin, E. J. and Ferrell, C. B. *J. clin. Invest.* 42 (1963) 986

[276] Thompson, G. A. *Ph.D. Thesis*, University of London, 1964

[277] Bernlohr, R. W. and Novelli, G. D. *Archs Biochem. Biophys.* 103 (1963) 94

[278] Wood, H. G., Allen, S. H. G., Stjernholm, R. and Jacobson, B. *J. biol. Chem.* 238 (1963) 547

[279] De Vitry, F. *Expl Cell Res.* 31 (1963) 376

[280] Abraham, S., Katz, J., Bartley, J. and Chaikoff, I. L. *Biochim. biophys. Acta* 70 (1963) 690

[281] Taylor, K. W. and Parry, D. G. *Biochem. J.* 89 (1963) 94P (Abstract only)

[282] Canfield, R. E. and Anfinsen, C. B. *Biochemistry* 2 (1963) 1073

[283] Taylor, K. W., Parry, D. G. and Howard Smith, G. *Nature, Lond.* 203 (1964) 1144

[284] Verly, W. G., Dewandre, A. and Moutschen-Dahmen, J. *J. molec. Biol.* 6 (1963) 175

[285] Chidsey, C. A., Kahler, R. L., Kelminson, L. L. and Braunwald, E. *Circulation Res.* 12 (1963) 220

[286] Di Costanzo, P. *C. r. Séanc. Acad. Sci.* 254 (1962) 3576

[287] *Int. Conf. Uses Isotopically Labelled Drugs in Exp. Pharmacol.*, Chicago, June 7–9th 1964 (see ref. 458)

[288] Leevy, C. M. *J. Lab. clin. Med.* 61 (1963) 761

[289] Bianchi, P. A., Crathorn, A. R. and Shooter, K. V. *Proc. Symp. Tritium Phys. Biol. Sci.*, I.A.E.A. Vienna 2 (1962) 268

[290] Roche, J., Nunez, J. and Jacquemin, C. *Proc. Symp. Tritium Phys. Biol. Sci.*, I.A.E.A. Vienna 2 (1962) 395

[291] Nunez, J., Mauchamp, J. and Roche, J. *Biochim. biophys. Acta* 86 (1964) 361

[292] Barr, G. C. and Butler, J. A. V. *Biochem. J.* 88 (1963) 252

[293] Hagen, A. A. and Eik-Nes, K. B. *Biochim. biophys. Acta* 90 (1964) 593

[294] Cunningham, K. G. and Freeman, G. G. *Biochem. J.* 53 (1953) 328

[295] Luckner, M. and Mothes, K. *Tetrahedron Lett.* (23) (1962) 1035

[296] Barton, D. H. R., Kirby, G. W., Steglich, W. and Thomas, G. M. *Proc. chem. Soc.* (1963) 203

[297] Dawson, R. F., Christman, D. R., Anderson, R. L., Solt, M. L., Diamado, A. M. and Weiss, U. *J. Am. chem. Soc.* 78 (1956) 2645

[298] Dawson, R. F., Christman, D. R., D'Adamo, A. F., Solt, M. L. and Wolf, A. P. *Chemy Ind.* (1958) 100; *J. Am. chem. Soc.* 82 (1960) 2628

[299] Karlson, P. and Hoffmeister, H. *Hoppe-Seyler's Z. physiol. Chem.* 331 (1963) 298

[300] Karlson, P. and Hoffmeister, H. *Justus Liebigs Annln Chem.* 662 (1963) 1

[300a] Huber, R. and Hoppe, W. *Chem. Ber.* 98 (1965) 2353

[301] Arnstein, H. R. V. and Crawhall, J. C. *Biochem. J.* 67 (1957) 180

[302] Winstead, J. A. and Suhadolnik, R. J. *J. Am. chem. Soc.* 82 (1960) 1644

[303] Eidinoff, M. L., Fitzgerald, P. J., Simmel, E. B. and Knoll, J. E. *Proc. Soc. exp. Biol. Med.* 77 (1951) 225

[304] Lajtha, L. G. and Oliver, R. *Med. Lab. (Stuttgart)* 8 (1959) 214

[305] Plaut, W. *Nature, Lond.* 182 (1958) 399

[306] Dunham, C. L., *Hearings before the sub-committee on Research, Development and Radiation of the Joint Committee on Atomic Energy*—U.S. Congress; U.S. Government Printing Office, Washington 25 D.C., 1961, page 4

[307] Reichard, P. and Estborn, B. *J. biol. Chem.* 188 (1951) 839

[308] Verly, W. G. and Hunebelle, G. *Bull. Socs chim. Belg.* 66 (1957) 640

[309] Taylor, J. H., Woods, P. S. and Hughes, W. L. *Proc. natn. Acad. Sci. U.S.A.* 43 (1957) 122

[309a] Watson, J. D. and Crick, F. H. C. *Nature, Lond.* 171 (1953) 737

[310] Feinendegen, L. E., Bond, V. P., Shreeve, W. W. and Painter, R. B. *Expl Cell Res.* 19 (1960) 443

[311] Fitzgerald, P. J. and Vinijchaikul, K. *Lab. Invest.* 8 (1959) 319

[312] Painter, R. B. *Radiat. Res.* 13 (1960) 726

[313] Taylor, J. H. *Ann. N.Y. Acad. Sci.* 90 (1960) 409

[314] Gall, J. G. and Callan, H. G. *Proc. natn Acad. Sci. U.S.A.* 48 (1962) 562

[315] Prescott, D. M. and Bender, M. A. *Expl Cell Res.* 26 (1962) 260

[316] Schultze, B., Oehlert, W. and Maurer, W. *Biochim. biophys. Acta* 49 (1961) 35

[317] Carneiro, J. and Leblond, C. P. *Science, N.Y.* 129 (1959) 391

[318] Mueller, H. G. and Linnartz-Niklas, A. *Arch. Gynaek.* 194 (1960) 48

[319] Prescott, D. M. *J. Histochem. Cytochem.* 10 (1962) 145

[320] Prensky, W. and Smith, H. H. *Expl Cell Res.* 34 (1964) 525

[321] Dawson, K. B. and Field, E. O. *Expl Cell. Res.* 34 (1964) 507

[322] Rigas, D. A. *Bull. math. Biophys.* 20 (1958) 68; *The Kinetics of Cellular Proliferation* Ed. Stohlman, F., p. 408, 1959. New York and London; Grune and Stratton

[323] Baserga, R. and Kisieleski, W. E. *Atompraxis* 8 (10) (1962) 386

[324] Baserga, R. and Kisieleski, W. E. *Lab. Invest.* 12 (1963) 648

[324a] Baserga, R. and Kisieleski, W. E. *Scient. Am.* 209 (2) (1963) 103

[324b] Oehlert, W. *Umschau* 64 (1964) 518

[324c] Cattaneo, S. M., Quastler, H. and Sherman, F. G. *Nature, Lond.* 190 (1961) 923

324d Young, R. W. *J. Cell Biol.* 14 (1962) 357

324e Odartchenko, N., Cottier, H., Feinendegen, L. E. and Bond, V. P. *Expl Cell Res.* 35 (1964) 402

324f Post, J. and Hoffman, J. *J. Cell. Biol.* 22 (1964) 341

324g Van't Hof, J. and Ying, H-K. *Nature, Lond.* 202 (1964) 981

324h Wimber, D. E. and Quastler, H. *Expl Cell Res.* 30 (1963) 8

324i Owen, M. and Macpherson, S. *J. Cell Biol.* 19 (1963) 33

324j Pelc, S. R. *Expl Cell Res.* 29 (1963) 194

324k Yoon, C. H. and Sabo, J. *Expl Cell Res.* 34 (1964) 599

324l Verly, W. G., Petitpas-Dewandre, A. *Nature, Lond.* 203 (1964) 865

324m Davies, D. R. and Wimber, D. E. *Nature, Lond.* 200 (1963) 229

325 Lima-de-Faria, A. *Prog. in Biophys. biophys. Chem.* 12 (1962) 281

326 Lima-de-Faria, A. *Hereditas* 45 (1959) 632 (Bibliography)

327 Vennesland, B. *Discuss. Faraday Soc.* (20) (1955) 240

328 Loewus, F. A., Vennesland, B. and Harris, D. L. *J. Am. chem. Soc.* 77 (1955) 3391

329 Hurlock, B. and Talalay, P. *J. biol. Chem.* 233 (1958) 886

330 Dixon, M. and Webb, E. C. *Enzymes* p. 343, 1960. London; Longmans

331 Levy, H. R., Talalay, P. and Vennesland, B. *Progress in Stereochemistry* Eds. de la Mare, P. B. D. and Klyne, W., vol. 3, p. 299, 1962, London; Butterworths

332 Cornforth, J. W., Ryback, G., Popjak, G., Donninger, C. and Schroepfer, G. *Biochem. biophys. Res. Commun.* 9 (1962) 371

333 Krakow, G., Ludowieg, J., Mather, J. H., Normore, W. M., Tosi, L., Udaka, S. and Vennesland, B. *Biochemistry* 2 (1963) 1009

334 Blakley, R. L., Ramasastri, B. V. and McDougall, B. M. *J. biol. Chem.* 238 (1963) 3075

335 Samuelsson, B. and Goodman, D. S. *Biochem. biophys. Res. Commun.* 11 (1963) 125

336 Samuelsson, B. and Goodman, D. S. *J. biol. Chem.* 239 (1964) 98

337 Abraham, S., Matthes, K. J. and Chaikoff, I. L. *Biochim. biophys. Acta* 47 (1961) 424

338 Pohl, S., Law, J. H. and Ryhage, R. *Biochim. biophys. Acta* 70 (1963) 583

339 Wenzel, M. and Günther, T. *Proc. Conf. Methods Preparing and Storing Marked Molecules.* European Atomic Energy Community, Euratom, EUR 1625e (May, 1964) p. 47

340 Matthes, K. J., Abraham, S. and Chaikoff, I. L. *Biochim. biophys. Acta* 70 (1963) 242

341 Wakil, S. J. *J. Lipid Res.* 2 (1961) 1; cf. Abraham, S., Katz, J., Bartley, J. and Chaikoff, I. L. *Biochim. biophys. Acta* 70 (1963) 690

342 Iodice, A. A. and Barker, H. A. *J. biol. Chem.* 238 (1963) 2094

343 Loyarte, J. M. G. and Sune, N. O. *Energia nucl.* 6 (24) (1962) 45

344 Glascock, R. F. and Hoekstra, W. G., *Proc. 2nd Int. Conf. peaceful Uses Atom. Energy,* Geneva 27 (1958) 104

344a Burg, S. P. and Burg, E. A. *Science, N.Y.* 148 (1965) 1190

345 Jansen, E. F. *J. biol. Chem.* 238 (1963) 1552

346 Jansen, E. F. *J. biol. Chem.* 239 (1964) 1664

347 Loewus, F. A. *Archs Biochem. Biophys.* 105 (1964) 590

348 Gordon, C. C. and Stein, O. L. *Radiat. Biol.* 2 (1962) 7

349 Boonsong, C. and Wright, S. E. *Aust. J. Chem.* 14 (1961) 449

350 Smith, S. H. and Schlegel, D. E. *Science, N.Y.* 145 (1964) 1058

351 Huff, R. L. and Parrish, D. *Proc. Int. Conf. peaceful Uses Atom. Energy*, Geneva 10 (1956) 236

352 Brucer, M. *Oak Ridge Inst. Nuclear Studies Rep.* ORINS 20 (1958)

353 Knisley, R. M., Andrews, G. A. and Harris, C. C. (Eds.) Progress in Medical Radioisotope Scanning'. *Proc. Symp. at the Medical Division of the Oak Ridge Inst. Nuclear Studies*, Oct. 22–26th (1962). *U.S.A.E.C. Rep.* TID–7673

354 Paoletti, R. and Poggi, M. *Proc. Conf. on Methods of Preparing and Storing Marked Molecules*, Brussels (Nov. 1963). European Atomic Energy Community-Euratom, EUR 1625e (May, 1964) p. 1137

355 Snell, J. F. *Adv. Tracer Methodol.* 1 (1963) 234

356 Whitby, L. G., Hertting, G. and Axelrod, J. *Nature, Lond.* 187 (1960) 604

357 Smith, A., Fabrykant, M., Gitlow, S. and Wortis, S. B. *Nature, Lond.* 193 (1962) 577

358 Hertting, G. and Axelrod, J. *Nature, Lond.* 192 (1961) 172

359 Heidelberger, C., Bosch, L., Chaudhuri, N. K. and Danneberg, P. B. *Fedn Proc. Fedn Am. Socs exp. Biol.* 16 (1957) 194 (Abstract only)

360 Eidinoff, M. L., Knoll, J. E. and Klein, D. *Archs Biochem. Biophys.* 71 (1957) 274

361 Dumont, A. E. and Sohn, N. *Nature, Lond.* 199 (1963) 617

362 Paul, J. and Struthers, M. G. *Biochem. biophys. Res. Commun.* 11 (1963) 135

363 Grünther, H. L. and Prusoff, W. H. *J. biol. Chem.* 238 (1963) 1091

364 Easterbrook, K. B. and Davern, C. I. *Virology* 19 (1963) 509

365 Potter, L. T. and Axelrod, J. *J. Pharmac. exp. Ther.* 140 (1963) 199

366 Hertting, G. *Biochem. Pharmac.* 12 (suppl.) (1963) 32

367 McDonald, G. O., Stroud, A. N., Svoboda, B. R. and Brues, A. M. *U.S.A.E.C. Rep.* TID–16709 (June, 1962)

368 Tamaoki, T. and Mueller, G. C. *Biochem. biophys. Res. Commun.* 11 (1963) 404

369 Mitchell, J. S. *Studies in Radiotherapeutics* 1960. Oxford; Blackwell

370 Cater, D. B. *G. ital. Chemioter.* 6–9 (1962) 235

371 Marrian, D. H., Marshall, B. and Mitchell, J. S. *Chemotherapia* 3 (1961) 225

372 Marrian, D. H., Marshall, B., Mitchell, J. S. and Simon-Reuss, I. *Proc. Symp. Tritium Phys. Biol. Sci.*, I.A.E.A. Vienna 2 (1962) 211

373 Simon-Reuss, I. *Acta radiol.* 56 (1961) 49

374 Andrews, K. J. M., Bultitude, F., Evans, E. A., Gronow, M., Lambert, R.W. and Marrian, D. H. *J. chem. Soc.* (1962) 3440

375 Mitchell, J. S. *Symp. on Chemotherapy of Cancer. Proc. R. Soc.* (Aug. 1963) 654

375a Mitchell, J. S. *Clin. radiol.* 16 (1965) 305

375b Mitchell, J. S. *Strahlentherapie* 127 (1965) 497

376 Silver, I. A., Cater, D. B., Marrian, D. H. and Marshall, B. *Acta Radiol.* 58 (1962) 281

377 Ficq, A. *Expl Cell Res.* 34 (1964) 581

378 Marrian, D. H. and Evans, E. A. *Brit. Patent 937,682* (25th Sept. 1963)

379 Suhadolnik, R. J., Fischer, A. G. and Zulalian, J. *Proc. Chem. Soc.* (1963) 132

380 Folca, P. J., Glascock, R. F. and Irvine, W. T. *Lancet* 2 (1961) 796

381 Laland, S. G. and Serck-Hanssen, G. *Biochem. J.* 90 (1964) 76

382 Hayhoe, F. G. J. and Quaglino, D. *Nature, Lond.* 205 (1965) 151

[383] Eggers, H. J., Reich, E. and Tamm, I. *Proc. natn Acad. Sci. U.S.A.* 50 (1963) 183

[384] Gottlieb, L. I., Fausto, N. and van Lancker, J. L. *J. biol. Chem.* 239 (1964) 555

[385] Bieliavsky, N. *Expl Cell Res.* 32 (1963) 342

[386] Easterbrook, K. B. *Virology* 21 (1963) 508

[387] Glowinski, J. and Axelrod, J. *Nature, Lond.* 204 (1964) 1318

[388] Creese, R. and Taylor, D. B. *Nature, Lond.* 206 (1965) 310

[389] Sinclair, N. R. and McCarter, J. A. *Nature, Lond.* 203 (1964) 521

[390] Yamamoto, Y. L., Feinendegen, L. E. and Bond, V. P. *Radiat. Res.* 21 (1964) 36

[391] Noteboom, W. D., Gorski, J. *Proc. natn Acad. Sci. U.S.A.* 50 (1963) 250

[391a] Taylor, D. B., Creese, R., Nedergaard, O. A. and Case, R. *Nature, Lond.* 208 (1965) 901

[392] Karaboyas, G. C. and Koritz, S. B. *Biochim. biophys. Acta* 100 (1965) 600

[393] Guzek, J. W. *Nature, Lond.* 201 (1964) 930

[394] Taylor, E. W. *J. Cell Biol.* 19 (1963) 1

[395] Jackson, J. F. and Lindahl-Kiessling, K. *Expl Cell Res.* 34 (1965) 515

[396] Banerjee, M. R. *Expl Cell Res.* 34 (1964) 351

[397] Palme, G. and Liss, E. *Klin. Wischr.* 41 (1963) 291

[398] Brenner, R. M. *Am. J. Anat.* 112 (1963) 81

[399] Kit, S. and Dubbs, D. R. *Expl Cell Res.* 31 (1963) 397

[400] Barka, T. *Expl Cell Res.* 37 (1965) 662

[401] Jensen, E. V., Ford, E. and Huggins, C. *Proc. natn Acad. Sci. U.S.A.* 50 (1963) 454

[402] Trakatellis, A. C. and Axelrod, A. E. *Biochem. J.* 95 (1965) 344

[403] Dewey, W. C. and Humphrey, R. M. *Expl Cell Res.* 35 (1964) 262

[404] Trosko, J. E., Chu, E. H. Y. and Carrier, W. L. *Radiat. Res.* 24 (1965) 667

[405] Stewart, P. A., Quastler, H., Skougaard, N. R., Wimber, D. R., Wolfsberg, M. F., Perrotta, C. A., Ferbel, B., Carlough, M. *Radiat. Res.* 24 (1965) 521

[406] Devik, F. *Int. J. Radiat. Biol.* 5 (1962) 59

[407] Looney, W. B., Chang, L. O., Williams, S. S., Forster, J., Haydock, I. C. and Banghart, F. W. *Radiat. Res.* 24 (1965) 312

[408] Alvarez, M. R. *Nature, Lond.* 206 (1965) 950

[409] Gracheva, N. D. *Radiobiologiya* 3 (1963) 81

[410] Foley, W. A., Cole, L. J., Ingram, B. J. and Crocker, T. T. *Nature, Lond.* 199 (1963) 1267

[411] Terasima, T. and Tolmach, L. J. *Biophys. J.* 3 (1963) 11

[412] Djordjevic, B. and Djordjevic, O. *Nature, Lond.* 206 (1965) 1165

[413] Evans, T. C. and Kim, J. H. *Radiat. Res.* 19 (1963) 186 (Abstract only)

[414] Kim, J. H. and Evans, T. C. *Radiat. Res.* 21 (1964) 129

[415] Harding, C. V., Thayer, M. N., Eliashof, P. A. and Rugh, R. *Radiat. Res.* 25 (1965) 305

[416] McGrath, R. A. *Radiat. Res.* 19 (1963) 526

[417] Billen, D., Hewitt, R. and Jorgensen, G. *Biochim. biophys. Acta* 103 (1965) 440

[418] Kent, E., C.N.A.E.M. 16 (Sept. 1964). Paper Submitted to the *3rd U.N. Int. Conf. peaceful Uses Atom. Energy*, Geneva, Aug.–Sept. 1964

[419] Zuppinger, A., Poretti, G., Schwarz, K., Zao Ralek, P. and Aebi, H. *Radiol. Clin.* 32 (1963) 402

[420] Avoy, D. R., Swyryd, E. A. and Gould, R. G. *J. Lipid Res.* 6 (1965) 369

[421] Leive, L. *Biochem. biophys. Res. Commun.* 18 (1965) 13
[422] Zeman, W. *Proc. natn Acad. Sci. U.S.A.* 50 (1963) 626
[423] Clever, U. *Science, N.Y.* 146 (1964) 794
[424] Creasy, W. A. and Markiw, M. E. *Biochim. biophys. Acta* 87 (1964) 601
[425] Sassen, A., Reuter, A., Kennes, F. and Franssen, J. *Preparation and Bio-Medical Applications of Labelled Molecules, European Atomic Energy Community* Euratom, EUR 2200 e (Dec. 1964) page 175

REVIEWS ON OR INCLUDING APPLICATIONS OF TRITIUM

1947
[426] Lyubarskii, G. D. *Usp. Khim.* 16 (1947) 422. 'The radioactive Isotope of Hydrogen (Tritium) and its Applications in Chemical Reactions'
1950
[427] Croxton, F. E. and Schwind, S. B. *U.S.A.E.C. Rep. TID–371* (1950). 'Tritium (H³). A Bibliography of Unclassified Literature'
1952
[428] Verzaux, P. *J. Phys. Radium, Paris* 13 (1952) 94. 'Tritium the Isotope of Hydrogen of Mass 3; bibliography'
1953
[429] *Chem. Engng News* 31 (1953) 3184. 'Tritium finds Increasing Application in Tracer Chemistry'
1954
[430] Thompson, R. C. *Nucleonics* 12 (9) (1954) 31. 'Biological Applications of Tritium'
1955
[431] Brown, W. G., Kaplan, L., Van Dyken, A. R. and Wilzbach, K. E. *Int. Conf. peaceful Uses Atom. Energy,* Geneva (15) (1955) 16. 'Tritium as a Tool in Industrial and Chemical Research'
1956
[432] Brown, L. M., Friedman, A. S. and Beckett, C. W. *Natn. Bur. Stand. Circ.* 562 (1956). 'Bibliography of Research on Deuterium and Tritium Compounds (1945–1952)'
1957
[433] Cason, M. *Univ. Calif. Radiation Lab. Rep.* UCRL–5069 (March, 1957). 'Tritium: A Bibliography'
[434] *Proc. Symp. Tritium Tracer Applications,* New York City, Nov. 1957 (New England Nuclear Corp.)
1958
[435] Bolin, B. *Proc. 2nd Int. Conf. peaceful Uses Atom. Energy,* Geneva 18 (1958) 336. 'On the Use of Tritium as a Tracer for Water in Nature'
[436] *Nucleonics* 16 (3) (1958) 62. 'Tritium Tracing—A Rediscovery'
[437] *Proc. Symp. Adv. Tracer Applications Tritium,* New York City, Oct. 1958 (New England Nuclear Corp.)
[438] Kisieleski, W. E. and Smetana, F. *Atompraxis* 4 (7/8) (1958) 261. 'Tritium in Biological Studies'
[439] Verly, W. G. *Centre D'Etude de L'Energie Nucleaire,* CEN–R 1426 (1958). '*Tritium in Biology*'

1959
440 Graul, E. H. and Hundeshagen, H. *Atompraxis*, 5 (1959) 154. 'Methods and Techniques in the Synthesis and Analysis of Tritium Labelled Compounds'
441 Oklahoma Conf.—Radioisotopes in Agriculture, *U.S.A.E.C. Rep.* TID–7578 (1959)
1960
442 Kühn, W. and Herrmann, F. *Kerntechnik* 2 (1960) 268. 'Application Possibilities of Tritium Bremsstahlung in Industry'
443 Verly, W. G. *Bull. Inst. Agron. Stns. Rech. Gembloux* Extra Vol. 2 (1960) 720. 'The Use of Tritium in Biology'
444 Verly, W. G. *I.A.E.A., Vienna Review Series*, No. 2 (1960). 'Tritium Determination, Preparation of Labelled Molecules and Biological Applications'
1961
445 Segel, K. H. *Isotopen-Technik.* 1 (5/6) (1961) 169 (CEA–tr–A–1108) 'Tritium in Industry and Technology'
446 Simon, H. *Angew. Chem.* 73 (1961) 481. 'Use of Tritium in Organic Chemistry and Biochemistry'
447 Tupitsyn, I. F. *Heavy Hydrogen Isotopes Deuterium and Tritium* 1961. Moscow; Gosatomizdat
1962
448 Evans, E. A. *Rep. Prog. appl. Chem.* (1962) 111. 'Tritium Labelled Compounds'
449 Nalborczyk *Postepy Biochem.* 8 (1) (1962) 95. 'Tritium in Biochemical and Biological Investigations'
450 *Tritium in the Physical and Biological Sciences*, Volumes I and II, I.A.E.A., Vienna, 1962
451 Wenzel, M. and Schulze, P. E. *Tritium labelling: Preparation, Measurement and Applications of Wilzbach Tritiated Compounds.* 1962. Berlin; Walter De Gruyter
1963
452 Clayton, D. W. *Int. Conf. Operating Experience and Future Development of Power Reactors and on Radioisotopes*, Montreal, May 1963. (CONF–9–10)
453 *Advances in Tracer Methodology* The Use of Radioactive Tracers in Pulp and Paper Research. 1963. Ed. S. Rothchild, vol. 1. New York; Plenum Press. (Incorporates references 434 and 437)
1964
454 *Proc. Conf. Methods of Preparing and Storing Marked Molecules*, Brussels, Belg. Nov. 1963. Ed. J. Sirchis. European Atomic Energy Community, Euratom EUR 1625e (May 1964)
455 *Int. Symp. Preparation and Bio-Medical Applications of Labelled Molecules*, Venice, Aug. 1964. Ed. J. Sirchis. European Atomic Energy Community, Euratom EUR 2200e (Dec. 1964)
456 *Advances in Tracer Methodology.* Ed. S. Rothchild. Vol. 2. 1964. New York; Plenum Press
1965
457 Wang, C. H. and Willis, D. L. *Radiotracer Methodology in Biological Sciences*, 1965. Prentice-Hall Inc.
458 *Isotopes in Experimental Pharmacology.* A compendium of lectures from an Int. Conf. Uses of isotopically labelled drugs in experimental pharmacology. Univ. Chicago Jun. 7–9 (1964). Ed. L. S. Roth. Univ. of Chicago Press, 1965

CHAPTER 3

PRECAUTIONS IN TRITIUM HANDLING

The pre-eminent importance of tritium and carbon-14 as biological tracers makes it fortunate that both are weak β-radiation-emitting isotopes. The handling difficulties would have made a great deal of work impracticable if these isotopes had an associated γ-radiation. This chapter deals with some of the problems encountered during the production and use of tritium compounds, and with methods for their handling.

Tritium is indeed one of the least toxic of radioisotopes, but this simple unqualified statement would be misleading, because there are certain special features of tritium which make it in some ways more difficult to control than some other, more toxic nuclides.

First of all there is the relatively large (curies) quantity often used, and the large difference in requirements for preparative and tracer use. Next is the rather tedious procedure necessary for laboratory monitoring (see page 80). A third feature is the actual chemical character of tritium as a hydrogen isotope. This leads to it being used in a great diversity of chemical forms, and the toxicity will depend very much indeed on the chemical form involved. It means also that large amounts are handled in the form of oxide (water) and all organic forms tend to be converted, whether rapidly or slowly, to tritium-labelled water. Water is a rather troublesome form to deal with; there is no means of separating the tritium from it easily, it is used in large volumes, it is rapidly absorbed through the skin or the lungs, and it is held tenaciously not only (for example) by organic materials, but by less likely substances such as glass.

No person setting out to work with tritium or its compounds should therefore take precautions too lightly. Although the amount of tritium activity handled may not easily cause a 'health hazard', it may be sufficient if 'mishandled' to easily set up an embarrassing level of contamination in the laboratory.

1. *Personnel Monitoring and Dosimetry*

For the benefit of readers who are not familiar with the units in which radiation doses are measured, the following terms are defined:

The RÖNTGEN is the quantity of x- or γ-radiation such that the associated corpuscular emission per $0 \cdot 001293$ g of air, produces in air, ions carrying 1 electrostatic unit (e.s.u.) of electric charge.

The RAD is the unit of absorbed dose of any ionizing radiation, and corresponds to the absorption of 100 ergs/g in the absorbing medium. In soft tissue the röntgen and the rad are approximately equal.

The REM. Equal doses of different types of radiation (expressed in rads) have different degrees of biological effectiveness. Consequently it is necessary to introduce a unit—the REM—to express the quantity of any ionizing radiation such that the energy imparted to the biological system per gramme of living matter by ionizing particles present in the locus of interest has the same biological effectiveness as 1 rad of 200–250 kV x-rays.

$$1 \text{ REM} = 1 \text{ RAD} \times \text{RBE}$$

The relative biological effectiveness (RBE) for tritium β-radiation is taken as $1 \cdot 7$[1, 2], but as pointed out by Mitchell and colleagues[3] this value, which relates only to tritiated water, may require modification for other forms of tritium.

The recommendations[1] of the International Commission on Radiological Protection (ICRP) for occupational exposure to tritium are:

(a) the maximum permissible body burden (mpbb) occupational exposure is 1 mc. Thus 1 mc of tritium maintained in the body will deliver a dose of $0 \cdot 1$ rem/week. The tritium concentration in body fluids necessary to maintain this dose is $0 \cdot 028$ μc/ml[4]. Thus a value of $0 \cdot 028$ μc/ml in the urine indicates 1 mpbb.

(b) the maximum permissible concentration in air
as tritiated water vapour 5×10^{-6} μc/ml
or as tritium gas $\quad\quad\quad 2 \times 10^{-3}$ μc/ml

(c) the maximum permissible level in drinking-water is $0 \cdot 1$ μc/ml.

These figures relate strictly to the uptake of tritium in simple chemical forms such as tritiated water or tritium gas, for persons classed as occupationally exposed.

Although the most common form of personnel monitoring is by film-badge dosimeters, it is unsatisfactory for determining the intake of tritium by personnel. This is best done by regular urine analysis[4-6].

When film badges are exposed to tritium atmospheres, uniform fogging of the film is normally observed[6] whereas exposures to other forms of β- or γ-radiation usually results in differential fogging of the film beneath the shield and open window of the film holder. Tests have shown[6] that the fogging effect due to tritium is not the result of Bremsstrahlung radiation but probably results from tritium permeating the film packet directly. Gibson[7] has shown that the A.E.R.E. film dosimeter exposed to tritium as tritiated water at room temperature and 50 per cent relative humidity, results in a film fogging which is proportional to the exposure dose of tritium and to the storage time after exposure before developing. The accuracy of calibration is only 50 per cent over the range 0·1–2·5 rem corresponding to tritium in air activities in the range 150 to 20,000 permissible concentrations per cubic centimetre. Thus, the film-badge method really reveals information concerning the dose to the film which may be the result of a 'splash' of tritiated material onto the badge rather than an intake into the body.

In order to determine the intake of tritium into the body by urine analysis, the elimination of tritium should be followed (for at least a week), the individual biological half-life (see page 85) determined, and the urine tritium concentration at the day of the intake found by extrapolation. If this is C_0 μc/ml, and T_b the biological half-life of the tritium in the body, the accumulated dose at any time d days after the intake may be calculated from equation (3.1)[4]:

$$D = \frac{0 \cdot 512}{\lambda_b} C_0 (1 - e^{-\lambda_b d}) \text{ rem} \quad . \quad . \quad . \quad (3.1)$$

where
$$\lambda_b = \frac{0 \cdot 693}{T_b}$$

The 'infinity dose' is thus (3.2)

$$D = 0 \cdot 74 \, T_b C_0 \quad \quad . \quad . \quad . \quad (3.2)$$

2. *Licensing Requirements and the Disposal of Tritiated Wastes*

Every organization in Great Britain using radioactive materials must conform to the general requirements of the 1960 Radioactive Substances Act[8]. Application for authorization to use or hold radioactive materials should be made at present to the Minister of Housing and Local Government (England and Wales), the Minister of State (Scotland) or the Minister of Health (Northern Ireland). Beginners are strongly recommended to read the *Introductory Manual on the Control of Health Hazards from Radioactive Substances*, a publication produced by the Medical Research Council[9], and the Ministry of Labour *Code of Practice for the Protection of Persons Exposed to Ionising Radiations in Research and Teaching*[10].

In accordance with the 1960 Radioactive Substances Act[8], users of radioactive materials must obtain authorization for the disposal and accumulation of specified quantities of tritium (and other radio-isotopes), from the Ministry concerned (*vide supra*).

The United Kingdom Atomic Energy Authority have agreed to accept for disposal radioactive wastes for which the Ministry of Housing and Local Government (or the Department of Health for Scotland) will not permit local disposal. Details of this service, for which a charge is made, can be obtained from these departments.

As precise recommendations specifically for the disposal of tritiated wastes have not yet been published[11], it is perhaps relevant to comment only briefly on some aspects of tritium-waste disposal.

Disposal of liquid wastes—Whereas carbon-14 compounds in liquid wastes are bacterially oxidized to carbon dioxide-C14 which equilibrates with the carbon dioxide present in the atmosphere, tritium compounds on the other hand are oxidized to tritiated water, the radiation decaying with the half-life of the isotope. Ultimately some of this tritium ends up in drinking-water which to the 'man in the street' may seem a calamity.

Looking at the problem more logically, most tritium wastes will end up in sea-water. Now even after the release of many tens of thousands of curies of tritium in the course of nuclear-weapon testing the level in sea-water rarely exceeded 500 T.U. $(16 \times 10^{-7} \ \mu c/ml)$ which is about 1,000 times *less* than the internationally recommended maximum permissible level in drinking-water $(0 \cdot 003 \ \mu c/ml)$ and about 10^5 times *less* than the occupational permissible concentration in drinking-water[1]. It is inconceivable that wastes from the production of tritium or its compounds, let alone tracer uses of tritium, could approach the quantity of tritium released during nuclear-weapon testing. In short, discharge of tritium wastes to sea, in any quantities which may be expected to arise from current tracer uses, can hardly be open to criticism on any reasonable grounds. Discharge to water-courses by way of sewers is only likely to be troublesome when water is subsequently withdrawn again for public supply. The licensing procedure takes full account of this possibility.

A conservative estimate of the water flow in an organic or bio-chemical laboratory would be 100 gal. daily for each worker, and the daily effluent from a moderately sized institution could easily exceed 5,000 gal. To attain the maximum permissible (occupational) level in 'drinking-water' in the laboratory effluent (approximately 450 $\mu c/gal.$) would require discharging in the region of 200 mc of tritium per day. This will of course be considerably diluted, often by factors of at least 10^3, in the public sewers. Permissible discharges of (say) 200 mc/day in liquid effluent are indeed unlikely to handicap tracer uses of tritium.

Small-bulk liquid effluent at high activity containing perhaps a few curies of tritium, is conveniently disposed of by absorption onto vermiculite or kieselguhr and sealed in glass containers (with outer metal containment). These can then be collectively disposed of through the U.K.A.E.A. effluent-disposal service.

For the small quantities (millicuries) often used in research laboratories, systematic monitoring of tritium in effluent is likely to be tedious, expensive and unnecessary. Licensing may more often be determined by the maximum quantities of tritium allowed to be held or used in the laboratory.

Gaseous effluent—Care should be taken to ensure that radioactive gases and particulate wastes should not be discharged in such a manner that they may conceivably constitute a health hazard; for example such discharges should always be clear of windows or other air intakes to buildings.

A recommended figure[12] for the discharge of carbon-14 dioxide in the exhaust system of a standard chemical laboratory hood that has a linear air flow of at least 50 ft./min, is at a rate not to exceed 100 μc/h/ft.[2] of air intake in the face of the hood as operated. Allowing for the lower energy of the tritium β-radiation and the same dilution with air as for carbon dioxide-C14, a figure of (say) 1 mc/h/ft.[2] for tritium would again seldom handicap the tracer user of tritium.

The washout of tritiated water from gaseous effluents by rain-water is discussed by Chamberlain and Eggleton[13], and the diffusion of large amounts of tritium in the atmosphere is discussed by Doury[13a].

Garbage—As a rough guide, again allowing for the lower energy of the tritium β-radiation and the higher mpbb, recommended levels for the disposal of tritiated garbage can be taken as (say) 10 times those of carbon-14[11,12,14].

It must be emphasized that the *permissible* levels for the disposal of any radioactive waste will be those agreed between the institution concerned and the Ministry.

3. *Types of Radioactive Laboratory*

It is often asked what kind of laboratory and what special facilities are necessary for working with tritium? There are clearly two main types of radioactive laboratory; first the specially equipped laboratory for handling multicurie quantities of tritium used for example in the preparation of tritium compounds; and second, the class of laboratory for tracer uses of tritium. Most laboratories using tritium fall into this second class, using perhaps a maximum of 100 c/year. On the other hand laboratories used for the preparation of tritium compounds or sources may well be required to process many thousands of curies per annum.

There are many good publications on design of radioactive laboratories[15–21, 21a] but existing conventional laboratories can often be suitably adapted for the tracer use of tritium compounds. A photograph of a typical laboratory for the production of tritium compounds is shown in *Figure 3.1*.

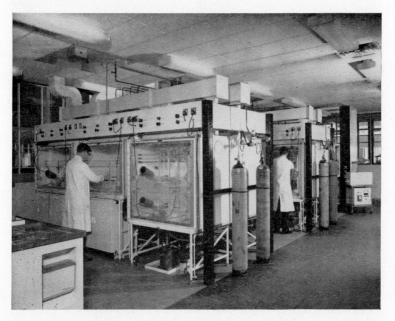

Figure 3.1. A general view of a laboratory with facilities for multicurie operations with tritium and its compounds

Specially constructed cabinets and process boxes are used for the regular handling of multicurie quantities of tritium compounds. A closer view of a typical process box of the type used at the Radiochemical Centre, is shown in *Figure 3.2*. The box is made of steel with dimensions roughly as follows: width 52 in., height 38 in. and

75

horizontal depth 30 in. The working aperture is 42 in. wide and 8 in. in height cut into the front panel of the box, the panel being made of perspex. The flow of air through the aperture can be controlled but it is normally fixed at not less than 150 linear ft./min for the safe working

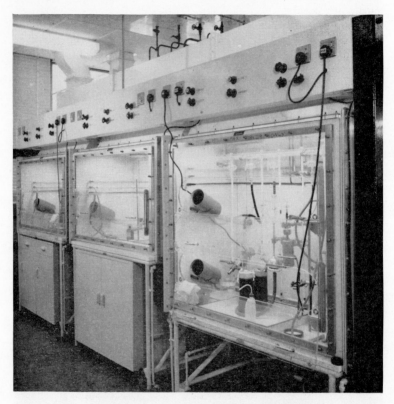

Figure 3.2 (a). A bank of process boxes for multicurie operations with tritium compounds. Note the glove washers situated on each side of the boxes

with multicurie quantities of tritium in any chemical form. The base of the box is fitted with a trough for washing contaminated apparatus prior to removal from the box. Hand-washing facilities are provided at the sides of the box and consist of two concentric steel tubes welded together; the inner tube is drilled with small holes and circulation of water under pressure between the two tubes results in fine sprays of water onto the hands or gloves (see *Figure 3.4*). The water feed is operated by a foot valve situated at ground level.

Figure 3.2 (b). A close view of a process box used for multicurie hydrogenations with tritium gas. Tritium gas from the ampoule (centre of photograph) is transferred to the reaction flask by means of the Toepler pump and the contents of the flask stirred magnetically

Figure 3.3 shows a process cabinet, which is really no more than a modification of the more conventional type of fume cabinet.

The cabinet is also fitted with a drain trough and hand-washing facilities. This is most suitable for tracer and median tritium activities. There is no fundamental advantage of boxes over cabinets, except that they can give a rather higher ratio of air throughput to fixed volume which may have some advantage for work at the higher levels of activity.

Segregation of high level tritium work (multicurie) from tracer or lower level experimental work is even more necessary than in the case of carbon-14[14] because of the greater range of activities used. A separate room for instruments and measurement equipment is desirable but essential only for segregation from multicurie quantities of tritium. A summary and arbitrary division of the scale of use of tritium is shown in Table 3.1.

Figure 3.3. A process cabinet showing hand washers and vacuum-transfer manifold line on the right

TABLE 3.1

Quantity of tritium	Preparative work	Applications	Grade laboratory[9]
10–10,000 μc	Seldom except for measurement and analytical samples	Frequent use as tracers	C
10–10,000 mc	Frequent	Occasional tracer use	C
10–100 c	Frequent for compound production in specialist laboratories	Frequent for industrial tracer use	B
Above 100 c	Compound production in specialist laboratories	Seldom	B or A

Laboratories handling tritium in any form should have adequate ventilation particularly if the tritium is in a volatile form. The need

Figure 3.4. Hand or glove washer for decontamination after multicurie operations with tritium

for careful and intelligent working has been stressed many times before [22] but cannot be stressed too often.

Protective clothing—Apart from the normal laboratory clothing (overalls or coat) worn by personnel, surgical rubber gloves are recommended for use in handling tritium at all but the microcurie level of activity. It is hardly possible to assess accurately the amount of personal uptake which occurs from contact of the hands (skin) with tritiated apparatus, but it has certainly been shown that it can be substantial [23, 24, 24a].

Handling multicurie quantities of tritiated water and other tritiated solvents, results in a high degree of contamination of rubber gloves.

TABLE 3.2

Age of water wash bath weeks	Volume l.	Total activity mc
2	4·5	70
1	1·5	10
1	2	15
1	2	30
1	2	70
2	2	100
2	2	192

Working with glass apparatus and a tritium throughput of about 500 c/week for example, average typical results of contamination rinsed from surgical gloves are shown in Table 3.2.

These collective glove-washings from one operator stress the need for frequent rinsing of surgical gloves while the operator is still wearing them. Gloves used for multicurie work should also be changed regularly, perhaps once a day if in constant use.

Apparatus—It is essential to segregate apparatus used for high activity from that for low activity preparative work. Glass apparatus which has been used for high activities cannot be effectively cleaned to remove all traces of tritium contamination. Such apparatus should never for example, be used for analytical work of any kind. Even prolonged treatment by soaking in chromic–sulphuric acids does not remove the last traces of tritium.

High-vacuum grease on vacuum taps, mercury and pump oil become heavily contaminated with tritium and are a constant potential source of contamination[6].

Glass apparatus which is used for tracer work can usually be satisfactorily cleaned by the usual cleaning fluids such as chromic–sulphuric acids, nitric–permanganic acids and detergents, but apparatus which has been used for multicurie preparative work must be regarded as permanently contaminated and only used again for experiments at the multicurie level.

It is impossible to remove contamination from rubber, and contaminated rubber tubing for example should be replaced by new.

4. *Control of Laboratory Contamination*

Only constant and intelligent care can prevent some degree of laboratory contamination. It is only too easy to let familiarity breed contempt resulting in short-cuts being taken and finally a spill of radioactive material; the cleaning-up of such spills wastes very much time and effort.

Any radioactive laboratory should be kept clean and tidy. Common sources of laboratory contamination are, dirty apparatus left lying around the laboratory, unrecognized or unreported spills and general uncleanliness. Perfection is rarely achieved in practice and the precaution of always working over spill trays (shown in *Figures 3.5* and *3.6*) is invaluable in minimizing the effects of truly accidental spills.

Laboratory monitoring—Frequent monitoring of radioactive laboratories is an essential requirement for the control of laboratory contamination. The difficulty of detecting tritium makes it even more important (tedious as it may seem) for regular and frequent examination of the laboratory for tritium contamination.

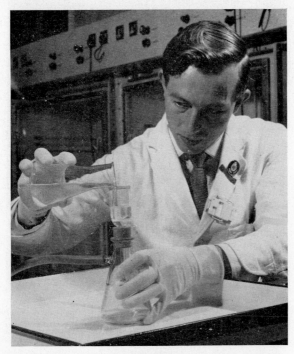

Figure 3.5. Filtration of a tritiated compound. Note the operation over a spill tray

Air monitors capable of detecting 0·1 to 100 times the maximum permissible concentration of tritium in air (page 71) by recording continuously the activity of a continuous air flow through an ionization chamber, have been described[6, 25-27]. These are suitable for use in laboratories where multicurie quantities of tritium in a volatile form are handled[27], but they are unnecessary in tracer laboratories.

This type of air monitor is not suitable for the detection of contaminated bench tops, handles of doors, apparatus etc., which is probably a more appropriate problem to the majority of users of tritium compounds. For such purposes a portable gas-flow monitor which consists of a windowless counter through which a gas flows such as helium–isobutane (98:2) or argon–methane (90:10), has been described [28]. The normal limit of detection for this type of instrument is about 0·1 μc while the efficiency at best is not more than 10 per cent.

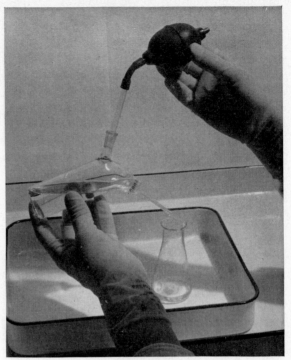

Figure 3.6. Filtration using a glass filter beaker. Again note the operation carried out over a spill tray

Disadvantages of such monitors are

(a) they very easily become contaminated,
(b) they need time to reach equilibrium,
(c) their geometry restricts their effective use to flat surfaces only and over a relatively small surface area at a time.

It is more practicable to take wipes of the surface by rubbing metal discs over the surface under examination. Removable tritium adsorbed on the metal wipe is then measured in a 2π-proportional gas-flow counter and compared with that of a reference source. Such a source can be a piece of filter paper with a known amount of tritium in the form of a non-volatile compound, adsorbed on it.

Even this method of course has its limitations, in that a large number of wipes may be necessary to track down the exact spot of contamination and tritium contamination in the 'odd' corner can easily be missed. However, such monitoring performed methodically and diligently is a most satisfactory means for obtaining a quick check on possible contamination over a fairly wide area of the laboratory.

Where it is undesirable to rub the surface with a metal disc, a similar procedure which involves wiping the surface with moist cotton wool or filter paper and measuring the activity by β-liquid scintillation counting, can be adopted. In this case although care must be taken to ensure that any recorded counts are not due to activation of the scintillant by chemiluminescence or phosphorescence (see Chapter 5); the high efficiency of measurement (20–50 per cent depending on the instrument) permits contamination levels down to 0·001 μc per wipe to be detected.

Yet another method which has been tested[29] consists of leaving small bottles of liquid scintillant exposed to the air in the laboratory. Airborne tritium contamination can be qualitatively detected but the method has not been tested quantitatively.

A simple 'cold strip' apparatus for monitoring for volatile airborne tritium has been described by Iyengar et al.[29a], consisting of an aluminium strip the bottom part of which is immersed in liquid nitrogen. Water condenses on the upper part of the metal strip and the tritium content of the condensate is then measured by β-liquid scintillation. This apparatus overcomes the disadvantage of the liquid nitrogen cooled cold trap apparatus for air sampling, which often gets blocked. However, it is also necessary to know fairly accurately the relative humidity during the period of condensation. There is close agreement between the results obtained by the two methods.

5. *Manipulation of Tritium Compounds*

Compounds at very high specific activity should whenever possible be manipulated in solution to avoid the possible spreading of contamination as highly active dust particles. Volatile compounds should be handled by transfer on vacuum manifolds, when appropriate. This is the only method for the quantitative transfer of volatile material on the semi-micro scale as is entailed with compounds of very high specific activity.

Paper chromatography for preparative as well as analytical work, is a frequent technique used in laboratories. When handling paper chromatograms with large amounts of tritium activity dispersed on them (say 10 mc/in.^{2}) there is the possibility of inhalation of paper fibres from dry papers and the use of disposable surgical masks is recommended to minimize any hazard involved. The same recommendation applies of course to the handling of preparative thin-layer chromatography plates, where the possible hazard from tritiated powdered silica gel (for example) is considerably increased over that from paper.

An experiment carried out at the Radiochemical Centre[30] to assess the amount of activity accumulated on a surgical mask when processing 3 to 4 c of tritiated thymine and thymidine, compounds which are routinely purified by paper chromatography, revealed less than 1 μc of tritium activity on the mask. It has in fact been proved that very little activity is passed from the paper to the operator in the case of carbon-14 compounds[14].

Sintered-glass filters are normally used for collecting crystalline solids or, alternatively, filter beakers of the type described for use with carbon-14 compounds[14] (see *Figures 3.5* and *3.6* respectively).

Hydrogenation of compounds in organic solvents with tritium gas invariably results in highly active solvents which can easily give rise to radiation exposures if these solvents are not carefully removed by distillation in closed vacuum systems.

Compounds which have been exposed to the curie quantities of tritium gas required for labelling by the Wilzbach (and related) procedure (see Chapter 4), often contain several curies of labile tritium, some due to strong adsorption of the tritium gas on the surface of the compound. Extreme care should be taken *never* to open ampoules containing such irradiated material in the open laboratory; well-ventilated fume cabinets should be used not only to avoid personal radiation exposures but to prevent general laboratory contamination.

6. *Biological Effects of Tritium and the Toxicity of Tritium Compounds*

The external radiation to the body from tritium contributes a negligible health hazard. The horny layers of the skin (assumed to be about 70 μ thick[31]) are more than sufficient to prevent penetration of the low-energy β-particles. The Bremsstrahlung (x-ray) dose is even smaller being only about 4×10^{-5} of the direct beta dose at the surface. This may be calculated from the usual x-ray formula[32] (3.3)

$$\epsilon = 10^{-9} \, ZV \qquad \dots \quad (3.3)$$

ϵ = the fraction of the electron energy appearing as x-radiation
Z = the atomic number of the target (6 for carbon)
V = the energy of electrons in volts (5,700 for the average tritium β-radiation).

No special shielding from radiation is therefore necessary when handling tritium or its compounds, at any level of specific or total activity. However, the ingestion of tritium in any form (as with other radioactive materials) does constitute a potential health hazard and it is necessary to protect personnel from breathing air contaminated with volatile tritium, such as tritiated water or solvent vapours, and dust carrying particulate tritium from solid tritium compounds.

Biological half-life—The time taken for half the assimilated activity to be excreted from the body following a single dose of tritium (corrected for radioactive decay), is termed the biological half-life. The effective half-life in the body, the biological half-life of the compound and the radioactive half-life are related by the equation (3.4):

$$T_e = \frac{T_b \, T_r}{T_b + T_r} \qquad \qquad \cdots \cdots \quad (3.4)$$

where

T_e = the effective half-life in the body
T_b = the biological half-life of the material
T_r = the radioactive half-life of tritium.

For most practical purposes the biological half-life and the effective half-life in the body, are identical for tritium.

The biological half-life has been extensively studied for tritiated water[33] and found to vary from 9 to 14 days in various humans. An average value of 12 days is usually accepted as the normal effective half-life of tritium in the form of tritiated water in the body. However, a more recent evaluation[34] provides a figure of 8·5 days and results show, as one might expect, that the value of the effective half-life of tritiated water is very much a function of the individual's response to his climatic environment as well as normal body function. A value as low as 7·5 days has been recorded under tropical conditions[35].

The Savannah River Plant in the U.S.A. is a major centre for the production of tritium and over the past 10 years some 309,000 urine samples from personnel have been measured for their tritium content. Butler and Leroy[35a] discuss the significance of these measurements. It was found that the biological half-life of the tritium in personnel ranged from 4–18 days having a mean value of 9·5 ± 4·1 days, with a trend towards a shorter effective half-life in older personnel and during the warmer months, as indeed might be expected (*vide supra*).

In cases of acute exposure, which is very unlikely in tracer laboratories, the effective half-life of the tritium in the body may be decreased by increasing the intake of body fluids.

It is perhaps of interest to note the very short effective half-life of tritium as tritiated water in cattle; being only 3·5 days which is remarkably short in relation to their size[36].

Toxicity of tritium—The toxicity of tritium has been related to that of hydrocyanic acid in that 'one breath is lethal'[37]. Such comparisons are misleading, are unsupported experimentally and can often lead to an exaggerated conception of the hazards of radioactivity; to attempt to equate radioactive and chemical toxicity of a compound is irrational. Assimilation of toxic levels of chemicals normally produces immediate biological effects whereas the effects of radioactivity may not be apparent for many years.

The early investigations on the toxicity of tritium were concerned almost entirely with tritium gas and tritiated water, for control of health hazards to personnel engaged on the production of tritium for nuclear weapons[2, 38-48]. Many of the references pertaining to the early health physics aspects of tritium, are collected in a bibliography by Bost[49], and more recently by McKown[47].

Because of the low solubility of tritium (or hydrogen) in body fluids it is generally considered[38, 46] that tritiated water presents a greater biological hazard than tritium gas. The principal conclusions reached by Anderson and Langham[38] of the hazards associated with acute exposure to high concentrations of tritium gas were

(*a*) the hazard from the exposure to tritium gas was at least 10^3 less than from tritiated water,

(*b*) the greatest danger from an acute exposure to a mixture of tritium gas in air, is the conversion of the tritium to its oxide by ignition of the explosive mixture,

(*c*) the dose rate to 1 μ layer of respiratory surface following an inhalation of tritium gas would be very high (thousands of rems/sec). As Lassen has pointed out[46a-b], the low solubility of tritium (also krypton-85 and xenon-133) in tissues and blood as compared to air implies that the lungs act as very efficient filters and further that the lungs and airways must be considered the critical organs receiving the highest radiation dose. It is however interesting to note that a total dose of approximately 135,000 rem to the lung surfaces in mice, produced no histological evidence for acute lung changes[46],

(*d*) the contribution to whole-body exposure from direct solution of the tritium in body fluids and from biological oxidation of the tritium followed by absorption of the tritiated water, are about of equal consequence. The hazard is not a lethal one; a 10 sec exposure to pure tritium gas would result in a dose of only about 6 rem. If the air in a room was 10 per cent tritium, a 10 min exposure would result

86

in a dose of about 40 rem (in a small laboratory which may have a volume of 150–300 m^3, a 10 per cent tritium atmosphere corresponds to a release of approx. 4–7×10^7 c).

(e) the dose from Bremsstrahlung radiation even at very high tritium concentrations, can be neglected because of its low intensity and penetrating power.

(f) the oxidation of tritium by its own radiation field [49a] appears to be negligible compared with biological oxidation. Results obtained by Smith, Emerson, Temple and Galbraith [50] suggest that the bacterial content of the intestines may be a principal agent in the oxidation of tritium within the animal body.

The toxicity of tritiated water to mice was studied [51] in 1952 with the result that an LD_{50} of 30 days was established for a dose of 1 mc/g body weight when given in a single injection. Autopsy findings and haematological observations confirmed that deaths were due to acute radiation disease. The lethal dose (LD_{50}) for humans on this basis would be about 70 c for a 70 kg man. However, one cannot extrapolate from mice to humans with any degree of certainty.

With tritiated water vapour, 86–100 per cent of the inspired water vapour molecules pass from the mammalian lung into the body [52]. A level of 200 µc of tritium will be maintained in the human body if air containing 10^{-6} µc of tritiated water per cubic centimetre is breathed for 48 h/week.

Problems do arise from tritiated water contamination, for example, in the air surrounding heavy water moderated reactors [24, 24b]. In such reactors there is a small continuous production of tritium by the nuclear reaction (3.5):

$$_1^2H + {}_0^1n \rightarrow {}_1^3H \qquad \cdots \qquad (3.5)$$

but in tracer laboratories the health problems from contamination due to tritium or tritiated water are negligible.

In Table 3.3 is shown the distribution of tritium in various tissues of the rat following an exposure to tritium gas or tritiated water for 4 h; the concentration of tritium being 200 µc/ml in both cases [53]. The observed average initial concentration of tritium in the body was 60 µc/ml for the rats exposed to tritium gas and 127 µc/ml for the rats exposed to tritiated water.

The interesting features about these early experiments were the reasonably uniform distribution of tritiated water among the various tissues following the exposure to tritium gas, and the retention of firmly bound tritium in certain tissues which appears to be greater following exposure to tritium gas than from tritiated water. The

TABLE 3.3

| Tissue | Gas-exposed rats | | THO-exposed rats |
	Tissue water μc/ml	Bound tritium % average tritium concentration*	Bound tritium % average tritium concentration*
Liver	69	4·4	2·7
Spleen	49	4·2	—
Kidney	62	2·7	1·0
Heart	43	2·5	0·6
Brain	63	2·2	0·5
Lung	58	1·8	0·7
Muscle	60	1·2	0·13
Large intestine	59	1·2	1·0
Stomach	70	1·1	1·2
Small intestine	62	0·9	1·9

$$* \quad \frac{\text{Bound tritium } (\mu c/g, \text{ moist tissue})}{\text{Average initial tritium content of body water } (\mu c/ml)} \times 100$$

difference is especially marked in the muscle and apart from the suggestion that this may be due to appreciable amounts of tritium being directly incorporated into tissue compounds (for example, unsaturated fats may become hydrogenated) without first being converted into tritiated water; there does not seem to be another obvious explanation.

DeLong[54] has studied the percutaneous absorption of tritium gas using excised skin from mice, rats and man. The absorption rates found were for mice $(254 \pm 44) \times 10^{-6}$; for rats $(207 \pm 26) \times 10^{-6}$; and for man $(72 \pm 16) \times 10^{-6}$ μc tritium absorbed/cm^2/min/μc tritium/cm^3 atm. The average rate constant for the percutaneous absorption of tritiated water through human skin was found to be $0·28 \pm 0·08$ μc/cm^2 skin/min/μc tritium/cm^3 atm.[41]. Although these figures are only intended as a rough guide they do demonstrate that tritiated water vapour is much more rapidly absorbed by the skin than tritium gas.

Moore[55] demonstrated that after 3 h following an intravenous injection (in humans) of tritiated water, the concentration of tritium in the expired air (water vapour) was 94 per cent of that in the blood and plasma; the concentration of tritium in the plasma and urine were equal and the tritium content of the red cell water was slightly less than in the plasma.

Toxicity of tritium compounds—Potentially the most serious radiological hazard to humans from tritium compounds is associated with substances at high specific activity. Those which are ingested and undergo slow metabolism (or catabolism) or become concentrated in certain tissues, cells or organs, are likely to be the most dangerous.

Lanz and McCall[56] have produced a nomogram for estimating tissue doses from internally deposited beta-emitting radioisotopes (3.6):

$$D = 74 \, ET_eC \qquad \dots \dots \quad (3.6)$$

where

D = the dose in rads absorbed by tissue after complete decay,

E = the average energy of the β-particles in MeV.

T_e = the effective half-life in days,

C = the concentration of the isotope in $\mu c/g$.

At a concentration of 1 $\mu c/g$ tissue for example, would receive a dose of approximately 5 rads assuming an effective half-life of 12 days. However, the effective half-life will vary not only for each compound, but also for the different tissues of the body[3]. For example, the T_e for glyceryl tristearate-T in the human is 30 to 40 days[57] which is about three times longer than for tritiated water.

Substances incorporated into cells, for example nucleosides and amino acids, can deliver large local doses and calculations of the radiation dose rates and isodose curves about a point source of tritium in unit density tissue have been published[58-60]. Radiation dose calculations in cells containing intranuclear tritium have also been made[60, 61]. Goodheart for example[61] calculated that such intra-cellular tritium would deliver a radiation dose of 0·271 rad/disintegration to the cell. On this basis the ingestion of 1 mμc (10^{-3} μc) of a tritiated compound, all of which is incorporated into a single cell, results in a dose of approximately 10 rads to the cell.

It is not difficult therefore, to appreciate the possible serious radiation damage and other effects of localized radiation due to tritiated compounds in various organs, but in order to obtain a clear perspective as to what is meant by 'radiological toxicity' of tritium compounds, it is important to differentiate between

(a) human personal uptake as a 'hazard' and

(b) possible radiation effects influencing the results obtained from a tracer use of tritium in biological experiments.

The current lack of *quantitative* information relating to uptake, distribution and radiation effects from an ingested 'dose' of a tritium-labelled compound, makes it impossible at the present time to assess realistically the problem of the 'hazard to humans'. There has been a tendency for isolated observations on the effects of tritiated compounds in biological experiments to be related to possible toxicity in humans. This would appear (in the absence of direct experimental evidence which admittedly is much more difficult to obtain) quite logical but may tend to exaggerate the hazards of working with tritium and its compounds. The absence of appreciable haemato-logical changes in patients with essentially normal bone marrow following intravenous doses of 10 c of tritiated tetrasodium 2-methyl-1,4-naphthaquinol diphosphate[3] provides a remarkable example of low toxicity for this chemical form.

Attempts to obtain quantitative information have been made for tritiated water (*vide supra*) but the only tritiated organic compound for which there has been investigation in any detail is thymidine. Tritiated thymidine and other labelled nucleosides are incorporated into the DNA of living cells and are built into the polynucleotide chains of the chromosomes. The genetic damage arising by irradi-ation from this *in situ* labelled thymidine, has consequently been the subject of numerous publications.

In conducting any experiments of this kind on the toxicology of tritiated compounds, one should bear in mind the possibility that short-term experiments (hours/days) may not show the radiation effects experienced in the longer-term experiments (weeks/months), and this perhaps accounts (in part) for the variation in the results of radiation effects, observed by different research workers. A simple example will illustrate this more clearly. The growth of HeLa cells is inhibited in tritiated water but at a dose level of 30 rads/day, it is over 1 week before the growth inhibition is observed[62].

Whether one should consider the chromosomal 'break' resulting from the primary disintegration (transmutation effect) as being more damaging than the secondary effect (ionization effect) caused by the ejected β-particle, is debatable[63]. This is the kind of dilemma which confronts the user of labelled compounds in cytological studies today. Stacey[64] (for example) concluded that 'cell death following decay of ^{32}P or ^{14}C were due overwhelmingly to transmutation of the atoms, rather than to ionizations, whereas ionizations caused by the very soft β-particles contributed a large part of the effects due to tritium decay'. However, Person[65] concluded from the results obtained with experiments on the comparative killing efficiencies for decays of tritium compounds in *E. coli*, that deaths were due very largely to chemical changes associated with the transmutation of tritium, rather than to the effects of ionizing radiation.

Although Guild[66] calculated that tritiated thymidine can deliver doses to the chromosomes or radiosensitive cells from 50 to 50,000 times those delivered by an equal activity of tritiated water, *in vitro* results with hamster cells[67] suggest that the effectiveness for breaking chromosomes is about the same for thymidine incorporated into DNA as for tritiated water or cobalt-60 γ-radiation. It is also interesting to note the work of McQuade[68] on chromosome aberrations in the meristemotic cells of onion seedling root-tips. After treatment in embryo with tritiated thymidine some of the seedlings died but many recovered the normal phenotype. This suggests that the undamaged or partly damaged cells survive within the injured organs to proliferate and eventually produce normal structures.

Other effects which have been attributed to tritiated thymidine include death to some bacteria (*E. coli*)[69,70] and chromosome aberrations and decrease in mitotic index in root-tips of plants exposed to activities of 1 μc/ml[71-73]. Mutations have also been observed in experiments with *Drosophila melanogaster*[74].

There are in fact many examples of the toxicity of tritiated thymidine in mammalian systems and some are summarized in Table 3.4.

The effect of an increased specific activity of the administered tritiated thymidine to cells is initially an increased net uptake of activity. This is subsequently followed by increased cell death and loss of a portion of the cell population with a net decrease in the resultant thymidine retention[76]. These observations were also confirmed by Samuels and Kisieleski[92] who make the suggestion (with Hiley)[93] that consideration of the actual disintegrations per cell may be a more useful guide in the measurement of the toxicity of tritiated thymidine (and other compounds) in biological systems. For example, the radiation dose to a cell from 125 disintegrations assuming 4·2 μ diameter nucleus of mass $3·84 \times 10^{-11}$ g, is 300 rads (taking the average energy of the tritium β-particles as 6 keV). Dewey, Humphrey and Jones[99], working with cells of the Chinese hamster, applied this approach for studying the intracellular effects of tritiated thymidine. They deduced that if all the energy from a tritium β-particle with an average energy of 5·7 keV were absorbed in a nucleus of radius 4·0 μ the radiation dose would be 0·34 rad. This value is reduced to 0·23 rad by the energy lost in the cytoplasm. The dose calculated for a radius of 2·0 μ is 1·41 rad and for a 5·0 μ radius is 0·126 rad. It is therefore important to know the size of the nucleus accurately. By and large their[99] results agreed with those obtained earlier by Guild[66] in that the β-particles from tritiated thymidine were less effective for producing chromosomal aberrations than the β-particle emitted from tritiated water distributed in the nucleus, or from γ-irradiation absorbed in the cells. However, they found the somewhat surprising result that 1,700 tritium disintegrations originating in the DNA were required to produce one visible chromosome aberration. It thus appears that a large number of tritium disintegrations must occur in the DNA of the chromosome to produce a noticeable biological effect and that either

TABLE 3.4

Effects of Tritiated Thymidine in Mammalian Systems

Biological system	Administered dose of tritiated thymidine in μc/ml of medium or μc/g of animal	Effect	References
Rat	2	Polyploidy liver	75
Rat	1	Chromosome aberrations (liver)	76
Mouse	1	Atypical cells (testis)	77
Mouse	1 to 10	Binucleate and pycnotic cells, Ehrlich ascites tumour (EAT)	78
HeLa tissue culture	0·02	Gross morphological changes	76, 79
HeLa cells	100–1000	Growth inhibition	62
HeLa cells	—	Growth inhibition	80
Mouse	20	Growth inhibition in bone-marrow transplants Cytological damage	81
Chick embryo	10 to 50 per embryo	Growth inhibition in Ehrlich ascites tumour	82
Mouse	1	Growth inhibition-regenerating liver Mutations	78
Rat	2	Malformations	83
Mouse	7·5	Neoplasm induction	84
Mouse	0·25 to 10	Cell death	85
Mouse	1	Testis cell death	86, 87
Tissue culture (lymphocytes)	1	Cell death in various tissues	88
Mouse	1	Inhibition of DNA synthesis	77, 89
Mouse	1 to 10	Disruption of cell cycle rhythm; delayed DNA synthesis; reduced number of cells in mitosis	90
Landschütz ascites Tumour cells	10		91
Rat	1 to 40		103

a single disintegration is relatively ineffective or the damage is largely repaired. Dewey and colleagues [99] also observed that in cells chronically irradiated by tritiated water or ^{60}Co γ-rays, during the S and G_2 periods (see page 43) many of the chromosomal breaks remained open for an hour or more. They concluded that energy absorption in or near the chromosomes is primarily responsible for producing aberrations and that the transmutation process (i.e. the decay of tritium to helium) in the tritiated thymidine of the DNA is relatively ineffective for inducing aberrations. About 25 per cent of the tritium β-particles have energies between 0·6 and 3·0 keV and it is interesting to note that this is the energy range for electrons suggested by Lea[100] as being the most effective for breaking chromosomes.

At present, the difficulty in determining the precise number of disintegrations occurring (or the total activity present) in a single cell severely limits the accuracy of such investigations.

From these various observations, it is apparent that in order to minimize the radiation artefact from tritiated thymidine (or other compounds used similarly) used in biological investigations, the minimum amounts of activity should be used, more especially when the experiment extends over more than a short time (a few hours). With the exception of one result[76] no toxic effects have been reported from concentrations below 0·05 μc/g of tissue or medium, a level which is quite satisfactory for autoradiography (see Chapter 5). It is acknowledged[92] that the toxicity of tritiated thymidine is best related to uptake and retention rather than to the administered dose.

The health hazard to the tracer user of tritiated thymidine (and other nucleosides), has perhaps been overemphasized[94, 95]. Normally, tritiated thymidine is handled in solution where the only means of body assimilation is by subcutaneous absorption from splashing on the skin. It is not expected that anyone would drink it; like other radioactive solutions it should never be pipetted by mouth. It is also a very difficult task to determine the radiological biological effectiveness (RBE) of the tritium β-radiation from intranuclear tritium compounds (such as thymidine), and until more *quantitative* information is available one must be cautious in correlating observed effects with the toxicity of tritium compounds in man.

Tritium sources and luminous compounds—The 'health physics' aspect of two other important applications of tritium is worthy of mention. The possible radiological hazard from tritium adsorbed on titanium sources, is reviewed by Gibson[96]. The rate of loss of tritium from sources kept at room temperature is less than 20 μc/8 h per curie of adsorbed tritium. Such sources thus present little hazard provided they are kept in adequately ventilated places[102], and precautions taken to avoid ingestion of the titanium tritide which may rub off (say) a damaged or worn source. Possible laboratory contamination from tritium on titanium or zirconium sources is also discussed by Chrusciel, Lasa and Salach[101].

The tritium losses from these sources when heated can be quite appreciable; under such conditions as used in gas chromatography. For example, a 50 mc source heated to 240° C in a nitrogen stream may lose 0·5 mc of tritium per day while at 285° C the loss is about 4 mc[97]. The results of some experiments carried out by the author[30] on the exchange of tritium from titanium tritide sources upon heating with organic compounds, are shown in Table 3.5. The loss of tritium from the sources at room temperature was about 10 μc/24 h per curie.

Sources were heated with 0·25 ml of the organic compound for about 1·5 h in a sealed tube.

TABLE 3.5

Source activity mc	Organic compound	Temperature °C	Total activity in solution mc	Percentage exchange of tritium
3,500	Acetic acid	100°	1·5	0·04 ⎫
3,500	Acetic acid	150°	30	0·92 ⎬ 35*
3,500	Acetic acid	200°	45	1·3 ⎭
1,000	Pyridine	100°	0·5	0·05 ⎫
1,000	Pyridine	150°	4°	0·4 ⎬ 50*
1,000	Pyridine	200°	200	20 ⎭
500	Benzene	100°	0·05	0·01 ⎫
500	Benzene	150°	0·05	0·01 ⎬ 10*
500	Benzene	200°	0·5	0·1 ⎭

* Overall loss of tritium from the source determined by ion current measurement at the end of the experiments.

Although the sources were subjected to rather extreme conditions as regards contact with the relatively large amount of organic vapour and liquid, the results do indicate that over a period of time acidic and basic compounds will strip out the adsorbed tritium and damage the titanium tritide surface. In preparative gas-chromatography a quantity of 0·25 g of an organic compound passed through a column during one hour is often carried out, but of course only a fraction may pass through the detector containing the source. It is therefore advisable to lead the outlet of the detection device containing the source into an air extract or a fume hood.

The potential hazard from the ingestion of tritiated luminous compounds (see Chapter 2) would appear no greater than from any other tritiated compound of long effective half-life in the body[98]. The most serious hazard arises from particulate luminous compound dust (i.e. 'tritiated' zinc sulphide) being lodged in the lungs which could result in quite large localized radiation doses. The same precautionary measures should be taken when handling tritiated zinc sulphide powders, as for handling solid tritium compounds (see page 84).

Summary

The effects of tritium radiation in biological systems (particularly in cytology), has only recently been made possible with tritium compounds now available at very high specific activities. This rather brief discussion of some aspects of tritium 'health physics' and of the possible radiation effects encountered in the use of tritium compounds, will perhaps (it is hoped) be generally useful to the newcomer to tritium tracer work.

In concluding this chapter the remarks made by Catch[22] for the precautions with carbon-14 compounds, would also be appropriate for tritium (and indeed other radioactive materials) in that the most important single factor in the safe handling of tritium and its compounds is the sense of responsibility and alertness of all concerned.

REFERENCES

[1] I.C.R.P. Publication 2—*Report of Committee II on Permissible Dose for Internal Radiation*, Pergamon Press (1959)

[2] Pinson, E. A. and Langham, W. H. *J. appl. Physiol.* 10 (1957) 108

[3] Mitchell, J. S., King, E. A., Marrian, D. H. and Chipperfield, B. *Acta radiol.* (New Series) 1 (1963) 321

[4] Fry, R. M. *A.E.R.E. Harwell Rep.* AERE HP/M137 (1958)

[5] Lawrence, J. N. P. *Los Alamos Sci. Lab. Rep.* LAMS–2163 (Nov. 1957)

[6] Butler, H. L. and van Wyck, R. W. Health Physics Section Savannah River Plant, *E.I. du Pont de Nemours & Co., Rep.* DP–329 (Feb. 1959)

[7] Gibson, J. A. B. *A.E.R.E., Harwell Rep.* AERE–M770 (Nov. 1960); *Physics Med. Biol.* 6 (1961) 283

[8] Radioactive Substances Act, 1960; 8 and 9, Eliz. 2, Ch. 34, H.M.S.O., London.

[9] *Introductory Manual on the Control of Health Hazards from Radioactive Materials.* Report of the Committee on Protection against Ionizing Radiations. *Med. Res. Coun. Memo.*, No. 39, 1961. London; H.M.S.O.

[10] Ministry of Labour. *Code of Practice for the Protection of Persons Exposed to Ionizing Radiations in Research and Teaching.* 1964. London; H.M.S.O.

[11] *The Control of Radioactive Wastes*, Cmnd. 884, 1959. London; H.M.S.O.

[12] *Recommendations for the Disposal of Carbon-14 Wastes.* Handbook No. 53, U.S. Dept. of Commerce, National Bureau of Standards, Washington, D.C. (1953)

[13] Chamberlain, A. C. and Eggleton, A. E. J. *A.E.R.E., Harwell, Rep.* AERE–R3970 (April, 1962)

[13a] Doury, A. *Minerva nucl.* 9 (1965) 1

[14] Catch, J. R. *Carbon-14 Compounds*, 1961. London; Butterworths

[15] Wang, C. H., Adams, R. A. and Bear, W. K. '*Adv. Tracer Methodol.*' 2 (1964) 303. Ed. S. Rothchild, Plenum Press N.Y. 1965

[16] Ward, D. R. *Laboratory Planning for Chemistry and Chemical Engineering.* Ed. Lewis, H. F., p. 156, 1962. New York; Reinhold Pub. Comp., London; Chapman and Hall

[17] Mackintosh, A. D. *U.S.A.E.C. Rep.* AECU–210 (ORNL–335) (1949)

[18] Tompkins, P. C. and Levy, H. A. *Ind. Engng Chem.* 41 (1949) 228

[19] Millett, R. J. *A Selected Reading List on Radiological Protection and Laboratory Design*—1946 to 1956; *A.E.R.E. Harwell, Rep.* AERE I/M 43 (1956)

[20] 'Design and Construction of Laboratory Buildings' *Analyt. Chem.* 34 (10) (1962) 25A

21 *Design and Construction of Radiochemical Laboratories;* a selected list of unclassified references *U.S.A.E.C. Service Rep.* TID–3013 (1951)

21a *The design and construction of radioisotope laboratories. A list of references.* AERE Harwell, Isotope Research Division, Wantage Research Laboratories, May, 1964

22 Catch, J. R. *Research, Lond.* 9 (1956) 479

23 Vaughan, B. E. and Davis, A. K. *U.S. Naval Radiol. Def. Lab. Rep.* USNRDL–TR–505 (April, 1961)

24 Morecraft, W. T. *Am. ind. Hyg. Ass. J.* 24 (1963) 87

24a Hutchin, M. E. and Vaughan, B. E. *Hlth. Phys.* 11 (1965) 1047

24b Butler, H. L. *Nuclear Safety* 4 (1963) 77

25 Brinkerhoff, J., Ziegler, C. A., Bersin, R. and Chleck, D. J. *Nucleonics* 17 (2) (1959) 76

26 Cowper, G. and Simpson, S. D. *Atomic Energy of Canada Ltd., Rep. AECL–1049* (July, 1960)

27 Engelke, M. J. and Bemis, E. A. *Los Alamos Sci. Lab. Rep.* LA–2671 (1962)

28 Karraker, D. G. *E. I. du Pont de Nemours & Co., Rep.* DP–34 (Dec. 1953)

29 Dr. R. J. Bayly (Radiochemical Centre)

29a Iyengar, T. S., Sadarangani, S. H., Somasundaram, S. and Vaze, P. K. *Hlth Phys.* 11 (1965) 313

30 Evans, E. A. (Radiochemical Centre)

31 Maximow, A. A. and Bloom, W. *A Textbook of Histology* 6th edn 1952. p. 311. Philadelphia; Saunders

32 Compton, A. H. and Allison, S. K. *X-Rays in Theory and Experiment* 2nd edn 1935, reprinted 1946, p. 90. New York; Van Nostrand

33 Pinson, E. A. and Anderson, E. C. *U.S.A.E.C. Rep.* AECU–937 (Nov. 1950); *Los Alamos Sci. Lab. Rep.* LA–1218 (March, 1951)

34 Wylie, K. F., Bigler, W. A. and Grove, G. R. *Hlth Phys.* 9 (1963) 911; 11 (1965) 62

35 Foy, J. M. and Schnieden, H. *J. Physiol., Lond.* 154 (1960) 169

35a Butler, H. L. and Leroy, J. H. *Hlth Phys.* 11 (1965) 283

36 Black, A. L., Baker, N. F., Bartley, J. C., Chapman, T. E. and Phillips, R. W. *Science N.Y.* 144 (1964) 876

37 Eutsler, B. C., Evans, G. L., Hiebert, R. D., Mitchell, R. N., Robbins, M. C. and Watts, R. J. *Nucleonics* 14 (9) (1956) 114

38 Anderson, E. C. and Langham, W. *Los Alamos Scient. Lab. Rep.* LA–1646 (Feb. 1954)

39 Pinson, E. A., Anderson, E. C. and Lotz, V. *Los Alamos Scient. Lab. Univ. Calif.,* Los Alamos, New Mexico, *Rep.* LAMS–1469 (Oct. 1952) (Classified)

40 Pinson, E. A., Anderson, E. C. and Lotz, V. *Los Alamos Scient. Lab. Rep.,* LA–1468 (Oct. 1952) (Classified)

41 Delong, C. W. *Rep.* AECD–4207 (July, 1951) Hanford Works, Richland, Washington, U.S.A.

42 Pinson, E. A., Anderson, E. C. and Lotz, V. *Los Alamos Scient. Lab. Rep.* LAMS–1465 (June, 1952)

43 Kingsley, W. H. and Hirsch, F. G. *Rep.* AECU–3394 (June, 1956) Sandia Corp., Albuquerque, New Mexico

44 Barker, R. F. *Isotopics* 6 (1) (1956) 10

45 Pinson, E. A. *Los Alamos Scient. Lab. Rep.* LAMS–1464 (June, 1952)

[46] Trujillo, T. T., Anderson, E. C. and Langham, W. H. *Los Alamos Scient. Lab. Rep.*, LA–1986 (Dec. 1955)

[46a] Lassen, N. A. *Int. J. appl. Radiat. Isotopes* 15 (1964) 495 (Abstract)

[46b] Lassen, N. A. *Radioactive Isotopes in Medicine and Research*, p. 36, Vol. 6 (1965). Munich-Berlin; Urban and Schwarzenberg

[47] McKown, D. A. *Los Alamos Scient. Lab. Rep.* LAMS–2946 (March, 1964) (Bibliography)

[48] Reinig, W. C. and Albenesius, E. L. *Am. ind. Hyg. Ass. J.* 24 (1963) 276

[49] Bost, W. E. *U.S.A.E.C. Rep.* TID–3570 (Dec. 1961) (Bibliography)

[49a] Casaletto, G. J., Gevantman, L. H. and Nash, J. B. *U.S. Naval Radiological Defence Lab. Rep.* USNRDL–TR–565 (1962)

[50] Smith, G. N., Emerson, R. J., Temple, L. A. and Galbraith, T. W. *Archs Biochem. Biophys.* 46 (1952) 22

[51] Brues, A. M., Stroud, A. N. and Rietz, L. *Proc. Soc. exp Biol. Med.* 79 (1952) 174

[52] Campbell, I. G., White, D. F. and Payne, P. R. *Br. J. Radiol.* 24 (1951) 682

[53] Smith, G. N., Hollis, O. L. and Thompson, R. C. *G.E.C. Hanford Works Rep.* HW–30437 (1954), p. 81

[54] Delong, C. W., Thompson, R. C. and Kornberg, H. A. *Radiat. Res.* 1 (1954) 214; *Am. J. Roentg.* 71 (1954) 1038

[55] Moore, R. *Hlth Phys.* 7 (1962) 161

[56] Lanz, H. and McCall, M. S. *Int. J. appl. Radiat. Isotopes* 7 (1959) 44

[57] Lubran, M. and Corsini, G. *Minerva nucl.* 4 (1960) 130

[58] Robertson, J. S. and Hughes, W. L. *Proc. First Nat. Biophysics Conf.*, p. 278, 1959. New Haven, Conn; Yale University Press

[59] Robertson, J. S., Bond, V. P. and Cronkite, E. P. *Int. J. appl. Radiat. Isotopes* 7 (1959) 33

[60] Künkel, H. A. *Strahlentherapie* 118 (1962) 46

[61] Goodheart, C. R. *Radiat. Res.* 15 (1961) 767

[62] Nias, A. H. W. and Lajtha, L. G. *Nature, Lond.* 202 (1964) 613

[63] Yamaguchi, H. *Radio-Isotopes, Tokyo* 10 (1961) 165

[64] Stacey, K. A. *Radiation Effects in Physics, Chemistry and Biology* Eds. M. Ebert and A. Howard, p. 96, 1963. Amsterdam; North Holland Pub. Co. (*Proc. 2nd Int. Conf. Radiat. Res.*, Harrogate, Aug. 5–11, 1962)

[65] Person, S. *Biophys. J.* 3 (1963) 183

[66] Guild, W. R. *Science, N.Y.* 128 (1958) 1308

[67] Dewey, W. C., Humphrey, R. M. and Jones, A. *Radiat. Res.* 19 (1963) 187 (Abst. only)

[68] McQuade, H. A. *Radiat. Res.* 20 (1963) 451

[69] Apelgot, S. *Proc. Symp. Tritium Phys. Biol. Sci.*, I.A.E.A., Vienna 2 (1962) 167

[70] Apelgot, S. and Latarjet, R. *Biochim. biophys. Acta* 55 (1962) 40

[71] Wimber, D. E. *Proc. natn Acad. Sci. U.S.A.* 45 (1959) 839

[72] McQuade, H. A. and Friedkin, M. *Expl Cell Res.* 21 (1960) 118

[73] Natarajan, A. T. *Expl Cell Res.* 22 (1961) 275

[74] Hughes, A. M., *Univ. Calif. Radiat. Lab. Bio-organic Chemistry Quart. Rep.* UCRL–10032 (Sept.–Nov. 1961) (1962)

[75] Post, J. and Hoffman, J. *Radiat. Res.* 14 (1961) 713

[76] Drew, R. M. and Painter, R. B. *Radiat. Res.* 11 (1959) 535

[77] Johnson, H. A. and Cronkite, E. P. *Radiat. Res.* 11 (1959) 825

78 Lisco, H., Nishimura, E. T., Baserga, R. and Kisieleski, W. E. *Lab. Invest.* 10 (1961) 435

79 Drew, R. M. and Painter, R. B. *Radiat. Res.* 16 (1962) 303

80 Peterson, D. F. p. 233 *Mathematical Problems in the Biological Sciences* 1962. Am. Maths. Soc.

81 Smith, W. W., Brecher, G., Stohlman, F. and Cornfield, J. *Radiat. Res.* 16 (1962) 201

82 Sauer, M. E. and Walker, B. E. *Radiat. Res.* 14 (1961) 633

83 Grisham, J. W. *Proc. Soc. exp Biol. Med.* 105 (1960) 555

84 Bateman, A. J. and Chandley, A. C. *Nature, Lond.* 193 (1962) 705

85 Greulich, R. C. *Radiat. Res.* 14 (1961) 83

86 Lisco, H., Baserga, R. and Kisieleski, W. E. *Nature, Lond.* 192 (1961) 571

87 Baserga, R., Lisco, H. and Kisieleski, W. E. *Proc. Soc. exp. Biol. Med.* 110 (1962) 687

88 Osgood, E. E. *The Kinetics of Cellular Proliferation* Ed. F. Stohlman, p. 184, 1959. New York; Grune and Stratton

89 Samuels, L. D., Kisieleski, W. E. and Hiley, P. C. *Radiat. Res.* 19 (1963) 244 (Abstr. only)

90 Garder, K. H. and Devik, F. *Int. J. Radiat. Biol.* 6 (1963) 157

91 Zajicek, G. and Gross, J. *Expl Cell Res.* 34 (1964) 138

92 Samuels, L. D. and Kisieleski, W. E. *Radiat. Res.* 18 (1963) 620

93 Kisieleski, W. E., Samuels, L. D. and Hiley, P. C. *Nature, Lond.* 202 (1964) 458

94 Samuels, L. D., Kisieleski, W. E. and Baserga, R. *Atompraxis* 10 (1964) 144

95 Oliver, R. and Lajtha, L. G. *Nature, Lond.* 186 (1960) 91

96 Gibson, J. A. B. *A.E.R.E. Harwell Rep.* AERE–M1169 (1963)

97 Shoemake, G. R., Lovelock, J. E. and Zlatkis, A. *J. Chromat.* 12 (1963) 314

98 Remy, J., Meunier, J. and Aeberhardt, A. *CEA–2155* (1962)

99 Dewey, W. C., Humphrey, R. M. and Jones, B. A. *Radiat. Res.* 24 (1965) 214

100 Lea, D. E. in *Actions of Radiation on Living Cells*, 2nd edn. p. 261, 1956. London; Camb. Univ. Press

101 Chrusciel, E., Lasa, J. and Salach, S. *Nukleonika* 10 (1965) 115

102 Kahn, L. and Goldberg, M. C. *J. Gas Chromatog.* 3 (8) (1965) 287

103 Post, J. and Hoffman, J. *Radiat. Res.* 26 (1965) 422

CHAPTER 4

THE PREPARATION OF TRITIUM-LABELLED COMPOUNDS

Labelling methods with tritium are determined largely by the following factors:

1. Substitution (directly or indirectly) or addition of hydrogen is always involved; this is often possible even with complex molecules, without any synthesis or partial synthesis in respect of carbon structure.
2. The primary forms of tritium are as gas (hydrogen) or liquid (water) with isotopic abundances being sometimes nearly 100 per cent.
3. Tritium is a comparatively cheap radioisotope.
4. Only very soft β-radiation is emitted.
5. The half-life is conveniently long.

There are some obvious consequences. Preparative yields are much less important than with the expensive carbon-14, but contamination and personal exposure are more troublesome because of the large amounts of tritium activity handled. Operations are much less difficult than with shorter-lived isotopes such as I-131 or P-32, because there is no overriding need for fast work and no penetrating radiation. On the other hand there is commonly less certainty about the position or distribution of labelling in the molecule than with other radioisotopes. The inevitable attempt to work with the highest possible specific activities makes self-decomposition much more troublesome than it is for example, with carbon-14 compounds (see Chapter 6).

This chapter describes the methods which are in current use for the preparation of tritium compounds. Many of the reactions and methods described have already been published and readers are referred to the original papers for practical details.

Any compound containing hydrogen atoms can be labelled with tritium by one or more of the methods now available. In practice tritium attached to atoms other than carbon is often labile because of its acidic or basic nature and consequently most of the preparative methods described are primarily for labelling organic molecules and relate in particular to the formation of carbon–tritium bonds.

There are four general approaches for preparing tritium compounds which are:

1. Isotope exchange reactions.
2. Direct chemical synthesis.
3. Biochemical methods.
4. Recoil labelling.

Wide use is made of isotope exchange reactions and chemical synthesis, with biochemical methods next in importance; but recoil tritium reactions are seldom used for preparative labelling.

1. ISOTOPE EXCHANGE REACTIONS

The preparation of tritium-labelled compounds by isotope exchange reactions can undoubtedly be regarded as the most important general technique for the introduction of tritium atoms into molecules. The method permits the labelling of very complex molecules which otherwise could not be labelled with tritium or indeed, in many cases, with any other isotope.

Exchange labelling methods for the introduction of isotopes into compounds have been known for many years, their possibility being first investigated by Hevesy[1,2] fifty years ago. Isotope exchange reactions are the reversible processes by which two isotopes of the same element $(^mZ, ^nZ)$ exchange places as shown in the equation (4.1):

$$A.^mZ + B.^nZ \rightleftharpoons A.^nZ + B.^mZ \quad . \quad . \quad . \quad (4.1)$$

Such reactions have the advantage of being relatively quick compared with some chemical syntheses with isotopes[3].

In any exchange labelling process it is essential to use a chemically pure substance as starting material, because any impurity in the parent compound will of course become labelled in the exchange reaction. This will then further complicate the purification of the tracer compound[33]. Impurities may also be labelled at a different rate from the parent compound giving rise either to very highly tritiated compounds or unlabelled chemical impurities.

Basically there are two general exchange labelling procedures which are currently applied to the preparation of tritium compounds. These are:

A. the gas-exposure method,
B. catalytic exchange in solution.

Both these methods are used frequently and the procedure selected depends on the nature and behaviour of the compound to be labelled under the experimental conditions.

A. Gas-Exposure Methods

The tritium gas-exposure method was first published in 1956 by Wilzbach[4] and is consequently also called 'Wilzbach' labelling. This has been by far the most widely used method and the subject of many publications on tritium labelling[5]. An excellent book has been published (in German)[6] on the preparation, measurement and uses of Wilzbach-labelled compounds.

The method consists of allowing a compound to remain in contact with tritium gas for a number of days or weeks. During this time the radiation induces exchange reactions between the hydrogen atoms of the compound and the tritium gas. The excess gas is then recovered, purified if necessary and used again, while the tritiated compound is purified by methods such as crystallization, distillation, sublimation etc.; although these conventional techniques are usually quite inadequate and chromatographic methods (paper, thin-layer, gas–liquid or ion exchange) are more frequently required in addition. This seemingly simple technique, when first discovered, added great impetus to furthering the uses of tritium compounds but the limitations of the method were soon apparent.

Limitations

The energy required for the introduction of a tritium atom into a particular molecule is about 300 eV in the most favourable cases and 5×10^5 eV in the least favourable[7]. The decay energy available from one tritium atom per day is about one electron volt or $1 \cdot 82 \times 10^{16}$ eV/day per millicurie which is considerably less than the energy of a recoil tritium atom (namely $2 \cdot 7$ MeV from the $^6Li(n, \alpha)^3H$ reaction). Consequently, if one compares the two labelling methods one would expect much less gross radiation damage to the compound in Wilzbach labelling than in recoil labelling. This is quite true in practice and most gas-exposure labelling techniques give high *chemical* yields. However, the most serious limitation is the formation of highly tritiated impurities which can arise by direct irradiation damage of the target material and by decomposition of the tritiated products by self-irradiation. These impurities often have a similar chemical

. . . . (4.2)

constitution to the parent compound, and although only present in trace chemical quantities they can represent a substantial part of the incorporated tritium activity. An excellent illustrative example is the attempted tritiation of the natural antifungal antibiotic griseofulvin [8,8a] (4.2).

Exposure of this compound to tritium gas resulted in less than 3 per cent of the total tritium incorporated being associated with the purified griseofulvin [9]. Although it was not proved, addition of tritium to the cyclohexenone ring system is more likely than substitution, as is found with the Wilzbach labelling of 3-keto-Δ^4-steroids[10].

The impurities are usually difficult to remove or even to detect and searching purity tests must therefore be applied to compounds produced by Wilzbach labelling before they can confidently be used as tracers. Some of the pitfalls of tritium analysis are discussed in Chapter 5.

Side reactions which occur during the irradiation include polymerization of unsaturated compounds, and addition reactions take place almost predominantly when compounds containing ethylenic, acetylenic or other unsaturated linkages are used [11,12]. Addition of tritium is not confined to carbon–carbon double bonds but can also take place across carbon–nitrogen double bonds[13].

Compounds which have been labelled by the Wilzbach technique are listed in Tables 4.1–4.7. At this point the reader should remember the difficulty of purifying compounds, especially complex compounds, when studying these examples. It would be unrealistic to assume that all the products are radiochemically pure in the strict sense.

It can be seen from these tables that another limitation of the gas-exposure method is the low specific activity of the purified compound. This is normally in the range 0·1 to 10 mc/mM except when large quantities of tritium gas are used in favourable cases[14]. Although this is an improvement over the recoil labelling method where specific activities less than 0·1 mc/mM are obtained, it is still much less than that required for many applications of tritium compounds (see Chapter 2).

Improvements

The simplicity of the Wilzbach method has prompted many investigations to improve the efficiency of tritium incorporation and to reduce the impurities formed. The efficiency of labelling has been considerably improved but to date the impurity problem remains unsolved.

Under the normal exposure of an organic compound to tritium gas, the rate of incorporation of tritium is about 1 per cent per day of the total tritium activity present in the system. This exchange can occur with any hydrogen atom in the compound and the distribution of tritium in the labelled products can be almost uniform, specific or general depending on the type of compound irradiated. More detailed information on the distribution of tritium in labelled materials is given in Chapter 5.

(a) *Tritium gas activation*—About the same time as Wilzbach's discovery (1956), Wolfgang, Pratt and Rowland[15] attempted to label organic compounds by bombardment with tritium ions accelerated to an energy of up to 100 eV. Unpurified products having a specific activity about 0·1 mc/mg were obtained. In 1959 Lemmon and colleagues[16] improved the efficiency of the tritium labelling by passing an electric discharge through the tritium gas during the exposure. Some comparisons between this technique and the normal method are given in Table 4.8. A Tesla-coil leak tester can be used as a source for the electric discharge[17]. Another technique employed is the mercury-sensitization of the mixture[18], which was first tried[19] in 1954 but was not used again until 1961.

Other methods for energizing the reaction system include irradiation with ultra-violet light[20–22], γ- and x-irradiation[16, 23], addition of iodine[42], and microwaves[24]. Shimojima, Nagao and Kamada[87], suggest the microwave discharge technique to be much superior to the high-voltage discharge method because of the simpler discharge tube required and the smaller amounts of tritiated impurities produced. However, their findings were based on the tritiation of a simple organic compound (acetic acid) only, and may not be generally true for other, more complex, compounds. From Tables 4.1–4.8 it can be seen that all these methods tend to increase the rate of incorporation of tritium into the molecule and in some cases the specific activity of the final purified product is much higher than the normal procedure. However, there is generally an increased amount of decomposition products which makes purification of the parent compound difficult and sometimes impossible[25, 26].

Activation of the tritium by atomizing the gas with a hot filament, has recently been described for labelling some carbohydrates[27]. Specific activities in the range 0·2 to 30 μc/mg using less than 50 mc of tritium gas, during a 30 min reaction time, were obtained.

(b) *Charcoal absorption*—If one assumes that Wilzbach labelling depends on a collision between tritium atoms or molecules, and a molecule of the compound, either in the ground or excited energy states, then an increased rate of labelling might be achieved by

103

bringing the molecules together in closer proximity. This can be done by adsorbing the compound on charcoal or even by just mixing the compound with charcoal, and then introducing the tritium gas into the ampoule. It is known that 1 g of activated charcoal at 15° C adsorbs 4·7 ml of hydrogen at one atmosphere pressure. This would be equivalent to the adsorption of 12 c of tritium gas per gramme of charcoal at one atmosphere pressure[35].

Work of this nature on charcoal-adsorbed products has been confined to simple organic compounds[28]. Results have been promising although an insufficient variety of compound classes have been studied to assess fairly the merits and usefulness of such a technique. Some results compared with the normal gas-exposure method are shown in Table 4.9. Claims have been made[29] that the amount of impurities are also reduced by the charcoal-compound gas-exposure technique and this would in itself be a considerable advance, but the usefulness of the method has been disputed[30].

Other adsorption methods have been used. Tritium adsorbed on pyrophoric uranium can be used to label hydrocarbons[31]. The hydrocarbon vapour is condensed onto the pyrophoric tritium-containing uranium. The rate of introduction of the tritium into the compound is 0·2 to 10 per cent per hour which is intermediate between that observed in the Wilzbach method and the gaseous discharge method. A survey by Rothchild[32] indicates that the former method introduces tritium into hydrocarbons at a (median) rate of 0·19 mc per curie-day ($7·9 \times 10^{-4}$ per cent/h) whereas the gaseous discharge method can incorporate tritium at the rate of 1·7 per cent per hour[16] to about 12 per cent per hour[34].

(c) *Catalysed gas-exposure method*—A most promising approach to improving the Wilzbach gas-exposure technique consists of exposing an intimate mixture of the compound with a noble-metal catalyst such as platinum or palladium black[36, 37] (prepared by reduction of the corresponding oxides), to the tritium gas. The results obtained in labelling compounds by this catalysed gas-exposure technique are shown in Table 4.10. It is seen that by using this procedure specific activities of 3 to 2,000 times higher than the normal method are obtained. The increase in labelling varies considerably with the different classes of compounds and usually the relative degree of labelling is higher for aromatic than for aliphatic compounds possibly because of stronger chemisorption of aromatic compounds on the catalyst[36, 37]; alternatively, the π-electrons of aromatic compounds may complex more readily with T^+ (HeT^+ or HT^+) than with the σ-electrons of aliphatic compounds.

Other catalysts which have been tried include Raney nickel[36, 38] and nickel oxide[36]. These have little effect on solids at room temperature but volatile hydrocarbons have been labelled at 60° C by exposure to tritium gas in the presence of Raney nickel[38].

Wenzel and colleagues[39] have tried to improve the Meshi and Takahashi catalysed-exposure method by combining the charcoal-adsorption technique with a platinum catalyst, with a view to obtaining substantially higher specific activities without a concomitant increase in radiation damage. Success was achieved with the steroid digitogenin but much more experimentation with a wide variety of compounds is required before the general applicability and usefulness of the combined techniques can be assessed.

Effect of Temperature and Pressure

At lower temperatures the amount of tritium gas adsorbed on the charcoal, catalyst or compound should increase and one may expect an increase in the efficiency of labelling. On the other hand, although chemical decomposition (and possibly some secondary radiation effects) will undoubtedly be reduced at the lower temperatures, the labelling efficiency may also be reduced as the thermal energy of the tritium and compound molecules is lowered. Experiments with valine[36] showed that labelling is more efficient at room temperature than at 80° C, while results obtained at the Radiochemical Centre[40] suggest that there is little advantage, as far as increasing the labelling efficiency, in conducting the catalytic-charcoal exchange below room temperature (20° C). These findings have been subsequently confirmed by other investigators[39, 41] (see Table 4.11). However, one must still bear in mind that low temperatures (down to −196° C) may be advantageous for sensitive compounds, for example to minimize denaturation of proteins.

These results conflict with those obtained by the normal Wilzbach procedure[7] where it is found that although the labelling in the decomposition products appears to be independent of temperature, labelling in benzoic acid (for example) increases with temperature. This could of course be related to an increase in pressure in the system and although the experiments with benzoic acid indicate the labelling to be independent of the pressure of the tritium (or concentration), for other compounds it may be a pressure effect rather than temperature. It may also be connected with the volatility of the compound under investigation.

The formation of decomposition products is almost proportional to the pressure of the tritium[7]. The addition of helium promotes the formation of side-products without affecting the formation of labelled benzoic acid but xenon increases the efficiency of labelling by 50 per cent and a three to fourfold increase in the side-products. The addition of diluent gases does not therefore offer any advantages.

Illustration

For the purpose of illustrating the Wilzbach method, let us consider the case of a hypothetical compound (4.3) and what might be expected to occur during an exposure of say 0·5 g to tritium gas (100 c, 40 ml, 98 per cent isotopic purity) for 14 days at room temperature at about 0·5 atm pressure.

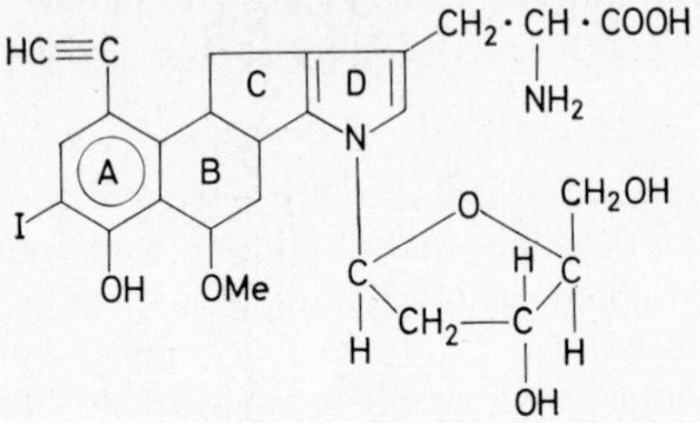

$$\qquad \cdots \quad (4.3)$$

Assuming a rate of incorporation of tritium to be 1 per cent per day, at the end of the irradiation the crude product would have about 14 c of activity associated with it. There are six labile hydrogen positions: phenolic —OH (ring A), amino group —NH_2 (side-chain ring D), deoxyribose —OH groups and the carboxyl —OH (side-chain ring D).

It is not possible to predict how much tritium is associated with these labile hydrogen atoms but it can be several curies. The labile tritium is removed by mixing the compound with water or other hydroxylic solvents and freeze-drying to avoid decomposition by heating. This is repeated several times with perhaps 5–10 ml quantities of solvent until the distillate contains practically no tritium. It is not necessary for the compound to dissolve in the hydroxylic solvent so long as there is thorough mixing. It is most important to remove this labile tritium as soon as possible after the irradiation to minimize further decomposition by self-irradiation.

Examining the various types of chemical bond present, the reader will immediately observe the presence of weak links. The weakest bonds in the molecule are the carbon–iodine bond (ring A) and the carbon–nitrogen bonds (amino acid side-chain and glycoside link of the sugar with ring D). For guidance some bond energies are listed in Table 4.12.

One would therefore expect specific labelling in ring A due to the replacement of the iodine atom with tritium[11, 43], and partial or complete reduction of the acetylenic side-chain of ring A[44-48]; ring D may also become saturated. These reactions will produce tritium-labelled impurities at high specific activity, indeed theoretically 'carrier-free'.

Hydroxyl groups are sometimes eliminated from the molecule especially in aliphatic compounds[113, 49]. For example, the 2,3-hydroxyl groups in tartaric acid are replaced by tritium 60 times faster than carbon-bound hydrogen atoms.

Substitution in the aromatic nucleus is usually favoured and thus ring A will contain (possibly) a higher proportion of the tritium than the rest of the molecule.

Splitting of carbon–nitrogen bonds will give rise to tritiated deoxyribose and deamination of the ring D side-chain.

One is then left with the original compound plus many impurities in trace chemical amounts which are nevertheless heavily tritiated. Purification from these impurities, some of similar chemical structure to the parent compound, may or may not be successfully achieved by chromatographic methods for example.

In general the more complex the structure of the compound (macromolecules like proteins are an example) the more difficult it is to achieve a radiochemically pure product.

Mechanism of Wilzbach Labelling

Although the detailed mechanism of tritium labelling by gas exposure is not fully worked out, in its simplest form the following states can arise:

(1) reaction of recoiling tritium atoms with the substrate

$$T_2 \rightsquigarrow (T^3He)^+ \quad + \quad R \cdot H \longrightarrow R \cdot T$$

(2) reaction of excited or ionized tritium molecules with the compound

$$T_2 \rightsquigarrow T_2^* \longrightarrow 2T$$

$$T \quad + \quad R \cdot H \longrightarrow R \cdot T \quad + \quad H \cdot T$$

(3) reaction of excited or ionized compound molecules with tritium

$$RH \rightsquigarrow R \cdot H^+ \quad + \quad e^-$$

$$R \cdot H \rightsquigarrow R \cdot H^*$$

$$R \cdot H^+ \; + \; T_2 \; \longrightarrow \; R \cdot T \; + \; H \cdot T$$

$$R \cdot H^* \; + \; T_2 \; \longrightarrow \; R \cdot T \; + \; H \cdot T$$

Reactions (2) and (3) probably contribute mainly to the labelling process and reaction (1) to a much lesser extent purely on the grounds of the number of recoiling tritium atoms produced during an irradiation[50, 51].

The Wilzbach method is a radiation-induced exchange procedure and the electronically excited states in the various parts of the compound molecules, induced by the β-radiation, would produce a generally labelled product (G) rather than a uniformly labelled one (U). This is in accordance with the experimental observations on the distribution of tritium in compounds labelled by gas-exposure techniques, an aspect dealt with more fully in Chapter 5.

There is some evidence[12, 52, 52a] that free radical processes are also operative.

Special Features

Although one would generally advise the use of the Wilzbach gas-exposure labelling technique as 'a last resort' for the preparation of tritium compounds, there are nevertheless some academically interesting features and applications of the method.

(*a*) Configurational changes which occur during the exchange of hydrogen atoms for tritium have received particular attention[52–58]. Unlike recoil labelling (see page 192), optical and geometrical configurations are usually affected to some extent.

Gordon, Intrieri and Brown[52] labelled 1,2,3,5-tetra-O-acetyl-D-ribofuranose with apparent complete retention of configuration; however, in this particular investigation the isomers could have been missed during the purification of the tritiated compound. Crawford and Garnett[54] reported a predominant but not exclusive retention of configuration in labelling (+) and (−)-2-octyl phthalate but Wilzbach and Riesz[53] showed that 30 per cent racemization occurred during the tritiation of (−)-mandelic acid.

Wilzbach labelling of crystalline (−)-inositol proceeds with a high retention of configuration, whereas its liquid hexa-O-methyl derivative undergoes predominant inversion[55]. It is suggested that the difference in behaviour is due (in part) to the rigidity of the molecular lattice (by intermolecular hydrogen bonding) in the crystalline inositol restricting conformational changes during the exchange[56].

A number of publications describe the Wilzbach labelling of L-amino acids[26, 36, 59], and although the chemical and radiochemical purity is established by paper chromatography, the 'radiochemical optical purity' (i.e. the percentage of the radioactivity which is in the stated optical form of the pure compound) is seldom proved. The degree of racemization can be established by reverse carrier dilution analysis with the L- and D-amino acid carriers. Table 4.13 shows some results obtained at the Radiochemical Centre[40], which indicate that some racemization can occur during the tritiation.

There is as yet no direct experimental evidence to support changes in configuration of the L- or D-amino acid components of a peptide chain, for example in proteins, during Wilzbach labelling, but the possibility should be borne in mind.

(*b*) Stereoselective saturation of a carbon–carbon double bond under Wilzbach conditions has recently been described[57]. Predominantly *trans*-addition of tritium occurs when 3β-hydroxy-androst-5-en-17-one is exposed to carrier-free tritium gas, yielding 3β-hydroxyandrostan-17-one-5α,6β-T (4.4):

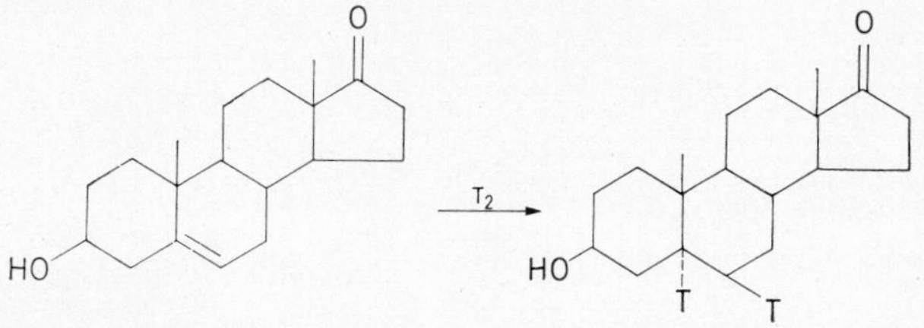

$$\dots \dots (4.4)$$

These results are in agreement with some earlier work by Bradlow, Fukushima and Gallagher, in that addition to the Δ^5-steroids give 5α-T products[61].

The addition of tritium to triple bonds on the other hand, is not stereospecific and a mixture of tritiated *cis*- and *trans*-olefins is obtained[47, 62].

(*c*) The radiation sensitivity of carbon–iodine bonds (for example) can sometimes be made use of in the specific labelling of organic compounds with tritium by the Wilzbach technique. Feng and Greenlee[43] showed that over 95 per cent of the tritium in benzoic acid-T was situated in the *p*-position after exposing *p*-iodobenzoic acid to tritium gas. A similar result with specific labelling in the *o*-position was obtained when *o*-iodobenzoic acid was used. The labelled benzoic acids obtained in this manner are of course the 'impurities' or 'decomposition products', and are theoretically labelled carrier-free in the specific positions indicated.

TABLE 4.1

Wilzbach-Labelled Amino Acids, Proteins and Peptides

Compound	Weight g	Tritium c	Time	Specific activity mc/g Crude	Specific activity mc/g Pure	Remarks	References
DL-Alanine (from α-hydroxyimino-propionic acid)	—	—	—	—	4·4	Electric discharge	13
Albumin (human)	0·25	4	4 days	—	25		63
Albumin (human)	1	7	10 days	123	—	Irradn at 0° C	40
Albumin (blood serum)	0·1	1	4 days	—	6·5		64
Albumin (blood serum)	0·1	1	30 days	—	12		64
Albumin (blood serum)	0·18	0·051	—	—	5		64
Angiotensin-II (asparoginyl-valyl-angio-tensin-II)	0·016	5·76	30 min	—	300	Mercury electric discharge	65
L-Cystine	—	5·85	19 days	2·73	0·12		26
Cycloserine	0·1	—	—	—	55	Microwave	66
S-(1,2-Dichloro-vinyl)-L-cysteine	—	—	—	—	—	Impure products	26
D-ββ-Dimethyl-cysteine	—	3	14 days	—	14·7		67
L-ββ-Dimethyl-cysteine	—	3	14 days	—	14·7		67
γ₂-Globulin	—	—	7 days	1–10	—		74
γ-Globulin	0·15	3	3 days	—	13·4		63
β-Hydroxy-γ-amino butyric acid	0·3	21	15 days	—	13·9		68
Hydroxylysine		1·2	14 days	—	71		69
L-Hydroxyproline	1	3	3 days	—	nil		70
L-Hydroxyproline	0·1	20	7 days	—	10		40
Insulin	1	2·2	14 days	18	4·6		71, 72
L-Isoleucine	0·1	0·9	21 days	—	8·2		59
L-Isoleucine	0·05	0·3	40 min	—	53	2 kV electric discharge	59
DL-Leucine	0·1	5	5 days	—	31·2		73a
DL-Leucine	—	5	3 days	—	20·1		73
L-Leucine	0·1	0·9	21 days	—	20·5		59
L-Leucine	0·3	0·3	20 min	—	13·8	2 kV electric discharge	59
L-Lysine HCl	0·1	0·9	21 days	—	39		59
Lysine-vasopressin	0·02	1·1	8 days	—	300		75, 75a
Lysozyme	0·237	1·8	3 days	—	—		76, 77
DL-Methionine	0·1	0·9	21 days	—	0·8		59
L-Methionine	0·4	0·1	30 days	—	1·6		59
L-Methionine	0·4	0·1	40 days	—	2·0		59
D-Methionine	0·4	0·1	60 days	—	2·9		59
α-Methyl-DL-glutamic acid	4·74	12	14 days	—	248		78, 79, 80
Oxytocin	0·153	3	7 days	175	12·4	at 4° C	81
DL-Phenylalanine	—	—	—	—	—		82
L-Phenylalanine	0·1	0·9	21 days	—	3·7		59
L-Phenylalanine	0·3	0·3	20 min	—	15	Electric discharge	59
L-Proline	1	3	3 days	40	2		70
L-Proline	1	100	14 days	2,450	1,230		40
L-Proline	0·1	20	7 days	—	560		40
Ribonuclease	0·57	6·73	2 days	—	—		76
DL-Threonine	0·1	0·9	21 days	—	0·25		59
DL-Threonine	0·4	0·1	30 days	—	0·96		59
DL-Threonine	0·4	0·1	40 days	—	1·0		59
DL-Threonine	0·4	0·1	60 days	—	1·03		59
L-Tryptophan	0·1	0·9	21 days	—	2·4		59
L-Tryptophan	0·3	0·3	20 min	—	—	Electric discharge	59
DL-m-Tyrosine	—	—	—	—	—		82
DL-Valine	0·1	0·9	21 days	—	1·8		59
L-Valine	0·3	0·3	20 min	—	9	5 kV electric discharge	59
L-Valyl-L-leucine	1	154 curie-days		705	192		83

110

The success of this method depends upon the rate of substitution of tritium for iodine being much greater than tritium for hydrogen, and is thus likely to be applicable to simple molecules only. Other limitations include:

(i) the availability of suitable iodinated intermediates,
(ii) the ability to separate the product required,
(iii) the rate of decomposition of the highly tritiated product by self-irradiation,

TABLE 4.2
Wilzbach-Labelled Aliphatic Compounds

Compound	Weight g	Tritium c	Time	Specific activity mc/g		Remarks	References
				Crude	Pure		
Aminopropanol	1	10	28 days	—	—		84
Artemisiaketone	0·1	10		—	4,940	Some addn	179
n-Butyl sulphide	1	1·72	28 days	161	15		85
n-Butyl disulphide	1	2·5	21 days	481	50		85
t-Butyl mercaptan	1	2·5	34 days	385	1		85
N,N-bis-(β-chloro-ethyl)-N-O-propy-lene phosphoric ester diamide (Endoxan)	—		3–5 days	—	—		86
N,N-bis(β-chloro-ethyl)-amido-phos-phoric acid dichloride	1·4	10	14 days	233	32		84
Cyclohexane	—	0·01	5 days	—	0·22	U.V.-Hg	18
Cyclohexane	—	0·01	5 days	—	0·0005		18
Cyclohexene	—			—	—	16% subs. 84% addn	44
Cyclohexene	1	2·25	28 days	267	6		85
Cyclohexane thiol	1	1·36	35 days	87	18		85
Dibromostearic acid amide	2	3·7	30 min	75·7	2·5	Electric discharge	34
Di-(2-ethylhexyl)-adipic acid ester	10	1	6 days	—	0·002		88
N,N-Dimethyldode-cylamine hydro-chloride	10	1·8	30 min	70	0·35	Electric discharge	34
2,5-Dimethylhexa-1,5-diene	1·0	1·95	28 days	845	67		85
2,5-Dimethylhexa-2,4-diene	1	2·5	21 days	722	12		85
2,2-Dimethyl-3,4-dithia-hexane	1	2·36	37 days	298	—		85
Ethylene oxide	0·435	0·064	—	—	—	Microwave	64
Ethylene oxide	0·26	0·124	—	—	—	Microwave	64
2-Ethylhexane thiol	1	1·78	28 days	118	—		85
n-Heptane	1·37	6·9	9·8 days	17·5	1·3		4
n-Heptane	1	1·51	35 days	96	8		85
Hept-3-ene	1	2·25	28 days	274	18		85
Hexadecanol	2	2·3	30 min	275	5·2	Electric discharge	34
γ-Hexachlorocyclo-hexane	0·2	2	7 days	—	—		10
Hexa-1,5-diene	1	4·78	0·04 days	38	—	Electric discharge	85
Hexa-1,5-diene	1	3·67	0·04 days	151	—	Electric discharge	85
Isoamylmercaptan	1	1·28	35 days	79	—		85
Isobutylene	—			—	—	47% subs. 53% addn	44
Maleic acid	0·115	5	3 days	—	0·11		91
Methylcyclohexane	1	4·77	0·04 days	131	—	Electric discharge	85
2-Methyl-1-butane thiol	1	2·35	28 days	96	—		85

111

TABLE 4.2 (continued)

Compound	Weight g	Tritium c	Time	Specific activity mc/g		Remarks	References
				Crude	Pure		
Methylhexyl sulphide	1	2·55	36 days	300	—		85
Methyl myristate	—	5	8 days	—	—		45, 46
Methyl oleate	1	1	18 days	—	—	100% addn	45, 46
2-Methyl-2-n-propyl-1,3-propanediol dicarbamate	1	5·5	3 days	350	303		89
2-Methyl-2-n-propyl-1,3-propanediol dicarbamate	—	—	—	—	—		90
2-Methyl-2-pentane thiol	1	1·81	28 days	73	—		85
Methyl laurate	—	5	7 days	—	—		45, 46
Methyl linoleate	1	1	18 days	—	—	100% addn	45, 46
Methyl linolenate	1	1	17 days	—	—	100% addn	45, 46
Methyl palmitate	—	1	4 days	—	—		45, 46
Methyl stearate	1	—	13 days	—	—		45, 46
Methyl sorbate	—	—	—	—	—		44
Mineral oil	1·5	3	10 min	57	41	Electric discharge	34
Oleic acid amide	2	3·2	30 min	187	0·3	Electric discharge	34
Palmitic acid	20	10	11 days	41	15		78
Palmitic acid	0·254	—	6 min	42	3·5	Electric discharge	78
Palmitic acid	0·35	1	5 min	32	4·7	Electric discharge	78
Palmitic acid	0·35	1·8	5 min	230	7·9	Electric discharge	34
n-Propyl disulphide	1	2·55	36 days	276	—		85
Succinic acid	0·238	—	—	—	0·052		29
Succinic acid	0·088	—	—	—	0·345		29
Succinic acid	0·283	—	—	—	0·244		29
Stearic acid	1	1·9	10 min	230	7·9	Electric discharge	34
1,1,1-Trifluoro-2-chloro-2-bromo-ethane	6	2·3	14 days	42	2·9		93
2,2,4-Trimethyl-pentane	1	4·6	0·04 days	282	30	Electric discharge	85
2,2,4-Trimethyl-pentane	1	3·98	0·04 days	434	—	Electric discharge	85

TABLE 4.3
Wilzbach-Labelled Aromatic Compounds

Compound	Weight g	Tritium c	Time	Specific activity mc/g		Remarks	References
				Crude	Pure		
p-Acetophenetidine	0·21	4	11 days	—	0·126		29
p-Aminosalicyclic acid	0·03–0·1	1·6–2·6	1–165 h	—	0·15–14	Series of expts	97
Anthanthrene	0·025	12	21 days	1,750	900		94
Aniline	1	1·83	28 days	557	92		85
Anisole	2	—	30 days	—	—		95
Anthracene	0·22	113	63 days	203,000	—		96
Benzene	0·088	0·076	—	—	225	Microwave	64
Benzene	0·088	0·075	—	—	—	Microwave	64
Benzene	0·035	0·087	—	—	70	Microwave	64
Benzene	0·6	0·04	60 min	—	1·7	Electric discharge	16
Benzene	0·6	0·46	300 min	—	33	Electric discharge	16
Benzene	0·6	0·025	1 day	—	0·008	γ-irradn.	16
Benzoic acid	—	0·5	10 days	—	0·68		30
Benzoic acid	—	5	4 days	—	0·5		29
Benzoic acid	1·31	6·4	5 days	119	14		101

TABLE 4.3 (*continued*)

Compound	Weight g	Tritium c	Time	Specific activity mc/g		Remarks	References
				Crude	Pure		
Benzoic acid	0·4	1·9	30 min	540	12	Electric discharge	102
3,4-Benzpyrene	0·05	12·5	21 days	1,690	990		94
3,4-Benzpyrene	0·5	—	14 days	800	45		99
Benzylacetamidomalonate	0·498	6·98	9·8 days	260	26·6		140
s-Butylbenzene	1	2·97	0·04 day	1,381	241	Electric discharge	85
t-Butylbenzene	1	2·5	34 days	1,015	228		85
Chloramphenicol	—	—	—	—	—		103
Chlorobenzene	2	0·3	30 days	—	9		95
p-Chlorobenzoic acid	0·06	4	6 days	—	0·2		91
1,1-Diamino-4,5-dimethylbenzene	2·84	7·2	14 days	—	5·1		79, 80
1,2,5,6-Dibenzanthracene	0·05	11·5	21 days	240	150		94
1,2,3,4-Dibenzanthracene	0·05	12·3	21 days	360	190		94
N,N-Dimethylaniline	—	—	—	—	—		104
9,10-Dimethyl-1,2,5,6-dibenzanthracene	0·027	13	56 days	32,300	2,400		94
9,10-Dimethyl-1,2-benzanthracene	0·05	12	21 days	320	140		94
9,10-Dimethyl-1,2-benzanthracene	0·5	—	14 days	460	18		99
1,3-Dimethylindene	1	2·3	28 days	130	20		85
2,7-Dimethylnaphthalene	1	2·5	21 days	246	102		85
2,4-Dihydroxy-acetophenone	4·8	11	14 days	—	8·4		79, 80
3,5-Dinitrobenzamide	3	4·36	29 days	—	118		79, 80
Diphenyl	0·29	208	42 days	476,000	—		96
Diphenyl	1	136	4 days	27,700	—		96
p-Dichlorobenzene	0·52	1·5	3 days	44	32		102
p-Dichlorobenzene	0·49	0·4	3 min	65	20	Electric discharge	102
3-Fluoro-10-methylbenzanthracene	0·045	12	23 days	1,790	970		94
4-Fluoro-10-methylbenzanthracene	0·042	12	25 days	770	320		94
4-Hydroxyphthalide	4·6	10	14 days	—	2·4		79, 80
bis-(Hydroxydichlorophenyl) sulphide	2	2·5	10 min	16	0·78	Electric discharge	34
p-Iodobenzoic acid	1	3	14 days	—	—	Benzoic acid isolated	43
Indane	1	3·98	0·04 day	541	—	Electric discharge	85
Indene	1	2·5	21 days	694	26		85
Isopropyl benzene	1	2·97	0·04 day	329	84	Electric discharge	85
DL-Kynurenine	1	2·4	14 days	290	1·98	Product diluted	105
L-Mandelic acid	—	—	—	—	—	Racemization	53
10-Methylbenzanthracene	0·047	12	23 days	1,600	650		94
4-Methylbenzanthracene	0·035	12	25 days	1,090	660		94
3-Methylbenzanthracene	0·04	12	25 days	2,430	2,200		94
3-Methyl-1-benzene thiol	1	1·19	35 days	137	38		85
3-Methylcholanthrene	0·05	12·5	21 days	2,300	1,780		94
20-Methylcholanthrene	0·5	—	14 days	700	170		106
1-Methylnaphthalene	1	2·5	21 days	719	172		85
2-Methylnaphthalene	1	3·28	0·04 day	1,504	87	Electric discharge	85
α-Methyl styrene	1	2·5	34 days	1,571	787		85
Naphthalenes (mixed)	1	2·32	28 days	216	52		85
Naphthalene	1	3·4	0·8 day	28	7·2		17
Naphthalene	0·25	292	49 days	360,000	—		96
Naphthalene	0·52	0·8	5 min	52	4·5	Electric discharge	102
Naphthalene	0·58	0·4	5 min	—	4·1	Electric discharge	102
Nitrobenzene	2	—	30 days	—	—		95
3-Nitrophthalic acid	4·5	11	14 days	—	32		79

TABLE 4.3 (continued)

Compound	Weight g	Tritium c	Time	Specific activity mc/g		Remarks	References
				Crude	Pure		
1-Phenylbut-2-ene	1	1·93	28 days	681	52		85
Phenol	1	2	28 days	445	159		85
2-Phenylphenanthrene 3,2'-dialdehyde	0·03	12	21 days	60	40		94
Salicylic acid	0·275	5	3 days	—	0·075		29
Salicylic acid	—	0·5	10 days	—	0·71		100
Sulphanilamide	0·155	3·2	6 days	—	0·23		29, 91
p-Terphenyl	0·21	113	30 days	6,500	—	⎫	96
p-Terphenyl	0·53	137	16 days	6,600	—	⎪	96
p-Terphenyl	2	155	10 days	4,700	—	⎪	96
p-Terphenyl	2	155	20 days	6,900	—	⎬ Addition	96
p-Terphenyl	2	155	30 days	9,000	—	⎪ products	96
p-Terphenyl	2	155	55 days	12,000	—	⎪	96
o-Terphenyl	0·25	110	64 days	14,600	—	⎪	96
m-Terphenyl	0·26	98	63 days	33,900	—	⎭	96
Tetralin	1	2·5	21 days	610	187		85
Tetrasodium 2-methyl-1,4-naphthaquinol diphosphate	0·3	200	14 days	—	420		40
Thiophenol	1	2·5	21 days	120	14		85
Toluene	0·86	7·5	2·9 days	42·7	22·2		4
Toluene	—	0·01	5 days	—	1·78	U.V.-Hg vapour	18
Toluene	—	0·01	4 days	—	0·73	U.V.-Hg vapour	18
Toluene	—	0·01	5 days	—	0·0053		18
1,2,4,5-Tetramethylbenzene	1	2·5	21 days	672	81		85
Trichlorophenyl carbanilide	0·53	1·7	10 min	4·4	0·49	Electric discharge	34
Triphenylene	0·2	85	81 days	4,000	—		96

TABLE 4.4

Wilzbach-Labelled Carbohydrates

Compound	Weight g	Tritium c	Time	Specific activity mc/g		Remarks	References
				Crude	Pure		
N-Acetyl glucosamine	0·175	3	30 days	—	80		123
D-Allose	0·2–1	—	14–21 days	—	27·3		124
1,5-Anhydro-D-glucitol	0·2–1	—	14–21 days	—	9·5		124
1,5-Anhydro-D-mannitol	0·2–1	—	14–21 days	—	5·6		124
6-Deoxy-1,5-anhydro-D-glucitol	0·2–1	—	14–21 days	—	12·2		124
6-Deoxy-D-galactose	0·2–1	—	14–21 days	—	8·2		124
6-Deoxy-D-glucose	0·2–1	—	14–21 days	—	2·2		124
2-Deoxy-D-glucose	0·2–1	—	14–21 days	—	4·4		124
7-Deoxy-D-glucoheptose	0·2–1	—	14–21 days	—	2·7		124
2-Deoxyribose-5-phosphate	0·1	4	21 days	—	1		79
Glucosamine hydrochloride	0·25	5	3 days	—	2·18		125
D-Glucose	0·5	25	15 days	—	244		40
Hexa-O-methyl(−)inositol	0·9	2	56 days	—	1,045	Mixed isomers	126
(−)Inositol	0·3	2	56 days	—	3,050	Mixed isomers	126
2-Methoxy-D-glucose	0·2–1	—	14–21 days	—	0·26		124
3-O-Methyl-D-glucose	0·2–1	—	14–21 days	—	4·6		124
D-Ribose	—	3	14 days	—	66·7		67
Sucrose	4	14	6·7 days	110	5		4
1,2,3,5-Tetra-O-acetyl-D-ribofuranose	1	1·2	15 days	—	—		52
Tri-(N-acetyl)-chitotriose	0·012	5	24 days	—	56		126

114

TABLE 4.5
Wilzbach-Labelled Heterocyclic Compounds

Compound	Weight g	Tritium c	Time	Specific activity mc/g		Remarks	References
				Crude	Pure		
Adenine	—	3	14 days	—	81·5		67
Aminopterin	—	—	—	—	—		108
2-Aminopurine	—	3	14 days	—	960		67, 107
2-Aminopyrimidine-5-carboxylic acid	—	3	14 days	—	7·2		67
Benzothiophene	1	2·5	21 days	777	155		85
Cardiazol	—	3	14 days	—	195		67
Diethylbarbituric acid	0·09	5	11 days	—	1·6		91
6-Dimethylamino-9-(3′-aminoribosyl)purine (aminonucleoside)	0·35	4·5	12 days	—	8		109
2,5-Dimethylpyrrole	1	3·67	0·04 day	405	—	Electric discharge	85
2-Ethylthiophene	1	2·5	34 days	965	—		85
5-Fluorouracil	—	3	14 days	—	7·7		67
N-Furfuryladenine (kinetin)	—	3	14 days	—	500		67
Imidazole dicarboxyamide	1·95	3·24	17 days	—	8		79
2-Isobutylthiophene	1	2·5	34 days	468	—		85
2-Isobutylthiophene	1	2·5	0·04 day	798	74	Electric discharge	85
3-Methylpyridine	1	2·18	37 days	351	—		85
2-Methylpyridine	1	3·28	0·04 day	387	89	Electric discharge	85
N-Methylpyrrole	1	2·18	37 days	247	110		85
Nicotinic acid	—	3	14 days	—	4·07		67
Nicotinic acid amide	0·06	5	5·5 days	—	0·18		91
Pentobarbital (5-ethyl-5-(1-methylbutyl)barbituric acid)	1	1	31 days	—	0·64	on 5 g 'hyflo'	110
Phenylethylbarbituric acid	0·23	4	11 days	—	0·12		29
Purine	—	3	3 days	—	6·7		67, 107
Pyrrole	1	2·88	32 days	220	—		85
Pyrrolidine	1	2·5	34 days	290	—		85
Quinoline	1	2·88	0·04 day	1,199	107	Electric discharge	85
Spartein sulphate	—	3	14 days	—	64		67
Thiacyclohexane	1	2·55	36 days	485	—		85
Thymidine	0·1	4·5	10 days	—	174		63
Thymidine	—	—	14 days	604	62		111
Thymidine	0·3	100	21 days	—	322		40
2,4,6-Trimethylpyridine	1	1·83	28 days	423	103		85
Tryptamine HCl	0·1	20	8 days	—	262		40

TABLE 4.6
Wilzbach-Labelled Steroids

Compound	Weight g	Tritium c	Time	Specific activity mc/g		Remarks	References
				Crude	Pure		
3β-Acetoxy-Δ⁵-pregnen-20-one	—	—	—	—	—	17% sub. 66% addn	61
Δ¹-Androstenolone	—	—	—	—	—		106
Aldosterone	0·005	6	10 days	—	—		112
Cholesterol	0·04	5	4 days	—	0·82		28
Cholesterol	1·88	7·2	5 days	—	64		4
Cholesterol	—	—	5 min	140	1·7	Electric discharge	102
Cholesterol	—	—	30 min	750	0·5	Electric discharge	102
Cholesterol	—	—	—	—	—	55% sub. 45% addn	44, 46
Cholic acid	0·005	1	28 days	—	3,200		114
Corticosterone	0·005	6	10 days	—	—		112
Cortisol	0·005	6	10 days	—	—		112

TABLE 4.6 (*continued*)

Compound	Weight g	Tritium c	Time	Specific activity mc/g		Remarks	References
				Crude	Pure		
7-Dehydrocholesterol	3	15	14 days	—	53·7		118
Dehydroepiandrosterone	—	—	—	—	—	95% addn	61
11-Desoxycortisol	0·005	6	10 days	—	—		112
11-Desoxycorticosterone	0·005	6	10 days	—	—		112
Digitoxin	0·45	7·5	6 days	513	77		115
Digitoxin	0·45	7·5	7 days	513	75		116
Digitoxin	0·5	7·5	6 days	256	90		4
Ecdysone	0·03	33	29 days	—	56·1	on charcoal at −196°C	41
Ergosterol	1	3	14 days	—	10		118
Hydrocortisone	—	—	—	21	—	10% sub. 10% addn	79
Hydrocortisone	—	—	—	—	—	10% sub 80% addn	10
17-Hydroxycorticosterone	2·5	2·4	29 days	21	—		79
17α-Hydroxyprogesterone	—	—	—	280	—		119
4-Hydroxy-17α-methyl-testosterone	0·571	2·61	18 days	—	1·5		100
6α-Methyl-17α-hydroxy-progesterone	0·574	2·35	3 days	—	1·95		100
	0·584	2·26	3 days	—	3·78	(light 500 Å)	100
	0·580	2·8	3 days	—	6·4	(u.v.-light 257 Å)	100
1-Methyl-Δ¹-androstenolone	—	—	—	10	—	15% sub. 80% addn	10
5α-Pregnan-17α,21-diol-3,11,20-trione 21-acetate	0·03	33	29 days	—	2,330		41
Δ¹-5α-Pregnen-17α,21-diol-3,11,20-trione 21-acetate	0·03	33	29 days	—	2,100		41
β-Sitosterol	0·42	2·5	14 days	—	—	90% sub. 10% addn	120
Testosterone propionate	0·05	1·8	13 days	3·1	0·4		91
Triamcinolone	1·4	2·3	14 days	270	0·7		121
Triamcinolone	1·01	2·5	14 days	—	4·7		121
3α,7β,12α-Trihydroxy-cholic acid	—	—	—	120	—		122

TABLE 4.7

Miscellaneous Wilzbach-Labelled Compounds

Compound	Weight g	Tritium c	Time	Specific activity mc/g		Remarks	References
				Crude	Pure		
Atropine	0·29	100	22 days	—	3,200		14
Atropine	0·1	2	16 days	139	57		129
Atropine	0·15	0·5	10 min	—	278	Electric discharge	129
Aureomycin (chlorotetracycline)	0·35	1	28 days	—	0·8		130
Bilirubin	0·02	6·23	21 days	890	110		131
Bilirubin	0·02	6·23	21 days	880	30	γ-irradn 2·9 × 10⁷rads	131
Chloramphenicol	0·35	1	28 days	—	6·07		130
Coenzyme-Q₀	—	—	—	—	18·4		165
Cytostaticum DG 428	—	3	14 days	—	—		67
Cytostaticum U 8344	—	3	14 days	—	—		67
Deoxyribosenucleic acid	0·085	2·4	14 days	860	—		132
Deoxyribosenucleic acid (sodium salt)	0·5	20	14 days	585	—		40
Dextran	0·1	1	21 days	5·1–15·2	—		133, 134
Dihydrostreptomycin	0·35	1	28 days	—	0·12		130
Dioctyl adipate	—	—	—	—	0·002		88
Endotoxin	0·1–0·5	3	10 days	300–4,000	35–130	at 0°C	136
Endoxan	—	—	3–5 days	—	—		86

116

TABLE 4.7 (*continued*)

Compound	Weight g	Tritium c	Time	Specific activity mc/g		Remarks	References
				Crude	Pure		
Folic acid	0·5	15	10 days	0·22	0·012		137
Geranyllinalol	—	—	—	—	—		142a
Gibberellic acid	1·6	5	20 days	—	108		138
Gibberellic acid	1·7	4·3	10 days	—	129		79
Gonadotrophin	0·199	3·5	14 days	—	24		63
Griseofulvin	—	3	14 days	—	5		9
Humic acid	—	—	—	—	0·3		139, 141
Hyaluronic acid	0·055	4·5	6 days	—	68·8		63
Hyaluronic acid	0·1	4·5	4·75 days	—	60		63
Inositol	—	—	—	—	—		142
Insulin	0·1	7	14 days	3,800	—	at 0° C denaturation	40
Morphine	—	—	—	—	—		143
Neomycin-B sulphate	8·5	13·4	30 min	680	0·88	Electric discharge	34
Nicotine .	—	—	—	—	—		145
NorCocaine	0·17	2	33 days	—	8·7		129
Nor-Morphine hydrochloride	—	—	—	—	5–10	some addn to 5,8-positions	144
Paraformaldehyde	0·5	25	15 days	6,400	—		40
Penicillin-G	0·35	1	28 days	—	19·5		130
Penicillin-V	0·35	1	28 days	—	18·4		130
Purpurogallin	—	—	—	—	0·568		141
Puromycetin	—	3	14 days	—	48		67
Pyridoxine hydrochloride	0·47	100	30 days	—	2,136		40
Streptomycin	0·35	1	28 days	—	0·033		130
Tetanus Toxin	—	5	2·5 days	—	—		151
Tetracycline	0·1	5	14 days	—	40		147
Tetracycline	0·35	1	28 days	—	0·13		130
Trans-Stilbene	—	—	—	28	0·22		146
Tricyclohexyl borane	—	—	—	—	—		148–150
Triphenyl lead	0·05	5	7 days	—	—		152
Triphenyl tin	0·05	5	7 days	—	—		152
Uridine diphosphate-N-acetylglucosamine	0·1	—	—	210	10		153, 154
Uridine diphosphate-N-acetylmuramic acid	0·05	—	—	360	—		153, 154
Uridine diphosphate-glucuronic acid	0·1	—	—	200	8		153, 154
Vasopressin	—	—	—	—	400	Electric discharge	75
Vincaleukoblastine	0·65	15	14 days	1,230	61·4	no addn	155*
Vincaleukoblastine sulphate	0·95	15	14 days	193	15·5	addn	155
Vinblastine sulphate	0·14	3	14 days	30	15	some addn	157
Vitamin-A acetate	—	—	—	—	1·6		44
Vitamin-A acetate	—	5	14 days	—	—		139
Vitamin-B12	0·1	0·005	22 days	—	0·0045		79
Vitamin-B12	—	3	14 days	—	240		67
Vitamin-D3	0·5	50	39 days	2,700	216	at − 196° C	156

* McMahon[155] found that addition of tritium only occurred when vincaleukoblastine (vinblastine) sulphate was used. Beer[157] *et al.*, isolated both tritiated dihydrovinblastine and vinblastine when the sulphate was used for the labelling. The different results may be due to the difficulty in separating vinblastine from dihydrovinblastine; a problem now resolved[157].

TABLE 4.8
Comparative Results of the Wilzbach and Electric-Discharge Methods

Compound	Method	Tritium c	Exposure time	Specific activity mc/g	References
Benzoic acid	Wilzbach	6·4	5 days	14	4
Benzoic acid	Elect. discharge	—	0·5 h	100	15
p-Dichlorobenzene	Wilzbach	1·5	3 days	32	102

TABLE 4.8 (*continued*)

Compound	Method	Tritium c	Exposure time	Specific activity mc/g	References
p-Dichlorobenzene	Elect. discharge	0·4	3 min	20	102
Hex-1-ene	Wilzbach	4·1	8 weeks	1,110	160
Hex-1-ene	Elect. discharge	3·7	1 h	1,500	160
1-Methylnaphthalene	Wilzbach	2·5	21 days	172	85
1-Methylnaphthalene	Elect. discharge	3·28	1 h	87	85
Tertiary butyl-benzene	Wilzbach	2·5	34 days	228	85
Tertiary butyl-benzene	Elect. discharge	2·97	1 h	241	85

TABLE 4.9

Comparative Results of the Wilzbach and Charcoal-Absorption Methods

Compound	Weight g		Tritium c	Time	Specific activity purified mc/g	References
	Compound	Charcoal				
p-Acetophenetidine	0·21	nil	4	11 days	0.126	29
p-Acetophenetidine	0·212	1	4	11 days	0·236	29
p-Acetophenetidine	0·095	1	4	11 days	0·48	29
Benzoic acid	0·136	nil	5	4 days	0·5	29
Benzoic acid	0·136	1	5	4 days	13·7	29
Benzoic acid	—	nil	0·5	10 days	0·68	30
Benzoic acid*	—	x	0·5	45 min	0·547	30
Benzoic acid*	—	x	0·5	60 min	0·41	30
p-Chlorobenzoic acid	0·06	nil	4	6 days	0·2	91
p-Chlorobenzoic acid	0·06	0·38	4	6 days	0·84	91
Cholesterol	0·040	nil	5	4 days	0·82	28
Cholesterol	0·035	0·185	5	4 days	1·4	28
Cholesterol	0·045	0·488	5	4 days	3·1	28
Diethylbarbituric acid	0·09	nil	5	11 days	1·6	91
Diethylbarbituric acid	0·08	1·23	5	11 days	5·1	91
Digitogenin	0·0198	nil	2	7·5 h	0·072	39
Digitogenin	0·0214	0·355	2	7·5 h	1·97	39
Maleic acid	0·115	nil	5	3 days	0·11	91
Maleic acid	0·56	0·188	5	3 days	1·0	91
Maleic acid	0·24	0·208	5	3 days	2·2	91
Nicotinic acid amide	0·06	nil	5	5·5 days	0·18	91
Nicotinic acid amide	0·06	0·436	5	5·5 days	0·9	91
Phenylethyl-barbituric acid	0·15	nil	4	11 days	0·12	29
Phenylethyl-barbituric acid	0·228	1	4	11 days	0·226	29
Phenylethyl-barbituric acid	0·088	1	4	11 days	0·345	29
Prednisolone	0·1	nil	0·1	22 days	0·4	36
Prednisolone	0·1	0·1	0·1	22 days	0·28	36
5α-Pregnan-17α,21-diol-3,11,20-trione 21-acetate	0·03	nil	33	29 days	2,330	41

TABLE 4.9 (*continued*)

Compound	Weight g		Trit- ium c	Time	Specific activity purified mc/g	Refer- ences
	Compound	Charcoal				
5α-Pregnan-17α,21-diol-3,11,20-trione 21-acetate	0·03	2	33	29 days	3,830	41
Δ¹-5α-Pregnen-17α, 21-diol-3,11,20-trione 21-acetate	0·03	nil	33	29 days	2,100	41
Δ¹-5α-Pregnen-17α, 21-diol-3,11,20-trione 21-acetate	0·03	2	33	29 days	1,230	41
Δ¹-5α-Pregnen-17α, 21-diol-3,11,20-trione 21-acetate	0·03	2	33	29 days (at −196° C)	91.8	41
Salicylic acid	0·275	nil	5	3 days	0·075	29
Salicylic acid	0·275	1	5	3 days	0·98	29
Salicylic acid	0·047	1	5	3 days	9·8	29
Salicylic acid	—	nil	0·5	10 days	0·71	30
Salicylic acid*	—	x	0·5	45 min	0·55	30
Salicylic acid*	—	x	0·5	60 min	0·57	30
Salicylic acid	0·1	nil	0·15	2 days	0·05	36
Salicylic acid	0·1	0·1	0·15	5 days	0·06	36
Salicylic acid	0·1	nil	0·1	3 days	0·068	36
Salicylic acid	0·1	0·1	0·1	3 days	0·09	36
Salicylic acid	0·1	0·2	0·1	3 days	0·06	36
Sulphanilamide	0·155	nil	3·2	6 days	0·23	161
Sulphanilamide	0·155	1·013	3·2	6 days	1·3	161
Sulphanilamide	0·155	1·013	3·2	6 days (at −196° C)	9·8	161
Testosterone propionate	0·05	nil	1·8	13 days	0·4	91
Testosterone propionate	0·05	0·434	1·8	13 days	1·64	91
L-Valine	0·1	nil	0·1	20 days	0·3	36
L-Valine	0·1	0·1	0·1	20 days	0·26	36

* Electric discharge.

TABLE 4.10
Catalysed Gas-Exposure Method

Compound	Weight mg	Catalyst	Weight mg	Tritium mc	Exposure time	Specific activity mc/g	Increase factor	Refer- ences
Benzoic acid	100	—	nil	100	5 days	0·1	1	36
Benzoic acid	100	Pt black	100	100	5 days	21·0	210	36
Digitogenin	22·6	10% Pt/C	355	2,000	7·5 h	6·6	91·5	39
Digitogenin	19·8	—	nil	2,000	7·5 h	0·072	1	39
Inositol	100	—	nil	100	4 days	0·24	1	36
Inositol	100	Pt black	100	100	4 days	4·55	19	36
L-Methionine	200	—	nil	7,000	6 days	14	1	40
L-Methionine	200	10% Pd/C	200	7,000	7 days	125	9	40
Prednisolone	100	—	nil	100	22 days	0·4	1	36

TABLE 4.10 (*continued*)

Compound	Weight mg	Catalyst	Weight mg	Tritium mc	Exposure time	Specific activity mc/g	Increase factor	References
Prednisolone	100	Pt black	100	100	22 days	2·32	5·8	36
Salicylic acid	100	—	nil	150	2 days	0·05	1	36
Salicylic acid	100	Pd black	100	150	3 days	13·8	276	36
Salicylic acid	100	Pt black	100	150	5 days	108	2,018	36
Salicylic acid	100	Pt/PtO$_2$·H$_2$O	65/35	150	5 days	146	2,920	36
Salicylic acid	100	PtO$_2$·H$_2$O	100	150	5 days	1·0	20	36
Salicylic acid	100	Pd/PdO	50/50	150	3 days	20	400	36
Salicylic acid	100	Raney Ni	100	150	2 days	0·06	1·2	36
Salicylic acid	100	Ni oxide	100	150	2 days	0·007	1	36
Salicylic acid	100	—	nil	100	3 days	0·068	1	36
Salicylic acid	100	Pd black	100	100	3 days	11·8	173	36
Salicylic acid	100	Pt black	100	100	3 days	88	1,290	36
Salicylic acid	100	Pt Black	200	100	3 days	128	1,880	36
Succinic acid	500	10% Pt/C	500	100,000	9 days	195	—	40
Thiamine	100	—	nil	100	7 days	0·95	1	36
Thiamine	100	Pt black	100	100	7 days	3·05	3·2	36
Thymidine	200	—	nil	7,000	7 days	20	1	40
Thymidine	200	10% Pd/C	200	7,000	7 days	1,510	75·5	40
L-Valine	100	—	nil	100	20 days	0·3	1	36
L-Valine	100	Pd black	100	100	7 days	0·57	1·9	36
L-Valine	100	Pt black	100	100	20 days	8·6	20	36
L-Valine	100	Pt black	200	100	20 days	6·2	21	36

TABLE 4.11

Influence of Temperature on Catalysed Gas Exposure

Compound	Weight mg	Catalyst	Weight mg	Tritium mc	Exposure time	Temp. °C	Specific activity mc/g	Increase factor	Reference
Digitogenin	19·8	—	nil	2,000	7·5 h	20°	0·072	1	39
Digitogenin	22·6	10% Pt/C	355	2,000	7·5 h	20°	6·6	91·5	39
Digitogenin	22·6	10% Pt/C	355	2,000	7·5 h	−196°	2·44	18·5	39
L-Methionine	200	—	nil	7,000	6 days	20°	14	1	40
L-Methionine	200	—	nil	7,000	6 days	−80°	16	1·1	40
L-Methionine	200	10% Pd/C	200	7,000	7 days	20°	125	9	40
L-Methionine	200	10% Pd/C	200	7,000	6 days	−80°	129	9	40
L-Methionine	200	10% Pd/C	200	7,000	6 days	−80°	85	6	40
L-Methionine	200	10% Pd/C +PtO$_2$	200/25	7,000	6 days	−80°	96	7	40
Thymidine	200	—	nil	7,000	7 days	20°	20	1	40
Thymidine	200	10% Pd/C	200	7,000	7 days	20°	1,510	75·5	40
Thymidine	200	10% Pd/C	200	7,000	7 days	−80°	850	42·5	40
Thymidine	200	10% Pd/C	200	7,000	7 days	−196°	310	15·5	40
L-Valine	100	—	nil	100	7 days	20°	0·45	1	36
L-Valine	100	Pt black	100	100	7 days	20°	106	235	36
L-Valine	100	—	nil	100	4 days	+80°	0·58	1·3	36
L-Valine	100	Pt black	100	100	4 days	+80°	2·25	5	36

TABLE 4.12

Bond Energies [163,164]

Bond Type	C≡C	C=C (Aromatic)	C—C	CH—H	CH$_2$—H
Energy (kcal/mole)	200	145	83	124	88

Bond Type	CH$_3$—H	C—N	C—O	C=O	C—I	N—H
Energy (kcal/mole)	101	72	86	179	57	104

120

TABLE 4.13

Racemization of L-Amino Acids during Wilzbach Labelling [40]

L-*Amino acid*	*Weight* mg	*Charcoal* mg	*Tritium* c	*Expos-ure time* days *at* 20° C	*Specific activity* mc/mM	*Racemiz-ation** %
L-Methionine	510	nil	25	7	2	<5
L-Methionine	200	500	25	7	6·5	9
L-Proline	1,000	nil	100	14	141	<5
L-Proline	500	nil	100	14	224	<5
L-Proline	200	500	25	7	3	25
L-Tryptophan	500	nil	25	7	4·5	50
L-Tryptophan	500	500	25	7	14	50

* Percentage radioactivity in the DL-form.

B. Catalytic Exchange in Solution

Labelling compounds with tritium by catalytic exchange in a tritiated solvent is undoubtedly the most useful general method and although widely used it has not received the same publicity as the Wilzbach technique. For the routine production of tritium compounds in high radiochemical yield and at high specific activity (greater than 50 mc/mM), the exchange reaction between the compound and a tritiated solvent in the presence of a catalyst is second best only to chemical synthesis, when that is a practical proposition.

The applicability of the technique is only restricted by the stability of the compound under the exchange conditions and is admirably suitable for compounds which are moderately stable in solution at temperatures up to 150° C.

1. *Exchange into Labile Positions*

When a compound is dissolved in a tritiated solvent, for example tritiated water, isotope exchange occurs between the tritium atoms of the water and hydrogen atoms in the compound which are attached to N, O or S (see Chapter 6). Exchange into these labile positions in a molecule occurs almost instantaneously at room temperature, an equilibrium is established and a tritiated compound remains after removal of the tritiated solvent by evaporation. For example, although ammonium ions exchange relatively slowly with deuterium oxide[166] tritiated ammonium salts are readily prepared by simply dissolving the salt in tritiated water and removing the water by evaporation (4.5):

$$(NH_4)_2SO_4 + THO \rightleftharpoons (NH_3T)_2SO_4 + H_2O \quad . \quad . \quad . \quad (4.5)$$

By heating the tritiated ammonium salts with soda-lime in the dry state, tritiated ammonia can be prepared. With the amino acid glycine only the hydrogen atoms attached to the amino- and carboxyl groups are exchanged with tritiated water (4.6):

$$NH_2 \cdot CH_2 \cdot COOH + 2THO \; \rightleftharpoons \; NHT \cdot CH_2 \cdot COOT + 2H_2O$$

$$\dots \quad (4.6)$$

Another interesting example of exchange forming labile tritium linkages is the reaction between malonic acid and tritiated water (4.7):

$$CH_2(COOH)_2 + THO \; \overset{fast}{\rightleftharpoons} \; CH_2(COOT)_2 + 2H_2O$$

$$CH_2(COOT)_2 + THO \; \overset{slow}{\rightleftharpoons} \; CHT(COOT)_2 + H_2O$$

$$\dots \quad (4.7)$$

This is an example of a labile tritium atom attached directly to a carbon atom. When the malonic acid is dissolved in tritiated water, exchange with the carboxyl hydrogen atoms is almost instantaneous but the hydrogen atoms of the methylene group exchange at a much slower measurable rate which is dependent on the temperature of the exchange reaction. The kinetics of this reaction have been studied in detail[167], equilibrium being reached in 8 h at 80° C. Qualitatively the rate of exchange is greater in both acid and alkaline solution[168].

Exchange reactions such as (4.5, 4.6 or 4.7) are of course reversible and if the tritiated compound obtained is now dissolved in water (or other hydroxylic solvents) re-equilibration takes place and the specific activity of the compound is reduced. By successive equilibrations in water all the tritium can be removed from the compound, which makes such labelled compounds normally quite useless as tracers for most purposes. In spite of this papers are still published describing methods for labelling compounds with tritium in labile positions. One such example is the tritiation of alcohols, phenols, enols, carboxylic acids and amines by passage over a gas–liquid chromatography column impregnated with tritiated water[169]. Such compounds would have a very limited use as tracers indeed.

2. *Exchange into Stable Positions*

Normally little or no exchange occurs into the non-labile hydrogen positions of a compound in the absence of a catalyst. For example, the methylene hydrogens of glycine (equation 4.6) are not exchanged on dissolving glycine in tritiated water or even on heating to boiling point under alkaline or acid conditions. In the absence of a catalyst only the amino- and carboxyl-hydrogen atoms are exchanged.

Adenine (4.8) is labelled only on the hydrogen atoms attached to nitrogen atoms by exchange in tritiated acetic acid; the presence of a catalyst is required to exchange the stable hydrogens at the 2- and 8-position[170].

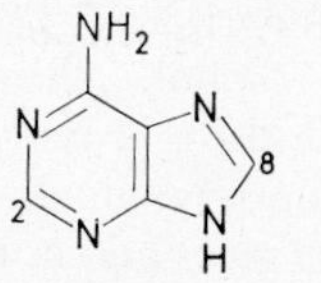

. . . . (4.8)

Some organic compounds contain no non-labile hydrogen positions and therefore cannot be usefully labelled with tritium. An example is 8-azaguanine (4.9).

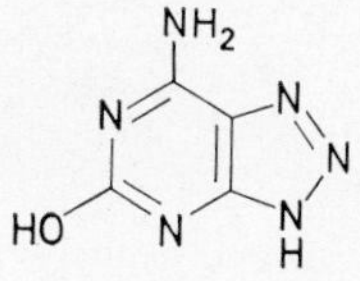

. . . . (4.9)

Stable carbon-tritium bonds are formed by shaking a mixture of the compound with a tritiated solvent (tritiated water or acetic acid are the most popular) in the presence of a hydrogen transfer catalyst. Normally heating to temperatures in the range 50–150° C is required to achieve high specific activities and to reach equilibrium in the shortest time. However, for sensitive compounds a suitable degree of labelling can sometimes be obtained even at room temperature. For example, vitamin-D_3 can be labelled by stirring in tritiated acetic acid at room temperature in the presence of a platinum catalyst[171].

Homogeneous catalysis—Both homogeneous and heterogeneous catalysis can be employed. In the former the most widely used catalysts are sulphuric acid[172,173], phosphoric acid[178], perchloric acid[175], trifluoroacetic acid[40,176], tritiated water containing aluminium chloride which forms the strong Brönsted acid $H[AlCl_3OH]$[177,177a] and tritiated phosphoric acid–boron trifluoride complex[178]. All these strongly acidic reagents have the disadvantage that they cannot be used for acid-sensitive compounds. They are suitable for labelling many aromatic compounds and at lower temperatures competing reactions such as sulphonation are not a serious disadvantage. The polyyne Artemisiaketone, isolated from *Artemisia vulgaris*, has recently been labelled with tritium by exchange in tritiated sulphuric acid for 60 h at 70°[179]. The specific activity of the *trans*-tetradecatri-2,4,6-yne-8-ene-12-one was 0·25 mc/mg using tritiated sulphuric acid at approximately 0·17 c/ml.

With some simple aliphatic compounds, such as *n*-propyl alcohol, heating to 100° C with 8M-tritiated perchloric acid results in rearrangement to isopropyl alcohol. Although no exchange into non-labile positions occurs with the *n*-propyl alcohol starting compound, the rearranged product isopropyl alcohol is tritiated[174].

The H[AlCl₃OH] *reagent* gives higher reaction rates than the other acidic tritiated solutions and some compounds which can be labelled using this reagent[177] are shown in Table 4.14.

TABLE 4.14
Labelling by Tritiated H[AlCl₃OH]

Compound	Moles	Methylene dichloride ml	Temperature °C	Reaction time h	Specific activity d.p.s./mole
Benzene	0·1	nil	25°	0·5	$2 \cdot 2 \times 10^9$
Benzene	0·1	nil	25°	1	$4 \cdot 5 \times 10^9$
Benzene	0·1	nil	25°	1·5	$6 \cdot 7 \times 10^9$
Chlorobenzene	0·1	nil	100°	3	$3 \cdot 6 \times 10^8$
2,4,6-Collidine	0·1	20	41–42°	3	$7 \cdot 5 \times 10^6$
2,4,6-Collidine	0·1	20	41–42°	7	1×10^7
2,6-Di-tertiary-butyl-4-picoline	0·1	20	41–42°	3	$2 \cdot 5 \times 10^7$
2,6-Di-tertiary-butyl-4-picoline	0·1	20	41–42°	7	4×10^7
Fluorobenzene	0·1	nil	86°	3	$1 \cdot 85 \times 10^9$
2,6-Lutidine	0·1	20	41–42°	7	$4 \cdot 8 \times 10^6$
Nitrobenzene	0·15	25	41–42°	12	8×10^4
Pyridine	0·1	25	41–42°	12	5×10^5

Tritiated water (0·05 mole) at a specific activity of $3 \cdot 96 \times 10^9$ d.p.s./mole containing aluminium trichloride (0·1 mole), was used in each experiment.

The results reflect the order of decreasing reactivity towards electrophilic substitution with benzene ≃ fluorobenzene > chlorobenzene > 2,4,6-collidine > 2,6-lutidine > pyridine > nitrobenzene. The 2,6-di-tertiary-butyl-4-picoline exchanges the most rapidly of the pyridines studied because this compound is not protonated and therefore substitutes as a pyridine more easily than as a pyridinium salt.

The phosphoric acid–boron trifluoride reagent[178,180] is prepared by dissolving phosphorus pentoxide in tritiated water and bubbling the boron trifluoride through the solution until the theoretical amount is absorbed. The tritiated phosphoric acid–boron trifluoride complex

($TH_2 \cdot PO_4 \cdot BF_3$) labels compounds by exchange at room temperature. This is useful for compounds which are heat sensitive, and this is the main advantage in employing the reagent.

Equilibrium exchange labelling can be readily achieved in both aromatic hydrogen positions and in other compounds at hydrogen positions adjacent to a tertiary carbon atom. The theoretical specific activity which can be achieved with the reagent can be calculated from the equation (4.10):

$$A = \frac{A_0}{\dfrac{3}{166} \cdot \dfrac{M}{N_H} + \dfrac{W_a}{W_T}} \qquad \cdots \quad (4.10)$$

where A = Specific activity of the compound
A_0 = Specific activity of the reagent
M = Molecular weight of compound
W_a = Weight of compound used
W_T = Weight of reagent used
N_H = Number of exchangeable hydrogen positions in the compound.

In the case of aromatic compounds, substituents which withdraw electrons from the aromatic nucleus inhibit the labelling reaction. For example, —COOH, —NO_2, —COOEt, —NH_2 and —CHO groups completely inhibit the labelling reaction under mild conditions. Labelling proceeds to a limited extent with milder deactivating groups such as chlorine and sulphydryl present, particularly at higher temperatures. Conversely substituent groups which introduce electrons into the aromatic ring strongly accelerate the labelling reaction. Groups in this category include —OH, alkyl and ethers. However, in aliphatic compounds containing a tertiary hydrogen atom, the presence of a hydroxyl group inhibits the exchange reaction.

Nuclear magnetic resonance studies on cumenes labelled with deuterium using the corresponding deuterated phosphoric acid–boron trifluoride complex show that the tertiary hydrogen atoms act as a gate for aliphatic compound labelling but do not themselves become labelled[180].

These various points will be obvious to readers upon examination of Table 4.15 which lists a number of examples of compounds tritiated by this reagent.

Disadvantages

1. Isotope exchange is prevented by salt formation with basic compounds

TABLE 4.15

Compounds Labelled by Exchange with $TH_2PO_4 \cdot BF_3$

Compound	N_H	Temperature °C	Reaction time h	Specific activity μc/g		
				Reagent	Product	Theoretical
Acetone	6	23	3·5	41·4	13·8	22·4
Acetophenone	3	23	20	41·4	37·7	32·5
n-Amyl alcohol	2	23	17·5	41·4	0·41	24·7
iso-Amyl alcohol	2	23	17·5	41·4	0·0	24·9
Aniline	5	75	4	37·4	1·6	83·8
Anisole	5	45	24	40·7	80·4	81·2
Anisole	5	23	20	63·3*	30·1	53·0
Benzene	6	21	1	41·6	0·9	126·6
Benzene	6	21	100	41·6	90·9	126·6
Benzene	6	60	1	41·6	17·1	126·6
Benzene	6	60	50	41·6	127·1	126·6
Benzaldehyde	1	23	20	41·4	0·1	16·8
Benzoic acid	5	23	22	41·4	0·0	81·2
Benzoic acid (methyl ester)	3	23	20	41·4	0·0	14·7
Benzoic acid (methyl ester)	3	75	20	41·4	0·1	22·4
Benzylamine	5	23	17	40·7	34·3	82·5
Benzylamine	5	80	16·5	37·4	135	75·8
iso-Butane	10	45	24	40·7	136	169
iso-Butane	10	45	172	40·7	150	169
iso-Butane	10	45	198	40·7	143	169
iso-Butane	10	45	551	40·7	144	169
Chlorobenzene	3	23	16	37·4	0·2	29·6
Chlorobenzene	3	65	16·5	37·4	20	29·6
Chloroform	1	23	17	40·7	0·005	15·89
Chloroform	1	23	42	40·7	0·013	15·89
o-Cresol	4	45	24	40·7	65·1	75·8
Cumene	12	31	0·5	33·4	1·34	122·6
Cumene	12	31	360	33·4	99·7	122·6
Cumene	12	60	1	33·4	12·29	129·9
Cumene	12	60	100	33·4	116·23	129·9
Cumene	6	25	24	41·6	80·7	85·8
Decalin	2	45	162	40·7	47·6	30·31
Heptan-2-one	5	23	20	41·4	21·7	83·8
Methylcyclohexane	8	45	216	41·4	71·3	128·9
Nitrobenzene	5	23	20	41·4	0·0	38·2
p-Nitrotoluene	4	75	40	40·7	8·65	60·6
Pyridine	1	23	22	40·7	0·07	24·6
Pyridine hydro-chloride	1	23	22	40·7	0·9	26·1
Pyridine N-oxide	1	70	45·5	40·7	29·8	22·3
Quinoline	4	23	22	41·4	0	47·2
Tetralin	4	23	5·5	1400	521	545
Thiophenol	1	23	0·5	37·4	11·0	11·9
Thiophenol	3	23	17	37·4	10·5	20·5
Toluene	5	31·5	1	41·6	10·4	98
Toluene	5	31·5	5	41·6	36·7	98
Toluene	5	45	24	41·6	97·4	98
Toluene	5	31·5	54·75	41·6	97	98
Thiophen	2	23	20	63·3*	35	34

* TH_2PO_4 only.

2. Carbohydrates and other readily dehydrated compounds, are dehydrated during the exchange
3. The reagent attacks glass-ware and must be stored in polythene bottles; this perhaps is more of an inconvenience than a disadvantage
4. It is likely that at high specific activity the reagent would have to be prepared freshly each time because of decomposition of the complex by self-irradiation.

Advantages

1. Labels at room temperature, as previously mentioned
2. In the cases of successful labelling there is no evidence of side effects due to radiation; the specific activity of the tritiated product before and after purification is virtually the same, in contrast to the gas-exposure labelling methods. Some examples are shown in Table 4.16. However, caution is necessary here as the results published use the reagent at tracer level only where radiation effects would not be apparent.

TABLE 4.16
Labelling Compounds with $TH_2PO_4 \cdot BF_3$ at $23°C$ [182]

Compound	Weight g	Weight of reagent g	Reaction time h	Specific activity μc/g	
				Before purification	After purification
Benzene	71·4	37·7	6	106·6	108·2
Cyclohexane	69·1	34·7	6	0·964	0
Decalin	69·3	35·3	6	32·2	31·4
trans-Decalin	49·2	—	6	—	23·8
cis-Decalin	20·4	—	6	—	52·5
Methylcyclohexane	69·6	36·8	6	9·25	9·36
Naphthalene	7·05	34·8	7	1,422	1,440
Tetralin	71·9	36·5	5·5	536	531
Toluene	70·9	35·3	6·5	550	554

3. Another advantage (over Wilzbach labelling) is that the use of multicurie quantities of tritium gas is avoided; the prior requisite of a high vacuum gas-transfer system is thus not essential.

Use of the Yavorsky–Gorin procedure has been made recently to label a series of insecticides and naphthalene (see Table 4.17), but again only at relatively low specific activity[181].

Heterogeneous catalysis—Exchange reactions in solution under the influence of heterogeneous hydrogen transfer catalysts, are carried out by heating a mixture of the compound, a tritiated solvent and the catalyst.

Most widely used are the noble-metal catalysts prepared by the

TABLE 4.17
Labelling Insecticides with $TH_2PO_4 \cdot BF_3$ Reagent[181]

Compound	Temp. °C	Time h	W_a/W_T	Specific activity mc/mM	Yield %	Theoretical labelling %
2,2-Bis(p-chlorophenyl)-1,1,1-trichlorethane (DDT)	23	20	0·5	0·04	79·2	0·1
2,2-Bis(p-methoxyphenyl)-1,1,1-trichloroethane (methoxychlor)	23	20	0·5	15·5	60·1	35·4
Diethyl 3-chloro-4-methyl-7-coumarinyl phosphorothionate (Co-ral)	23	20	0·5	0·42	40·0	1·7
Diethyl p-nitrophenyl phosphorothionate (parathion)	23	20	0·5	0·27	2·5	1·0
	23	20	0·25	1·10	2·0	3·6
3,5-Di-isopropylphenyl-N-methylcarbamate	23	20	0·5	9·75	72·8	48·8
Dimethyl 3-methyl-4-methyl-thiophenyl phosphorothionate (Baytex)	23	20	0·5	2·03	10·3	9·8
3,5-Dimethyl-4-methylthiophenyl N-methylcarbamate	23	20	0·5	5·86	69·7	40·4
Dimethyl p-N-dimethyl-sulphamoyl-phenyl phosphate	50	6	0·5	0·00045	19·1	0·0015
3-Isopropylphenyl-N-methyl-carbamate	23	20	0·5	0·90	76·2	3·9
2-Isopropoxyphenyl-N-methyl-carbamate	23	20	0·5	4·34	58·2	18·5
1-Naphthyl-N-methyl-carbamate (Sevin)	23	20	0·5	3·26	70·0	10·2
Naphthalene	23	20	0·5	11·28	65·3	42·7

W_a/W_T is the weight ratio of insecticide (or naphthalene) to reagent.

reduction of their oxides with hydrogen. Both platinum and palladium are very satisfactory and the catalysed exchange in solution method can be used to label a very wide range of compounds indeed. These include amino acids[183], polycyclic aromatic hydrocarbons[184], purines[170], pyrimidines and nucleosides[186-188], alicyclic compounds[189] and steroids[190]. This procedure for generally labelling organic compounds with tritium has been used at the Radiochemical Centre for many years[40], in preference to gas-exposure methods.

Tritiated acetic acid (70 per cent) and water are normally the tritiated solvents employed. However, variations in pH or the addition of a second solvent may be necessary to increase the solubility of the compound in the exchange medium.

Several factors govern the degree of tritium labelling and the final specific activity achieved, which are:

1. the stability of the compound in the exchange medium,
2. the equilibrium constant for the reaction,
3. the specific activity of the tritiated solvent used,
4. the temperature of the exchange reaction,
5. the reaction time,
6. the efficiency of the hydrogen transfer catalyst,
7. the degree of chemisorption of the compound on the catalyst surface,
8. the solubility of the compound in the exchange solution.

Each factor plays an important part in the success or failure to label a particular compound, and careful consideration should be given to them before choosing the conditions for the exchange reaction.

Stability—One of the main attractions of the catalytic exchange in solution is that compounds are usually very much easier to purify after the exchange reaction than those labelled by the Wilzbach and similar tritium gas-exposure methods already described. This is because the decomposition products are mainly those produced by chemical breakdown under the exchange reaction conditions and are not radiation-produced fragments.

Side-products often arise by partial hydrolysis or, when acetic acid is used as a solvent, compounds sometimes become acetylated. The important point to realize is that these side-products are usually labelled to the same extent as the compound required. There is not the same risk of having a product contaminated with material at very high specific activity present in trace chemical amounts, as with Wilzbach-labelled products. An example will illustrate this point: Inosine (the riboside of hypoxanthine) is labelled by an exchange reaction between tritiated water and inosine in the presence of a platinum catalyst. Under the reaction conditions, partial hydrolysis of the ribonucleoside occurs (4.11):

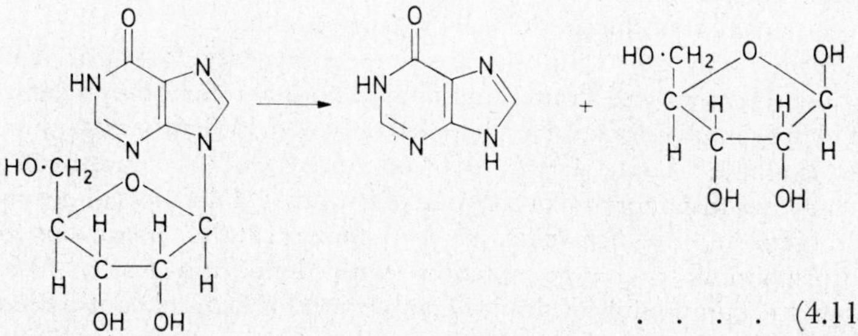

$$\dots \dots (4.11)$$

The tritiated inosine is purified by chromatography on paper which also serves to separate and purify the side-product hypoxanthine. Measurement of the specific activity of the inosine and hypoxanthine show that they are similar in magnitude (see Table 4.21). Similar results are obtained when deoxyadenosine is labelled by the same procedure[40].

Equilibrium constant—Measurements for a number of compounds labelled with deuterium by catalysed exchange in deuterium oxide have been published[191], but little quantitative information is available for reactions in tritiated water.

The rate at which equilibrium is attained increases, as one might expect, with increasing temperature of the exchange reaction. At room temperature the incorporation of tritium into non-labile hydrogen positions is very slow, but a satisfactory degree of labelling can usually be achieved by heating at temperatures in the range 50–150°C. The actual temperature selected will naturally depend on the type and stability of the compound being labelled, but usually temperatures in excess of 100°C are required for the preparation of compounds at high specific activity. The dependence of the resulting specific activity of the purified product on the temperature of the exchange reaction is clearly seen from Tables 4.18–4.22.

Solvent activity—Increasing the specific activity of the solvent of course not only increases the specific activity of the product but also the proportion of any products which are formed by radiation decomposition of the substrate. Tritiated solvents having an isotopic abundance of 1 to 10 per cent tritium are mostly used.

Reaction time—Satisfactory labelling is normally accomplished within 20 h, although the specific activity of the compound may be much lower than the calculated value at equilibrium. After the exchange reaction has been completed, the tritiated solvent and labile tritium should be removed as soon as possible to minimize decomposition of the products by self-irradiation.

Catalyst efficiency—Catalysts are notoriously easy to poison, consequently compounds containing catalyst poisons reduce the efficiency of hydrogen transfer, and are labelled only with difficulty. Ethionine for example (Table 4.18), requires quite vigorous conditions to achieve a satisfactory incorporation of tritium. Molecules containing nitrogen, sulphur or arsenic, are well-known catalyst poisons in the corresponding exchange reactions with deuterium oxide. With aromatic compounds of similar complexity, for example anthracene and phenanthrene, the degree of catalyst poisoning decreases with increasing ionization potential[192].

Solubility and chemisorption—The compound to be labelled does not have to dissolve completely in the exchange medium, although the exchange is more efficient if it does. The part played by chemisorption of the compound on the catalyst surface and just how this is related to the efficiency of the exchange process, are still rather obscure but Garnett and colleagues have published the results of some interesting experiments in an attempt to formulate a reaction mechanism[191–195] (see page 133).

There are a number of advantages and disadvantages with hetero-geneous catalytic exchange in solution[196] in comparison with tritium gas-exposure methods.

Advantages

1. The outstanding advantage is the much higher specific activities which are obtained. Compare for example, the tritiation of 6-di-methylamino-9-(3'-amino-ribosyl) purine by the Wilzbach method (Table 4.5) and by platinum-catalysed exchange in tritiated water (Table 4.21); the latter process yields a product having a specific activity almost 1,000 times higher than the Wilzbach method. There are many such examples.

2. Only a short labelling time is required (2 to 20 h); this ensures the minimum radiation damage to the compound.

3. The tritiated solvent can be recovered and used again. It does of course become reduced in specific activity during each exchange.

4. Unsaturated compounds, i.e. compounds containing carbon–carbon double bonds or acetylenic bonds, do not become hydro-genated under the exchange reaction conditions. Highly tritiated addition compounds are therefore not produced. However, un-conjugated double bonds do tend to move into conjugation. For example, sodium oleate or elaidate will tend to give some tritiated Δ^1-octadecenoic acid where the 9,10-double bond has moved into conjugation with the carboxyl group. Kritchevsky *et al.*[197] have successfully labelled glyceryl trioleate by catalytic exchange in solution at low specific activity (16 uc/g); at Amersham exchange labelling has given only solid products, which presumably arise by bond migration.

5. Compounds are usually easier to purify than Wilzbach-labelled compounds, as previously mentioned. The products from the exchange reaction in solution are normally quite different from one another in their chemical structure which facilitates their separation.

6. Compounds containing halogen substituents (except iodine) are not normally dehalogenated but here again caution must be exercised as some types of compounds are dehalogenated under the exchange conditions. For example, the exchange reaction between tritiated acetic acid and 5-bromouracil in the presence of a platinum catalyst yields only tritiated uracil (4.12), while 5-bromo-2'-deoxy-uridine under the same conditions gives both tritiated 2'-deoxy-uridine and tritiated uracil[40] (4.13); complete debromination occurring in both examples.

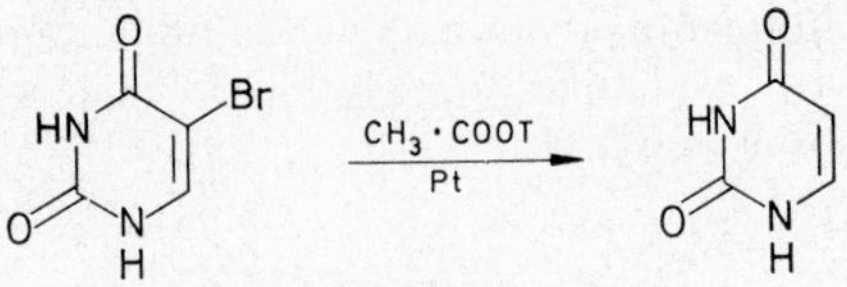

. . . . (4.12)

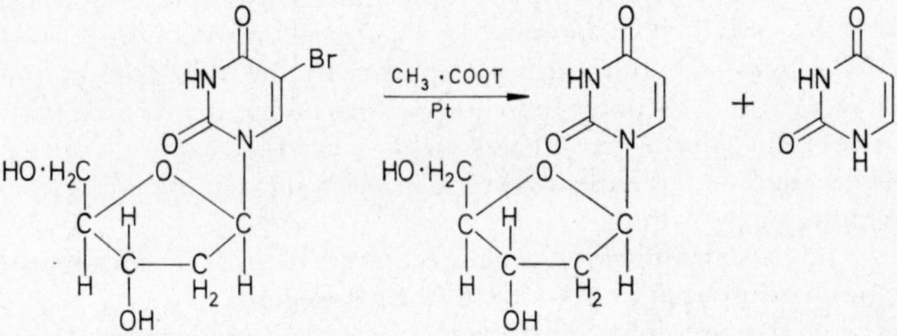

. . . . (4.13)

At Amersham attempts to label iodine-containing compounds for example, thyroxine, by the catalytic exchange in solution has always resulted in partial or complete removal of iodine atoms from the molecule [40].

Disadvantages

1. The distribution and amount of tritium in the molecule cannot be predicted with any accuracy and can vary from exchange to exchange even though the experimental conditions appear to be identical[198]. This is in fact a disadvantage common to all the exchange labelling methods.

2. Aliphatic compounds are less readily labelled than aromatic compounds.

3. The presence of iodine or nitro groups inhibits labelling namely compounds containing catalyst poisons are labelled with difficulty.

4. Compounds which tend to disproportionate for example, cyclohexene, have to be separated carefully from their disproportionated tritiated products[189].

5. To achieve high specific activities tritiated solvents at very high specific activity are necessary, which does present a possible contamination hazard and such exchange reactions should not be ventured unless proper facilities for doing so are available. This of course applies equally to multicurie Wilzbach labelling.

6. Only under very carefully controlled conditions can L- or D-amino acids be labelled: racemization readily occurs[195a].

132

7. Dehalogenation occurs with some types of halogen compounds.

8. Macromolecules such as proteins, peptides and polymers are either degraded or further polymerized.

There is little doubt that the advantages of the method easily outweigh the disadvantages, and the wide applicability as a labelling procedure is illustrated in Tables 4.18–4.22 of various classes of compounds labelled at the Radiochemical Centre.

Mechanism of Catalytic Exchange in Solution

Homogeneous catalysis with acids for example is explained by the formation of an addition complex carbonium ion[180] (4.14). For example:

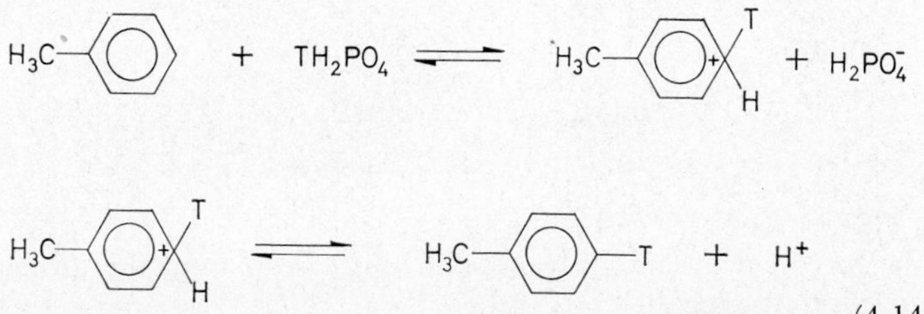

$$\dots \dots (4.14)$$

The principles of hydrogen isotope exchange reactions in solution have been reviewed in more detail by Gold and Satchell[199].

It is not yet possible to formulate a general reaction mechanism for the heterogenous catalysis of tritium–hydrogen exchange reactions in solution. The situation is complicated by the fact that different mechanisms are likely to be operative for the various metal catalysts[200]. However, a π-complex intermediate has been postulated in connection with the platinum-catalysed deuteration of aromatic compounds[195,196,196a]. The existence of a π-bonded species has also been proposed during the exchange of aliphatic hydrocarbons with deuterium[201].

Experiments by Garnett and colleagues[194] suggest that the exchange is not a simple π-complex substitution mechanism, since this does not adequately explain ring orientation effects and the ready exchange between two aromatic species. Garnett and Sollich[194] have therefore proposed two new mechanisms for the catalytic exchange reaction:

(*a*) the Associative π-Complex Substitution Mechanism and (*b*) Dissociative π-Complex Substitution Mechanism.

133

Both mechanisms do involve a π-complex-chemisorbed aromatic nucleus which occupies a horizontal position on the catalyst surface (4.15):

$$\dots \quad (4.15)$$

In mechanism (a) the π-bonded aromatic nucleus is attached by a chemisorbed deuterium atom giving a transition state similar to the conventional aromatic substitution reactions (4.16):

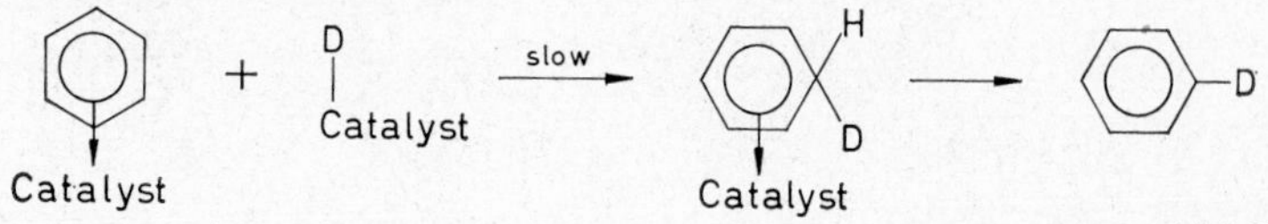

$$\dots \quad (4.16)$$

The direction of charge transfer in this case is from the aromatic nucleus to the metal.

The dissociative mechanism (b) involves reaction of the π-bonded aromatic nucleus with a metal radical in a rapid conventional type of substitution reaction. During this process, the molecule rotates through 90 degrees and results in σ-bonded (edge-on) chemisorption (4.17):

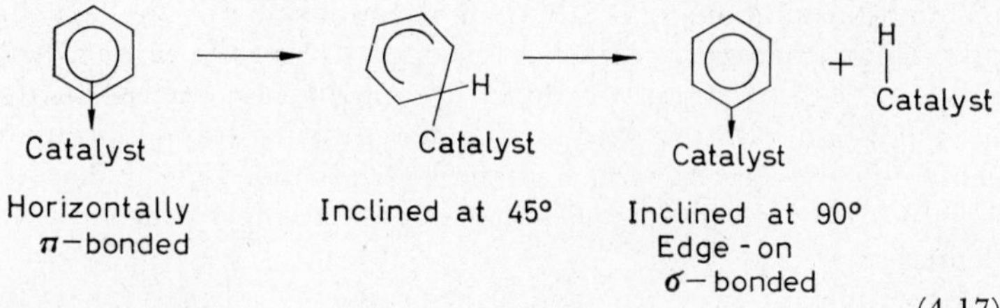

$$\dots \quad (4.17)$$

In the σ-bonded state, the aromatic nucleus undergoes a further but slower substitution reaction with a chemisorbed deuterium atom (4.18).

Present evidence suggests that the Dissociative π-Complex Substitution Mechanism is of major importance in the platinum-catalysed exchange reactions in solution[185,194,194a].

. . . . (4.18)

These mechanisms proposed for deuterium exchange reactions would, of course, equally apply to those of tritium, but the additional effects of the radiation upon the catalyst and local charge distribution, must also be taken into account.

Isotope effects are always possible in the rate-determining step (see Chapter 6).

TABLE 4.18
Tritiated DL-Amino Acids by Catalysed Exchange in Solution

DL-Amino acid	Weight g	Catalyst g	Tritiated water		Temp. °C	Time h	Chem. yield %	Specific activity mc/mM
			Volume ml	Specific activity mc/mM				
α-Alanine	0·5	0·2	2	1,090	158	16	30	445
α-Alanine	0·5	0·2	2	1,800	140	16	30	1,130
Aspartic acid	0·5	0·2	2	1,350	130	15	68	466
α:ε-Diaminopimelic acid	0·6	0·3	2	1,350	110	17	67	40
3,4-Dihydroxy-phenyl-alanine	0·5	0·2	2	1,350	125	16	35	268
Ethionine	0·5	0·27	2	1,260	110	17	62	41
Ethionine	0·5	0·3	2	1,580	150	6	46	74
Glutamic acid	0·5	0·2	2	1,580	115	6	13	44
Glutamic acid	0·5	0·2	2	1,800	130	15	15	74
Glycine	0·5	0·2	2·5	1,035	100	8·5	58	176
5-Hydroxy-tryptophan	0·1	0·1	1·5	1,200	130	5	43	921
Isoleucine	0·5	0·15	3	420	120	16	54	50
Isoleucine	0·5	0·2	2·5	1,800	155	16	40	314
Leucine	0·44	0·14	2·4	540	100	40	70	5
Leucine	0·3	0·2	2·4	540	120	66	47	102
Lysine hydrochloride	0·6	0·2	2	1,800	110	7	67	139
Lysine hydrochloride	0·6	0·2	2	2,250	115	20	67	307
Methionine	0·44	0·22	4	1,575	110	23	19	148
Methionine	0·5	0·3	2	1,350	110	17	22	145
Ornithine hydrochloride	0·5	0·22	4	1,115	115	16	18	46
3-Phenylalanine	0·5	0·2	2	1,800	140	16	38	441
3-Phenylalanine	0·5	0·2	2	2,160	140	16	50	1,800
Serine	0·5	0·2	2	1,440	130	15	60	138
Threonine	0·5	0·2	2	1,585	130	15	73	32
Tyrosine	0·44	0·3	2·5	720	100	18	46	18
Tyrosine	0·5	0·2	2	1,350	150	17	48	102
Tryptophan	0·5	0·5	3	1,440	100	18	28	685
Valine	0·25	0·2	1	1,080	120	16	80	20

135

TABLE 4.19

Tritiated L-Amino Acids by Catalysed Exchange in Solution

L-Amino acid	Weight g	Catalyst g	Tritiated water		Temp. °C	Time h	Chem. yield %	Specific activity mc/mM	Race-miz-ation* %
			Volume ml	Specific activity mc/mM					
Arginine hydrochloride	0·44	0·26	2·5	158	110	22	59	8	5
Arginine hydrochloride	0·65	0·36	4	1,125	110	2	38	27	5
Arginine hydrochloride	0·5	0·2	1·5	1,260	130	16	63	106	5
Arginine hydrochloride	0·5	0·2	2	2,250	132	16	66	760	30
Leucine	0·3	0·2	2·5	675	150	20	43	197	5
Lysine hydrochloride	0·5	0·2	2	1,800	150	16	22	136	5
Methionine	0·5	0·2	2·5	720	110	16	22	22	42
Methionine	0·5	0·3	2·5	720	130	16	43	100	90
Methionine	0·5	0·2	2·5	720	120	16	13	125	100
Methionine	0·5	0·2	3	305	130	15	72	9	5
Methionine	0·2	0·2	2	900	140	10	23	36	5
Methionine	0·5	0·2	2·5	720	115	20	40	36	36
Tryptophan	0·5	0·2	2	2,250	150	20	14	1,632	74
Tyrosine	0·3	0·2	3	1,800	145	16	12	1,023	28
Tyrosine	0·3	0·2	2	1,350	125	7	30	1,321	36

* % Racemization—percentage activity in the DL-form.

TABLE 4.20

Tritiated Aromatic Compounds by Catalysed Exchange in Solution

Compound	Weight g	Catalyst g	Tritiated solvent	Vol. ml	Specific activity	Temp. °C	Time h	Chem yield %	Specific activity mc/mM
Aniline	1	0·08	THO	2	90 mc/mM	130	65	50	40
Aniline hydrochloride	0·5	0·2	THO	2	1,575 mc/mM	140	20	90	1,516
Benzoic acid	1·6	0·4	THO	5	900 mc/mM	130	24	87	81
Benzoic acid (sodium salt)	0·45	0·26	THO	3	595 mc/mM	150	11	69	174
1,2-Benzanthracene	0·5	0·2	70% AcOT	2	150 c/ml	150	16	40	655
Benzimidazole	0·5	0·2	THO	2·5	720 mc/ml	130	20	68	268
3,4-Benzpyrene	0·37	0·16	70% AcOT	4	25 c/ml	160	16	64	451
4,5-Benzpyrene	0·3	0·2	70% AcOT	2·5	150 c/ml	150	17	44	242
Bromobenzene	0·75	0·22	THO	2	90 mc/mM	130	19	92	1·5
Congo red	0·2	0·05	THO	1·7	90 mc/mM	100	20	90	12
Coumarin	0·49	0·14	THO	3	360 mc/mM	120	16	39	16
Coumarin	0·5	0·2	THO	2·5	6,300 mc/mM	130	16	34	2,242
1,2,5,6-Dibenzanthracene	0·2	0·2	70% AcOT	3	33 c/ml	150	16	25	114
1,2,3,4-Dibenzanthracene	0·1	0·2	70% AcOT	3	33 c/ml	150	16	47	151
1,2,3,4-Dibenzanthracene	0·2	0·2	70% AcOT	2	225 c/ml	140	16	11	156
9,10-Dimethyl-1,2-benzanthracene	0·2	0·2	70% AcOT	3	30 c/ml	150	16	50	3,250
2,4-Dinitrochlorobenzene	0·66	0·2	THO	3	415 mc/mM	115	16	39	1·6
Malachite green	0·53	0·34	THO	3·4	470 mc/mM	100	15	64	49
Methyl p-amino-benzoate	0·5	0·2	THO	2	900 mc/mM	135	24	30	1,360
20-Methylcholanthrene	0·49	0·19	70% AcOT	1·5	40 c/ml	130	24	56	17
20-Methylcholanthrene	0·26	0·2	70% AcOT	1	100 c/ml	150	16	65	338
20-Methylcholanthrene	0·5	0·2	70% AcOT	2	225 c/ml	145	16	14	3,150
2-Methylnaphthalene	0·5	0·2	THO	2	90 mc/mM	130	20	60	8·5

TABLE 4.20 (*continued*)

Compound	Weight g	Catalyst g	Tritiated solvent	Vol. ml	Specific activity	Temp. °C	Time h	Chem yield %	Specific activity mc/mM
2-Methyl-1,4-naphthoquinone	0·5	0·2	70% AcOT	2	2·5 c/ml	130	18	11	72
1-Naphthylacetic acid	0·52	0·17	70% AcOT	3	15 c/ml	132	24	27	188
2-Naphthylamine	0·45	0·23	THO	2	900 mc/mM	130	16	48	1,660
Phenylacetic acid	0·5	0·2	70% AcOT	3	23 c/ml	155	16	74	111
Phthalic anhydride	0·5	0·2	THO	3	1,495 mc/mM	100	18	49	123*
Sodium phenate	0·5	0·2	THO	2·5	1,800 mc/mM	110	16	86	602

* As phthalic acid.

TABLE 4.21

Tritiated Heterocyclic Compounds by Catalysed Exchange in Solution

Compound	Weight g	Catalyst g	Tritiated solvent	Vol. ml	Specific activity	Temp. °C	Time h	Chem yield %	Specific activity mc/mM
Adenine	0·3	0·25	70% AcOT	3	67 c/ml	130	14	70	439
Adenosine	0·42	0·22	70% AcOT	2·4	20 c/ml	100	20	36	200
Adenosine	0·32	0·2	70% AcOT	4	63 c/ml	110	8	5	680
Caffeine	0·5	0·2	70% AcOT	2	25 c/ml	150	16	36	1,280
Cytidine (sulphate)	0·6	0·2	THO	3	70 c/ml	100	16	10	99
Cytosine	0·5	0·16	70% AcOT	2	15 c/ml	100	20	30	52
Cytosine	0·5	0·2	70% AcOT	4	40 c/ml	100	20	40	293
Deoxyadenosine	0·2	0·2	70% AcOT	3	67 c/ml	100	6·5	7	627
Deoxycytidine hydrochloride	0·5	0·2	THO	2·5	70 c/ml	130	16	0·4	1,527
Deoxyguanosine	0·5	0·2	THO	2	87 c/ml	120	3	0·2	1,000
Deoxyuridine	0·2	0·2	70% AcOT	3	33 c/ml	100	5	20	385
6-Dimethylamino-9-(3'-aminoribosyl)-purine	0·4	0·2	THO	2·5	200 c/ml	120	16	72	1,550
Guanine	0·52	0·22	70% AcOT	1·5	14 c/ml	170	65	86	5
Guanine hydrochloride	0·5	0·2	THO	2	70 c/ml	145	20	50	150
Guanosine	0·5	0·3	THO	2	90 c/ml	130	16	20	481
Hypoxanthine	0·3	0·21	70% AcOT	3	50 c/ml	150	15	30	630
Hypoxanthine			Isolated from inosine exchange below						631
Inosine	0·4	0·2	70% AcOT	3	50 c/ml	100	20	8	642
5-Methylcytosine	0·35	0·2	THO	2	100 c/ml	130	16	10	15,600
Nicotine	0·5	0·2	THO	2	35 c/ml	100	72	33	82
Nicotinic acid	0·5	0·2	THO	2	37·5 c/ml	130	16	66	320
isoNicotinic hydrazide	0·5	0·2	THO	2	100 c/ml	125	16	72	1,323
Orotic acid	0·54	0·18	70% AcOT	2	15 c/ml	95	40	56	3
Orotic acid	0·2	0·2	70% AcOT	1	250 c/ml	140	15	65	115
Pyridine	0·9	0·2	THO	2	60 c/ml	110	20	33	608
Pyridoxine hydrochloride	0·4	0·28	70% AcOT	1·5	13 c/ml	100	24	20	6
Theophylline	0·5	0·2	70% AcOT	2	75 c/ml	140	16	21	1,480
Thymidine	0·5	0·44	0·1N-KOH THO	1·5	50 c/ml	100	40	39	72
Thymidine[202]	0·8–1·6	—	THO	5	540 c/ml	—	—	—	550
Thymidine[187]	0·205	0·2	THO	1	2 c/ml	100	24	50	14·9
Thymine	0·26	0·23	70% AcOT	2	100 c/ml	170	15	20	8,600
Thymine	0·5	0·2	70% CF₃COOT	2	225 c/ml	145	16	59	7,056
Thymine	0·5	0·2	70% CF₃COOT	2	225 c/ml	160	16	63	7,182
Uracil	1·0	0·2	70% AcOT	3	50 c/ml	155	16	50	482
Uracil			Isolated from deoxyuridine exchange above						495
Uridine	0·5	0·14	70% AcOT	2	15 c/ml	100	20	70	62
Uridine	0·5	0·2	70% AcOT	2	75 c/ml	120	16	35	10,08

TABLE 4.22

Tritiated Steroids by Catalytic Exchange in 70 per cent Acetic Acid

Compound	Wt. g	Catalyst g	Exchange-solution Volume ml	Activity c/ml	Temp. °C	Time h	Chem. yield %	Specific activity mc/mM
Δ^4-Androstene-3,17-dione	0·6	0·29	1	40	150	48	50	3,400
Cholesteryl acetate	1·0	0·5	1·5	50	150	16	81	294
Cholesterol	0·45	0·27	2	75	130	64	50	314
Cholesterol	0·5	0·2	2·5	180	155	16	23	1,620
Corticosterone acetate	0·2	0·2	2	38	130	16	32	1,590
Cortisone acetate	0·31	0·32	1·8	12	125	24	44	35
Oestra-3,17β-diol	0·5	0·2	2	37	145	8	68	100
Oestra-3,17β-diol	0·5	0·2	2	200	140	16	12	174
Oestrone	0·54	0·2	1·8	14	130	90	56	188
Prednisolone	0·5	0·2	2·5	160	150	5	10	685
Progesterone	0·5	0·2	2	88	140	16	43	509

TABLE 4.23

Miscellaneous Tritium Compounds by Catalytic Exchange in Solution

Compound	Weight g	Catalyst g	Exchange solvent	Vol. ml	Specific activity c/ml	Temp. °C	Time h	Yield %	Specific activity mc/mM	Ref.
Arginine HCl	0·3	0·5 (Pt/C)	THO	0·5	0·2	100	24	80	0·22	208 209
Aromatic amines	1	—	0·3N– HTSO₄	—	—	100	7	—	—	207
Deoxycytidine	0·8– 1·6	Pt	THO	5	540	—	—	—	2,160	188
Ethylene glycol	1	0·2	THO	3	33	130	15	50	48	40
D-Glucose	0·5	0·2	THO	2·5	40	135	15	14	12	40
Glycine ethyl ester hydrochloride	0·5	0·2	THO	2	37·5	140	6	80	34	40
Methotrexate	0·025	0·028	AcOT	10	1	80	16	—	778	247
DL-Nα-Methyl-tryptophan	—	—	THO/ HCl	1·5	0·2	110	—	—	5·56	246
1-Phenyl-2-amino-propan-1,3-diol triacetate	—	—	AcOT	—	0·013	100	24	—	0·15	205
Resorcinol	10⁻⁵– 10⁻⁴	—	THO	—	5	—	—	—	1·88	210
Sodium formate	0·5	0·2	THO	2	50	140	24	90	20	40
Sodium malonate	3	nil	THO	3	33	80	1	100	172	40
Stearic acid	0·2	0·02	0·2N–KOT	0·4	0·05	135	168	90	1·76	203
Stearic acid	7·5	1	0·17N–KOT	—	—	135	200	95	—	206
Stilboestrol	0·5	0·1	THO	3	10	140	5	42	295	40
α-Tocopherol	0·75	0·2	THO	3	60	130	16	38	51	40
Triolein	6	1	KOT	6	—	130	28	87 (crude)	0·014	197
Vitamin-B₁₂	0·15	0·15	THO	2·5	80	140	20	50	4,604	40

Tables 4.18–4.23 illustrate the high specific activities (compared with gas-exposure methods) which can be obtained by catalysed exchange in a tritiated solvent. The weight of catalyst referred to is the weight of platinum oxide used prior to reduction in hydrogen.

Certain steroids, for example progesterone, have been shown to exchange with tritiated aqueous alcohols such as *n*-amyl alcohol, without the use of a catalyst [211]. The process is very inefficient and at least 60 per cent of the tritium is located on the carbon atom adjacent to the keto groups, which of course is readily removed under alkaline conditions. As a labelling method this procedure offers no advantages over the heterogeneous catalytic process.

Exchange methods of questionable value appear in the literature from time to time. One publication [213] describes the ring labelling of nicotinic acid by keeping the compound for 3 to 5 *weeks* at − 30° C in concentrated tritiated sulphuric acid. The specific activity and yield achieved were not quoted. Another process labels *p*-nitrobenzoic acid by exchange with the vapour from a mixture of concentrated sulphuric acid–phosphorus pentoxide and tritiated water at 250° C [212].

These rather extreme labelling conditions are quite unnecessary and are far inferior to the other methods available for catalytic exchange in solution.

A number of commercial suppliers of radioactive chemicals operate 'Tritium Labelling Services' for people who require a particular tritiated compound but who do not wish to handle the multicurie quantities of tritium required in the primary exchange labelling process.

2. DIRECT CHEMICAL SYNTHESIS

Synthesis by direct chemical methods is the most precise and reliable way of labelling compounds with tritium. It is the only practical approach for obtaining compounds with specific labelling, and is particularly valuable when very high specific activities are required.

The preparations of these specifically labelled compounds are not discussed in detail as many of the methods are conventional reactions described many times in the literature. Instead, an outline of the synthetic routes and comments on any unusual features, is presented.

Starting Materials

Just as a gas (carbon-14 dioxide) is the usual starting material for many syntheses with carbon-14, so tritium gas is the raw material for all syntheses involved in the preparation of tritium compounds.

The production of tritium gas has been outlined in Chapter 1, and next in importance is its oxide, tritiated water.

There are two procedures which can be used for preparing tritiated water, the method of choice depending upon the specific activity required. For water of the highest isotopic abundance (say greater than 70 per cent), it is best to oxidize the tritium catalytically by combination with oxygen using a palladium catalyst (4.19). Alternatively, tritium can be used to reduce a metal oxide such as copper oxide (4.20). These methods have been fully described by Wilson[214, 215].

$$2T_2 + O_2 \rightarrow 2T_2O \qquad \text{. . . .} \quad (4.19)$$

$$T_2 + CuO \rightarrow T_2O + Cu \qquad \text{. . . .} \quad (4.20)$$

For low specific activities, say 0·1 to 1 per cent isotopic abundance, the tritium gas may be shaken or stirred with water in the presence of a platinum catalyst[216] preferably under slightly acidic conditions[40]. A fairly rapid exchange reaction occurs with the water until equilibrium is attained.

$$T_2 + HOH \rightleftharpoons HTO + HT \quad \text{. . . .} \quad (4.21)$$

$$HT + HOH \rightleftharpoons HTO + H_2 \quad \text{. . . .} \quad (4.22)$$

Mahadevan[217] has made a study of the isotope exchange between water and deuterium in the presence of a palladium–charcoal catalyst. Reaction mechanisms for the exchange are proposed involving activation of the chemisorped deuterium, which could be applicable to a similar exchange with tritium.

General Methods

Standard techniques of organic or inorganic chemical preparative work are used, with special modifications for the handling of small (chemical) quantities of compounds at very high specific activities. Frequent use is therefore made of vacuum distillations for the transfer of volatile compounds, and of paper, thin-layer, column and gas chromatography. Many compounds at high specific activity are not isolated in the solid state but are always kept in solution.

One often reads about the preparation of deuterium compounds involving the use of deuterium or deuterium oxide at 99 per cent isotopic abundance. Reference is commonly made at the end of such publications 'that by using tritium or tritiated water, tritium compounds at very high specific activity may be prepared'[218, 219]. In theory this is true but it is not always practically possible. Tritium gas at greater than 98 per cent isotopic abundance is of course frequently used for the preparation of tritium compounds on the millimolar scale (1 mM of tritium gas, 22·4 ml at S.T.P., is equivalent to 58·24 c). Tritiated water at greater than 98 per cent isotopic abundance on the other hand is seldom used. This perhaps is not very surprising when one considers that 1 ml of pure tritium oxide contains about 2,650 c; it is self-luminescent and irradiates itself at the rate of 6×10^{17} eV ml^{-1}sec^{-1} (approximately 10^9 rads/day). Consequently any chemical dissolved in tritium oxide would undergo considerable radiation damage during the course of an experiment. Tritiated water also undergoes quite rapid self-radiolysis which is further discussed in Chapter 6, and this is another reason why it is seldom used at the maximum isotopic abundance.

In chemical syntheses and for the exchange reactions described earlier in this chapter, tritiated water of 1 per cent isotopic abundance (580 mc/mM) is usually sufficient to produce compounds with a specific activity of at least 100 mc/mM.

In addition to the more specific chemical syntheses, there are two general reactions which can be advantageously used for preparing tritium compounds at very high specific activity:

1. Reduction of unsaturated compounds.
2. Catalytic halogen–tritium exchange.

Both these methods involve the use of tritium gas.

1. *Reduction of Unsaturated Compounds*

Types of reactions which may be envisaged are shown in the equations (4.23 to 4.27):

$$R \cdot CH = CH \cdot X \xrightarrow{T_2} R \cdot CHT \cdot CHT \cdot X \quad \ldots \quad (4.23)$$

$$R \cdot C \equiv C \cdot X \xrightarrow{T_2} R \cdot CT \cdot CT \cdot X \quad \ldots \quad (4.24)$$

$$R \cdot C \equiv C \cdot X \xrightarrow{T_2} R \cdot CT_2 \cdot CT_2 \cdot X \quad \ldots \quad (4.25)$$

$$R \cdot C \equiv N \xrightarrow{T_2} R \cdot CT_2 \cdot NH_2 \quad \ldots \quad (4.26)$$

$$RR'C = O \xrightarrow{T_2} RR'CT \cdot OH \quad \ldots \quad (4.27)$$

Hydrogenation of unsaturated compounds by the catalytic addition of tritium gas or tritium–hydrogen mixtures is one of the most convenient and simplest methods for the introduction of tritium into a compound.

The usual procedure is to hydrogenate the unsaturated compound dissolved in a suitable solvent with tritium gas in the presence of a catalyst. Most of the well-known catalysts may be used for example, Adams' catalyst (reduced PtO_2), platinum or palladium supported on charcoal, calcium carbonate or alumina, and rhodium on alumina. By a suitable choice of catalyst selective or partial reduction of carbon–carbon triple bonds may sometimes be accomplished, thus producing a tritiated ethylenic compound. Two recent examples of the partial reduction of acetylenic bonds are the preparation of oleic acid-9,10-T from stearolic acid[220, 221] (4.28) and the partial reduction of octadeca-9,12-diynoic acid to give linoleic acid-9,10,12,13-T[222] (4.29).

$$CH_3(CH_2)_7C\equiv C(CH_2)_7 \cdot COOH \xrightarrow{T_2}$$

$$CH_3(CH_2)_7CT = CT(CH_2)_7 \cdot COOH \quad \ldots \quad (4.28)$$

$$CH_3(CH_2)_4C\equiv C(CH_2) \cdot C\equiv C(CH_2)_7 \cdot COOH$$

$$\Big\downarrow T_2$$

$$CH_3 \cdot (CH_2)_4 \cdot CT = CT \cdot CH_2 \cdot CT = CT \cdot (CH_2)_7 \cdot COOH$$
$$\ldots \quad (4.29)$$

When maximum specific activities are required, hydrogenations are best carried out in non-polar solvents, that is, solvents which do not contain any labile hydrogen positions. These include hydrocarbons, dioxan, tetrahydrofuran, ethyl acetate (and other esters) and dimethyl sulphoxide. This does not mean that tritiations cannot be performed in polar solvents such as alcohols or water. On the contrary successful hydrogenations to give very high specific activity compounds are possible in say ethanol in the presence of a platinum catalyst[40]. It is then best to keep the volume of solvent to a minimum and the hydrogenation rate to a maximum such that the rate of exchange (4.30) is much slower than the rate of hydrogenation.

$$R \cdot OH + T_2 \rightleftharpoons R \cdot OT + TH \quad \ldots \quad (4.30)$$

Nevertheless, solvents without labile hydrogen positions are generally to be preferred.

The specific activity of the final product from the hydrogenation, also depends on the functional groups R, R′ and X. If any of these contain a labile hydrogen atom, for example hydroxyl or carboxyl groups, the hydrogen atoms in these positions exchange rapidly with the tritium until equilibrium is attained (4.31).

$$R \cdot CH = CH \cdot COOH + T_2 \rightleftharpoons R \cdot CH = CH \cdot COOT + HT$$
$$\ldots \quad (4.31)$$

This has the effect of reducing the specific activity of the hydrogenating gas mixture and consequently the specific activity of the final product is lower than in the absence of these labile hydrogen atoms. To achieve maximum specific activities it is therefore necessary to block any labile hydrogen positions by the preparation of suitable derivatives, such as the methyl ester, methyl ether or acetate, thus preventing the alternative competing exchange reaction. The beneficial effects of these techniques or 'dodges' can clearly be seen from Table 4.24.

Instead of preparing derivatives for the hydrogenation, a very large excess of tritium gas can be used to reduce the hydrogen 'dilution effect' to a minimum. This is not always practically possible and also has the disadvantage, and potential hazard, of manipulating large amounts of tritium gas. The derivative method is to be preferred from this point of view.

When mixtures of tritium and hydrogen are used, some workers have reported that preferential formation of carbon–tritium bonds over carbon–hydrogen bonds occurs[223, 224] by a factor of about 1.2. A similar preferential formation of carbon–deuterium bonds occurs during the reduction of ketones with hydrogen–deuterium mixtures using Raney nickel catalyst[225]. Bigeleisen[226] put forward a possible explanation of this phenomenon by assuming that the tritium atoms are 'loosely bound' to the catalyst surface during the hydrogenation, such that the difference between the isotopic zero-point energies of tritium and hydrogen is small. If the reaction then involves such 'free' (i.e. not bound to the catalyst as a complex) tritium atoms, the rate of reaction (hydrogenation) in the order of rate constants is $k_T > k_D > k_H$.

A good account of the use of noble-metal catalysts in hydrogenations is given by Wells[204] who rightly points out that there is (unfortunately) no technique yet available for the *direct* determination of the chemisorbed states of reactants, intermediates and products *during* catalytic reactions.

Disadvantages—The principal disadvantage of the catalytic reduction of unsaturated compounds with tritium gas is the tendency for tritium to be attached to carbon atoms other than those of the unsaturated bond[227], a point which is further discussed in Chapter 5. Although this effect is not so serious in the reduction of acetylenes to olefines where less than 10 per cent of the tritium is associated with carbon atoms other than those forming the triple bond[221, 228, 229]; it can be much more evident in the saturation of olefins[227]. It is only to be expected that some degree of non-specific labelling will occur, since conditions for catalytic hydrogenation are also essentially those for hydrogen–tritium exchange, proceeding slowly at room temperature (see page 130).

Another disadvantage is that acetylenes are particularly prone to polymerization on noble-metal catalysts[230], and at very high specific activities there is the added possibility of polymerization of the unsaturated starting material by the radiation. The latter effect can usually be overcome by carrying out the hydrogenation in dilute solution.

To perform reactions of the type (4.26) and (4.27), it is sometimes necessary to use higher than room temperatures or greater than atmospheric pressures. For safety and convenience such conditions are best avoided if possible and alternative methods employed, for example by the use of tritiated metal hydrides.

Reductions with tritiated metal hydrides—Frequent use is made of the tritiated metal hydrides and mixed metal hydrides such as sodium or lithium borotritides and lithium aluminium tritide, for the reduction of acids, esters, aldehydes, ketones and nitriles (see page 149 *et seq.*). Note that in this case the labelling is strictly specific and the tritium atoms are located only on the carbon atom forming the unsaturated group. For example, the hormones adrenaline (4.32; R = Me) and noradrenaline (4.32; R = H) are labelled exclusively at the 7-position by the reduction of the corresponding ketones with sodium boro-tritide (4.32) [231, 232]:

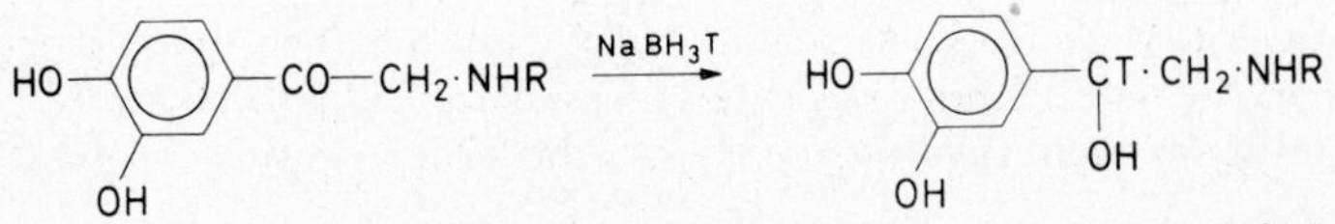

$$HO-\underset{\underset{OH}{|}}{\bigcirc}-CO-CH_2 \cdot NHR \xrightarrow{Na\,BH_3T} HO-\underset{\underset{OH}{|}}{\bigcirc}-\underset{\underset{OH}{|}}{CT} \cdot CH_2 \cdot NHR$$

. . . . (4.32)

2. *Catalytic Halogen–Tritium Exchange*

The second of the more general synthetic tritiation procedures involves the replacement of halogen atoms by tritium under catalytic conditions (4.33):

$$R \cdot hal + T_2 \rightarrow R \cdot T + T \cdot hal \quad . \quad . \quad . \quad (4.33)$$

Fluorine, chlorine, bromine or iodine atoms can readily be exchanged for tritium under conditions similar to those used for hydrogenation reactions. In this type of reaction both polar and non-polar solvents can be used but it is usually necessary to neutralize the tritium halide formed during the reaction, with a basic compound. If this is not done the halide poisons the catalyst and rapidly slows the dehalogenation process [40].

From the equation (4.33) it can be seen that half the tritium is lost as the tritiated halide. This of course is not a serious disadvantage as regards utilization of the isotope, but particularly at high specific activities, the accumulation of this tritium in the reaction solvent increases the possibility of side-reactions and radiation damage to both the unlabelled halogen compound and the tritiated product.

A very wide variety of compounds has now been labelled by this method, ranging from simple molecules such as uracil to the more complex compounds like tetracycline, and some are listed in Table 4.25.

Although supported palladium catalysts are more popular for the

TABLE 4.24

Reduction of Unsaturated Compounds with Tritium

Starting compound	Solvent	Catalyst	Final product	Specific activity mc/mM		References
				Observed	Calc.	
Acetylene dicarboxylic acid (dimethyl ester)	—	5% Pd/C	Succinic acid-2,3-T	—	—	242
Arterenone	Water/H+	Pd/C	Dopamine-7-T	—	—	238
But-2-yne-1,4-diol	Dioxan	Pt	Butan-1,4-diol-2,3-T	35	200	40
But-2-yne-1,4-diol	—	—	Butan-1,4-diol-2,3-T	—	—	236
n-Dec-1-ene	Dioxan	Pt	n-Decane-1,2-T	200	200	40
Dienoestrol	Acetone	10% Pd/C	Hexoestrol-T	—	—	239
Dienoestrol	Dioxan	10% Pd/C	Hexoestrol-T	—	—	234
Dieneoestrol	Dioxan	Pd/C	Hexoestrol-T	35	200	40
Elaidic acid	Dioxan	Pd/C	Stearic acid-T	—	—	241
Elaidic acid	Dioxan	Pt	Stearic acid-T	100	250	40
Ethyl linoleate	Ethyl acetate	Pt	Stearic acid-T	—	—	203
Glyceryl trioleate	Dioxan	Pt	Glyceryl tri-(stearate-T)	200	200	40
n-Hexadec-1-ene	Dioxan	Pt	n-Hexadecane-1,2-T	200	200	40
Lysergic acid	AcOT	10% Pd/C	1-Methyl-9,10-dihydrolysergamide-9,10-T	—	—	100
Methyl acrylate	Dioxan	Pt	Methyl propionate-2,3-T	200	200	40
Methyl cinnamate	Dioxan	Pt	β-Phenylpropionic acid-αβ-T	200	200	40
Morphine	Ethyl acetate	Pd	Dihydromorphine-T	—	—	285a
Maleic acid	Dioxan	Pt	Succinic acid-2,3-T	18	200	40
trans-Muconic acid	Dioxan	Pt	Adipic acid-T	—	—	88, 40
Myoinosose-2	Water	Pt	Myoinositol-2-T	—	—	240
Octadeca-9,12-diynoic acid	n-Hexane + 5% of 0·2% quinoline in hexane	Lindlar	Linoleic acid-9,10,12,13-T	357	—	222
Palmitoleic acid	Dioxan	Pt	Palmitic acid-T	200	350	40
Prostaglandin E₂	Ethyl acetate	5% Pd/C	Prostaglandin-E₁-5,6-T	5 × 10⁴	—	202
Selachyl alcohol	Cyclohexane	Pt	D-Batyl alcohol	—	—	301a
Stearolic acid	Ethyl acetate	5% Pd/C	Stearic acid-T	—	—	221
Stearolic acid	Ethyl acetate (20% pyridine)	5% Pd/C	Oleic acid-9,10-T	—	—	220
Streptomycin HCl	D₂O/dimethyl sulphoxide	Pt	Dihydrostreptomycin-T	—	—	237

145

halogen–tritium exchange reactions, platinum is sometimes pre-ferred [233] as it absorbs less tritium during the process.

An apparatus suitable for microhydrogenations (or dehalogenations) with tritium gas is described by Glascock and Pope [234].

Tritium compounds prepared by catalytic halogen–tritium exchange are essentially specifically labelled, but the reaction conditions are again similar to those for general exchange labelling. A few per cent of tritium may sometimes be found in positions other than those previously occupied by halogen atoms (see Chapter 5).

A catalytic halogen–tritium exchange procedure has recently been described [235] involving the *in situ* generation of tritium from a tritiated sodium hydroxide solution by aluminium–Raney nickel or cobalt alloys. Under the reaction conditions complete substitution of fluorine, chlorine, bromine or iodine for tritium may be achieved. An example is the preparation of tritiated acetic acid from trifluoroacetic acid (4.34):

$$CF_3 \cdot COOH \xrightarrow[\text{NaOH/THO}]{\text{Al—Ni}} CH_2T \cdot COOH \quad . \quad . \quad . \quad (4.34)$$

TABLE 4.25

Catalytic Halogen–Tritium Exchange Reactions

Starting compound	Solvent	Catalyst	Final product	Reference
8-Bromoadenosine	aq. Dioxan	Pd/C	Adenosine-8-T	40
5-Bromocytidine	aq. Dioxan	Pd/CaCO₃	Cytidine-5-T	40
5-Bromo-2′-deoxycytidine	aq. Dioxan	Pd/CaCO₃	2′-Deoxycytidine-5-T	40
5-Bromomethyl-1,4-diacetoxy-2,3-dimethoxybenzene	Dioxan/Et₃N	Pd/C	Coenzyme-Q₀-5-methyl-T	244
2-Bromomethyl-1,4-diacetoxynaphthalene	Dioxan/Et₃N	Pd/C	2-Methyl-T-1,4-naphthoquinone	245
5-Bromouracil	aq. Dioxan	Pd/CaCO₃	Uracil-5-T	40
5-Chloromethyluracil	Dioxan/Et₃N	Pd/C	Thymine-methyl-T	40
5-Chloromethyluracil	—	—	Thymine-methyl-T	251
7-Chlorotetracycline (aureomycin)	Dioxan/Et₃N	Pd/C or Pt	Tetracycline-7-T	147 233 250 40
3′,5′-Dibromofolic acid	aq. Dioxan	Pd/C	Folic acid-3′,5′-T	40
3′,5′-Dichloromethotrexate	NaOH	Pd/C	Methotrexate-3′,5′-T	40
3-Iodo-anisole	NaOH	Raney nickel	Anisole-3-T	243
5-Iodo-cytidine	aq. Dioxan	Pd/CaCO₃	Cytidine-5-T	40
5-Iodo-2′-deoxycytidine	aq. Dioxan	Pd/CaCO₃	2′-Deoxycytidine-5-T	40
5-Iodo-2′-deoxyuridine	aq. Dioxan	Pd/CaCO₃	2′-Deoxyuridine-5-T	40
Iodo insulin	Dimethylformamide	Pd/C	Insulin-T	289
5-Iodo-orotic acid	aq. Dioxan	Pd/CaCO₃	Orotic acid-5-T	40
Iodo oxytocin	Dimethylformamide	Pd/C	Oxytocin-T	289
Iodo lysine vasopressin	Dimethylformamide	Pd/C	Lysine vasopressin-T	289
4-Iodo-salicylic acid	NaOH	Raney Ni	Salicylic acid-4-T	248
5-Iodo-uridine	aq. Dioxan	Pd/CaCO₃	Uridine-5-T	40
2-Methyl-(6-iodo- or 5,6,7-tribromo)-1,4-naphthaquinol bis-(disodium phosphate)	Dioxan/NaOH	Pd/C	2-Methyl-1,4-naphthaquinol-(6- or 5,6,7-T)-bis(disodium phosphate)	249

146

The greater problems of manipulating compounds in tritiated solvents at very high specific activities limits the practical use of the method to the preparation of compounds at relatively low specific activity.

Other Methods

The more specific syntheses for introducing tritium atoms into molecules are assembled under the following headings which are likely to be familiar to the reader;

1. Aliphatic compounds
2. Aromatic compounds
3. Amino acids, peptides and proteins
4. Carbohydrates and polyhydric alcohols
5. Heterocyclic compounds
6. Steroids
7. Organo-metallic compounds
8. Miscellaneous syntheses
9. Inorganic tritium compounds

1. *Aliphatic Compounds*

Acids—The simplest member of the series, formic acid, can be prepared by exchange[40, 252], by decarboxylation of tritiated oxalic acid[253] (4.35), or by hydrolysis of cyanide with tritiated water at $170°$ C[254] (4.36).

$$(COOT)_2 \rightarrow T \cdot COOH \quad \ldots \ldots \quad (4.35)$$

$$NaCN \xrightarrow[170°C]{THO} T \cdot COONa \quad \ldots \ldots \quad (4.36)$$

Acetic acid labelled in the methyl group, a key intermediate for numerous syntheses (some examples 4.38) is best prepared by decarboxylation of malonic acid at $180°$ C[167,168, 241]. The labile tritium attached to the carboxyl group is removed by conversion of the acid to the sodium salt. Acetic acid-(*methyl*-T) is then regenerated with dry hydrogen chloride (4.37):

$$CH_2(COOH)_2 + THO \rightarrow CHT(COOT)_2 \xrightarrow{-CO_2} CHT_2 \cdot COOT$$

$$\downarrow NaOH$$

$$CHT_2 \cdot COOH \xleftarrow{HCl} CHT_2 \cdot COONa$$

$$\ldots \ldots \quad (4.37)$$

Some reactions of acetic acid-(*methyl*-T) (4.38):

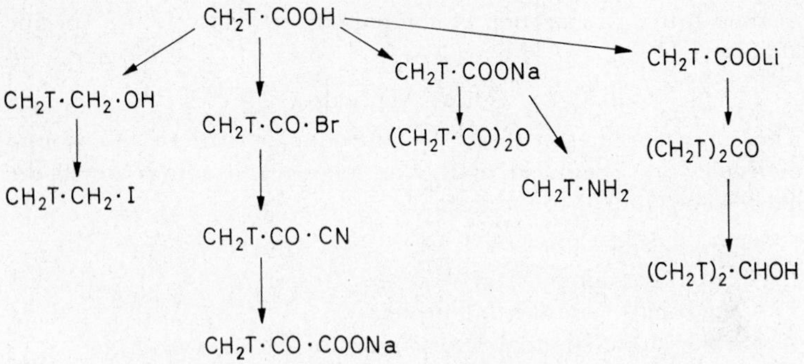

$$
\begin{array}{c}
CH_2T \cdot COOH \\
\end{array}
$$

CH$_2$T·CH$_2$·OH

CH$_2$T·CH$_2$·I

CH$_2$T·CO·Br

CH$_2$T·CO·CN

CH$_2$T·CO·COONa

CH$_2$T·COONa

(CH$_2$T·CO)$_2$O

CH$_2$T·COOLi

(CH$_2$T)$_2$CO

CH$_2$T·NH$_2$

(CH$_2$T)$_2$·CHOH

. . . . (4.38)

A novel approach is the conversion of thiophene acids into their open-chain analogues by simultaneous desulphurization and reduction with Raney nickel in alkaline tritiated water [218] (4.39):

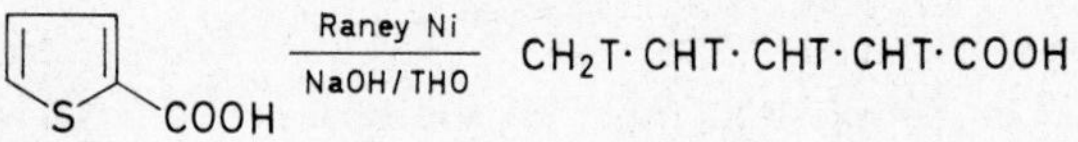

$$ \underset{S}{\bigcirc}\!\!-COOH \xrightarrow[\text{NaOH/THO}]{\text{Raney Ni}} CH_2T \cdot CHT \cdot CHT \cdot CHT \cdot COOH $$

. . . . (4.39)

The method gives general labelling.

Acid anhydrides (in particular the useful analytical reagent acetic anhydride-T) are prepared from acetic acid-(*methyl*-T) by reaction of the anhydrous sodium salt with the theoretical quantity of acetyl bromide (4.40) or *p*-toluene sulphonyl chloride (4.41). With the sulphonyl chloride method there is no dilution of the isotope, and the molar specific activity of the acetic anhydride-T is therefore twice that of the starting sodium acetate-T.

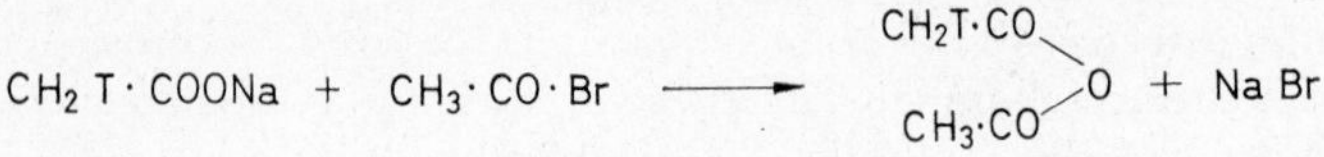

$$ CH_2T \cdot COONa + CH_3 \cdot CO \cdot Br \longrightarrow \begin{array}{c} CH_2T \cdot CO \\ CH_3 \cdot CO \end{array}\!\!>\!\!O + Na\,Br $$

. . . . (4.40)

$$ 2CH_2T \cdot COONa + Cl \cdot SO_2 \cdot C_6H_4 \cdot CH_3 \rightarrow $$
$$ (CH_2T \cdot CO)_2O + HSO_3C_6H_4 \cdot Me $$

. . . . (4.41)

Alcohols—Aliphatic alcohols can be labelled on the methylene or methine hydrogen positions by the reduction of acids, esters [239, 254, 256, 256a], aldehydes or ketones [257] with lithium aluminium tritide or lithium borotritide (4.42–4.44):

$$R \cdot CHO + LiAlH_3T \rightarrow R \cdot CHT \cdot OH$$
$$\cdots \quad (4.42)$$

$$R \cdot COOH \text{ or } R \cdot COOR' + LiAlH_3T \rightarrow R \cdot CHT \cdot OH$$
$$\cdots \quad (4.43)$$

$$RR'CO + LiAlH_3T \rightarrow RR'CT \cdot OH$$
$$\cdots \quad (4.44)$$

Tritiated ethanol can be prepared by the reduction of acetaldehyde with tritium gas over a nickel-on-kieselguhr catalyst at 170° C [258]. However, for preparative work especially at high specific activities, high temperature and pressure reactions with tritium gas are usually avoided, not only from the potentially greater hazard but because high temperatures often lead to isomerization or movement of the tritium atoms to other parts of the molecule. For example, ethanol-T prepared from acetaldehyde and tritium over the nickel catalyst, contained $11\cdot3$ per cent tritium in the methyl group [258].

Sometimes it is possible to combine the advantages of simple exchange procedures with chemical synthesis. Methanol-T can be prepared by reduction of carbon dioxide with lithium aluminium tritide [256], but is often more conveniently prepared by the hydrolysis of methyl-T naphthoate [259] or benzoate [258]. These esters are readily prepared by exchanging the carboxyl group hydrogen atom with tritiated water followed by esterification of the tritiated acid with diazomethane in ethereal solution (4.45) [258, 259]:

$$R \cdot COOH + THO \rightarrow R \cdot COOT + HOH$$
$$R \cdot COOT + CH_2N_2 \rightarrow R \cdot COOCH_2T$$
$$R \cdot COOCH_2T + KOH \rightarrow R \cdot COOK + CH_2T \cdot OH$$
$$\cdots \quad (4.45)$$

Ethyl alcohol can be labelled in the methylene group by a similar process using diazoethane [40], but reduction of acetic acid with lithium aluminium tritide is the more usually described procedure [260, 261].

Similar reductions are described for the preparation of *n*-propyl alcohol-(*methyl*-T-) [262] and isopropyl alcohol-2-T [257].

Aldehydes and ketones—Formaldehyde-T can be prepared by the photochemical-induced reaction between carbon monoxide and tritium gas [263], by periodate fission of glucose-6-T [264], or by the oxidation of glycine-2-T with ninhydrin [265], although direct exchange between tritium gas and paraformaldehyde is sometimes more convenient [40].

Other aldehydes can be prepared by the oxidation of tritiated primary alcohol, oxidation of amino acids-T with ninhydrin or from alkyl halides or tosylates by heating in dimethyl sulphoxide at 150° C [266].

Acetone-T is prepared by the pyrolysis of lithium acetate-T at 400° C. This is a particularly useful method which results in acetone at double the molar specific activity of the starting acetate (4.46):

$$2CH_2T \cdot COOLi \xrightarrow{400°C} CH_2T \cdot CO \cdot CH_2T + Li_2CO_3$$

$$\text{. . . . (4.46)}$$

Acetone-T at a high specific activity (above 5 c/mM) has been observed to exhibit a purple-violet self-phosphorescence [40].

Other ketones may be prepared by more conventional reactions such as the oxidation of tritiated secondary alcohols.

A point to remember however, is that tritium atoms attached to carbon atoms adjacent to keto groups lose the tritium by enolization under alkaline conditions (4.47):

$$R \cdot CHT \cdot CO \cdot R' \rightleftharpoons R \cdot CH{=}\underset{\underset{OT}{|}}{C}{-}R' \underset{T^+}{\overset{H^+}{\rightleftharpoons}} R \cdot CH{=}\underset{\underset{OH}{|}}{C} \cdot R'$$

$$\text{. . . . (4.47)}$$

Alkyl halides—Simple intermediates such as methyl or ethyl iodide labelled with tritium can be prepared by the reaction of the corresponding tritiated alcohols with hydriodic acid (4.47) or by the hydrolysis of tritiated esters (4.48) [267].

$$R \cdot OH + HI \rightarrow R \cdot I + H_2O \quad \text{. . . . (4.47)}$$

$$R \cdot COO \cdot CHT \cdot R' + HI \rightarrow R' \cdot CHT \cdot I + R \cdot COOH$$

$$\text{. . . . (4.48)}$$

There is no observed exchange of tritium during these processes indicating the stability of the tritium atoms to the acidic conditions [40].

Treatment of the complex, obtained by the reduction of esters with lithium borotritide, with halogen acids is another method. An example is the preparation of ethyl bromide-1-T from ethyl acetate (4.49) [268].

$$CH_3 \cdot COOC_2H_5 + LiBH_3T \rightarrow LiB(O \cdot CHT \cdot CH_3)_4 \xrightarrow{HBr}$$

$$CH_3 \cdot CHT \cdot Br \quad \text{. . . . (4.49)}$$

150

Hydrocarbons—Methane-T may be prepared by the reaction of tritiated water with aluminium carbide [269] (4.50):

$$Al_4C_3 + THO \rightarrow CH_3 \cdot T + Al(OH)_3 \quad . \quad . \quad . \quad (4.50)$$

The tritiated methane from this reaction usually contains traces of hydrogen, oxygen, ammonia, hydrogen sulphide and other hydrocarbons. The purity of the methane depends very much on the quality of the aluminium carbide used. For this reason methane-T is normally prepared by a more general reaction which is applicable to the preparation of many tritiated hydrocarbons; the reaction of tritiated water with a Grignard reagent, in this example with methyl magnesium iodide or bromide (4.51).

$$Me \cdot MgI + THO \rightarrow Me \cdot T + MgOHI \quad . \quad . \quad . \quad (4.51)$$

(Grignard reagents are more precisely formulated as $R \cdot Mg \cdot MgX_2$ [270] but for simplicity the more conventional and familiar formula $R \cdot MgX$ where X = halogen is used throughout this book.)

The exchange of the THO with the MgOHI formed, can be eliminated by using bis-2-ethoxyethyl ether as solvent in which the MgOHI is converted into Mg_2OI_2 [271].

The preparation of tritiobutane from tritiated water and *n*-butylmagnesium bromide forms the basis of the tritium measurement method of Glascock and others [241, 271].

Hydrogenation of unsaturated hydrocarbons with tritium gas is another general procedure and some examples are given in Table 4.24.

A novel route to tritiated hydrocarbons involves passing a halogen compound over a chromatographic column containing calcium tritide, at $100-200° C$ [273]. A halogen–tritium replacement reaction takes place (4.52):

$$2R \cdot hal + CaT_2 \rightarrow 2R \cdot T + Cahal_2 \quad . \quad . \quad . \quad (4.52)$$

Unsaturated hydrocarbons of confirmed specific tritium labelling can be prepared by the newly developed hydroboration procedures (see page 178).

Partial hydrogenation of acetylenes using Lindlar and other catalysts, is also used to prepare tritiated olefins. An example is the preparation of oct-4-ene-4,5-T by the catalytic reduction of oct-4-yne [229].

Olefins have also been prepared from tritiated alkylenephosphines by the Wittig reaction [274, 274a].

Acetylene can be labelled with tritium by the reaction of tritiated water with calcium carbide (4.53):

$$CaC_2 + THO \rightarrow CT{\equiv}CH + Ca(OH)_2 \qquad \ldots \quad (4.53)$$

Note however that the hydrogen atoms of acetylenes are acidic and are readily exchanged in the presence of protonated solvents through a carbonium ion intermediate (4.54). For example, if acetylene is shaken with tritiated acetic acid-*hydroxyl*-T, tritiated acetylene may be obtained (4.54; R = H).

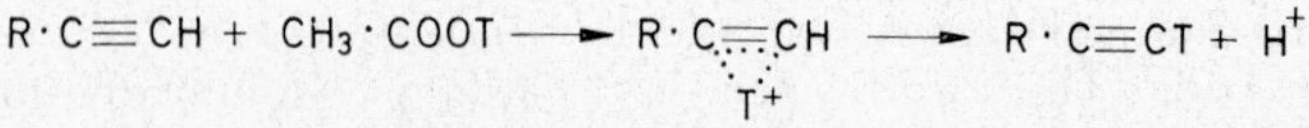

$$\ldots \ldots (4.54)$$

The rate of exchange is improved, without hydrogenation occurring, by the use of a 5 per cent rhodium on alumina catalyst[275]. Ethylenes exchange at a slower rate than the acetylenes but much faster than ethanes. The rhodium catalyst is not so easily poisoned, compared with platinum, and dichlorinated ethylenes have been labelled in this manner[275].

2. *Aromatic Compounds*

Tritiated aromatic acids, alcohols, aldehydes and ketones, may be prepared by similar reactions described for their aliphatic counterparts. Numerous reactions are described in the literature and many have been collectively assembled by Murray and Williams[276].

The ease of exchange of hydrogen for tritium in aromatic nuclei favours the use of exchange labelling procedures for the general labelling of aromatic rings.

Aryl halides—Intermediates such as bromo- or chloro-benzene are usually prepared by direct reaction of the halogen with tritiated benzene[277] (4.55):

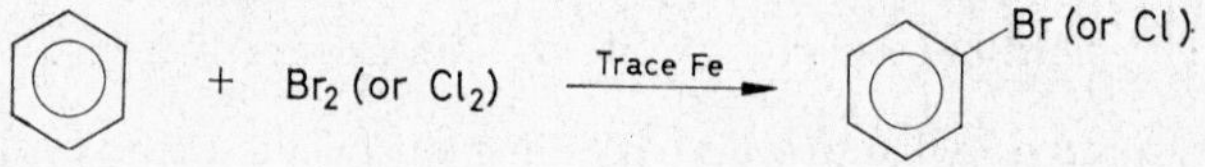

$$\ldots \ldots (4.55)$$

In such substitution reactions tritium is less readily substituted than hydrogen, and consequently there is often practically no change (less than 10 per cent) in the specific activity of the bromo- or chloro-benzene-T from that of the starting tritiated benzene; certainly at low isotopic abundances (less than 0·1 per cent tritium)[40]. The maximum change, neglecting any isotope effects, would be 16·7 per cent.

152

Hydrocarbons (ring-labelled)—Aryl hydrocarbons specifically labelled in the aromatic nucleus are prepared by the reaction of tritiated water with the appropriate Grignard reagent[278] (4.56) or lithium aryl[279,279a] (4.57).

$$Ar \cdot MgBr + THO \rightarrow Ar \cdot T + MgOHBr. \quad . \quad . \quad . \quad (4.56)$$

$$Ar \cdot Li + THO \rightarrow Ar \cdot T + LiOH \quad . \quad . \quad . \quad . \quad (4.57)$$

There is a large isotope effect during the Grignard reaction[280] and the resulting specific activity of the tritiated hydrocarbons is normally about 30 per cent of the theoretical value (see Table 6.1).

The general catalytic halogen–tritiated exchange reaction (see page 144) can of course be used for aryl hydrocarbons, and usually the halogen replacement is easier than with aliphatic compounds[40].

An unusual reaction for the preparation of tritiated benzene involves the decarboxylation of calcium mellitate (calcium benzene–hexacarboxylate) by heating at 500° C with an excess of tritiated calcium hydroxide[281] (4.58). The yield is only 64 to 72 per cent and is not so good as the methods described above which normally yield 80 per cent or more tritiated benzene. However, the decarboxylation method probably yields more general labelling in the benzene molecule compared with the other methods which give specific labelling.

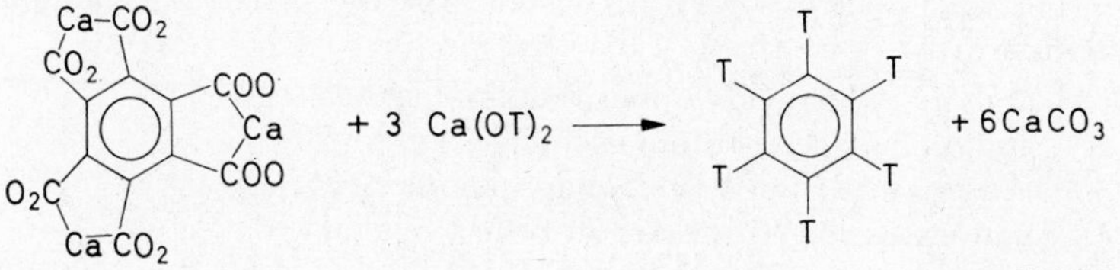

$$. \quad . \quad . \quad . \quad (4.58)$$

Another method consists of the low-temperature ($-30°$ to $250°$ C) cyclization of tritiated acetylene (prepared from tritiated water and barium carbide) using a niobium, tantalum or tungsten catalyst, in a solvent consisting of a mixture of aliphatic hydrocarbons[98]: 84·6 per cent yield conversion into benzene is recorded.

Side-chain—Labelling of aryl hydrocarbons in the side-chain is normally accomplished by hydrogenation of suitable intermediates with tritium gas. For example, stilbene-T is prepared by the partial reduction of diphenylacetylene with tritium gas in benzene solution using palladium on calcium carbonate as catalyst[282] (4.59):

$$Ph \cdot C{\equiv}C \cdot Ph + T_2 \rightarrow Ph \cdot CT{=}CT \cdot Ph \quad . \quad . \quad . \quad (4.59)$$

In this example mainly the *cis*-isomer is produced, which can be converted into *trans*-stilbene-T by heating at 315° C in a sealed tube.

Styrene-T can be labelled in the side-chain by a similar reaction from phenylacetylene (4.60), although the reaction only proceeds satisfactorily at tracer levels of activity. At higher specific activities (above 100 mc/mM) radiation polymerization of the phenylacetylene and tritiated styrene is likely to occur[40].

$$Ph \cdot C\!\!\equiv\!\!CH + T_2 \xrightarrow[\text{dioxan}]{\text{Pd/C}} Ph \cdot CT\!\!=\!\!CHT \quad \ldots \ldots (4.60)$$

Styrene is more usually labelled in the side-chain by reduction of acetophenone with tritium in the presence of a platinum catalyst followed by dehydration of the phenyl methyl carbinol with naphthalene- or *p*-toluenesulphonic acid[223] (4.61):

$$Ph \cdot CO \cdot CH_3 \rightarrow Ph \cdot \underset{\underset{OT}{|}}{CT} \cdot CH_3 \rightarrow Ph \cdot CT\!\!=\!\!CH_2 \quad \ldots (4.61)$$

3. *Amino Acids, Peptides and Proteins*

The amino acids and their associated condensation products, the peptides and proteins, form perhaps the most studied group of compounds. Practically all the important members of the amino acid class have been labelled with tritium.

The four principal methods for the specific tritiation of amino acids are:

1. Catalytic reduction of unsaturated precursors.
2. Catalytic halogen–tritium exchange.
3. Decarboxylation of α-acetamido-malonic acid derivatives.
4. Chain extension by the Arndt–Eistert reaction.

There are many examples of Methods 1 and 2 which can be seen from Table 4.26; DL-leucine-4,5-T for example is prepared by the reaction

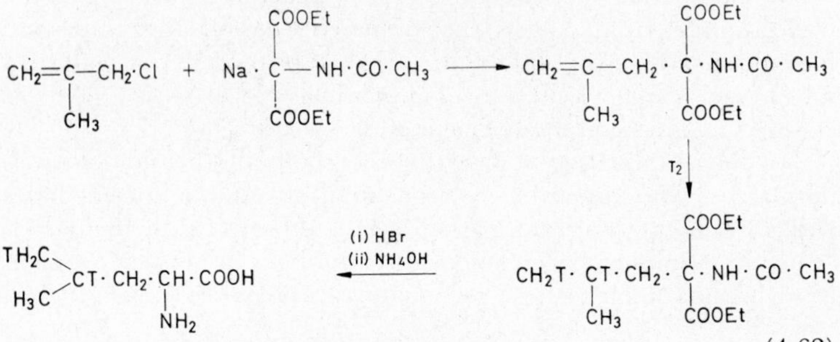

$$\ldots \ldots (4.62)$$

sequence (4.62) and involves reduction of ethyl 2-acetamido-2-ethoxycarbonyl-4-methyl-pent-4-enoate in dioxan solution with tritium in the presence of a platinum catalyst. Hydrolysis of the tritiated product with hydrobromic acid followed by treatment with ammonia gives an 83 per cent yield of DL-leucine-4,5-T[283].

The general technique of catalytic halogen–tritium exchange has been particularly useful for the preparation of aromatic ring-labelled amino acids such as phenylalanine, tyrosine and tryptophan. Aqueous alkaline solutions or methanolic potassium hydroxide are normally used as solvents. An example is the dehalogenation of 3,5-di-iodotyrosine to yield tyrosine-3,5-T[284] (4.63):

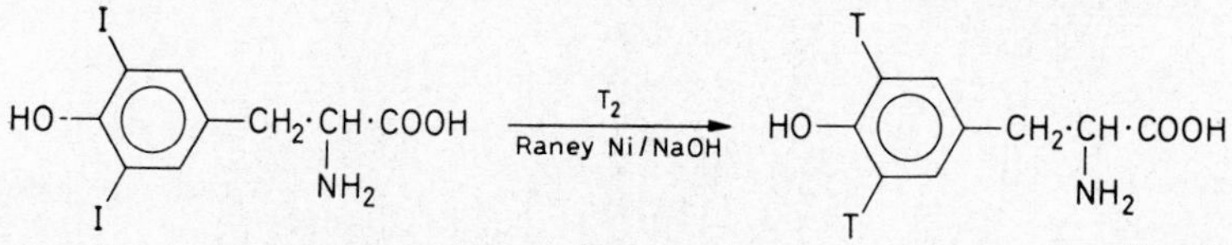

$$\cdots \cdots \text{(4.63)}$$

If optically active intermediates are used, it is necessary to examine the tritiated amino acid for racemization, particularly if the reaction is carried out under alkaline conditions. This is best done by reverse isotope dilution analysis with D- and L-amino acid carriers[60]. Other examples are given in Table 4.26.

With Method 3 the decarboxylation of α-acetamino-malonic acid derivatives is useful when specific labelling in the α-position is required. The reaction is normally carried out in acid solution of a tritiated solvent; for example, DL-leucine-2-T is prepared by the decarboxylation of 2-acetamino-2-carboxy-4-methyl-pentanoic acid, i.e. by using tritiated hydrobromic acid in reaction (4.62)[231]. The general reaction is (4.64)

$$\begin{array}{c} \text{COOH} \\ | \\ \text{R} \cdot \text{C} \cdot \text{NH} \cdot \text{CO} \cdot \text{CH}_3 \xrightarrow{\text{T}^+} \text{R} \cdot \text{CT} \cdot \text{COOH} \\ | \qquad\qquad\qquad\qquad | \\ \text{COOH} \qquad\qquad\qquad \text{NH}_2 \end{array}$$

$$\cdots \cdots \text{(4.64)}$$

The validity of tritiated amino acids labelled in the α-position, particularly as tracers in biological systems, is questionable (see Chapter 6), but they are still useful for the preparation of labelled aldehydes (see page 149).

By Method 4, tritiation in the position alpha to the carboxyl group may be achieved by treatment of diazoketones with tritiated water and silver oxide [285] (4.65):

$$R \cdot CH \cdot CO \cdot CHN_2 \rightarrow R \cdot CH \cdot CTH \cdot COOH$$
$$\underset{\displaystyle NH_2}{|} \qquad\qquad \underset{\displaystyle NH_2}{|}$$

. . . . (4.65)

However, it is doubtful whether this reaction for the tritiation of β-amino acids offers any advantage over the alternative route (4.66):

$$R \cdot CH \!=\! CH \cdot COOH$$
$$\downarrow \text{\footnotesize T. hal}$$
$$R \cdot CH \!-\! CHT \cdot COOH$$
$$\underset{\displaystyle \text{\footnotesize hal}}{|} \qquad \underset{\displaystyle \text{\footnotesize NH}_4\text{OH}}{|}$$
$$R \cdot CH \cdot CHT \cdot COOH$$
$$\underset{\displaystyle NH_2}{|}$$

. . . . (4.66)

The addition of tritiated hydrogen halides to $\alpha\beta$-unsaturated acids obeys the 'Markownikov Rule' giving the β-halogenated acid.

Most of the methods described give the DL-tritiated amino acid and optical resolution by chemical or biochemical techniques is frequently required to obtain the L- or D-acid. Few publications do in fact describe the determination of the amount of tritium activity in the stated optical form of the pure amino acid.

Peptides and proteins—The associated difficulties of purification when peptides, proteins or other macromolecules are labelled by the tritium gas-exposure methods [76, 286, 287], have promoted some investigation of alternative methods for their more specific labelling.

In *any* technique employed for the tritiation of proteins or peptides, it is imperative that the integrity of the tritium label be thoroughly examined. Even when the chemical and radiochemical purity are proven, the radioactivity may still only be associated with biologically inert material. The cautious experimentor will always bear this in mind, and for this reason it is often better to prepare such labelled biologically active material by biochemical methods (see page 183) or by *in situ* labelling using a tritiated amino acid precursor. For example, Caro and Palade [288] labelled protein *in situ* with leucine-4,5-T for studying intracellular protein movement in guinea pigs.

However, one of the more promising chemical approaches for the specific tritium labelling of peptides is by catalytic halogen–tritium exchange using iodinated peptides (or proteins) as precursors. Insulin, oxytocin and lysine vasopressin have all been labelled by de-iodinating the corresponding halogenated proteins with tritium gas in dimethylformamide in the presence of a palladium-on-charcoal catalyst[289]. Preliminary analysis showed that the labelling was mainly on the tyrosyl residues with some non-specific labelling of the aromatic amino acids (probably by tritium–hydrogen exchange under the catalytic conditions), and over 85 per cent of the biological activity was reported to be retained by the labelled protein. Note however that the gross retention of biological activity of the specimen *as a whole* cannot be taken as sufficient evidence of the retention of the biological activity of the *labelled molecules*; more stringent biological tests may be necessary to do this.

A synthetic analogue of the octapeptide angiotensin, valine 5-angiotensin II aspartyl-β-OH, has been tritiated on the phenylalanine group by a similar halogen–tritium exchange procedure[290].

An excellent short review by Margen and Tarver[291] of the labelling of proteins, particularly for turnover studies, reveals the need for further evaluation of their labelling.

TABLE 4.26

Specifically Labelled Tritiated Amino Acids

Starting compound	Method	Solvent	Catalyst	Amino acid	Ref.
α-Hydroxyimino-propionic acid	A	aq. Dioxan	Pt	DL-α-Alanine-α-T	292
α-Acetamido-acrylic acid ethyl ester	A	Tetrahydrofuran	10% Pd/C	DL-α-Alanine-αβ-T	293
γ-Phthalimidocrotonic acid ethyl ester	A	Ethanol	10% Pd/C	γ-Aminobutyric acid-αβ-T	293
Acetamino-3-carbethoxy-Δ^1-propenyl-malonic acid diethyl ester	A	Ethanol	10% Pd/C	DL-α-Aminoadipic acid-4,5-T	293
S-Benzyl-3-thio-2-carbethoxy-2-acetamido-propionic acid	Synthesis	—	—	DL-Cystine-α-T	265
Formaldehyde-T	Synthesis	—	—	DL-Cystine-β-T	265
2,5,6-Tribromo-O-diacetyl-N-acetyl-3,4-dihydroxy-phenylalanine methyl ester	B	Dioxan Et₃N	Pd/C	3,4-Dihydroxyphenylalanine-2,5,6-T	294
6-Bromo-O-diacetyl-N-acetyl-3,4-dihydroxyphenylalanine methyl ester	B	Dioxan Et₃N	Pd/C	3,4-Dihydroxyphenylalanine-6-T	294
2,5,6-Tribromo-3,4-dihydroxyphenylalanine	B	aq. Alcohol + KOH	Pd/CaCO₃	3,4-Dihydroxyphenylalanine-2,5,6-T	293
α-Acetamino-β-(3,4-diacetoxyphenyl)-acrylic acid	A	aq. Ethanol	10% Pd/C	DL-3,4-Dihydroxyphenylalanine-αβ-T	293

TABLE 4.26 (*continued*)

Starting compound	Method	Solvent	Catalyst	Amino acid	Ref.
Acetamino-(2-carb-ethoxyvinyl)-malonic acid diethyl ester	A	Ethanol	10% Pd/C	DL-Glutamic acid-$\beta\gamma$-T	293
L-2,5-Diiodohistidine	B	aq. Ethanol + KOH	Pd/CaCO₃	L-Histidine-2,5-T	293
4-Keto-DL-proline	NaBH₃T	—	—	DL-Hydroxyproline-4-T	295
N-Carbobenzyloxy-3-keto-DL-proline methyl ester	NaBH₃T	—	—	cis- and trans-3-Hydroxyproline-3-T	135
β-Ethyl-methyl-α-hydroxyiminopropionic acid	A	Dioxan	Pt	DL-isoLeucine-α-T	296
Ethyl 2-acetamino-2-carbethoxy-4-methyl-pent-4-enoate	A	Dioxan	Pd/C	DL-Leucine-4,5-T	283
Acetamino-(4-amino-$\varDelta^2$-butenyl)-malonic acid diethyl ester hydrochloride	A	Acetic acid	Pt	DL-Lysine-4,5-T	298
Acetamino-(4-amino-$\varDelta^2$-butenyl)-malonic acid diethyl ester hydrochloride	A	Methanol	10% Pd/C	DL-Lysine-4,5-T (and poly-L-lysine-T)	299
α-Acetamino-β(2-chloracetamino-ethyl) acrylic acid	A	aq. Ethanol	10% Pd/C	DL-Ornithine-$\alpha\beta$-T	128
3-Nitropyrid-2-one	A	Acetic acid	Pt	DL-Ornithine-$\alpha\beta\gamma\delta$-T	128
β-Phenyl-α-hydroxy-iminopropionic acid	A	Dioxan (40° C)	Pt	DL-Phenylalanine-α-T	296
L-2,4-Dibromo-phenylalanine	B	aq. Ethanol	Pd/CaCO₃	L-Phenylalanine-2,4-T	293
$\varDelta^1$-Pyrroline-2-carboxylic acid hydrochloride	A	Tetrahydrofuran-H₂O at pH 4·5	10% Pd/C	DL-Proline-2-T	293
3,4-Dehydroproline	A	—	Pt	DL-Proline-3,4-T	304
N,O-Ditosyl-allo-hydroxy-L-prolinol tetrahydropyranyl ether	LiAlH₃T	—	—	trans-L-Proline-4-T	127
N,O-Ditosyl-hydroxy-L-prolinol tetrahydropyranyl ether	LiAlH₃T	—	—	cis-L-Proline-4-T	127
Formyl-N-benzoyl-glycine ethyl ester	Redn.	Al/Hg in THO	—	DL-Serine-2,3-T	300
3,5-diiodo-L-thyronine	B	NaOH	Raney Ni	L-Thyronine-3,5-T	284 301
2-Acetylamino-4-(p-methoxyphenyl)but-3-enoic acid	A	Dioxan	Pt	DL-Tyrosine-$\beta\gamma$-T (and thyroxine by synthesis)	302
3-Iodo-L-tyrosine	B	aq. Ethanol	Pd/CaCO₃	L-Tyrosine-3-T	293
3,5-Di-iodo-L-tyrosine	B	aq. Ethanol	Pd/CaCO₃	L-Tyrosine-3,5-T and 3-iodo-L-tyrosine-5-T	293
3,5-Di-iodo-L-tyrosine	B	NaOH	Raney Ni	L-Tyrosine-3,5-T and 3-iodo-L-tyrosine-5-T	301
DL-5-Bromotrypto-phan	B	aq. Ethanol	Pd/CaCO₃	DL-Tryptophan-5-T	293
2-Phenyl-4-isopropyl-idene-oxazol-5-one	A	Tetrahydrofuran	Pt	DL-Valine-$\alpha\beta$-T	303

Method A—Hydrogenation with tritium or tritium–hydrogen mixtures.
Method B—Halogen replacement with tritium or tritium–hydrogen mixtures.

4. Carbohydrates and Polyhydric Alcohols

Specifically labelled carbohydrates and polyhydric alcohols are best prepared by the reduction of keto- (ketoses) or aldehydo- (aldoses) sugars with tritiated lithium or sodium borohydrides.

Ethylene glycol may be readily prepared from hydroxyacetalde-hyde, by reduction with tritiated sodium borohydride[40] (4.67):

$$HO \cdot CH_2 \cdot CHO \rightarrow HO \cdot CH_2 \cdot CHT \cdot OH$$

$$\dots \dots (4.67)$$

The three-carbon polyhydric alcohol glycerol is labelled on carbon-2 by reduction of dihydroxyacetone with lithium borohydride-T in pyridine[40] (4.68)

$$
\begin{array}{ccc}
CH_2 \cdot OH & & CH_2 \cdot OH \\
| & & | \\
CO & + \ LiBH_3T \rightarrow & CT \cdot OH \\
| & & | \\
CH_2 \cdot OH & & CH_2 \cdot OH
\end{array}
$$

$$\dots \dots (4.68)$$

or on carbon-1 (3) by the reduction of D-glyceraldehyde with sodium borohydride[305] (4.69)

$$
\begin{array}{ccc}
CHO & & CHT \cdot OH \\
| & & | \\
CH \cdot OH & + \ NaBH_3T \rightarrow & CH \cdot OH \\
| & & | \\
CH_2 \cdot OH & & CH_2 \cdot OH
\end{array}
$$

$$\dots \dots (4.69)$$

In a similar manner the reduction of aldonic lactones with lithium borotritide in pyridine solution yields the aldoses-1-T. In addition small amounts of the fully reduced alditols-1-T are formed. The use of pyridine suppresses the decomposition rate of the borotritide and minimizes the further reaction to the alditol[306]; for example, in the preparation of α-D-glucose-1-T from D-glucono-δ-lactone (4.70):

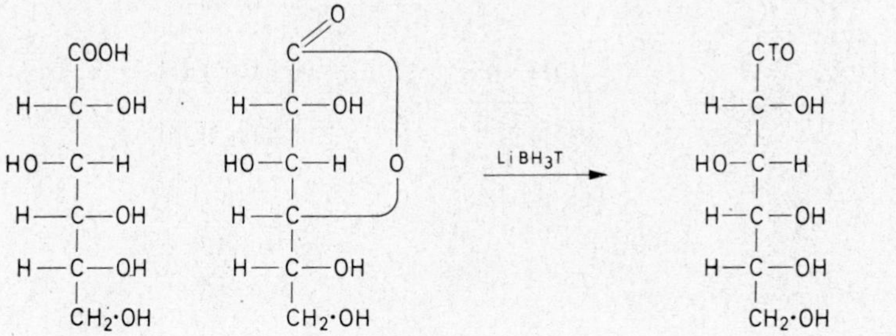

D- gluconic acid   D- glucono-lactone   α - D - glucose -1- T

$$\dots \dots (4.70)$$

The yield of the aldose-1-T is variable and depends upon the lactone used. Some typical figures obtained by Isbell and colleagues[307] are given in Table 4.27. The specific activity of the products is dependent upon the specific activity of the lithium borotritide used.

TABLE 4.27

Yields of Aldoses-1-T and Alditols-1-T Obtained by Reducing Aldonic Lactones with Lithium Borotritide in Pyridine

Lactone	Aldose-1-T	Yield %	Alditol-1-T	Yield %
D-Arabono-γ-	β-D-Arabinose	17·3	D-Arabinitol	8·3
D-Xylono-γ-	α-D-Xylose	35·7	D-Xylitol	4·2
D-Ribono-γ-	D-Ribose	8·7	D-Ribitol	3·7
D-Glucono-δ-	α-D-Glucose	52·8	D-Glucitol	0·6
D-Galactono-γ-	α-D-Galactose	25·2	D-galactitol	7·6
D-Mannono-γ-	α-D-Mannose	19·2	D-Mannitol	1·6
Maltobiono-δ-	β-Maltose (hydrate)	44·4	Maltitol	—
Lactobiono-δ-	α-Lactose (hydrate)	50·9	Lactitol	0·2
L-Rhamnono-γ-	α-L-Rhamnose (hydrate)	21·4	L-Rhamnitol	1·3

Although the alditols are a side-product in the preparation of the aldoses-1-T, the same reaction (that is, reduction of aldoses, aldonic lactones or ketoses) can be used for their preparation. Best yields are obtained when tetrahydrofuran is used as a solvent for the lithium borotritide[307] (4.71):

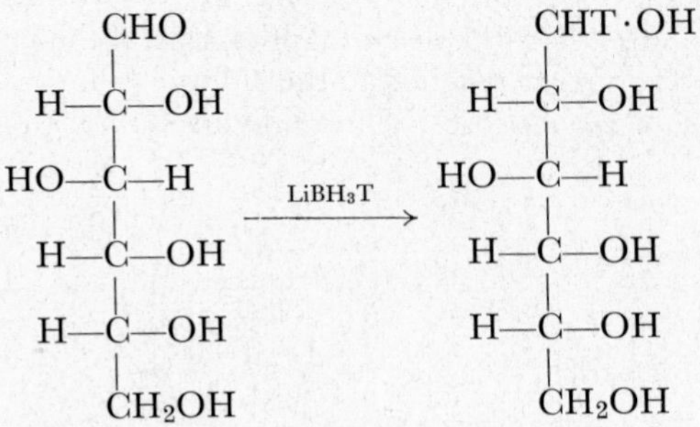

$$\text{α-D-Glucose} \xrightarrow{\text{LiBH}_3\text{T}} \text{α-D-Glucitol-1-T}$$

. . . . (4.71)

It is interesting to note that the alditol-1-T obtained by the reduction of the aldonic lactone (4.72) has twice the specific activity of that obtained by the reduction of the aldose (4.71).

Alditols labelled on carbon atom 2 with tritium can be prepared by the reduction of the corresponding ketose with lithium borotritide in

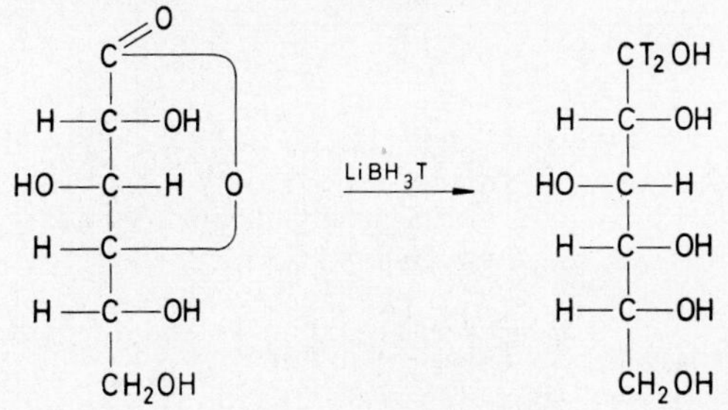

$$
\begin{array}{ccc}
\underset{\displaystyle \text{C}}{\overset{\displaystyle \text{O}}{\|}} & & \text{CT}_2\text{OH} \\
\text{H—C—OH} & & \text{H—C—OH} \\
\text{HO—C—H} \quad \text{O} & \xrightarrow{\text{LiBH}_3\text{T}} & \text{HO—C—H} \\
\text{H—C} & & \text{H—C—OH} \\
\text{H—C—OH} & & \text{H—C—OH} \\
\text{CH}_2\text{OH} & & \text{CH}_2\text{OH}
\end{array}
$$

$$\cdots \cdots \quad (4.72)$$

tetrahydrofuran. In this case a mixture of epimeric pairs is formed which are usually separated by fractional crystallization[307] (4.73):

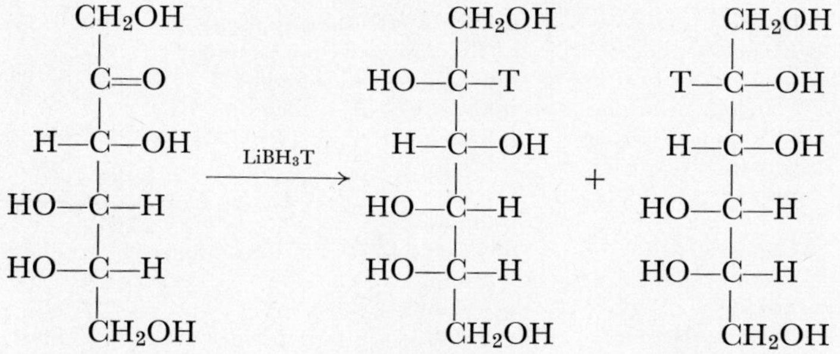

$$
\begin{array}{ccc}
\text{CH}_2\text{OH} & \text{CH}_2\text{OH} & \text{CH}_2\text{OH} \\
\text{C}=\text{O} & \text{HO—C—T} & \text{T—C—OH} \\
\text{H—C—OH} \xrightarrow{\text{LiBH}_3\text{T}} & \text{H—C—OH} \quad + & \text{H—C—OH} \\
\text{HO—C—H} & \text{HO—C—H} & \text{HO—C—H} \\
\text{HO—C—H} & \text{HO—C—H} & \text{HO—C—H} \\
\text{CH}_2\text{OH} & \text{CH}_2\text{OH} & \text{CH}_2\text{OH} \\
\text{L-Sorbose} & \text{L-Gulitol-2-T} & \text{L-Iditol-2-T}
\end{array}
$$

$$\cdots \cdots \quad (4.73)$$

The yields of alditols-T by reduction of the aldoses in anhydrous tetrahydrofuran are usually higher than by reduction of the corresponding lactones. Some results obtained by Isbell and colleagues[307] are shown in Table 4.28.

Aldoses-1-T can also be prepared by the reduction of the aldonic lactone with sodium amalgam in tritiated water as used for the preparation of 2-deoxy-D-glucose-1-T for example[117]. This procedure although suitable for low specific activity products is not as convenient as the borotritide procedure for the preparation of aldoses-1-T at very high specific activity.

TABLE 4.28

Yields of Alditols-T by reduction of Aldoses, Aldonic Lactones and Ketoses with
Lithium Borotritide in Tetrahydrofuran

Starting compound	Alditol-T	Yield %
D-Arabinose	D-Arabinitol-1-T	94
D-Arabono-γ-lactone	D-Arabinitol-1-T	79·2
D-Fructose	D-Mannitol-2(5)-T; D-Glucitol-2-T	43·2; 42·1
D-Galactose	D-Galactitol-1-T	90
D-Galactono-γ-lactone	D-Galactitol-1-T	71·5
D-Glucose	D-Glucitol-1-T	81
D-Glucono-δ-lactone	D-Glucitol-1-T	70·8
D-Glucono-γ-lactone	D-Glucitol-1-T	70·3
D-Gluco-heptulose	D-Glycero-D-gluco-heptitol-2-T	22·6
	D-Glycero-D-ido-heptitol-2-T	32·1
D-Glycero-D-gulo-heptono-γ-lactone	D-Glycero-D-gulo-heptitol-1-T	67·4
D-Gulono-γ-lactone	L-Glucitol-1-T (D-Glucitol-6-T)	66·6
Lactobiono-γ-lactone	4-O-D-Galactopyranosyl-D-Glucitol-1-T	61·3
D-Lyxose	D-Lyxitol-1-T (D-Arabinitol-5-T)	71
D-Manno-heptulose	D-Glycero-D-galacto-heptitol-2-T	33·2
	D-Glycero-D-talo-heptitol-2-T	60·0
D-Mannono-γ-lactone	D-Mannitol-1-T (D-Mannitol-6-T)	76·6
L-Rhamnono-γ-lactone	L-Rhamnitol-1-T	75·5
D-Ribose	D-Ribitol-1-T	80
L-Sorbose	L-Gulitol-2-T	27·9
	L-Iditol-2(5)-T	—
D-Tagatose	D-Galactitol-2-T; D-Talitol-2-T	22·9; 59·5
D-Talose	D-Talitol-1-T	67
D-Xylose	D-Xylitol-1-T	86
D-Xylono-γ-lactone	D-Xylitol-1-T	80

When sugars labelled in other positions are required reduction of
isopropylidene derivatives is often employed. Some examples are the
preparation of D-glucose-6-T from 1,2-O-isopropylidene-D-glu-
curono-6,3-lactone (4.74), α-D-xylose-5-T from 5-aldo-1,2-O-iso-
propylidene-D-xylopentofuranose (4.75) and D-mannitol-1-T from
2,3,5,6-di-O-isopropylidene-D-mannofuranose[308] (4.76).

The monoacetone-D-glucuronolactone (4.74) may also be reduced
with sodium borotritide to yield (after hydrolysis) D-glucose-6-T[309],
but lithium borohydride-T is normally used as it is easier to prepare
this metal hydride at high specific activity.

D-Glucose-4-T and D-galactose-4-T may be prepared by the reduc-

162

tion of di-O-isopropylidene-4-keto-D-glucose dimethyl acetal with lithium aluminium tritide[310] (4.77) (lithium borotritide would also be suitable) which gives a mixture of the two products. These are separated by paper chromatography.

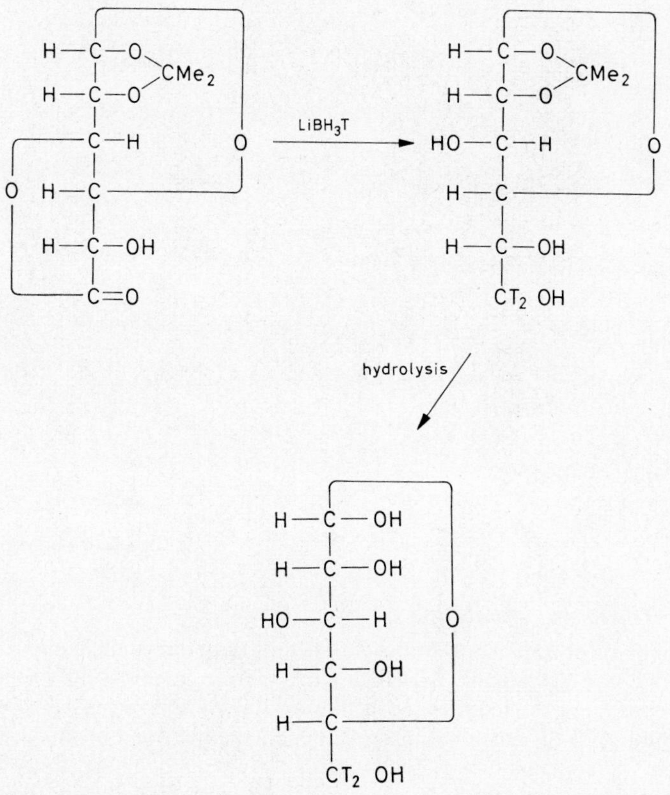

. . . . (4.74)

The reduction of methyl-2,3,6-tri-O-methyl-4-keto-D-glucopyrano-side with sodium borotritide may also be used as a method for the preparation of glucose-4-T[311], but in this reaction it is reported that some of the tritium is also incorporated into position-6.

The specificity of the tritium label and its stability in these types of compounds are discussed in Chapters 5 and 6 respectively.

163

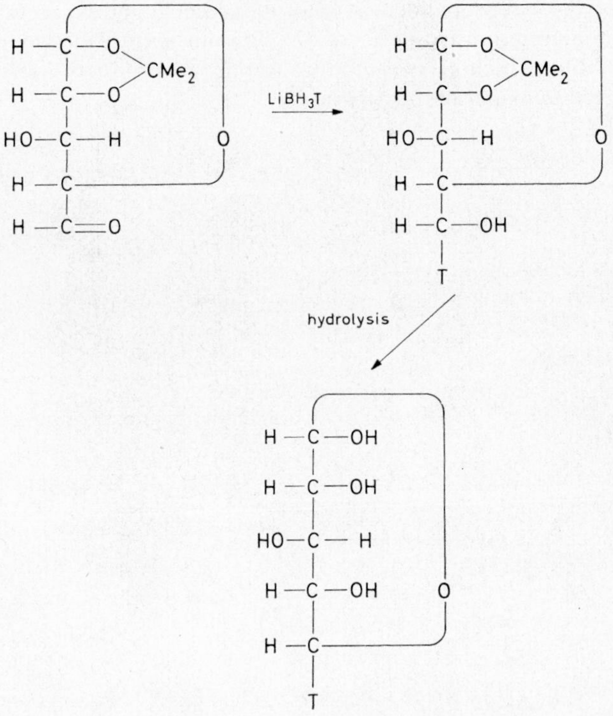

$$\ldots \ldots (4.75)$$

5. *Heterocyclic Compounds*

The most important and useful groups of heterocyclic compounds which are specifically labelled with tritium include the purines, pyrimidines, nucleosides, pyridines and a number of miscellaneous compounds of biological interest, which are included in this discussion.

The three principal reactions involved in the labelling of heterocyclic compounds are:

1. Halogen–tritium exchange of suitable halogenated intermediates.
2. Intramolecular migration of a tritium atom from a labile position into a non-labile position.
3. The reduction of compounds in tritiated solvents.

1. *Halogen–tritium exchange*—There is little published information on the use of catalytic halogen–tritium exchange reactions for the preparation of purines, pyrimidines or nucleosides, although such

LiBH3T
hydrolysis

. . . . (4.76)

(i)
LiAlH3T
(ii)
Hydrolysis
D - Glucose-4 - T
D - Galactose-4 - T

. . . . (4.77)

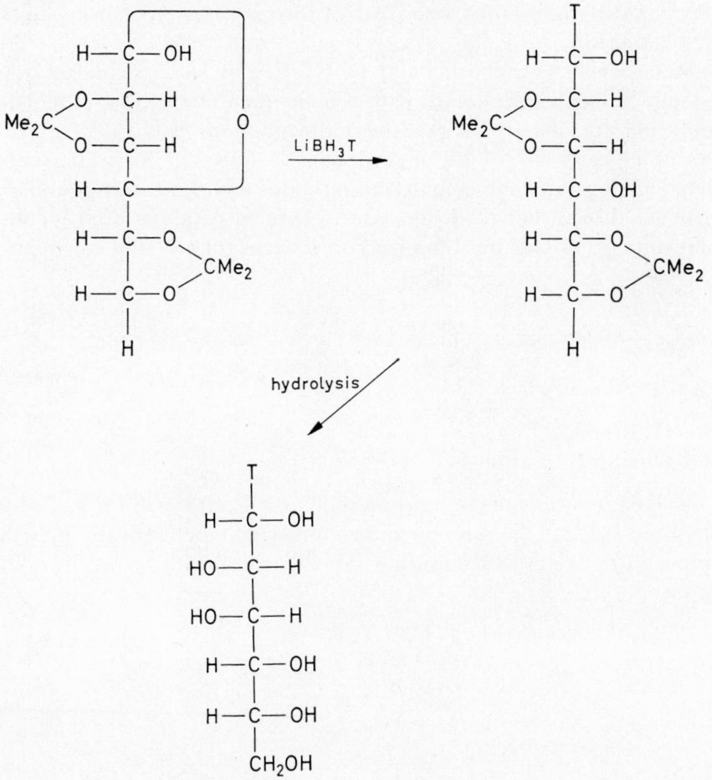

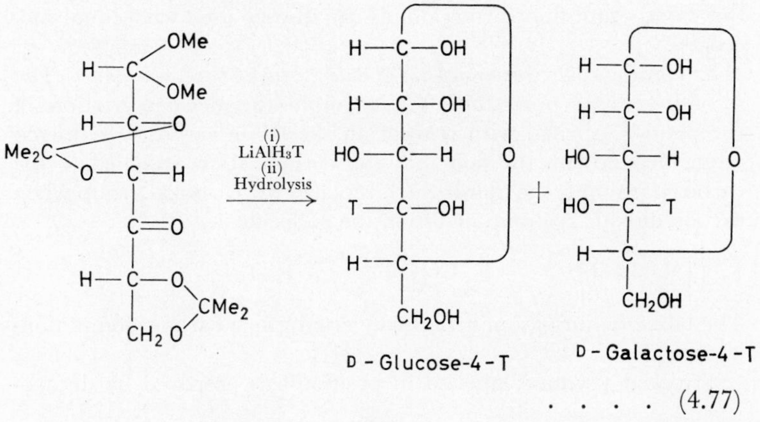

reactions are frequently described for the preparation of amino acids (for example).

Heterocyclic compounds may be labelled by catalytic dehalogenation of halogen compounds with tritium gas. The tritium enters the molecule specifically where the halogen atom is displaced. For example uracil-5-T (4.78) or uridine-5-T (4.79) can be prepared by dehalogenation of the corresponding iodo- or bromo-compounds in aqueous dioxan with tritium gas[40]. Typical catalysts used include platinum or palladium supported on charcoal or calcium carbonate.

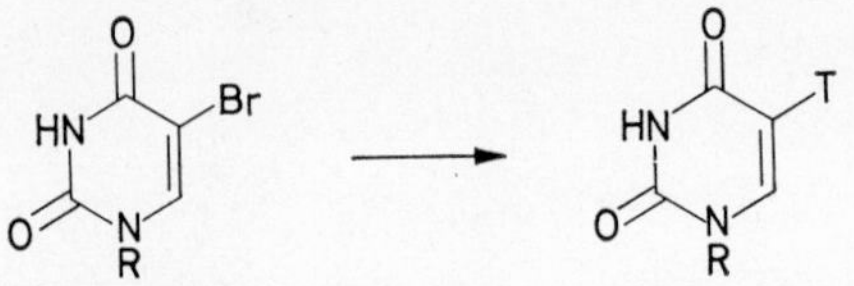

R = H; uracil-5-T (4.78)
R = -D-ribose; uridine-5-T (4.79)

Dehalogenation of 5-chloromethyl uracil with tritium gas gives thymine-*methyl*-T[251] which can be converted biochemically into the important nucleoside thymidine, labelled specifically in the 5-methyl group (4.80):

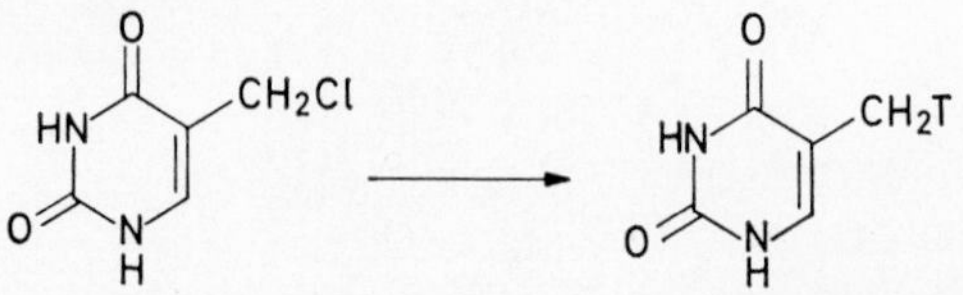

. . . . (4.80)

Iodo- and bromo-compounds are normally used as intermediates but chloro- and fluoro-compounds can also be used with equal success[312].

2. *Intramolecular conversion of labile tritium into non-labile*—The second general procedure, for example the decarboxylation of compounds labelled with tritium on the labile carboxyl hydrogen atom, depends on the fact that the tritium atom attached to the carboxyl group is the atom which replaces the carboxyl group when carbon dioxide is eliminated from the molecule (4.81).

$$R \cdot COOH + THO \rightarrow R \cdot COOT \xrightarrow{-CO_2} R \cdot T \quad . \quad . \quad . \quad . \quad (4.81)$$

The labile tritium atom is thus converted into a carbon-bound non-labile one.

Tritiated thymine labelled in position-6 is prepared by decarboxylation of the corresponding 6-carboxylic acid. In this example decarboxylation is difficult and is normally aided by mixing the compound with copper powder before heating at about $305° C$[313] (4.82).

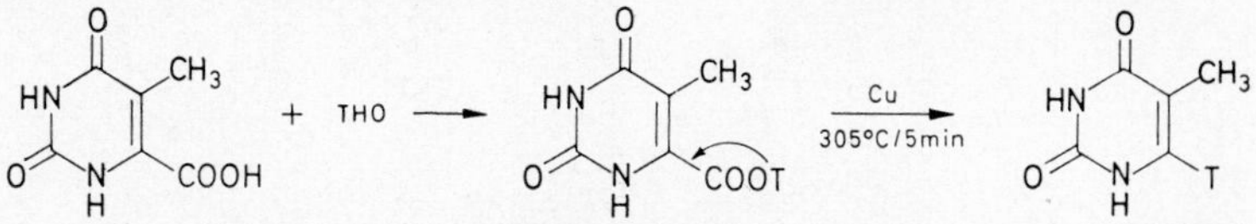

. . . . (4.82)

This reaction is particularly useful for the preparation of the 5-halogenated tritiated pyrimidines, where the halogen atoms facilitate the decarboxylation process.

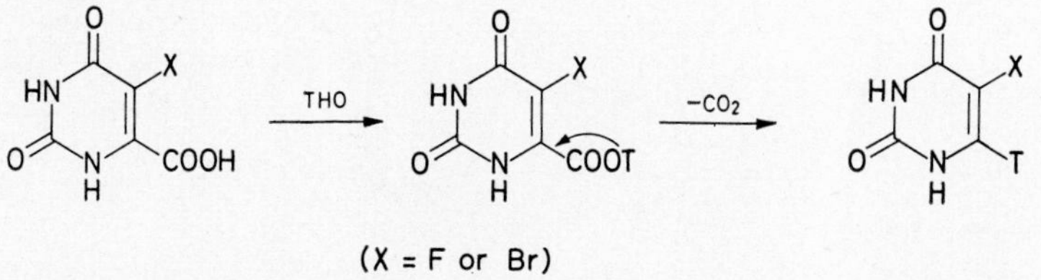

(X = F or Br)

. . . . (4.83)

5-Fluorouracil-6-T[40] and 5-bromouracil-6-T[314] are readily prepared by the decarboxylation of the corresponding tritiated carboxyl compounds (4.83). However, 5-iodouracil-6-T cannot be made successfully by this method[40] because the carbon–iodine bond of 5-iodo-orotic acid-T breaks at the high temperature required for decarboxylation forming uracil-6-T. 5-Iodouracil-6-T is therefore best prepared by direct iodination of uracil-6-T.

The carboxyl hydrogen atom is usually labelled by warming the compound in tritiated water followed by removal of the solvent by distillation *in vacuo*, prior to decarboxylation. As an alternative method, tritium gas can be used; in this case the compound is suspended or dissolved in a non-hydroxylic solvent such as dioxan, and stirred for several hours. To increase the rate of exchange a mild catalyst such as rhodium on alumina may be used as for example in the preparation of N-methyl pyrrole[315] (4.84):

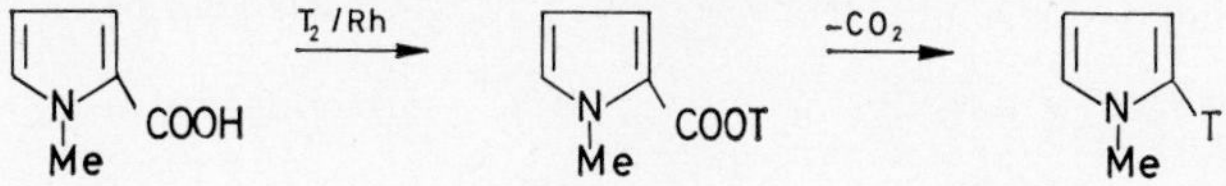

. . . . (4.84)

The decarboxylation procedure is used for the preparation of tritiated phenothiazines labelled in the 5-position[316] (4.85).

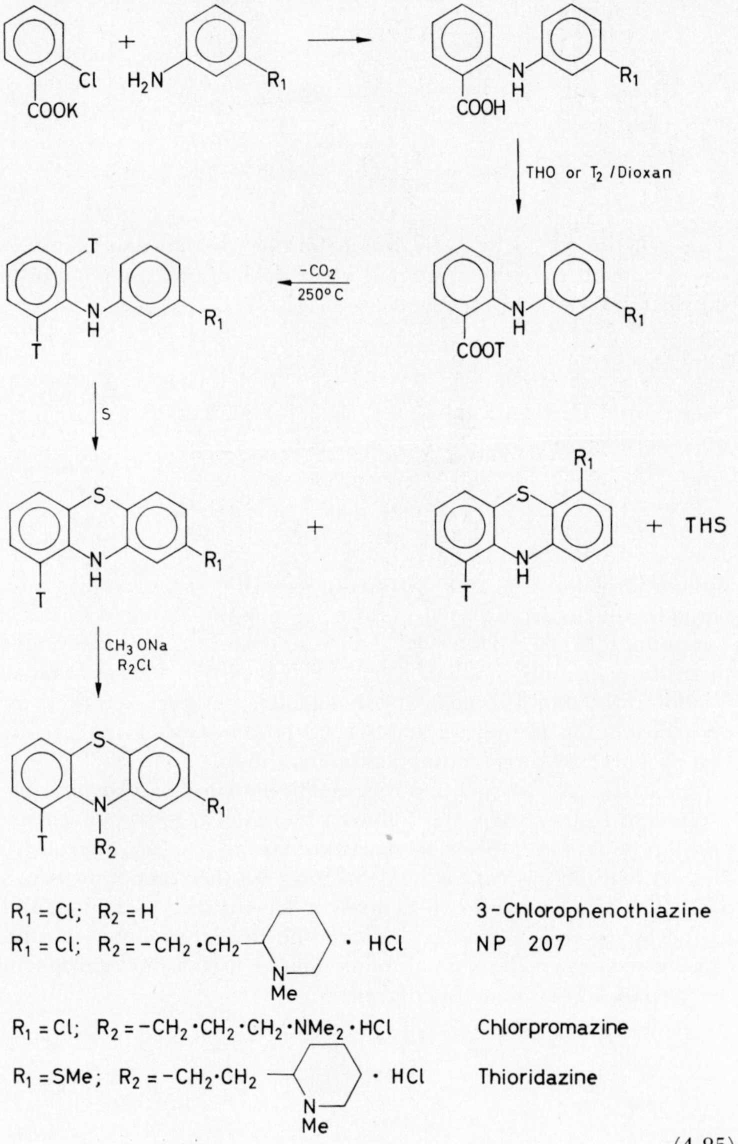

$R_1 = Cl; \quad R_2 = H$ 3-Chlorophenothiazine

$R_1 = Cl; \quad R_2 = -CH_2 \cdot CH_2 -$ [piperidine ring, N-Me] $\cdot HCl$ NP 207

$R_1 = Cl; \quad R_2 = -CH_2 \cdot CH_2 \cdot CH_2 \cdot NMe_2 \cdot HCl$ Chlorpromazine

$R_1 = SMe; \quad R_2 = -CH_2 \cdot CH_2 -$ [piperidine ring, N-Me] $\cdot HCl$ Thioridazine

$$. . . . (4.85)$$

168

3. *Reduction of compounds in tritiated solvents*—A most useful example of this type of reaction is the preparation of the pyridine nucleotides labelled in position-4 of the pyridine ring. For example, nicotinamide-adenine-dinucleotide is labelled by reduction with sodium hydro-sulphite in tritiated water, followed by biochemical oxidation with alcohol dehydrogenase [317]. The use of cyanide in tritiated water which gives rise to the equilibria (4.86) has also been employed for the labelling of NAD [318, 319].

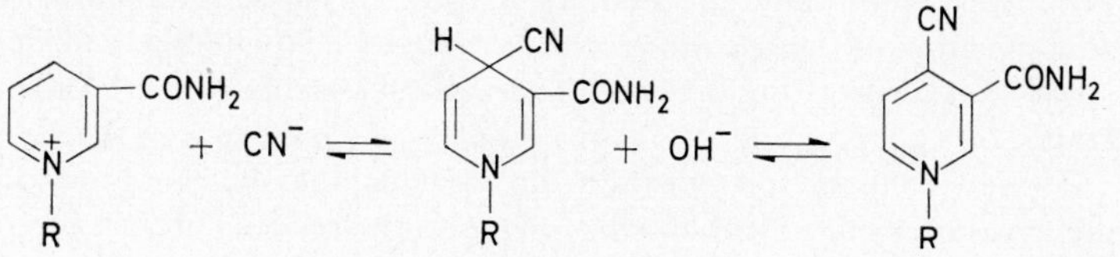

$$\ldots \ldots (4.86)$$

The trinucleotide (NADP) may be labelled in a similar manner.

Since both the hydrosulphite and KCN tritiation procedures are carried out under basic conditions, some labelling in the 2-position also occurs. Alternative methods for labelling NAD (DPN) or NADP (TPN) by reduction with tritiated sodium borohydride are described by Chaykin [319a].

6. *Steroids*

The biochemical importance of steroid hormones has resulted in much attention being given to their labelling. For many *in vivo* experiments physiological doses are required and the tritiated steroids are therefore normally required at exceptionally high specific activities. The methods described enable this to be accomplished.

For those readers who wish to refresh their memory with regard to the numbering of the steroid rings, the basic steroid skeleton with a cholesterol side-chain is shown in (4.87):

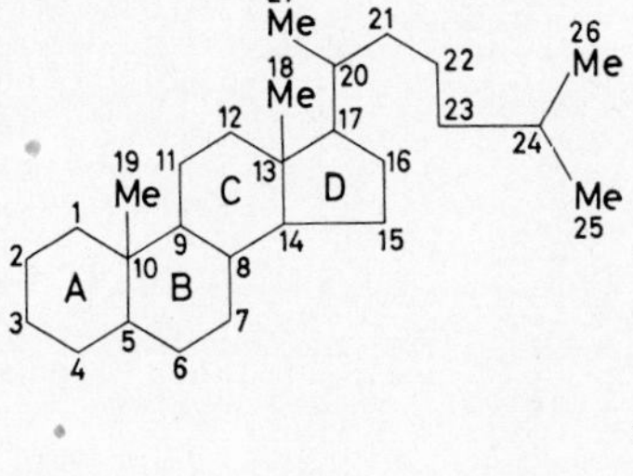

$$\ldots \ldots (4.87)$$

A dotted or broken line is used to denote the α-configuration for the attachment of atoms or groups to the nucleus, i.e., the atom or group lies behind the general plane of the ring system. A solid line denotes the β-configuration where the atom or group lies in front of the plane[320].

Specifically tritiated steroid hormones are prepared by the catalytic halogen–tritium exchange of suitable halogenated intermediates and by complete or selective reduction of unsaturated precursors. Whatever method is adopted, it is most important to know the configuration of the tritium atoms introduced, i.e. whether α or β, in order to interpret intelligently the results of biochemical transformations.

Table 4.29 lists the important steroids which have been tritiated in the various positions indicated. Owing to the relative importance of this group of compounds their labelling with tritium is discussed in some detail.

TABLE 4.29

Tritium-Labelled Steroids

Starting compound	Tritiation procedure	Final product	Position of label	References
Δ¹-Aldosterone 21-acetate	Hydrogenation	Aldosterone	1α,2α	332
Δ⁴,⁶-Androstene-3,17-dione	Hydrogenation	Δ⁴-Androstene-3,17-dione	6,7 and 7	333
Δ¹,⁴-Androstene-3,17-dione	Hydrogenation	Δ⁴-Androstene-3,17-dione	1,2	324
Δ¹,⁴-Androsten-3,17-dione	Hydrogenation	Androstane-3,17-dione	1,2,4,5	324
Cholest-5-ene-3-one	NaBH₃T redn.	Cholesterol	3α	272
Cholesteryl acetate	Hydrogenation	Cholestanol acetate	5,6	253
3β-Benzoyloxy-6β-chloro-cholest-4-ene	LiAlH₃T	Cholesterol	4β	272
7α-Bromocholesteryl acetate benzoate	Dehalogenation	Cholesterol	7α	322, 335 40
7β-Bromo-6-keto-cholest-anyl acetate	Dehalogenation	Cholesterol	7α and 7β	323
3β-Hydroxychol-5-enic acid	Anodic synthesis	Cholesterol	24,25	328
		Cholesterol	3α,4α,4β,6	334
Prednisolone (and bis-methylenedioxy derivative)	Hydrogenation	Cortisol	1α,2α	336
		Corticosterone	1α,2α	336
		Cortisone	1α,2α	336
Prednisone	Hydrogenation	Cortisone	1α, 2α	40
Δ⁶-Dehydrocortisol	Hydrogenation	Cortisol	6,7	255
Cymarin	Reduction with NaBH₃T	Cymarol	19	337
		Cholic acid	6α,6β,7β,8β	334
		Chenodeoxycholic acid	6α,6β,7β,8β	334
Dexamethasone-21-acetate	Pd/C/T₂ then SeO₂ in pyridine	Dexamethasone	1,2,4,	338
7α-Bromodehydroepi-androsterone	Dehalogenation	Dehydroepiandrosterone	7α	40
Δ⁵-Cholestene-3,22-dione	NaBH₃T	22-Ketocholesterol	3α,3β (mixed isomers)	159
Lanostadiene-3-one	KOH/THO	Lanostadiene-3-one	2	339

170

TABLE 4.29 (*continued*)

Starting compound	Tritiation procedure	Final product	Position of label	References
Lanostadiene-3-one	LiAlH$_3$T	Lanosterol	3	339
Lanostadiene-3-one-2-T	Reduction	Lanosterol	2	339
17α-Acetoxy-6α-methyl pregna-1,4-diene-3,20-dione	Hydrogenation	Medroxyprogesterone	1α,2α	346
		Megesterol acetate	1α,2α	346
2,4-Di-iodo-oestradiol	Dehalogenation	Oestradiol	2,4	284
Δ⁶-Oestradiol acetate	Hydrogenation	Oestradiol	6,7	342
16-Iodo-oestrone	Dehalogenation	Oestrone	16	340, 341
Δ⁶-Oestrone	Hydrogenation	Oestrone	6,7	343, 344
(3-Acetoxyderivative)		Oestradiol	6,7	343, 344
		Oestriol	6,7	343, 344
7α-Bromo-Δ⁵-pregnene-3β-ol-20-one acetate	Dehalogenation	Δ⁵-Pregnenolone	7α	345
		Progesterone	7α	345
17α-Bromoprogesterone	Dehalogenation (Zn/AcOT)	Progesterone	17α	350
Δ⁶-9β,10α-Progesterone	Reduction (Li/NH₃/THO)	9β,10α-Progesterone	4	347
		Δ⁶-Dehydroprogesterone	4	347
Pregna-11-ene-3,20-dione	Hydrogenation	Pregnane-3,20-dione	11α,12α	350
Δ⁴,⁶-Pregnadiene-3,20-dione	Hydrogenation	Progesterone	6,7 and 7	333
Δ⁻¹⁶-Pregnenolone acetate	Hydrogenation	Δ⁵-Pregnenolone	16	348
		Progesterone	16	348
Δ¹-Testosterone	Hydrogenation	Testosterone	1,2(1β)	324, (162)
Δ⁶-Testosterone acetate	Hydrogenation	Testosterone	6,7 and 7	326
Δ⁴-Androstenedione	NaBH₃T	Testosterone	17α	158
Δ⁸,²⁴-Cholestadienol	Reduction (Raney Ni)	Zymostenol	24,25	349

1. *Catalytic halogen–tritium exchange*—7α-Bromo-steroids are readily prepared by the reaction of N-bromosuccinimide (Wohl–Ziegler reaction) with the corresponding Δ⁵-3β-acetoxy or benzyloxy compounds [321] (4.88):

(R=CH₃·CO— or Ph·CO—)

. . . . (4.88)

The bromination is normally carried out in a mixture of carbon tetrachloride and petrol or hexane. It is important that the 7α-bromo-starting material should be pure and free from intermediates brominated in other positions. If this condition is not fulfilled then the tritiated steroid will contain tritium in other parts of the molecule (see Chapter 5). In this respect the 3β-benzoates are often more stable and easier to purify than the 3β-acetates; this is certainly true for cholesterol derivatives [40].

The halogen–tritium exchange reaction is usually carried out in ethyl acetate or dioxan as solvent, palladium supported on calcium carbonate as the catalyst, and carrier-free tritium gas to achieve high specific activities [322]. The maximum theoretical activity (29.12 c/mM) for the replacement of the halogen with a tritium atom is seldom achieved by this method, for reasons which are still obscure.

Raney nickel in sodium hydroxide solution may be used as the catalyst and solvent respectively, for the replacement of halogen atoms particularly in the aromatic rings of steroids, for example in the preparation of oestradiol-2,4-T [301] (4.89):

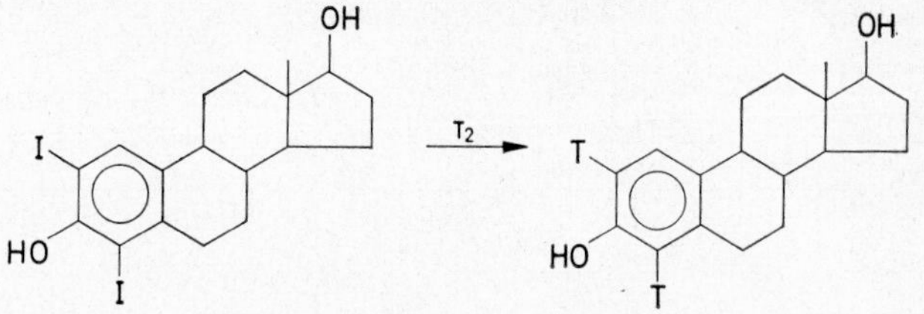

. . . . (4.89)

The stereospecific synthesis of the 7α- and 7β-tritiated steroids is exemplified by the work of Corey and Gregoriou [323] on the preparation of the 7α- and 7β-tritiated cholesterols, as outlined in the reaction scheme (4.90). 7α-Bromo-6-keto-cholesteryl-7β-T-3β-acetate, prepared by bromination of 6-keto-cholestanyl acetate with bromine in tritiated acetic acid–ether solution, is dehalogenated with zinc in acetic acid and the 6-keto group then reduced with sodium borohydride. The 6β-hydroxy-cholestanyl-7β-T acetate is dehydrated with phosphorus oxychloride in pyridine and the product treated with lithium aluminium hydride to yield cholesterol-7β-T. The cholesterol-7α-T is formed by using zinc in tritiated acetic acid for the dehalogenation stage, the subsequent reactions being the same as for the 7β-T compound. The configurations were established by the infra-red spectral analysis of the corresponding compounds labelled with deuterium.

2. *Reduction of unsaturated precursors*—The most used unsaturated

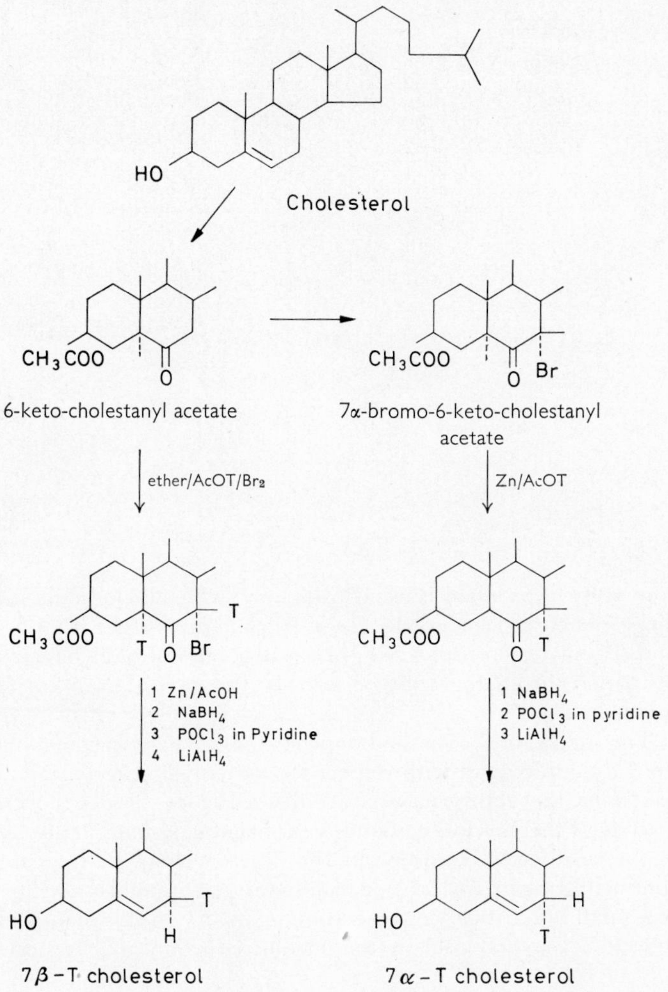
HO
Cholesterol
CH3COO
O
6-keto-cholestanyl acetate
CH3COO
O
Br
7α-bromo-6-keto-cholestanyl
acetate
ether/AcOT/Br2
Zn/AcOT
CH3COO
T
O
Br
T
CH3COO
O
T
1 Zn/AcOH
2 NaBH4
3 POCl3 in Pyridine
4 LiAlH4
1 NaBH4
2 POCl3 in pyridine
3 LiAlH4
HO
T
H
7β-T cholesterol
HO
H
T
7α-T cholesterol

. . . . (4.90)

precursors are the $\Delta^{1,4}$- and $\Delta^{4,6}$-steroid dienes. The partial hydrogenation of these steroid dienes with tritium gas is carried out in dioxan solution with a palladium on charcoal catalyst. For example, cortisol-1α,2α-T is prepared by the partial reduction of prednisolone (4.91) and cortisone-1α,2α-T from prednisone.

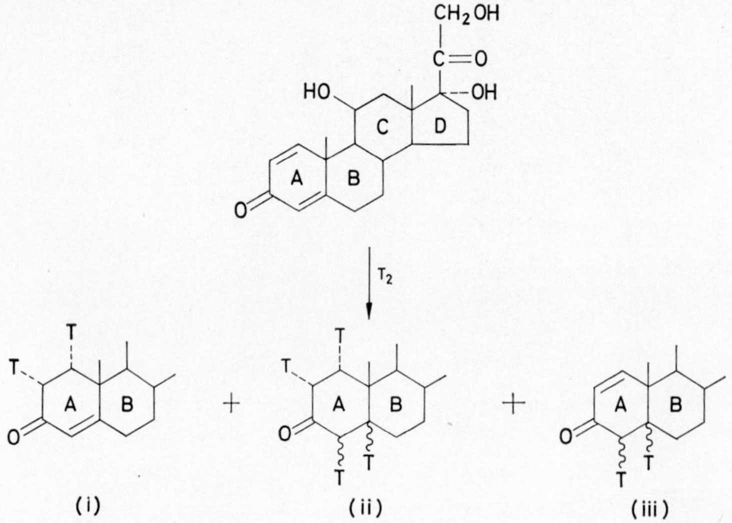

. . . . (4.91)

A mixture of products is usually obtained which include the starting diene (inactive), cortisol-1α, 2α-T (i), dihydrocortisol-1,2,4,5-T (ii) and Δ^1-dihydrocortisol-4,5-T (iii). These can normally be separated by paper chromatography [324] and by thin-layer chromatographic methods.

The success of the method depends upon the greater reactivity of the 1,2-double bond with respect to catalytic hydrogenation and of course on the ability to separate the reduction products. The reactivity of the 4,5-double bond is exceeded only marginally by that of the 6,7-double bond [325] but the difference can be increased by conducting the hydrogenation in anhydrous methanol in the presence of a small but critical concentration of alkali. In this manner testosterone-7-T is prepared by the partial reduction of Δ^6-testosterone

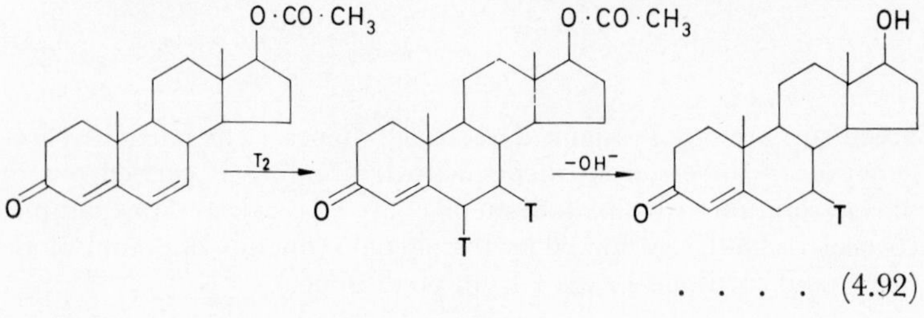

. . . . (4.92)

acetate with tritium gas [326] (4.92); the absolute configuration of the tritium atom at the 7-position, in this example, was not established. The tritium in the 6-position is lost by enolization during the alkaline hydrolysis of the testosterone-6,7-T acetate.

Tritiation of cholesterol in the 1 α- position may be achieved by the reactions shown (4.93). This has been used for the synthesis of vitamin-D$_3$-1 α-T [327].

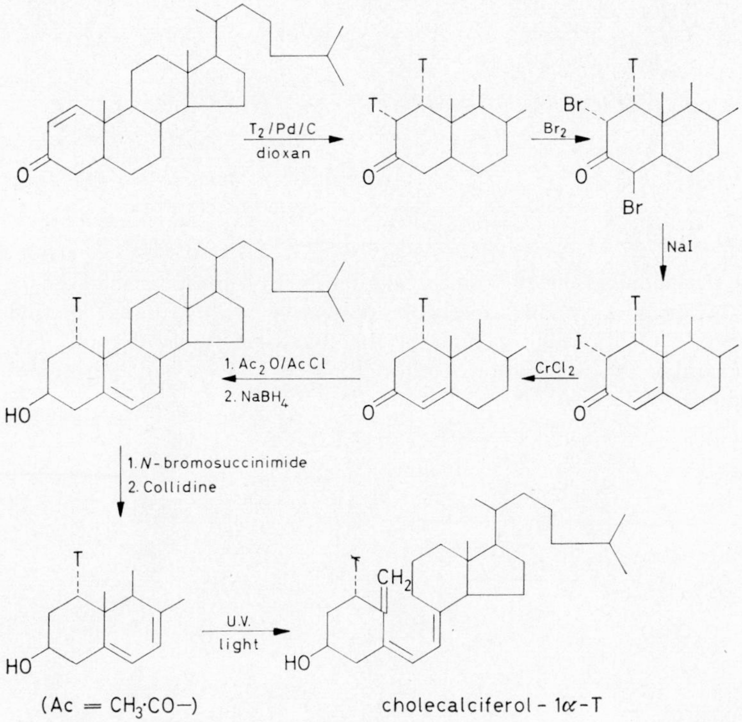

$(Ac = CH_3 \cdot CO-)$ cholecalciferol - 1 α-T

$$. \quad . \quad . \quad . \quad (4.93)$$

3. *Other methods*—Cholesterol labelled with tritium in the side-chain (positions 24 and 25) is prepared by anodic synthesis [327, 328], a rather novel reaction in the steroid field [329,329a]. A mixture of iso-valeric acid-2,3-T and 3 β-hydroxychol-5-enic acid is electrolysed yielding about 17 per cent (based on the bile acid used) of cholesterol-24,25-T (4.94):

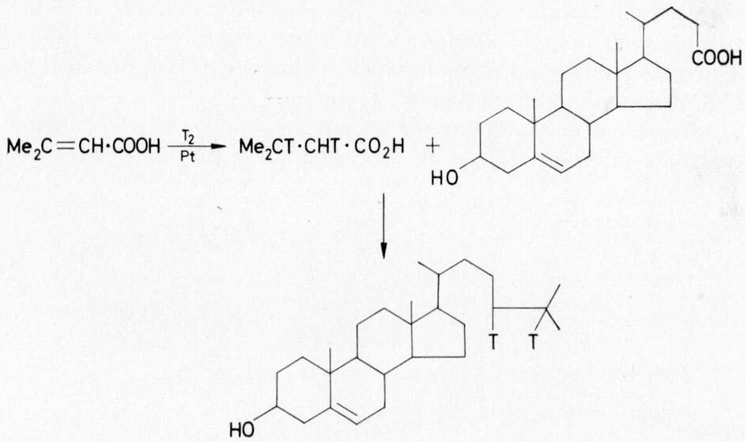

$$Me_2C=CH\cdot COOH \xrightarrow[Pt]{T_2} Me_2CT\cdot CHT\cdot CO_2H \; +$$

. . . . (4.94)

Labelling in the 19-position (angular methyl group) is achieved by alkylating a readily accessible derivative with tritiated methyl iodide or by ring opening of the 3-keto-5β,19-*cyclo*steroid. For example, the preparation of testosterone-19-T (4.95) and androstene-dione-19-T (4.96) [330].

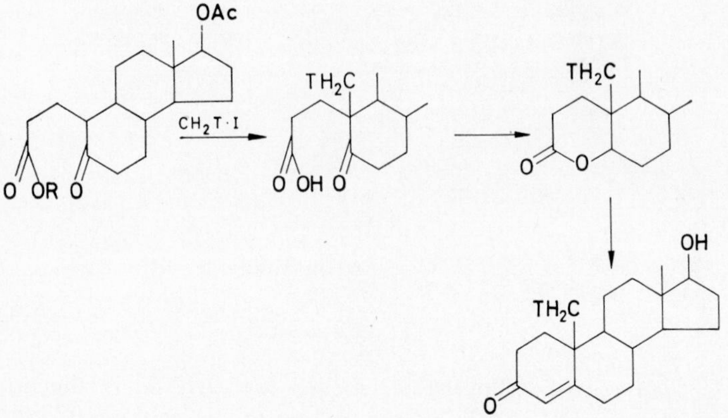

. . . . (4.95)

A short review of methods for tritiating steroids has been published by Osinski [331].

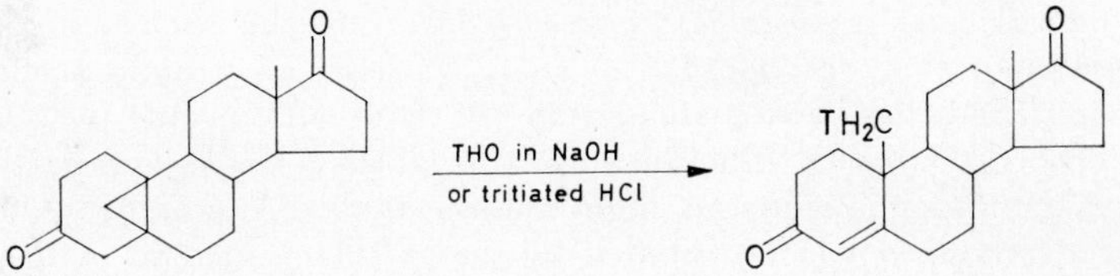

THO in NaOH
or tritiated HCl

. . . . (4.96)

7. Organometallic Compounds

In recent years the chemistry of organometallic compounds has interested many research workers and there is now a growing interest in the applications of tritiated organometallic compounds. Their present use is primarily as intermediates in the synthesis of tritiated organic compounds.

1. *Tritiated Grignard reagents*—There is no need to dilate on the possible uses of tritiated Grignard reagent in organic syntheses, as there are many reviews and books on the uses of these unlabelled reagents.

One example however, is the preparation of a synthetic oestrogen by the reaction of tritium-labelled ethylmagnesium bromide with 3,4-di-*p*-anisyl-4-oxo-*n*-butane (4.97), followed by dehydration of the tertiary tritiated alcohol to yield the synthetic oestrogen 3,4-di-*p*-anisyl-hex-3-ene-2-T[268].

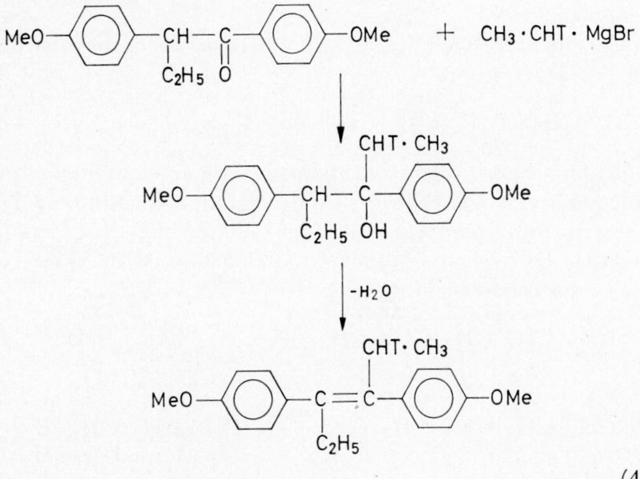

. . . (4.97)

2. *Tritiated organoboron compounds*—Recently the application of hydroboration reactions[351] for the synthesis of tritium-labelled compounds has been evaluated[148–150]. Examples include the conversion of tritiated diborane into the labelled trialkylboranes by reaction with olefines in high-boiling ethers. Alternatively, the trialkylboranes can be tritiated by the Wilzbach method, with its associated purification problems, or by catalytic exchange with tritium gas at room temperature, which would appear to be more satisfactory[148]. Tritiated diborane may be prepared by direct exchange with tritium gas[352] or more usually prepared *in situ* by the reaction of boron trifluoride etherate with sodium borotritide. The diborane is evolved quantitatively in accordance with the amount of sodium borotritide used (4.98):

$$3NaBT_4 + 4BF_3 \cdot OEt_2 \rightarrow 2B_2T_6 + 3NaBF_4 \qquad \ldots \quad (4.98)$$

The olefin is added to the diborane-T in diglyme or triglyme (dimethyl ether of di- and tri-ethylene glycols respectively). Addition of the boron–tritium atoms to the olefin occurs and appears to involve a simple 4-centre *cis*-addition mechanism[353] (4.99):

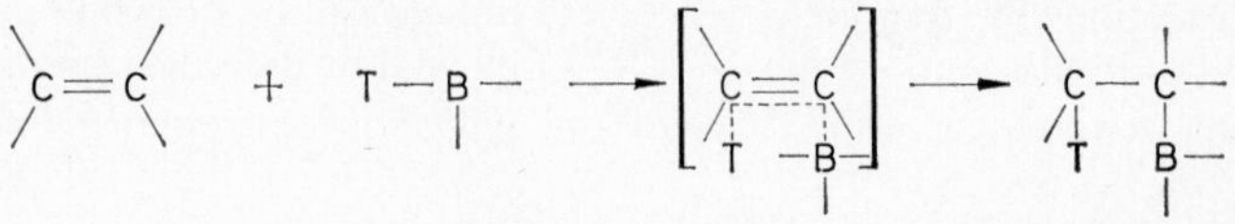

$$\ldots \quad (4.99)$$

Six molecules of the olefin react with one molecule of the diborane-T (4.100):

$$6R \cdot CH{=}CH_2 + B_2T_6 \rightarrow 2(R \cdot CHT \cdot CH_2T)_3B \quad \ldots \quad (4.100)$$

By heating the tritiated trialkylborane with an olefin higher in the homologous series than the one used to form the trialkylborane-T, one displaces the lower homologue giving a tritiated olefin. For example, by heating tri-*n*-hexylborane-T at 160–170° C with *n*-dec-1-ene, displacement occurs yielding *n*-hex-1-ene-T[148] (4.101):

$$(CH_3 \cdot CH_2 \cdot CH_2 \cdot CH_2 \cdot CH_2 \cdot CH_2)_3B + CH_3 \cdot (CH_2)_7 \cdot CH{=}CH_2$$

$$\downarrow 160°C$$

$$(CH_3 \cdot CH_2 \cdot CH_2 \cdot CH_2 \cdot CH_2 \cdot CH_2 \cdot CH_2 \cdot CH_2 \cdot CH_2 \cdot CH_2)_3B +$$
$$Me \cdot (CH_2)_3CH{=}CH_2$$
$$\ldots \quad (4.101)$$

The method is particularly useful for labelling unsaturated alicyclic hydrocarbons such as cyclohexene. Cyclohexene-T can be displaced from tricyclohexylborane-T by heating with n-dec-1-ene at 160–170° C[148]. Other methods for labelling cyclohexene with tritium are less successful[44, 189].

Specific labelling can also be achieved with acetylenic hydrocarbons. For example, the reaction of n-hex-1-yne with di-isoamylborane followed by protonation with tritiated acetic acid yields n-hex-1-ene-T. This method of labelling appears to be 100 per cent specific and in the last example all the tritium is attached to carbon-1 of the n-hexene molecule[148]. In a similar manner methyl oleate can be tritiated specifically in the 9,10-positions by the reaction of methyl stearolate with di-isoamylborane followed by protonation with acetic acid-T.

Oxidation of the tritiated trialkylboranes yields the corresponding saturated tritiated alcohol[148] (4.102):

$$(RCHT \cdot CH_2T)_3B \rightarrow 3R \cdot CHT \cdot CHT \cdot OH + B(OH)_3$$

$$\text{. . . . (4.102)}$$

Oxidation is usually effected with hydrogen peroxide in sodium hydroxide solution[354].

The many possible applications of tritiated boron compounds[351] promise to make them as useful as the Grignard reagents for the synthesis of tritium-labelled compounds.

3. *Tritiated organosilicon compounds*—Experiments with deuterium[355] have shown that silicon–hydrogen bonds are not readily labile and are somewhat analogous to carbon–hydrogen bonds. This stability is due in part to the polarization of the silicon–hydrogen bond Si^+—H^-. Isotope exchange can only take place by a mechanism which is unlikely because of the instability of nucleophilic H^-. Disregarding any radiation effects one would expect the same degree of stability to apply to the silicon–tritium bonds.

Exchange reactions between tritiated solvents and organosilicon compounds in the presence of hydrogen transfer catalysts do not appear to have been studied.

The preparation of tritiated trialkyl- or triarylsilanes may be achieved by the reduction of the corresponding chloro-compound with lithium aluminium tritide[356] (4.103):

$$R_3SiCl + LiAlH_3T \rightarrow R_3SiT \quad \text{. . . . (4.103)}$$

The triphenyl- and tri-n-propylsilanes labelled with tritium directly attached to the silicon atom are both prepared by this method[356].

The use of tritiated organosilicon compounds has yet to be explored but they would appear to have a more limited application for use in organic syntheses than the organoboron compounds.

8. *Miscellaneous Syntheses*

Under this heading are included a number of specifically labelled tritiated compounds and special methods for their preparation, which are not included in the classes already described.

1. *Polymers*—Tritiated polymers may become useful as reference compounds associated with tritium measurement and in the preparation of luminous compounds[434].

Methyl methacrylate-T which has been used as a reference source in autoradiographic efficiency determinations[357] can be prepared by converting a labile tritium atom attached to the carboxyl group of α-methylacrylic acid into a non-labile methyl tritium atom, by the reaction of the acid with diazomethane[40] (4.104):

$$CH_2{=}CMe \cdot COOH + THO \rightarrow CH_2{=}CMe \cdot CO_2T + CH_2N_2 \rightarrow$$
$$CH_2{=}CMe \cdot COOMe$$
$$. \quad . \quad . \quad . \quad (4.104)$$

If the specific activity of the tritiated ester is sufficiently high, it will polymerize by self-irradiation.

The preparation of tritiated styrene is described on page 154 and at specific activities in excess of 50 mc/mM the monomer polymerizes within a few hours if free radical scavengers are not present[40].

Tritiated polyvinyl alcohol is prepared from acetylene-T by the addition of acetic acid (which can also be tritiated on the carboxyl group), followed by polymerization of the vinyl acetate. Hydrolysis then gives the polyvinyl alcohol-T[358, 358a] (4.105):

$$. \quad . \quad . \quad (4.105)$$

180

Nylon-T is prepared by the polymerization of tritiated adipic acid with hexamethylenediamine in a manner similar to the preparation of the unlabelled polymer[40] (4.106):

$$\underset{\textit{cis-}\text{ or }\textit{trans-}\text{muconic acid}}{\text{MeOOC}\cdot\text{CH}{=}\text{CH}\cdot\text{CH}{=}\text{CH}\cdot\text{COOMe}} \xrightarrow{T_2} \text{MeOOC}\cdot\text{CHT}\cdot\text{CHT}\cdot\text{CHT}\cdot\text{CHT}\cdot\text{COOMe}$$

$$\text{NH}_2\cdot(\text{CH}_2)_6\cdot\text{NH}_2 + \text{HOOC}\cdot\text{CHT}\cdot\text{CHT}\cdot\text{CHT}\cdot\text{CHT}\cdot\text{COOH}$$

$$\downarrow$$

$$(\text{HOOC}\cdot\text{CHT}\cdot\text{CHT}\cdot\text{CHT}\cdot\text{CHT}\cdot\text{CO}\cdot\text{NH}\cdot(\text{CH}_2)_6\cdot\text{NH}\cdot\text{CO}\cdot\text{CHT}\cdot\text{CHT}\cdot\text{CHT}\cdot\text{CHT}\cdot\text{CO}\cdot\text{NH}{-})_n \quad \ldots\ldots (4.106)$$

A polymer which is used in the preparation of tritiated luminous compounds is a partially hydrogenated maleic acid-hexamethylene-diol. The tritiated material is cross-linked with hexamethylene di-isocyanate for stability[359].

The decomposition of tritiated polymers and other macromolecules is discussed in Chapter 6.

2. *Quaternization of tertiary bases*—The introduction of a tritiated methyl or ethyl group into a compound containing a tertiary nitrogen atom by forming the quaternary salt, is often a convenient way of labelling[267]. A simple example is the preparation of choline iodide-(*methyl*-T) by the quaternization of *N*-dimethylaminoethanol with tritiated methyl iodide[40] (4.107):

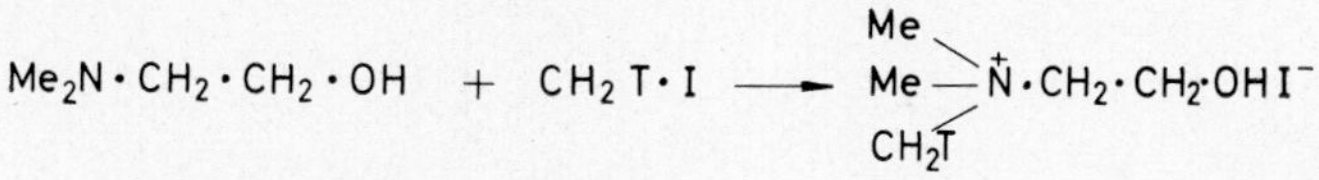

Me₂N · CH₂ · CH₂ · OH + CH₂T · I
Me
Me — N · CH₂ · CH₂ · OH I⁻
CH₂T

. . . . (4.107)

CH₃ · CONH
N
NH · CO · CH₃
CH₂T·I
CH₂T · I⁻
H₂O/HCl
H₂N
CH₂T · Cl⁻
NH₃⁺Cl⁻

. . . . (4.108)

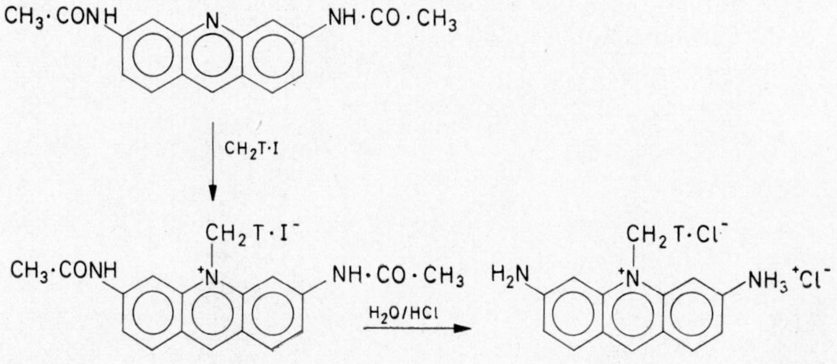

A more complex compound labelled by this simple technique is 3,6-diamino-10-methyl-T-acridinium chloride hydrochloride (acriflavin-T hydrochloride) [360] by the reactions shown (4.108):

3. *Reaction of tritiated hydrogen halides with double bonds*—When $\alpha\beta$-unsaturated α-amino acids are heated with tritiated hydriodic acid and red phosphorus, the $\alpha:\beta$-double bond is reduced giving a tritiated amino acid (4.109):

$$R \cdot CH = C \cdot COOH \xrightarrow{TI/P} R \cdot CHT \cdot CT \cdot COOH$$
$$\underset{NH \cdot CO \cdot Ph}{|} \qquad\qquad \underset{NH_2}{|} \qquad \cdots \cdots (4.109)$$

The unsaturated amino acid is normally added to the tritiated hydriodic acid prepared *in situ* from tritiated water, iodine and red phosphorus. The amino group is protected as the benzoyl or acetyl derivative which is subsequently hydrolysed during the reduction process. This reaction is widely used for the preparation of thyroxine and analogous compounds labelled in the side-chain with tritium [340, 341].

The addition of tritiated hydriodic acid to acrylic acid yields β-iodopropionic acid-T which can be converted into tritiated β-propiolactone-T [40] by the method of Westfahl and Gresham [361] (4.110):

$$CH_2 = CH \cdot COOH + TI \ \rightarrow \ CH_2 I \cdot CHT \cdot COOH \xrightarrow{Ag_2O}$$
$$\begin{array}{cc} CH_2 \cdot CHT \\ | \qquad | \\ O \!\!-\!\! C = O \end{array}$$
$$\cdots \cdots (4.110)$$

β-Propiolactone is one of the simplest known carcinogenic substances [246, 247].

The synthetic hormone hexoestrol can be labelled in positions 2 and 5 of the carbon chain as follows:

$$THO + SOCl_2 \ \rightarrow \ 2TCl + SO_2 \qquad \cdots \cdots (4.111)$$

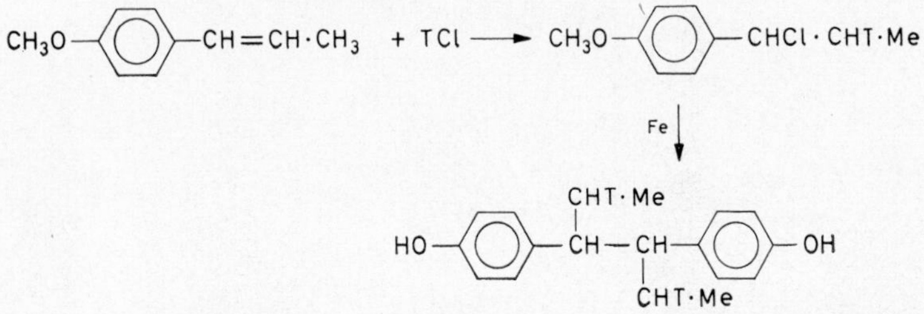

$$\cdots \cdots (4.112)$$

Tritiated hydrogen chloride, prepared from tritiated water and thionyl chloride (4.111), adds to the *p*-methoxyphenyl-prop-2-ene giving the 3-*p*-methoxyphenyl-3-chloropropane-2-T which is converted into hexoestrol by heating with iron followed by demethylation. Using tritiated water at 1 mc/ml hexoestrol at 66 μc/g is obtained[362]. The method is now of course superseded by the reduction of dienoestrol with tritium gas[234, 239].

Three other syntheses worthy of mention are the synthesis from 1,4-dihydroxybutane-T of tritiated 'myleran-T'[236] a drug used in the treatment of myeloid leukaemia, cyclophosphamide-T(endoxan)from ethyleneoxide-T[363], and *O,O*-dimethyl-5(methylcarbamoylmethyl)-phosphorodithioate from methanol-T[367].

9. *Inorganic Compounds*

At the present time there is less interest in tritiated inorganic compounds than in organic compounds, consequently much less effort has been put into devising methods for their preparation. There are several reasons for this:

1. Inorganic compounds are currently of little interest in the biological sciences which account for most of the uses of tritium compounds.
2. The chemical bond between tritium and elements other than carbon is often unstable in the sense that the tritium is very readily labilized and exchanged. There is, however, a general lack of knowledge concerning the stability of tritiated inorganic compounds.
3. Other radioisotopes are often of more practical value for inorganic chemical tracer investigations.

A review of the methods which have been applied to the preparation of a number of inorganic compounds labelled with tritium, has been published[364], but it does not discuss the relative efficiencies (or merits) of the methods described[365].

Although relatively little use is made of the tritiated metal hydrides and mixed metal hydrides in inorganic chemistry, they are of great importance and frequently used for the preparation of specifically labelled tritiated organic compounds, for example carbohydrates (see page 158). At present these are the most useful tritiated inorganic compounds (to the organic chemist) and are best prepared by heating the metal or metal hydrides in tritium gas.

Table 4.30 lists a number of these metal hydrides together with other inorganic tritium compounds.

3. BIOCHEMICAL METHODS

Biochemical methods for the preparation of carbon-14-labelled

TABLE 4.30

Tritium-Labelled Inorganic Compounds

Compound	Preparative method	References
Lithium hydride-T	$LiH + T_2 \xrightarrow{350°C} LiT + HT$	261
Lithium borohydride-T	$LiBH_4 + T_2 \xrightarrow{200°C} LiBH_3T + HT$	360, 366
Lithium aluminium hydride-T	$4LiT + AlCl_3 \rightarrow LiAlT_4 + 3LiCl$ $LiAlH_4(n,\alpha)LiAlH_3T$ (recoil)	261 384
Calcium tritide	$CaH_2 + T_2 \rightarrow CaHT + TH$	273
Sodium borohydride-T	$NaBH_4 + T_2 \xrightarrow{350°C} NaBH_3T + TH$	368
Boron hydride-T	$B_2H_6 + T_2 \xrightarrow{55°C} B_2H_5T + HT$	352
	$3NaBH_3T + 4BF_3 \rightarrow 2B_2H_5T + 3NaBF_4$	353
Hydrogen cyanide-T	$3T_2O$ (vapour) $+ P(CN)_3 \rightarrow$ $3TCN + P(OH)_3$	369
Hydrogen chloride-T	$2AgCl + T_2 \xrightarrow{700°C} 2TCl + 2Ag$	370
	$T_2 + Cl_2 \xrightarrow[\text{light}]{\text{u.v.}} 2TCl$	371
	$PCl_5 + THO \rightarrow TCl$	372
	$HCl + HTSO_4 \rightarrow TCl + H_2SO_4$	373
	$T_2 = HCl \xrightarrow[860°C]{Pt} TCl$	374
Hydrogen bromide-T	$T_2 + Br_2 \xrightarrow[\text{light}]{\text{u.v.}} 2TBr$	371
Hydrogen iodide-T	$P (red) + I_2 + THO \rightarrow TI + HI$	340
Ammonia-T	$NH_3 + T_2 \rightarrow NH_2T + TH$	364, 375
	$NH_4Cl + THO \xrightarrow{Na} NH_2T$	364
	$Mg_3N_2 + 6T_2O \xrightarrow{100-150°C}$ $2NT_3 + 3Mg(OT)_2$	376
Ammonium salts	$NH_4NO_3 + t\text{-}BuOT + CHCl_3 \rightarrow$ $NH_3T \cdot NO_3$	377
Phosphorous acid-T	$H_3PO_3 + THO \rightarrow H_2TPO_3 + H_2O$	378
Hafnium hydride-T	—	383
Uranium hydride-T	$UH_3 + T_2 \rightarrow UH_2T + TH$	29, 379, 380
Titanium hydride-T	$Ti + xT_2 \rightarrow TiT_x*$	381
Zirconium hydride-T	$Zr + xT_2 \rightarrow ZrT_x*$	382

* Non-stoichiometric compounds.

compounds are well known and include the growing of various species of algae in bicarbonate-C14 solution as a source of uniformly labelled L-amino acids, and the use of photosynthetic methods for the preparation of carbon-14-labelled carbohydrates. In contrast, similar biochemical methods of labelling with tritium have not as yet proved very useful, with a few specific exceptions. The basic reasons for this are the mobility of hydrogen atoms and the hydroponic character of all biological systems. These often nullify the advantages of cheapness and high specific activity of the isotope.

The relative ease of labelling, even of complex molecules, by isotope exchange makes many of the biosynthetic methods which have been used with carbon-14 (for example) unnecessary with tritium.

In this discussion only those procedures which appear to be useful for preparing useful labelled compounds will be considered. This distinction, from the great variety of tritium compounds arising in small yield and low specific activity from research with tritium tracers is necessarily arbitrary, but must be recognized.

Classification of the methods must also be arbitrary, but helps to present a rather confusing mass of information more clearly. The following divisions are adopted:

A. Reactions catalysed by specific enzymes
   1. Using organic substrates.
   2. Using inorganic substrates.

B. Reactions in non-specific systems
   1. Using tritiated water as substrate.
   2. Using tritiated compounds as substrate.

The actual efficiency of a biosynthetic process as a labelling method is sometimes difficult to ascertain from present publications. Specific activities of substrate or product are often omitted, or are stated as counts per minute per gramme without defining the method of measurement and counting efficiency. For many investigations of course, only relative values are necessary for the interpretation of the results, but it would present a more helpful picture if absolute values were stated.

A. Reactions catalysed by specific enzymes

1. *Organic Substrates*

Tritiated compounds at high specific activity are ideal substrates for small (chemical) scale enzyme-catalysed transformations, provided the tritium atoms in the molecule of the substrate are not labilized under the biological conditions. Examples include:

(*a*) the use of renal (pig kidney) D-amino acid oxidase for the conversion of tritiated DL-amino acids into L-acids and L-oxidase (rattlesnake venom) to obtain the D-tritiated acids[385]. However, use of either of these oxidases involves the loss of tritium atoms from the α-position of α-amino acids, and in some cases from the β-position also, by an exchange mechanism[386], an interesting observation which is further discussed in Chapter 6. DL-Amino acids tritiated in the α-position only cannot therefore be converted into the L- or D- acid by this process, which is otherwise of course very useful

(*b*) a crude enzyme extract used for a specific purpose, being itself far from specific, is thymidine phosphorylase isolated from cattle liver [387] which is used for the enzymic conversion of thymine-T at high specific activity into the deoxyribonucleoside thymidine [40, 388] (4.113):

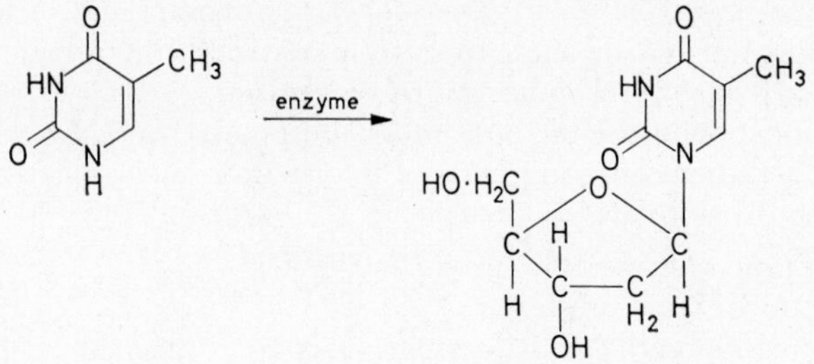

. . . . (4.113)

The enzyme *trans*-N-deoxyribosylase described by MacNutt [389], can also be used [251] although thymidine phosphorylase has the advantage of relative ease of preparation.

There is no loss of tritium from the 5- or 6-positions of the pyrimidine base by exchange during the enzyme reaction [40].

Other tritiated 2′-deoxyribonucleosides which can be prepared in this way include deoxyuridine (from uracil-5,6-T), 5-bromo- and 5-fluoro-2′-deoxyuridine (from the corresponding 5-bromo- and 5-fluorouracil-6-T) [40, 390].

This is a field of investigation where there is obviously much to be developed [391].

2. *Inorganic Substrate*

Here tritiated water is used as the substrate in conjunction with two co-enzymes of unique importance. These are the pyridine nucleotides, which have already been discussed in more detail in Chapter 2 (page 44).

In the presence of oxidases and reductases the tritium atoms may be transferred from the 4-position of the pyridine ring moiety to a specific position in the molecule of an organic compound. For example, L-lactic acid labelled specifically at carbon-2 has been prepared by the use of NADT [392]. The specific activity of the products obtained in this manner depends on the specific activity of the tritiated water used (i) for labelling the co-enzymes directly or (ii) for labelling the hydrogen positions used in the hydrogen transfer process.

For high specific activity compounds the method is less suitable than method A1, due to the radiation effects which are likely at high tritium isotopic abundance, including damage to the co-enzymes, and the greater hazards associated with the manipulation of tritiated water at very high isotopic abundance.

B. Reactions in Non-specific Systems

1. *Using Tritiated Water as Substrate*

Any organism grown in tritiated water will eventually incorporate some tritium into all its hydrogen-containing compounds. For example, the naturally occurring purines and pyrimidines, adenine, guanine, cytosine and uracil, were among the first compounds to be labelled with tritium by growing yeast on a substrate containing tritiated water[393]. The isolated nucleic acid-T was hydrolysed into the four bases by 70 per cent perchloric acid. In this case the levels of activity were too low to yield useful products, and served only to demonstrate the biosynthesis of tritiated compounds. Now, of course, no one would prepare these tritiated bases biosynthetically when much simpler chemical methods are available (*vide supra*).

The two classes of compounds attracting most attention are the carbohydrates and fatty acids. The isolation and separation of tritiated amino acids from algal protein has not been published.

Carbohydrates—The overall empirical equation for the photosynthetic formation of polysaccharides (4.114), suggests the immediate or ultimate use of the hydrogen atoms of water molecules as the reducing agent.

$$xCO_2 + yH_2O \rightarrow C_xH_{2y}O_x + xO_2 \qquad \ldots \quad (4.114)$$

The rate of incorporation of tritium into the carbohydrates can be conveniently followed by double isotope experiments with carbon-14[394]. For example, results obtained by growing *Chlorella* in tritiated water at 7 mc/ml containing carbon-14 bicarbonate, showed that the tritiated glucose and fructose (isolated by paper chromatography) to be of the same specific activity.

An entirely academic approach to photosynthetic studies with tritiated water is provided by the work of Calvin and colleagues[395], using tritiated water at 1 c/ml and *Chlorella pyrenoidosa*. The algae were grown over short times (minutes) only, and Calvin points out the difficulties of interpreting results of such biochemical studies with tritium because of non-specific exchange reactions.

Sucrose, fructose and glucose generally labelled with tritium at low specific activity (about 1 $\mu c/mM$) are obtained by circulating tritiated water vapour (from tritiated water at 10 mc/ml) around the leaves of the Soybean plant[396]. Even the use of tritium gas has been tried. Earlier experiments by Cline[297] showed that there was very little incorporation of tritium into non-labile hydrogen positions of compounds when leaves of *Phaseolus vulgaris* (red kidney bean) were exposed to tritium gas.

Fatty acids—Soybean plants cultured in a nutrient medium containing tritiated water can be used for the preparation of labelled fatty acids. After maturation of the beans, the oils are extracted and the glycerides *trans*-esterified with methanol. The methyl esters of the fatty acids which include linoleate, linolenate, oleate, palmitate, stearate and $C_{20\mp}$ acids, are separated into pure compounds by counter-current extraction. The specific activity of the isolated acids obtained by Dutton and colleagues[397] was however only about 0·03 mc/g.

Foster and Bloom[398] showed that the main portion of tritium activity was in the stearic and palmitic acids, when fatty acids were synthesized by rat liver slices in tritiated water (or using glucose-1-T as substrate).

Biochemical tritiation of fatty acids[398a] does not compete at all favourably with chemical methods, which are to be preferred.

Limitations of tritiated water as a substrate—The early work of Porter and colleagues[399-402] demonstrated that β-radiation can not only influence the yield and course of the reactions when *Chlorella pyrenoidosa* is grown in tritiated water, but produces also a gross reduction in viability (over 70 per cent of the cells being unable to form colonies when plated) when the specific activity of water exceeds 20 mc/ml. Chapman-Andresen[403] found that *Chaos Chaos* (Amoeba), *Scenedesmus* (Alga) and *Paramecium bursaria* (Ciliate), all died within 24 h in tritiated water at 167 mc/ml.

This is of course a disappointingly low level (less than 0·01 per cent isotopic abundance of tritium) for useful labelling, and is perhaps a little surprising when several species of algae can be grown in almost pure deuterium oxide[404, 405]. It does suggest that it is purely a radiation growth inhibition and certainly accounts for the lack of interest in this approach for labelling proteins or amino acids (for example) with tritium.

In any 'isotope farming' of this kind with tritium, because water constitutes a predominant part of the composition of the cells, the incorporation of the isotope is at a considerable disadvantage compared with carbon-14. A *Chlorella* cell (for example) grown in bicarbonate-C14 is not immediately exposed to the maximum radiation dose; much of the activity is in the circulating gas phase for a considerable part of the growth time. In the densest cultures commonly used this is not more than about 0·8 mc/ml in suspension. Assuming complete absorption of the β-radiation energy by the solution this only amounts to about 2×10^3 rads/day and even for a disintegration occurring in the cell, much of the energy is dissipated relatively harmlessly in the surrounding medium.

In tritium oxide, by contrast, the cell is immediately exposed to the maximum external dose; about 10^9 rads/day. Even to achieve useful labelling at (say) 100 mc/mM it would be necessary to use tritiated water of about 5 c/ml (neglecting any isotope effects). The dose rate to the algae in such a solution would be about 10^6 rads/day. The cell is very rapidly labelled internally by exchange of labile hydrogen atoms, and primary (internal and external) radiation effects are operative right from the start. As a result the culture dies at quite low isotopic abundances before growth can proceed far enough to produce useful labelling in non-labile positions.

Isotope effects are also unfavourable for labelling with tritiated water [399, 400].

These considerations will apply not only to *Chlorella* but to all biological systems, and it is very doubtful whether tritiated water as a substrate for biosynthesis will prove generally useful.

Fermentations—The failure to obtain the antibiotic paromomycin [406] (4.115) in a radiochemically pure state following labelling by exposure to tritium gas (perhaps not really surprising), prompted the attempt to label the compound by fermentation in a medium containing tritiated water at 10 mc/ml [407].

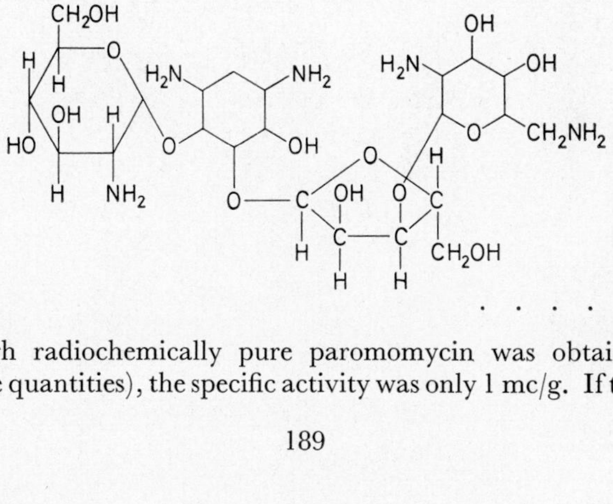

. . . . (4.115)

Although radiochemically pure paromomycin was obtained (in gramme quantities), the specific activity was only 1 mc/g. If this type of fermentation process could be carried out with tritiated water at say 10 c/ml or higher, then products at high activity (1 c/g), which are of real value as tracers, may be obtained. However, radiation effects, as with *Chlorella*, may again be the limiting factor.

2. *Using Tritiated Compounds as Substrate*

Tritiated compounds such as carbohydrates, amino acids, purines, pyrimidines, nucleosides, steroids etc., at high specific activity as substrates for the biosynthesis of labelled complex molecules, are likely to be much more useful than tritiated water; the radiation effects are much reduced compared with tritium oxide, even using several curies of the substrate and may be controlled to some extent by dilution of the growth medium. Some examples are:

(*a*) deoxyribosenucleic acid specifically labelled on the methyl group of the thymine residues is obtained by the incorporation of tritiated thymidine-*methyl*-T in normal tissue with rapid cellular turnover such as intestines or spleen, or Ehrlich tumour cells. The specific activity of the DNA isolated was 0·1 to 2 mc/g[408] rather low but still

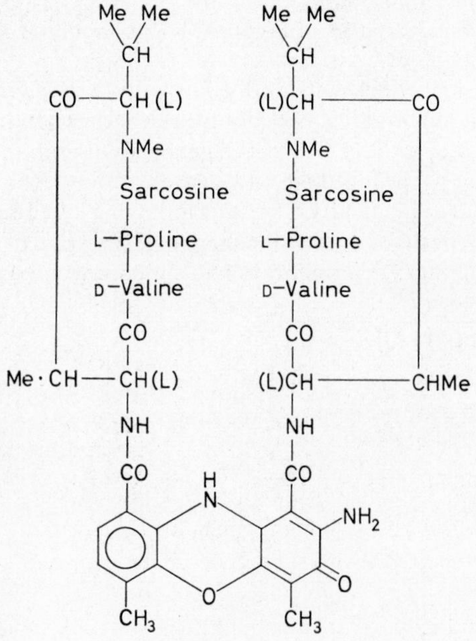

Actinomycin—C_1

. . . . (4.116)

useful for some purposes. The preparation of DNA-T from thymidine-T in *Bacillus subtilis* and *Escherichia coli* Phage T2, has also been described[409]. The activity of the isolated DNA was about 10^6counts/min/μM DNA-phosphorus.

Tritiated amino acids have been used as substrates for the biosynthesis of actinomycin (4.116). The labelled acids added to *Streptomyces antibioticus* strain V-187 are built up into the amino acid chains of the actinomycin which was isolated at 3–4 mc/mg[410]. Even using six tritiated amino acids (DL-glutamic acid-T; glycine-2-T; L-proline-T; DL-valine-T; DL-threonine-T and L-tryptophan-T) simultaneously as the substrate, only 5 per cent of the activity was incorporated into the antibiotic. However, this was 5 times higher than the incorporation of tritium when using glucose-6-T or DL-glutamic acid-T as substrates.

The amino acid chains of proteins can be built up from tritiated amino acids, for example lysozyme (from leucine-4,5-T)[411], thyroglobulin (from tyrosine-$\alpha\beta$-T)[412] and insulin (from leucine-4,5-T and isoleucine-T(G)[413–417, 417a]. The biosynthesized mammalian insulins-T were purified by specific immunological methods. After the precipitation with the antibody, the tritiated insulin may be regenerated with acid and finally purified by paper chromatography[417, 417a].

Bacitracin-A, an antibiotic produced by *Bacillus licheniformis*, contains 12 amino acids (4.117):

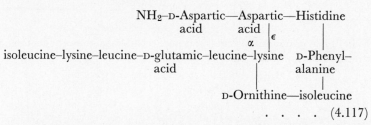

. . . . (4.117)

DL-Ornithine-T(G) (labelled by the Wilzbach method) at 4·85 mc/mM added to the medium in which *Bacillus licheniformis* cells were growing, yielded Bacitracin-T at 72·3 μc/mg[418].

One of the best described examples of the biosynthesis of tritiated steroids is provided by the work of Ayres, Pearlman, Tait and Tait[419], who prepared a series of corticosteroids labelled in the 16-position by incubating progesterone-16-T with isolated adrenal cortex tissue (from ox adrenal glands). The method has subsequently been improved by Ayres[420] who incubated 8·5 c of progesterone-16-T (specific activity 13·4 c/mM) with 4 kg of ox adrenal cortex tissue consisting mainly of zona glomerulosa plus capsule. The products

THE PREPARATION OF TRITIUM-LABELLED COMPOUNDS

were isolated by solvent extraction and purified by chromatographic procedures. The yield and specific activity of the isolated cortico-steroids are shown in Table 4.31

TABLE 4.31

Biosynthesis of Corticosteroids from Progesterone-16-T

Crystalline steroid isolated	Amount mg	Specific activity		Yield* approx. %
		c/mM	mc/mg	
Aldosterone-16-T	2·7	2·08	5·8 ∓ 0·1	1·5
Corticosterone-16-T	14·3	3·76	10·9 ∓ 0·05	7
Cortisol-16-T	3·9	1·88	5·2 ∓ 0·08	2

* Based on progesterone-16-T used.

In conclusion, only the methods A1 (page 185) and B2 (page 190) are likely to be of real value for preparative work. There is a real need for methods of labelling biologically active macromolecules such as proteins, deoxyribosenucleic acid and antibiotics (for example), to replace the present unpredictable exchange labelling techniques. Biochemical methods could fill this gap, for there is a very great advantage in using labelled compounds for biochemical investig-ations which themselves have been prepared by a biosynthetic method. The tritium label is almost certain to be associated with biologically active material in the purified compound, and such tritiated material can be used confidently for tracer investigations.

4. RECOIL LABELLING

(Hot-atom Reactions)

Labelling compounds by the reaction of recoil tritium atoms (tritons) from the nuclear reactions

$$^6Li(n,\alpha)^3H \quad \text{and} \quad ^3He(n,p)^3H$$

was first developed for the preparation of tritium compounds by Wolfgang, Rowland and Turton[421] in 1955. However, this method has subsequently proved to be of little value for useful preparative labelling with tritium. There are two main reasons for this:

1. Only low specific activities are attainable (less than 1 mc/g) which are usually much too low to be of use as tracers for many purposes.

2. Chemical and radiochemical yields are normally quite low due to the damage caused to the target material partly by the high neutron flux and γ-radiation, but mainly by the recoil tritons with their high kinetic energy (2·73 MeV from the lithium-6 reaction and 0·192 MeV from the helium-3 reaction). Other damage is caused by

the recoiling α-particle with kinetic energy 2·057 MeV or by the recoiling proton with energy 0·573 MeV [422].

Recoil tritium labelling becomes possible only when the kinetic energy of the recoil triton is such that after colliding with a molecule it can form a stable bond with one of the atoms in that molecule [423]. At a neutron flux of 10^{12} n/sec/cm^2 the number of tritium atoms produced per second by the ^{6}Li(n,α)^{3}H process is $7·13 \times 10^{12}$ per gramme of natural lithium and for the ^{3}He(n,p)^{3}H process $1·45 \times 10^{11}$ per cm^3 of helium-3; the tritons are positively charged at the instant of formation, they are slowed down in the medium, repeated charge exchange occurs and most of the recoil tritons with energies of several electron volts are neutralized [422, 424-426]. Chemical reactions of recoil atoms begin after they have 'cooled' to energies of a few electron volts and consequently, mainly uncharged tritons are involved in the recoil reactions. Thus one special feature of recoil triton reactions is that the tritons approach the region of chemical reaction from the direction of very large energies, which is of the exact opposite of the Wilzbach and similar tritium gas-exposure methods. It is not surprising therefore that much less *gross* damage to the target material occurs in Wilzbach labelling compared with the recoil method.

Condensed Phase Reactions

Compounds which are solid, liquid or liquified gases are normally mixed intimately with a lithium salt, about 10 per cent by weight, packed into aluminium cans and irradiated for several days in a nuclear reactor at a neutron flux of about 10^{12} n/sec/cm^2.

The favourable isotopic thermal neutron cross-section for the nuclear reaction ^{6}Li(n,α)^{3}H is 945 barns (1 barn = 10^{-24} cm^2) and the energy of the reaction is 4·787 MeV producing tritons which have a range of approximately 50 μ or 5 mg/cm^2 in the medium. The natural isotopic abundance of lithium-6 in lithium salts is 7·5 per cent; lithium salts such as the chloride can be electrolytically enriched in lithium-6 [427].

The activity (A) of the recoil tritium atoms produced in the nuclear reaction may be calculated from equation [203](4.118):

$$A = \frac{Wf\sigma\theta}{M} (1 - e^{-0·693t/T}) \, 6 \times 10^{23} \qquad \qquad \text{. . . . (4.118)}$$

where: σ = cross-section for the reaction = 945 barns
$\quad\quad\;\; W$ = weight of element of natural isotopic abundance in grammes i.e. weight of lithium salt

f = neutron flux
M = atomic weight of element (lithium)
θ = fractional abundance of the target isotope (lithium-6) in the natural element
t = irradiation time
T = half-life of isotope in units of t

The yield of the required compound depends not only on the extent of radiolysis of the target material (as one might expect) but also on the dimensions of the grains of the lithium salt. Less decomposition is observed when large particles of the lithium salt are used than with the finely ground salt. For example[441], irradiation of cholesterol mixed with 60 μ-particles of lithium oxalate gave a good yield of cholesterol with a specific activity of 200 μc/g. The same irradiation conditions with the use of 30 μ-particles gave greater decomposition, while the use of lithium myristate gel resulted in the formation of an insoluble product from which no cholesterol was isolated at all.

The yield does not essentially depend upon the intensity of the neutron flux and the chemical nature of the lithium salt does not influence the distribution or yield of the reaction products[429, 430]. Most commonly used lithium salts are the carbonate and fluoride.

In general, the stability (and hence the yield) of compounds under the irradiation conditions of recoil reactions, decreases with increasing molecular weight of the substance being irradiated.

Rowland and Wolfgang[431] have shown that if a compound is intimately mixed with up to 30 per cent of its weight of lithium carbonate, the specific activity induced during the irradiation can be calculated from the equation (4.119).

Specific activity $= 10^3\ EPft$ dis. per min per mg

$$\cdots \cdots \quad (4.119)$$

where E = per cent entry of tritium (generally 10–30 per cent)
P = per cent lithium carbonate in mixture
f = neutron flux (approximately 10^{12} n sec^{-1} cm^{-2})
t = irradiation time

E is a constant for the substance being irradiated.

It can be calculated that an irradiation of about 24 h can produce a compound with a specific activity of only 10^5–10^6 d.p.m./mg (0·1–1 μc/mg). As previously mentioned the maximum specific activities attained are very much dependent upon the rate of decomposition of the target material and cannot be very high even under the optimum irradiation time of 10 to 20 h.

A number of compounds which have been labelled by the $^6Li(n,\alpha)^3H$ process are listed in Table 4.32. As can be seen from this table the method has wide applicability but the specific activity of the purified compounds rarely exceeds 0·1 mc/mM and thus what promised to be a useful general method for the preparation of tritium compounds, has proved somewhat disappointing.

TABLE 4.32

Tritium Compounds from the $^6Li(n,\alpha)^3H$ Reaction

Compound irradiated	Neutron flux n sec^{-1}cm^{-2}	Irradn. time	Active products	Yield %	Specific activity μc/g	References
Acetic acid	$1·7 \times 10^{12}$	1 h	Acetic acid	18	1·7	432
			Hydrogen	33		
			Methane	13		
Acetone (liqud)	$1·8 \times 10^{12}$	2 h	Acetone	24	2·9	433
			Acetaldehyde	9·1		
Acetone (solid)	4×10^{12}	1 h	Acetone	24	3·6	433
			Acetaldehyde	5		
			isoPropanol	1·7		
L(+)-Alanine (14% in aq. soln.)	$1·8 \times 10^{11}$	21 h	Alanine	0·5	—	435
L(+)-Alanine	$1·8 \times 10^{12}$	24 h	Alanine	12	—	435
Acetone (30% water)	$1·8 \times 10^{12}$	1 h	Acetone	25	1·2	433
			Acetaldehyde	7·5		
Anthracene	1×10^{12}	72 h	Anthracene	—	150	434
Benzene	$3–4 \times 10^{12}$	30 min	Benzene	26	28	436
			Cyclohexa-1,4-diene	2·5		
			Cyclohexa-1,3-diene	1·2		
			C$_6$-Linear	0·3		
Benzene (deuterated)	$3–4 \times 10^{12}$	30 min	Benzene-D	24·2	26	436
			Cyclohexa-1,4-diene	2·6		
			Cyclohexa-1,3-diene	1·1		
			C$_6$-Linear	0·2		
Benzene (with lithium methyl)	$3–4 \times 10^{12}$	30 min	Benzene	52		
			Cyclohexa-1,4-diene	5·2	1·7	436
			Cyclohexa-1,3-diene	2·6		
			C$_6$-Linear	1		
Benzene clathrate	$3–4 \times 10^{12}$	30 min	Benzene	42·5	100	436
			Cyclohexadienes	trace		
Benzene	4×10^{12}	10 h	Benzene	—	40	437
Benzoic acid	2×10^{12}	40 h	Benzoic acid	35	100	431
Benzoic acid	1×10^{12}	72 h	Benzoic acid	—	96	421
Benzoic acid	2×10^{12}	154 h	Benzoic acid	66	1,000	431
Benzoic acid	2×10^{11}	15 h	Benzoic acid	—	14	438
Benzoic acid	2×10^{12}	700 h	Benzoic acid	56	1,000	431
Benzoic acid	1×10^{12}	72 h	Benzoic acid	25	90	431
Benzoic acid	1×10^{12}	168 h	Benzoic acid	16	150	440
Benzoic acids (substituted)						
o-, m- and p-Amino	5×10^{12}	2 h	Aminobenzoic acids	32–35	21·7	447
o, m- and p-Bromo	5×10^{12}	2 h	Bromobenzoic acids	36–42	26·7	447
o-, m- and p-Carboxy-	5×10^{12}	2 h	Carboxybenzoic acids	32	20	447
o-, m- and p-Chloro-	5×10^{12}	2 h	Chlorobenzoic acids	42–49	31·7	447
o- and m-Fluoro-	5×10^{12}	2 h	Fluorobenzoic acids	44–57	36·7	447
o- and m-Iodo-	5×10^{12}	2 h	Iodobenzoic acids	33–36	23·3	447
o-, m- and p-Hydroxy-	5×10^{12}	2 h	Hydroxybenzoic acids	31–43	26·7	447
o-, m- and p-Nitro-	5×10^{12}	2 h	Nitrobenzoic acids	27–29	1·6	447
n-Butyric acid	$2–4 \times 10^{12}$	1 h	n-Butyric acid	27		432
			Hydrogen	49		
			Methane	2·6		
			Propane	3·7		
iso-Butyric acid	$2–4 \times 10^{12}$	1 h	isoButyric acid	26		432
			Hydrogen	47		
			Methane	4·7		
			Propane	3·3		

TABLE 4.32 (continued)

Compound irradiated	Neutron flux n sec^{-1}cm^{-2}	Irradn. time	Active products	Yield %	Specific activity μc/g	References
n-Caproic acid	2–4 × 10^{12}	1 h	n-Caproic acid	27		432
			Hydrogen	46		
			Methane	1·3		
			Pentane	0·9		
t-Caproic acid	2–4 × 10^{12}	1 h	t-Caproic acid	33		432
			Hydrogen	34		
			Methane	2·8		
			s-Pentane	0·8		
Cholestane	2 × 10^{12}	29 h	Cholestane	17	200	437
Cholesterol	1 × 10^{12}	115 h	Cholesterol	—	154	441
cis-Cinnamic acid	5 × 10^{12}	2 h	cis-Cinnamic acid	15	10	440
trans-Cinnamic acid	5 × 10^{12}	2 h	trans-Cinnamic acid	30	18·3	440
trans-Cinnamic acid	1 × 10^{12}	72 h	trans-Cinnamic acid	—	100	431
trans-Cinnamic acid (sodium salt)	1·3 × 10^{12}	8 h	trans-Cinnamic acid (free acid + Na salt)	27	20	440
Cyclohexane	3–4 × 10^{12}	30 min	Cyclohexane	10	8	437
Cyclohexene	3–4 × 10^{12}	30 min	Cyclohexene	11	10	437
			Cyclohexane	9	90	
Cyclohexanol	4 × 10^{12}	5 h	Cyclohexanol	29·8		437
			Cyclohexane	3·9		
			H$_2$ + methane	66·3		
Cyclohex-1,4-diene	3–4 × 10^{12}	2 h	Cyclohexa-1,4-diene	17	60	437
			Cyclohexa-1,3-diene	5	65	
			Cyclohexene	15	330	
			Benzene	29	60	
Cyclohexa-1,3-diene	3–4 × 10^{12}	2 h	Cyclohexa-1,3-diene	3·3		437
			Cyclohexa-1,4-diene	2·6		
			Cyclohexene	14·1		
			Benzene	29		
Cyclohexylamine	4 × 10^{12}	5 h	Cyclohexylamine	32·8		437
			Cyclohexane	5·3		
			H$_2$ + methane	61·9		
Cumene	6·9 × 10^{12}	90 min	Cumene	—	12·6–24·7	439
Diacetone glucose	2 × 10^{12}	24 h	Diacetone glucose	—	100	431
Diethylmercaptyl-glucose	2 × 10^{12}	24 h	Diethylmercaptyl-glucose	—	100	431
Dimethyl ether	3 × 10^{12}	48 h	Dimethyl ether	16		442
			Ethylmethyl ether	3·2		
			Methane	4		
			Hydrogen	77		
Ethane (solid)	5 × 10^{12}	30 sec	Ethane	100	5	429
Ethanol	2 × 10^{12}	6 h	Ethanol	95	40	433
Ethyl benzene	6·9 × 10^{12}	90 min	Ethyl benzene	—	17·6–212	439
Fumaric acid	5 × 10^{12}	2 h	Fumaric acid	12	8·3	440
Galactose	1·8 × 10^{12}	27 hr	Galactose	12	11·3	444
Glucose	6 × 10^{9}	65 h	Glucose	10	3	444
Glucose	1·8 × 10^{12}	24 h	Glucose	22	266	445
Glucose	2·5 × 10^{11}	21 h	Glucose	89	20	446
Glucose	2 × 10^{12}	24 h	Glucose	22	15	444
Glucose (48% aq. soln.)	1·8 × 10^{12}	24 h	Glucose	1	1·7	445
α-Hydroximino-propionic acid	2·5 × 10^{11}	21 hr	Oxime	55	13	446
			Glycine	0·17	1,000	
			Alanine	0·34	1,900	
Lactose	2·5 × 10^{11}	21 h	Lactose	47	10	446
Methane (solid)	5 × 10^{12}	30 sec	Methane	49	5	429
Methanol	2 × 10^{12}	6 h	Methanol	23	40	433
Maleic acid	5 × 10^{12}	2 h	Maleic acid	10	6·7	440
Methyl cholate	2 × 10^{12}	24 h	Methyl cholate	17	150	437
Methylcyclohexane	4 × 10^{12}	5 h	Methylcyclohexane	35·2		437
			Cyclohexane	3·9		
			H$_2$ + methane	60·9		
α-Methyl glucoside	2 × 10^{12}	24 h	α-Methyl glucoside	—	100	431
2-Methyl-2-n-propyl-1,3-propandiol carbamate	2 × 10^{12}	72 h	2-Methyl-2-n-propyl-1,3-propandiol carbamate	6	50	431
Nicotinic acid	1 × 10^{12}	72 h	Nicotinic acid	23	100	431
Nicotinic acid	1·8 × 10^{12}	24 h	Nicotinic acid	—	3,200	449
Nicotinic acid	2 × 10^{12}	48 h	Nicotinic acid	6	150	437
Phenylacetic acid	7 × 10^{12}	2 h	Phenylacetic acid	30	34	450

196

TABLE 4.32 (continued)

Compound irradiated	Neutron flux n sec^{-1}cm^{-2}	Irradn. time	Active products	Yield %	Specific activity $\mu c/g$	References
Phenylacetic acid	2×10^{12}	3 h	Phenylacetic acid	31	100	450
o-Phthalic acid	1×10^{12}	72 h	o-Phthalic acid	24	100	431
isoPropylbenzoate	1×10^{12}	118 h	isoPropylbenzoate	16·8	188	448
isoPropylbenzoate	1×10^{12}	153 h	isoPropylbenzoate	10·2	217	448
Reserpine	$1·8 \times 10^{12}$	2 h	Reserpine	18	10	451
Reserpine	$1·8 \times 10^{12}$	72 h	Reserpine	18	100	451
Reserpine		240 h	Reserpine	—	400	452
Salicylic acid	1×10^{12}	72 h	Salicylic acid	31	100	431
Terpene	1×10^{12}		Terpene		1–14	488
Tetracycline	$1·4 \times 10^{12}$	300 h	Tetracycline	—	2,000	147
DL-Threonine	$2·5 \times 10^{11}$	17 h	DL-Threonine	—	82	454
			allo-Threonine		108	
			Glycine		11	
o-Toluidinic acid	1×10^{12}	72 h	o-Toluidinic acid	25	100	453
Toluene	1×10^{12}	97 h	Toluene	40	220	455
Toluene	3×10^{12}	11 h	Toluene	—	—	456
Toluene	$6·9 \times 10^{12}$	90 min	Toluene	—	12–26	439
o-Toluic acid	1×10^{12}	72 h	o-Toluic acid	25	100	431
n-Valeric acid	$2–4 \times 10^{12}$	1 h	n-Valeric acid	20		432
			Hydrogen	65		
			Methane	2		
			Butane	2·2		
isoValeric acid	$2–4 \times 10^{12}$	1 h	isoValeric acid	33		432
			Hydrogen	48		
			Methane	4·5		
			isoButane	2·1		
t-Valeric acid	$2–4 \times 10^{12}$	1 h	t-Valeric acid	20		432
			Hydrogen	43		
			Methane	9·6		
			s-Butane	6·8		
Water (liquid)	2×10^{9}	144 h	Hydrogen	10		457, 458
			Water	90		
Water (gas)	2×10^{9}	144 h	Hydrogen	4		457, 458
			Water	96		
Water (gas)+helium-4	2×10^{9}	144 h	Hydrogen	2		457, 458
			Water	98		
Water (gas)+NO	2×10^{9}	144 h	Hydrogen	4		457, 458
			Water	96		
Water (gas)+oxygen	2×10^{9}	144 h	Hydrogen	1·5		457, 458
			Water	98·5		

Gas-Phase Reactions

Experiments in the gas phase are usually carried out by mixing the compound with helium-3 in quartz ampoules and irradiating the mixture in a reactor at a neutron flux about 10^{12} n sec^{-1} cm^{-2}. The isotopic thermal neutron cross-section for the reaction $^3He(n,p)^3H$ is 5,400 barns and the energy of the nuclear reaction is 0·765 MeV [422].

The natural abundance of helium-3 is only about $1·3 \times 10^{-4}$ per cent, consequently helium-3 produced by the natural decay of tritium is quite often used and a purification process for the helium has been described by Pritchard, Urch and Welch[459], which consists of adsorbing the impurities on finely divided zirconium film. Erdman and colleagues[485] have described a method for the removal of traces of tritium in helium-3 by freezing-out the tritium after the addition of about 1 per cent of hydrogen, but the use of charcoal at $-196°$ C is reported to be more efficient[443].

Most gas-phase reactions with recoil tritium atoms have been

197

carried out with a view to establishing some facts relating to the mechanism of the 'hot-atom' reaction rather than as a means for preparing a particular tritiated compound. For this reason, and in view of the minor importance of the technique for useful preparative labelling with tritium, readers are referred to the listed references[460-480] for some of the many papers dealing with the academic implications of gaseous triton recoil reactions.

Special Features of Recoil Triton Reactions

An excellent review of the reactions of energetic tritium (and carbon) atoms with organic compounds has been given by Wolf[481], including current ideas on the mechanism of recoil triton reactions. It is perhaps only necessary therefore, to include a discussion of some special features which relate to the use of the method for preparing tritium-labelled compounds.

1. *Energy considerations*—One must always bear in mind that the reactions of the recoil tritons are occurring from the direction of high energies; this gives rise to decomposition products by breakdown of the excited states in addition to radiolytic breakdown.

Consideration of the bond energy of the bond undergoing rupture by reactions with recoil tritons, is only applicable when comparing similar molecules[469]. For example, Odum and Wolfgang[482] have shown that fluorine, chlorine, bromine and iodine atoms in the alkyl halides have a high probability of being displaced by tritons to give labelled hydrocarbons. The ease of displacement in the gaseous halides is the same as in the solid-phase reactions, $I > Br > Cl > F \simeq H$. When more than one halogen atom is present in the molecule, steric factors influence the course of the reaction rather than the bond energies. Pozdeev, Nesmeyanov and Dzantiev[483] have demonstrated that the yield of benzene depends on the energy of excitation of the complex and on the energy of the phenyl–halogen bond, when recoil tritons react with halogenated benzenes. Their results obtained during a 20 min irradiation at a neutron flux of 5×10^{12} n sec^{-1} cm^{-2} are shown in Table 4.33.

The marked dependence of the yield of labelled benzene on the bond energy with the halogen, again demonstrates that the tritium recoil atoms form labelled molecules when they have an energy of a few electron volts only. The presence of a free radical scavenger (iodine) supports a displacement reaction (non-radical reaction). The delocalization of the π-electrons in the aromatic molecule favours rapid propagation of the excitation of all the bonds of the excited molecule complex and the complex then breaks at the weakest bond.

TABLE 4.33
Interaction of Recoil Tritons with Halogenated Benzenes

Compound irradiated	Bond energy Ph-halogen	Iodine concn. moles	Yield of labelled benzene counts/sec
Fluorobenzene	117 kcal/mole	0	860
Chlorobenzene	85 kcal/mole	0	$1,870 \mp 140$
		1×10^{-2}	$1,730 \mp 90$
		5×10^{-2}	$1,880 \mp 90$
Bromobenzene	70 kcal/mole	0	$3,060 \mp 50$
		5×10^{-2}	$2,970 \mp 50$
Iodobenzene	56 kcal/mole	0	$4,900 \mp 300$
		1×10^{-2}	$5,300 \mp 100$
		5×10^{-2}	$5,500 \mp 100$
Benzene		0	4,000

Recoil tritons not only displace H or halogen atoms[486] or groups, but also groups such as $-NO_2$, $-NH_2$, $-COOH$, $-OH$[428], in the corresponding derivatives of benzoic acid for example[447]. Replacement may occur as a secondary process, for example the reaction of recoil tritons with carboxylic acids proceeds by formation and decarboxylation of excited molecules (4.120) or (4.121).

$$T^* + CH_3 \cdot COOH \rightarrow CH_2T \cdot COOH^* + H$$
$$\downarrow$$
$$CH_3T + CO_2 \qquad \ldots \ldots \quad (4.120)$$

$$T^* + CH_3 \cdot COOH \rightarrow CH_3T \cdot COOH^*$$
$$\downarrow$$
$$CH_3T + H + CO_2 \qquad \ldots \ldots \quad (4.121)$$

In the case of benzoic acid it has been shown[484] that the secondary decomposition can be reduced by the irradiation of lithium benzoate rather than the free acid.

2. *Stereochemistry*—One of the most interesting features of recoil labelling with tritium is that stereochemical configuration of the target material is predominantly retained during the process. The displacement of an atom by a recoil triton occurs rapidly (10^{-14} sec). This is comparable with bond vibration times. The excitation energy of the excited complex $(R \cdot T^*)$ does not always have time to spread over the whole molecule, so that only local bond disturbances occur while the molecular configuration is retained in the majority of cases[435, 445, 448, 463, 464].

The initial observation was made during reactions with D-glucose and galactose[444] which clearly demonstrated that the triton recoil reactions occurred with predominant retention of configuration about an asymmetric carbon atom. This has since been confirmed

199

with L(+)-alanine[435], s-butyl alcohol[465], (+) and (−)-2-octyl-phthalates[491], and the observations extended to liquid and gaseous phase reactions[463, 487].

In the stereochemical replacement of hydrogen by tritium in the solid phase, maleic and fumaric acids (for example) give the same geometrical isomers at least 20 times more frequently than the opposite isomer, during the recoil reactions[440]. Substitution occurs along the path which requires the least complex total motion of the various atoms or groups in the molecule. However, steric effects in the solid-state recoil reactions are often difficult to interpret as the blocking of paths of attack by the surrounding molecules must also be taken into account.

This predominant retention of configuration during recoil labelling contrasts with the Wilzbach labelling process where configuration is not generally retained.

3. *Addition reactions*—In reactions of recoil tritons with unsaturated compounds, the main reaction products apart from the parent compound and hydrogen are hydrogenated products. The probability of carbon–carbon bond rupture following addition of the tritons is lower for cyclic than for open-chain compounds[437, 490]. For example, cyclohexene yields cyclohexane and cyclohexadiene gives cyclohexene (Table 4.32). In the case of benzene, the labelled cyclo-hexadienyl radical is formed which is then transformed into cyclohexa-1,4-diene and cyclo-1,3-diene; addition reactions therefore also occur with aromatic compounds[489, 491, 492].

As these addition products are formed without carriers, they have a high specific activity and are sometimes of more value than the parent labelled compound. The situation here is similar to the Wilzbach technique in as much as the addition of tritium produces high activity impurities in the parent compound.

4. *Influence of radical scavengers on recoil reactions*—The main point to note is that the presence of radical scavengers has no influence on the yield of labelled products which are formed by the displacement of hydrogen or groups by the tritons. Small amounts of scavengers such as iodine, bromine, nitric oxide, oxygen (for gas-phase reactions) and diphenylpicrylhydrazyl (DPPH) (for liquid and solid), have a strong influence on the yields of individual products, formed by secondary processes. For example, DPPH decreases the yield of the benzene hydrogenation products in the reaction of recoil tritons with benzene[489].

5. *Effect of temperature and the phase state of the target compound on the yield of labelled products*—The yield of labelled products does not

depend substantially on the temperature in the range 0° to 200° C[424]. However, a change in the phase state has an appreciable influence on the quantitative composition of the products without affecting the qualitative composition. For example, the reaction of recoil tritons with *trans*-but-2-ene gives similar results at 20° C and −78° C, i.e., in the gaseous and liquid states respectively. In the solid state at −196° C there is a decrease of labelled but-2-ene and a substantial increase in the yield of *n*-butane-T[493]. Note that these results differ from those obtained by the exposure of unsaturated hydrocarbons to tritium gas. For example, with Wilzbach labelling about the same percentage addition of tritium to cyclohexene occurs at room temperature as at −196° C[62]. There is however a concomitant decrease in the yield of cyclohexene-T at the lower temperature which is similar to the results obtained from recoil reactions.

Reactions of recoil tritons with *trans*-but-2-ene and *trans*-hex-2-ene, give lower yields of labelled olefin in the liquid than in the gas phase[494, 495].

The distribution of the tritium atoms in a few of the compounds which have been labelled by these various methods is discussed in Chapter 5.

REFERENCES

[1] von Hevesy, G. and Rona, E. *Z. phys. Chem.* 89 (1915) 294
[2] von Hevesy, G. and Zechmeister, L. *Ber. dt. chem. Ges.* 53 (1920) 410
[3] Catch, J. R. *Carbon-14 Compounds* 1961. London; Butterworths
[4] Wilzbach, K. E. *Chem. Engng News* 1956; *J. Am. chem. Soc.* 79 (1957) 1013
[5] Whisman, M. L. and Eccleston, B. H. *Nucleonics* 20 (6) (1962) 98
[6] Wenzel, M. and Schulze, P. E. 'Tritium Markierung' *Preparation, Measurement and Uses of Wilzbach Labelled Compounds*, 1962. Berlin; Walter De Gruyter
[7] Wilzbach, K. E. *Proc. Symp. Tritium phys. Biol. Sci.* I.A.E.A., Vienna 2 (1962) 3
[8] Grove, J. F. *Q. Rev. chem. Soc.* 17 (1963) 1
[8a] Stork, G. and Tomasz, M. *J. Am. chem. Soc.* 86 (1964) 471
[9] Demis, J. D. and Walton, M. D. *J. invest. Derm.* 34 (1960) 181
[10] Schulze, P. E. Unpublished experiments see ref. 6
[11] Rajan, N. S. S. *Diss. Abstr.* 23 (1963) 2704
[12] Nystrom, R. F. and Rajan, N. S. *Chemy Ind.* (1961) 1165
[13] Sato, Y. and Takahashi, T. *Bull. chem. Soc. Japan* 34 (1961) 169
[14] Evans, E. A. *Chemy Ind.* (1961) 2097
[15] Wolfgang, R., Pratt, T. and Rowland, F. S. *J. Am. chem. Soc.* 78 (1956) 5132
[16] Lemmon, R. M., Tolbert, B. M., Strohmeier, W. and Whittemore, I. M. *Science, N.Y.* 129 (1959) 1740
[17] Dorfman, L. M. and Wilzbach, K. E. *J. phys. Chem., Ithaca* 63 (1959) 799
[18] Cacace, F., Guarino, A. and Montefinale, G. *Nature, Lond.* 189 (1961) 54
[19] Kaplan, L. *J. Am. chem. Soc.* 76 (1954) 1448

[20] Ghanem, N. A. and Westermark, T. *J. Am. chem. Soc.* 82 (1960) 4432
[21] Cacace, F., Ciranni, E., Ciranni, G. and Montefinale, G. *Energia nucl.* 8 (1961) 561
[22] Ache, H. J., Herr, W. and Thiemann, A. *Proc. Conf. Chemical Effects nucl. Transformations*, I.A.E.A., Vienna 2 (1961) 111
[23] Ahrens, R. W., Sauer, M. C. and Willard, J. E. *J. Am. chem. Soc.* 79 (1957) 3285
[24] Westermark, T., Lindroth, H. and Enander, B. *Int. J. appl. Radiat. Isotopes* 7 (1960) 331
[25] Wilzbach, K. E. *Atomlight* (15) (1960) 1
[26] Klubes, P. and Schultze, M. O. *Int. J. appl. Radiat. Isotopes* 14 (1963) 241
[27] Moser, H. C., Nordin, P. and Senne, J. K. *Int. J. appl. Radiat. Isotopes* 15 (1964) 557
[28] Wenzel, M., Schulze, P. E. and Wollenberg, H. *Naturwissenschaften* 49 (1962) 515
[29] Wenzel, M., Wollenberg, H. and Schulze, P. E. *Proc. Symp. Tritium Phys. Biol. Sci.*, I.A.E.A., Vienna 2 (1962) 37
[30] Chadha, M. S., Woeller, F. H., Lemmon, R. M. *Univ. Calif. Radiat. Lab., Bio-Organic Chemistry Quart. Rep.*, UCRL–10032 (Sept. to Nov., 1961) 94
[31] Felter, R. E. and Currie, L. A. (as ref. 29) 2 (1962) 61
[32] Rothchild, S. *Atomlight* (16) (1961) 6
[33] Jellinck, P. H. and Smyth, D. G. *Nature, Lond.* 182 (1958) 46
[34] Jackson, F. L., Kittinger, G. W., Krause, F. P. *Nucleonics* 18 (8) (1960) 102
[35] McBain, J. W. and Baker, A. M. *J. Am. chem. Soc.* 48 (1926) 690
[36] Meshi, T. and Takahashi, T. *Bull. chem. Soc. Japan* 35 (1962) 1510
[37] Meshi, T. and Sato, Y. *Bull. chem. Soc. Japan* 37 (1964) 683
[38] Long, M. A., Odell, A. L. and Thorp, J. M. *Radiochim. Acta* 1 (1963) 174
[39] Maurer, R., Wenzel, M. and Karlson, P. *Nature, Lond.* 202 (1964) 896
[40] Evans, E. A. and colleagues—Radiochemical Centre
[41] Karlson, P., Maurer, R. and Wenzel, M. *Z. Naturf.* 18b (1963) 219
[42] Ache, H. J., Thiemann, A. and Herr, W. *Angew. Chem.* 73 (1961) 707
[43] Feng, P. Y. and Greenlee, T. W. (as ref. 29) 2 (1962) 11
[44] Dutton, H. J. and Nystrom, R. F. *Adv. Tracer Methodol.* 1 (1963) 18
[45] Nystrom, R. F., Mason, L. H., Jones, E. P. and Dutton, H. J. *J. Am. Oil Chem. Soc.* 36 (1959) 212
[46] Dutton, H. J., Jones, E. P., Mason, L. H. and Nystrom, R. F. *Chemy Ind.* (1958) 1176
[47] Dutton, H. J., Jones, E. P., Davison, V. L. and Nystrom, R. F. *J. org. Chem.* 27 (1962) 2648
[48] Whisman, M. L. *Analyt. Chem.* 33 (1961) 1284
[49] Simon, H., Müllhofer, G. and Dorrer, H. D. *Proc. Conf. Methods Preparing and Storing Marked Molecules*, Brussels, Nov. 1963. European Atomic Energy Community, Euratom, EUR 1625e (May, 1964) p. 997
[50] Ache, H. J. and Herr, W. *Z. Naturf.* 17a (1962) 631
[51] Yang, K. and Gant, P. L. *J. phys. Chem.* 66 (1962) 1619
[52] Gordon, M. P., Intrieri, O. M. and Brown, G. B. *J. Am. Chem. Soc.* 80 (1958) 5161
[52a] Yang, J. Y., Ingalls, R. B. and Hardy, J. R. *J. Am. chem. Soc.* 84 (1962) 2831
[53] Riesz, P. and Wilzbach, K. E. *Abstracts Papers 134th Meet. Amer. Chem. Soc.*, Chicago (Sept. 1958) p. 27P

REFERENCES

54 Crawford, B. and Garnett, J. L. *Proc. Symp. Tritium Phys. Biol. Sci.*, I.A.E.A., Vienna 2 (1962) 10

55 Angyal, S. J., Garnett, J. L. and Hoskinson, R. M. *Aust. J. Chem.* 16 (1963) 252

56 Angyal, S. J., Garnett, J. L. and Hoskinson, R. M. *Nature, Lond.* 197 (1963) 485

57 Baba, S., Brodie, H. J., Hayano, M., Kwass, G. and Gut, M. *J. org. Chem.* 29 (1964) 2751

58 Angyal, S. J. and Fernandez, C. *Nature, Lond.* 202 (1964) 176

59 Sato, Y., Takahashi, T. and Meshi, T. *Radio-Isotopes (Tokyo)* 10 (1961) 488

60 Bayly, R. J. *Radioisotopes Phys. Sci. and Ind.* I.A.E.A., Vienna 2 (1962) 305

61 Bradlow, H. L., Fukushima, D. K. and Gallagher, T. F. *Atomlight* (9) (1959) 2

62 Nystrom, R. F. *Atomlight* (23) (1962) 5

63 Pany, J. *Naturwissenschaften* 46 (1959) 515

64 Ghanem, N. A. and Westermark, T. *Proc. Conf. Uses Radioisotopes Phys. Sci. Ind.*, I.A.E.A., Copenhagen 3 (1962) 43

65 Khairallah, P. A., Page, I. H., Bumpus, F. M. and Smeby, R. R. *Science, N.Y.* 138 (1962) 523

66 Hanngren, H., Hansson, E., Ullberg, S. *Antibiotics Chemother.* 12 (1962) 46

67 Träger, L. *Dissertation Techn. University*, Berlin, (1960)

68 Verly, W. G., Flamée, P. A. and Fallais, C. J. *Bull. Soc. chim. Belg.* 72 (1963) 50

69 Sinex, F. M., van Slyke, D. D. and Christman, D. R. *J. biol. Chem.* 234 (1959) 918

70 Decker, C. F., Norris, W. P. and Kisieleski, W. E. *Argonne Natn. Lab. Rep.*, ANL-6093 (1958) 24

71 von Holt, C., Nolte, I. and von Holt, L. *Proc. 2nd U.N. Conf. peaceful Uses Atom. Energy*, Geneva 25 (1958) 230

72 von Holt, C., Voelker, I., von Holt, L. *Biochim. biophys. Acta* 38 (1960) 88

73 Wenzel, M. *Atompraxis* 7 (1961) 86

73a Wenzel, M. and Schultze, P. E. *Z. analyt. Chem.* 201 (1964) 349

74 Rajam, P. C. and Jackson, A. L. *Nature, Lond.* 184 (1959) 375

75 Fong, C. T. O., Schwartz, J. L., Popence, E. A., Silver, L. and Schoessler, M. A. *J. Am. chem. Soc.* 81 (1959) 2592

75a Fong, C. T. O., Silver, L., Christman, D. R. and Schwartz, J. L. *Proc. Soc. Natn. Acad. Sci. U.S.A.* 46 (1960) 1273

76 Steinberg, D., Vaughan, M., Anfinsen, C. B., Gorry, J. D. and Logan, J. *Liquid Scintillation Counting* Ed. Bell, C. G. and Hayes, F. N. p. 230, 1958. London; Pergamon Press

77 Steinberg, D., Vaughan, M., Anfinsen, C. B. and Gorry, J. *Science, N.Y.* 126 (1957) 447

78 Riesz, P. and Wilzbach, K. E. *J. phys. Chem.* 62 (1958) 6

79 Rosenblum, C. *Nucleonics* 17 (12) (1959) 80

80 Rosenblum, C. and Meriwether, H. T. *Adv. Tracer Methodol.*, 1 (1963) 12

81 Du Vigneaud, V., Schneider, C. H., Stouffer, J. E., Murti, V. V. S., Aroskar, J. P. and Winestock, G. *J. Am. chem. Soc.* 84 (1962) 409

82 Winstead, J. A. and Suhadolnik, R. J. *J. Am. Chem. Soc.* 82 (1960) 1644

83 Burnett, J. P. and Haurowitz, F. *Hoppe-Seyler's Z. physiol. Chem.* 331 (1963) 67

THE PREPARATION OF TRITIUM-LABELLED COMPOUNDS

84 Graul, E. H., Hundeshagen, H. and Steiner, B. *Atompraxis* 7 (1961) 449

85 Whisman, M. L., Schwartz, F. G. and Eccleston, B. H. *U.S. Bureau of Mines Report of Investigation* 5717 (1961)

86 Bolt, W., Ritzel, F., Toussaint, R. and Nahrmann, H. *Arzneimittel-Forsch.* 11 (1961) 170

87 Shimojima, H., Nagao, H. and Kamada, T. *Radio-Isotopes (Tokyo)* 13 (1964) 287

88 Lindström, G. B. *Acta chem. scand.* 13 (1959) 848

89 Roth, L. J., Wilzbach, K. E., Heller, A. and Kaplan, L., *J. Am. Pharm. Ass. Sci. edn.* 48 (1959) 415

90 Agranoff, B. W., Bradley, R. M. and Axelrod, J. *Proc. Soc. exp. Biol. Med.* 96 (1957) 261

91 Wenzel, M., Wollenberg, H. and Schütte, E. *Lecture Natural-Substances Symp.* Brussels, June, (1962) and unpublished results—see ref. 6

92 Cacace, F. and Inam-Ul-Haq *Ricerca scient.* 30 (1960) 501

93 Hanna, C. *J. Am. Pharm. Ass. Sci. edn* 49 (1960) 502

94 Giovanella, B. C., Abell, C. W., Heidelberger, C. *Cancer Res.* 22 (1962) 925

95 Cacace, F., Guarino, A., Montefinale, G. and Possagno, E. *Int. J. appl. Radiat. Isotopes* 8 (1960) 82

96 Wilson, E. J. and Bultitude, F.—Radiochemical Centre

97 Rydberg, J. and Hanngren, A. *Acta chem. scand.* 12 (1958) 332

98 Ciba Ltd. *Brit. Patent 961,576* (June, 24th, 1964)

99 Lijinsky, W. and Garcia, H. *Nature, Lond.* 197 (1963) 688

100 Dubini, M. *Proc. Conf. on Methods of Preparing and Storing Marked Molecules*, European Atomic Energy Community, Euratom, EUR 1625e (May, 1964) p. 911

101 Brown, B. T., Ranger, D. and Wright, S. E. *J. Pharmac. exp. Ther.* 113 (1955) 353

102 Wilzbach, K. E. and Dorfman, L. M. *Conf. Use Radioisotopes Phys. Sci. Ind.*, I.A.E.A., Copenhagen 3 (1960) 3

103 Felsenfeld, H. and Carter, C. E. *J. Pharm. exp. Ther.* 132 (1961) 1

104 Galus, Z., White, R. M., Rowland, F. S. and Adams, R. N. *J. Am. chem. Soc.* 84 (1962) 2065

105 Hankes, L. V. and Segel, I. H. *Proc. Soc. exp. Biol. Med.* 97 (1958) 568

106 Schultze, P. E. and Wenzel, M. See ref. 6

107 Wacker, A., Kirschfeld, S. and Träger, L. *J. molec. Biol.* 2 (1960) 24

108 Silber, R., Huennekens, F. M. and Gabrio, B. W. *Archs Biochem. Biophys.* 100 (1963) 525

109 Wenzel, M. and Körtge, P. *Naturwissenschaften* 48 (1961) 431

110 Bernhard, K., Goetschel, J. D. and Wagner, H. *Helv. chim. Acta* 44 (1961) 1554

111 Gerber, G., Gerber, G. and Altman, K. I. *J. biol. Chem.* 235 (1960) 1433

112 Peterson, R. E. *Adv. Tracer Methodol.* 1 (1963) 265

113 Simon, H., Eder, W., Medina, R. and Hechtfischer, S. *Proc. Conf. on the Preparation and Bio-Medical Applications of Labelled Molecules*, European Atomic Energy Community, Venice, Aug. 1964 Euratom EUR 2200e (1964) 459

114 Bergström, S. and Lindstedt, S. *Acta chem. scand.* 11 (1957) 1275

115 Spratt, J. L. and Okita, G. T. *Proc. 2nd U.N. Conf. peaceful Uses Atom. Energy*, Geneva 25 (1958) 186

REFERENCES

[116] Spratt, J. L., Okita, G. T. and Geiling, E. M. K. *Int. J. appl. Radiat. Isotopes* 2 (1957) 167

[117] Kemp, R. G. and Rose, I. A. *J. biol. Chem.* 239 (1964) 2998

[118] Norman, A. W. and Deluca, H. F. *Biochemistry* 2 (1963) 1160

[119] Solomon, S., Carter, A. C. and Lieberman, S. *J. biol. Chem.* 235 (1960) 351

[120] Werbin, H., Chaikoff, I. L. and Imada, M. R. *Archs Biochem. Biophys.* 89 (1960) 213

[121] Florini, J. R. *J. biol. Chem.* 235 (1960) 367

[122] Samuelsson, B. *Acta chem. scand.* 14 (1960) 21

[123] Goecke, Cl., Günther, Th. and Wenzel, M. See ref. 6

[124] Crane, R. K., Drydale, R. and Hawkins, H. *Atomlight* (15) (1960) 4

[125] Günther, Th., Wenzel, M. and Greiling, H. *Hoppe-Seyler's Z. physiol. Chem.* 326 (1961–62) 212

[126] Wenzel, M., Lenk, H. P. and Schütte, E. *Hoppe-Seyler's Z. physiol. Chem.* 327 (1961–62) 13

[127] Fujita, Y., Gottlieb, A., Peterkofsky, B., Udenfriend, S. and Witkop, B. *J. Am. chem. Soc.* 86 (1964) 4709

[128] Birkofer, L., Hempel, K. and Nouvertné, W. *Chem. Ber.* 98 (1965) 3200

[129] Schmidt, H-L., and Werner, G. *Justus Leibigs Annln Chem.* 656 (1962) 149

[130] Giovannozzi-Sermanni, G. and Possagno, E. *Energia nucl.* 7 (1960) 797

[131] Grodsky, G. M., Carbone, J. V., Fanska, R. and Peng, C. T. *Am. J. Physiol.* 203 (1962) 532

[132] Borenfreund, E., Rosenkranz, H. S., Bendlich, A. *J. molec. Biol.* 1 (1959) 195

[133] Hanngren, A., Hansson, E., Ullberg, S. and Aberg, B. *Nature, Lond.* 184 (1959) 373

[134] Oeff, K., Palme, G., Lindner, J. and Kolm, H. See ref. 6

[135] Irreverre, F., Morita, K., Robertson, A. V. and Witkop, B. *J. Am. chem. Soc.* 85 (1963) 2824

[136] Schrader, W. H. and Woolfrey, B. F. *Am. J. Path.* 42 (1963) 225

[137] Johns, D. G., Sperti, S. and Burgen, A. V. S. *J. clin. Invest.* 40 (1961) 1684

[138] Baumgartner, W. E., Lazer, L. S., Dalziel, A. M., Cardinal, E. V. and Varner, E. L. *J. agric. Fd Chem.* 7 (1959) 422

[139] Scharpenseel, H. W. *Landw. Forsch.* 14 (1961) 42

[140] Krizek, H., Verbiscar, A. J. and Brown, W. G. *J. org. Chem.* 29 (1964) 3443

[141] Scharpenseel, H. W. *Z. Pfl-Ernähr. Düng. Bodenk.* 91 (136) (1960) 131

[142] Thompson, W., Strickland, K. P., Rossiter, R. J. *Biochem. J.* 87 (1963) 136

[142a] Verly, W. European Atomic Energy Community, *Euratom Rep.* EUR 2531f (1965)

[143] Achor, L. B. *J. Pharm. exp. Ther.* 122 (1958) 1A (Abstract)

[144] Misra, A. L. and Woods, L. A. *Nature, Lond.* 185 (1960) 304

[145] Parups, E. V., Hoffman, I. and Jackson, H. R. *Talanta* 5 (1960) 75

[146] Cameron, G. G., Grassie, N. and Thomson, S. J. *J. chem. Soc.* (1960) 1411

[147] André, T. *Antibiotics Chemother.* 8 (1958) 195

[148] Nystrom, R. F., Nam, N. H. and Russo, A. J. *Proc. Conf. on Methods of Preparing and Storing Marked Molecules*, Brussels, Nov. 1963. European Atomic Energy Community, Euratom, EUR 1625e (May, 1964) p. 47

[149] Nam, N. H., Russo, A. J. and Nystrom, R. F. *Chemy Ind.* (1963) 1876

[150] Numrich, R. W., Nam, N. H. and Nystrom, R. F. *Chemy Ind.* (1964) 1269

[151] Speirs, R. S. *Proc. Symp. Tritium Phys. Biol. Sci.* I.A.E.A., Vienna 2 (1962) 419

[152] Carson, A. S., Cooper, R. and Stranks, D. R. *Proc. Conf. on Radioisotopes Phy. Sci. Ind.*, I.A.E.A., Vienna 3 (1962) 495

[153] Markovitz, A., Cifonelli, J. A. and Dorfman, A. *J. biol. Chem.* 234 (1959) 2343

[154] Markovitz, A., Cifonelli, J. A. and Cross, J. I. *Atomlight* (16) (1961) 1

[155] McMahon, R. E. *Experientia* 19 (1963) 434

[156] Peng, C. T. *J. Am. pharm. Ass.* 52 (1963) 861

[157] Beer, C. T., Wilson, M. L. and Bell, J. *Can. J. Chem.* 42 (1964) 1

[158] Baulieu, E. E. and Mauvais-Jarvis, P. *J. biol. Chem.* 239 (1964) 1569

[159] Chaudhuri, A. C., Harada, Y., Shimizu, K., Gut, M. and Dorfman, R. I. *J. Biol. Chem.* 237 (1962) 703

[160] Whisman, M. L. *Analyt. Chem.* 33 (1961) 1284

[161] Wollenberg, H. and Wenzel, M. *Z. Naturf.* 18b (1963) 8

[162] Edwards, B. E. and Rao, P. N. *Biochim. biophys. Acta* 115 (1966) 518

[163] Pauling, L. *The Nature of the Chemical Bond* 1945. Ithaca; Cornell University Press

[164] Cottrell, T. L. *The Strengths of Chemical Bonds* (2nd edn) 1958. London; Butterworths

[165] Wagner, A. F., Lusi, A., Folkers, K. *Archs Biochem. Biophys.* 101 (1963) 316

[166] Brodskii, A. I. and Sulima, L. V. *Dokl. Akad. Nauk SSSR*, 74 (1950) 513

[167] Avivi, P., Simpson, S. A., Tait, J. F. and Whitehead, J. K. *Proc. Radio-isotope Conf.* Oxford, 1 (1954) 313

[168] Hodnett, E. M., Andrews, W. R. *Proc. Oklahoma Acad. Sci.* 40 (1960) 71

[169] Elias, H., Lieser, K. H. and Sorg, F. *Radiochimica Acta* 2 (1963) 30

[170] Eidinoff, M. L. and Knoll, J. E. *J. Am. chem. Soc.* 75 (1953) 1992

[171] Schachter, D., Finkelstein, J. D., Kowarski, S. *J. clin. Invest.* 43 (1964) 787

[172] Halvarson, K. and Melander, L. *Ark. Kemi.* 8 (1955) 29

[173] Avinur, P. and Nir, A. *Bull. Res. Coun. Israel*, 7A (1958) 74

[174] Gold, V. and Satchell, R. S. *J. chem. Soc.* (1963) 1938

[175] Aliprandi, B. and Cacace, F. *Annali Chim.* 49 (1959) 2011

[176] Aliprandi, B. and Cacace, F. *Annali Chim.* 51 (1961) 397

[177] Mantescu, C. and Balaban, A. T. *Can. J. Chem.* 41 (1963) 2120

[177a] Mantescu, C., Genunche, A. and Balaban, A. T. *J. Labelled Compounds* 1 (1965) 178

[178] Yavorsky, P. M. and Gorin, E. *Chem. Engng News* April 9th (1962) 50; *J. Am. chem. Soc.* 84 (1962) 1071

[179] Schulze, P. E. and Dornfeldt, W. *Naturwissenschaften* 51 (1964) 58

[180] Yavorsky, P. M. and Gorin, E. *Consolidation Coal Co. Rep.* NYO–10178 (June, 1963)

[181] Hilton, B. D. and O'Brien, R. D. *J. agric. Fd Chem.* 12 (1964) 236

[182] Yavorsky, P. M. and Gorin, E. *Consolidation Coal Co. Rep.* NYO–9143 (April, 1961)

[183] Graul, E. H. and Hundeshagen, H. *Atompraxis* 5 (1959) 154

[184] Crowter, D. G., Evans, E. A. and Rasdell, R. *Chemy Ind.* (1962) 1622

[185] Garnett, J. L. and Sollich-Baumgartner, W. A. *J. phys. Chem.* 68 (1964) 3177

[186] Taylor, J. H., Woods, P. S. and Hughes, W. L. *Proc. Natn. Acad. Sci. U.S.A.* 43 (1957) 122

REFERENCES

187 Verly, W. G. and Hunebelle, G. *Bull. Soc. chim. Belg.* 66 (1957) 640
188 Murray, A., Petersen, D. F., Hayes, F. N. and Magee, M. *Los Alamos Biol. Med. Res. Gp Rep. Hlth Div.* LAMS–2627 (Jan.–June, 1961) p. 51
189 Thompson, S. J. and Walton, A. *Trans. Faraday Soc.* 53 (1957) 821
190 Fukushima, D. K. and Gallagher, T. F. *J. biol. Chem.* 198 (1952) 871
191 Garnett, J. L., Henderson, L. and Sollich, W. A. *Proc. Symp. Tritium Phys. Biol. Sci.*, I.A.E.A., Vienna 2 (1962) 47
192 Ashby, R. A. and Garnett, J. L. *Aust. J. Chem.* 16 (1963) 549
193 Garnett, J. L. and Sollich, W. A. *Nature, Lond.* 201 (1964) 902
194 Garnett, J. L. and Sollich, W. A. *J. Catalysis* 2 (1963) 339, 350
194a Garnett, J. L. and Sollich-Baumgartner, W. A. *J. phys. Chem.* 69 (1965) 3526
195 Garnett, J. L. and Sollich, W. A. *Aust. J. Chem.* 14 (1961) 441
195a Calf, G. E., Garnett, J. L., Halpern, B. H. and Turnbull, K. *Nature, Lond.* 209 (1966) 502
196 Garnett, J. L. *Nucleonics* 20 (12) (1962) 86
196a Garnett, J. L. and Sollich-Baumgartner, W. A. *J. Phys. Chem.* 69 (1965) 1850
197 Kritchevsky, D., McCandless, R. F. J., Knoll, J. E. and Eidinoff, M. L. *J. Am. chem. Soc.* 77 (1955) 6655
198 Crowter, D. G., Evans, E. A. and Lambert, R. W. *Chemy Ind.* (1960) 899
199 Gold, V. and Satchell, D. N. P. *Q. Rev. Chem. Soc.* 9 (1955) 51
200 Ueda, T. and Hirota, K. *J. chem. Soc. Japan* 84 (1963) 882 (In Japanese)
201 Rooney, J. J., Gault, F. G. and Kemball, C. *Proc. chem. Soc.* (1960) 407
202 Samuelsson, B. *J. biol. Chem.* 239 (1964) 4091
203 Sato, Y., Meshi, T. and Takahashi, T. *Bull. chem. Soc. Japan* 34 (1961) 167
204 Wells, P. B. *Chemy Ind.* (1964) 1742
205 Otto, P. Ph. H. L. *Proc. Conf. on Methods of Preparing and Storing Marked Molecules*, Brussels, Nov. 1963. European Atomic Energy Community, Euratom, EUR 1625e (May, 1964) p. 799
206 Rosenthal, D. J. and Kritchevsky, S. *U.S.A.E.C. Rep.* UCRL–1331 (1951)
207 Fontana, B. J. *J. Am. chem. Soc.* 64 (1942) 2503
208 Graul, E. H. and Hundeshagen, H. *Atompraxis* 5 (1959) 154
209 Graul, E. H. and Hundeshagen, H. *Strahlentherapie* 4 (1959) 524
210 Schildkneckt, H. and Schlegelmilch, F. *Radioisotopes Phys. Sci. Ind.*, I.A.E.A., Vienna 3 (1962) 73
211 Weisz, I., Gosztonyi, T., Kemeny, V. and Marton, J. *Tetrahedron Lett.* 2 (1964) 69
212 Bradley, J. E. S. *Nature, Lond.* 178 (1956) 1193
213 Gumbley, J. M. and Wilson, A. T. *Biochim. biophys. Acta* 74 (1963) 163
214 Wilson, E. J. *Vacuum* 4 (1954) 303
215 Wilson, E. J. *A.E.R.E. Harwell Rep.* AERE I/M 28 (July, 1953)
216 Swain, C. G. and Kresge, A. J. *J. Am. chem. Soc.* 80 (1958) 5281
217 Mahadevan, E. G. *Indian J. Chem.* 2 (1964) 1
218 Buu-Hoi, N. P. *Nature, Lond.* 180 (1957) 385
219 van Bac, N., Buu-Hoi, N. P. and Dat Xuong, N. *Bull. Soc. chim. Fr.* (1962) 1077
220 Tenny, K. S. *Diss. Abstr.* 22 (1961) 1574
221 Tenny, K. S., Gupta, S. C., Nystrom, R. F. and Kummerow, F. A. *J. Am. Oil Chem. Soc.* 40 (1963) 172
222 Sgoutas, D. S. and Kummerow, F. A. *Biochemistry N.Y.* 3 (1964) 406

223 Berstein, I. A., Bennett, W. and Fields, M. *J. Am. chem. Soc.* 74 (1952) 5763

224 Eidinoff, M. L., Knoll, J. E., Fukushima, D. K. and Gallagher, T. F. *J. Am. chem. Soc.* 74 (1952) 5280

225 Anderson, L. C. and MacNaughton, N. W. *J. Am. chem. Soc.* 64 (1942) 1456

226 Bigeleisen, J. *J. chem. Phys.* 17 (1949) 675

227 Glascock, R. F. and Reinius, L. R. *Biochem. J.* 62 (1956) 529

228 Stoffel, W. *Hoppe-Seyler's Z. physiol. Chem.* 333 (1963) 71

229 Borcic, S., Strelkov, T. and Sunko, D. E. *Croat. chem. Acta* 34 (1962) 243

230 Bryce-Smith, D. *Chemy Ind.* (6) (1964) 239

231 Unpublished Experiments by Dr. W. R. Waterfield (Radiochemical Centre)

232 Labrossa, E. H., Axelrod, J., Kopin, I. J. and Kety, S. S. *Proc. Symp. Tritium Phys. Biol. Sci.*, I.A.E.A., Vienna 2 (1962) 407

233 Andre, T. and Ullberg, S. *J. Am. chem. Soc.* 79 (1957) 494

234 Glascock, R. F. and Pope, G. S. *Biochem. J.* 75 (1960) 328

235 Buu-Hoi, N. P., Dat Xuong, N. and van Bac, N. (as ref. 248, p. 1237)

236 Koch, G. *Bull. Socs chim. belg.* 68 (1959) 59

237 Andre, T. *Nature, Lond.* 177 (1956) 379

238 Senoh, S., Creveling, C. R., Udenfriend, S. and Witkop, B. *J. Am. chem. Soc.* 81 (1959) 6236

239 Williams, D. L. and Ronzio, A. R. *J. Am. chem. Soc.* 72 (1950) 5787

240 Hokin, L. E. and Hokin, M. R. *J. biol. Chem.* 233 (1958) 805

241 Glascock, R. F. *Isotopic Gas Analysis for Biochemists* 1954. New York; Academic Press

242 Williams, D. L. and Ronzio, A. R. *U.S.A.E.C. Rep.* AECU–2126 (1952)

243 Michel, R., Truchot, R., Tron-Loisel, H. and Poillot, B. *Bull. Soc. Chim. biol.* 42 (1960) 1207

244 Stoffel, W. and Martius, C. *Biochem. Z.* 333 (1960) 440

245 Billeter, M. and Martius, C. *Biochem. Z.* 333 (1960) 430

246 Smith, H. H. and Srb, A. M. *Science, N.Y.* 114 (1951) 490

247 Roberts, J. J. and Warwick, G. P. *Biochem. Pharmac.* 12 (1963) 1441

248 Michel, R. and Truchot, R. *Proc. Conf. on Methods of Preparing and Storing Marked Molecules*, Brussels (Nov. 1963). European Atomic Energy Community, Euratom, EUR 1625e (May, 1964) p. 1171

249 Andrews, K. J. M., Bultitude, F., Evans, E. A., Gronow, M., Lambert, R. W. and Marrian, D. H. *J. chem. Soc.* (1962) 3440

250 Takesue, E. I., Tonelli, G., Alfano, L. and Buyske, D. A. *Int. J. appl. Radiat. Isotopes* 8 (1960) 52

251 Winand, M. and Gouverneur, L. *Proc. Conf. on Methods of Preparing and Storing Marked Molecules*, Brussels (Nov. 1963). European Atomic Energy Community—Euratom, EUR 1625e (May, 1964) p. 1147

252 Block, J. and Schmid, H. *Z. phys. Chem. (Frankft. Ausg.)* 40 (1964) 137

253 Contractor, S. F. *Biochem. Pharmac.* 12 (1963) 821

254 Rachele, J. R., Kuchinskas, E. J., Knoll, J. E. and Eidinoff, M. L. *Archs Biochem. Biophys.* 81 (1959) 55

255 Werbin, H. and Chaikoff, I. L. *Biochim. biophys. Acta* 82 (1964) 581 (cf. Agnello, E. J. and Laubach, G. D. *J. Am. chem. Soc.* 82 (1960) 4293)

256 Zielinski, M. *Nukleonika* 7 (1962) 789

REFERENCES

256a Moyer, J. D. and Ochs, R. J. *Science N.Y.* 142 (1963) 1316
257 Kaplan, L. *J. Am. chem. Soc.* 77 (1955) 5469
258 Melander, L. *Ark. Kemi.* 3 (1951) 525
259 Verly, W. G., Rachele, J. R., Du Vigneaud, V., Eidinoff, M. L. and Knoll, J. E. *J. Am. chem. Soc.* 74 (1952) 5941
260 Kaplan, L. *J. Am. chem. Soc.* 76 (1954) 4645
261 Wilzbach, K. E. and Kaplan, L. *J. Am. chem. Soc.* 72 (1950) 5795
262 Grisebach, H., Achenbach, H. and Hofheinz, W. *Proc. Symp. Tritium Phys. Biol. Sci.*, I.A.E.A., Vienna 2 (1962) 139
263 Park, G. S. *J. Soc. Dyers Colour.* 76 (1960) 624
264 Simon, H. and Heubach, G. *Z. Naturf.* 18b (1963) 159
265 Arnstein, H. R. V. and Crawhall, J. C. *Biochem. J.* 65 (1957) 18P
266 Kornblum, N., Jones, W. J. and Anderson, G. J. *J. Am. chem. Soc.* 81 (1959) 4113
267 Weygand, F., Daniel, H. and Simon, H. *Chem. Ber.* 91 (1958) 1691
268 Hodnett, E. M. and Gallagher, R. *J. org. Chem.* 24 (1959) 564
269 White, D. F., Campbell, I. G. and Payne, P. R. *Nature, Lond.* 166 (1950) 628
270 Dessy, R. E., Handler, G. S., Wotiz, J. H. and Hollingsworth, C. A. *J. Am. chem. Soc.* 79 (1957) 3476
271 Ito, R., Morikawa, N. and Simamura, O. *J. chem. Soc.* (1962) 4724
272 Green, K. and Samuelsson, B. *J. biol. Chem.* 239 (1964) 2804
273 Stöcklin, G., Schmidt-Bleek, F., Herr, W. *Angew. Chem.* 73 (1961) 220
274 Bestmann, H. J., Kratzer, O. and Simon, H. *Chem. Ber.* 95 (1962) 2750
274a Atkinson, J. G., Fisher, M. H., Horley, D., Morse, A. T., Stuart, R. S. and Synnes, E. *Can. J. Chem.* 43 (1965) 1614
275 Smith, H. A. and Lindauer, M. *Proc. Conf. on Methods of Preparing and Storing Marked Molecules*, Brussels (Nov. 1963). European Atomic Energy Community—Euratom, EUR 1625e (May, 1964) p. 171
276 Murray, A. and Williams, D. L. *Organic Syntheses with Isotopes* 1958. New York; Interscience
277 Melander, L. *Ark. Kemi.* 2 (1950) 275
278 Melander, L. *Ark. Kemi.* 2 (1950) 260
279 Kresge, A. J. and Chiang, Y. *J. Am. chem. Soc.* 83 (1961) 2877
279a Blatchly, J. M. and Taylor, R. *J. Chem. Soc.* (1965) 4641
280 Assarsson, L. O. *Acta chem. scand.* 9(1955) 1399
281 Pichat, L., Sharefkin, D. and Herbert, M. CEA–2234 (1962)
282 Berstein, I. A., Bennett, W., Fields, M. and Farmer, E. C. *Nucleonics* 11 (2) (1953) 64
283 Done, J. and Payne, P. R. *Biochem. J.* 64 (1956) 266
284 Jacquemin, C., Michel, R., Nunez, J. and Roche, J. *C. r. hebd. Séanc. Acad. Sci. Paris* 249 (1959) 1904
285 Hempel, Kl. *Proc. Conf. on Methods of Preparing and Storing Marked Molecules*, Brussels (Nov. 1963). European Atomic Energy Community—Euratom, EUR 1625e (May, 1964) p. 1009
285a Hug, C. C. and Mellett, L. B. *Univ. Mich. Med. Bull.* 29 (1963) 165
286 Leonis, J. (as ref. 285, p. 983)
287 Baeyens, W., Zamorani, G. and Ledoux, L. (as ref. 285, p. 1191)
288 Caro, L. G. and Palade, G. E. *J. Cell Biol.* 20 (1964) 473
289 Dingman, J. F., Meyers, W. W., Agishi, Y. and Wysocki, A. P. *Fedn. Proc. Fedn Am. Socs exp. Biol.* 22 (2, Pt. 1) (1963) 386 (Abstract only)

290 Barbour, B. H. and Bartter, F. C. *J. clin. Endocr. Metab.* 23 (1963) 313

291 Margen, S. and Tarver, H. *Atomlight* (39) (1964) 1

292 Sato, Y., Meshi, T., Takahashi, T. and Sugimoto, N. *Jap. J. Pharm. Chem.* 32 (1960) 317

293 Birkofer, L. and Hempel, K. *Chem. Ber.* 96 (1963) 1373

294 Schreier, E., Pacha, W. and Rutschmann, J. *Helv. chim. Acta* 46 (1963) 954

295 Robertson, A. V., Katz, E. and Witkop, B. *J. org. Chem.* 27 (1962) 2676

296 Sato, Y., Takahashi, T. and Meshi, T. *Radio-Isotopes (Tokyo)* 10 (1961) 488

297 Cline, J. F. *Pl. Physiol., Lancaster* 28 (1953) 717

298 Birkofer, L. and Hempel, K. *Chem. Ber.* 93 (1960) 2282

299 Fridkin, M., Sokolovsky, M. and Katchalski, E. *J. Polym. Sci. Part D.* 2 (1964) 123

300 Weiss, B. *J. biol. Chem.* 238 (1963) 1953

301 Nunez, J., Jacquemin, C. and Roche, J. *Int. J. appl. Radiat. Isotopes* 13 (1962) 573

301a Tietz, A., Lindberg, M. and Kennedy, E. P. *J. biol. Chem.* 239 (1964) 4081

302 Tata, J. R. and Brownstone, A. D. *Nature, Lond.* 185 (1960) 34

303 Crawhall, J. C. and Smyth, D. G. *Biochem. J.* 69 (1958) 280

304 Robertson, A. V. and Witkop, B. *J. Am. chem. Soc.* 84 (1962) 1697

305 Bloom, B. and Foster, D. W. *J. biol. Chem.* 239 (1964) 967

306 Isbell, H. S., Frush, H. L., Holt, N. B. and Moyer, J. D. *J. Res. Nat. Bur. Stand.* 64A (1960) 177

307 Frush, H. L., Isbell, H. S. and Fatiadi, A. J. *J. Res. Nat. Bur. Stand.* 64A (1960) 433

308 Isbell, H. S., Frush, H. L. and Moyer, J. D. *J. Res. Nat. Bur. Stand.* 64A (1960) 359

309 Moss, G. *Archs Biochem. Biophys.* 90 (1960) 111

310 Kohn, B. D. and Kohn, P. *J. org. Chem.* 28 (1963) 1037

311 Bevill, R. D., Nordin, J. H., Smith, F. and Kirkwood, S. *Biochem. biophys. Res. Commun.* 12 (1963) 152

312 Duschinsky, R., Pleven, E. and Heidelberger, C. *J. Am. chem. Soc.* 79 (1957) 4559

313 Parkanyi, C. and Sorm, F. *Coll. Czech. chem. Commun. Engl. edn.* 28 (1963) 2491

314 Moravek, J. and Filip, J. *Coll. Czech. chem. Commun. Engl. edn.* 25 (1960) 2697

315 Lindauer, M. W. and Smith, H. A. *J. org. Chem.* 27 (1962) 2245

316 Kalberer, F. and Rutschmann, J. *Helv. chim. Acta* 46 (1963) 586

317 Pullman, M. E., San Pietro, A. and Colowick, S. P. *J. biol. Chem.* 206 (1954) 129

318 San Pietro, A. *J. biol. Chem.* 217 (1955) 579

319 Krakow, G., Ludowieg, J., Mather, J. H., Normore, W. M., Tosi, L., Udaka, S. and Vennesland, B. *Biochemistry* 2 (1963) 1009

319a Chaykin, S. *Atomlight* (43) (1965) 1

320 I.U.P.A.C. *Rules for the Nomenclature of Steroids* (1957), see 'Handbook for Chemical Society Authors' Special Publication No. 14, Chem. Soc. London, 1960, p. 132

321 Antonucci, R., Bernstein, S., Giancola, D. and Sax, K. J. *J. org. Chem.* 16 (1951) 1126

REFERENCES

[322] Gut, M. and Uskokovic, M. *J. org. Chem.* 25 (1962) 792

[323] Corey, E. J. and Gregoriou, G. A. *J. Am. chem. Soc.* 81 (1959) 3127

[324] Osinski, P. *Proc. Symp. Tritium Phys. Biol. Sci.* I.A.E.A., Vienna 2 (1962) 113

[325] Shepherd, D. A., Donia, R. A., Campbell, J. A., Johnson, B. A., Holysz, R. P., Slomp, G., Stafford, J. E., Pederson, R. L. and Ott, A. C. *J. Am. chem. Soc.* 77 (1955) 1212

[326] Coombs, M. M. and Roderick, H. R. *Nature, Lond.* 203 (1964) 523

[327] Thompson, G. A. National Institute for Medical Research, 'Chemical Studies in the Vitamin D Field', *Ph.D. Thesis*, University of London, 1964

[328] Bergström, S., Lindstedt, S. and Sen, D. *Acta chem. scand.* 11 (1957) 1692

[329] cf. Evans, E. A. and Whalley, M. *J. chem. Soc.* (1954) 3642

[329a] Björkem, I., Danielsson, H., Issidorides, C. and Kallner, A. *Acta chem. Scand.* 19 (1965) 2151

[330] Rakhit, S. and Gut, M. *J. Am. chem. Soc.* 86 (1964) 1432

[331] Osinski, P. A. *Proc. Conf. on Methods of Preparing and Storing Marked Molecules* Brussels (Nov. 1963). European Atomic Energy Community—Euratom EUR 1625e (May, 1964) p. 1177

[332] Laumas, K. R. and Gut, M. *J. org. Chem.* 27 (1962) 314

[333] Pearlman, W. H. *J. biol. Chem.* 236 (1961) 700

[334] Samuelsson, B. (as ref. 331, p. 251)

[335] Clayton, R. B. and Edwards, A. M. *J. biol. Chem.* 238 (1963) 1966

[336] Osinski, P. and Vanderhaeghe, H. *Recl Trav. chim. Pays-Bas. Belg.* 79 (1960) 216

[337] Segel, K. H. *J. prakt. Chem.* 13 (1961) 152

[338] Jerchel, D., Henke, S. and Thomas, Kl. (as ref. 331, p. 1115)

[339] Lindberg, M., Gautschi, F. and Bloch, K. *J. biol. Chem.* 238 (1963) 1661

[340] Roche, J., Nunez, J., Jacquemin, C. and Pommier, J. (as ref. 331, p. 1035)

[341] Nunez, J., Jacquemin, C. and Roche, J. *Int. J. appl. Radiat. Isotopes* 13 (1962) 611

[342] Uskokovic, M. and Gut, M. *J. org. Chem.* 22 (1957) 996

[343] O'Donnell, V. J. and Pearlman, W. H. *Biochem. J.* 69 (1958) 38P

[344] O'Donnell, V. J., Preedy, J. R. K. and Pearlman, W. H. *Biochem. J.* 90 (1964) 527

[345] Gut, M. and Uskokovic, M. *Naturwissenschaften* 47 (1960) 40

[346] Cooley, G. and Kellie, A. E. *Biochem. J.* 93 (1964) 8C

[347] Van Kamp, H., Westerhof, P. and Niewind, H. *Recl Trav. chim. Pays-Bas. Belg.* 83 (1964) 509

[348] Pearlman, W. H. *Biochem. J.* 67 (1957) 1

[349] Schroepfer, G. J. *J. biol. Chem.* 236 (1961) 1668

[350] Gut, M. and Hayano, M. *Atomlight* (23) (1962) 1

[351] Brown, H. C. *Hydroboration* 1962. New York; Benjamin

[352] Rigden, J. S. and Koski, W. S. *J. Am. chem. Soc.* 83 (1961) 3037

[353] Brown, H. C. and Subba Rao, B. C. *J. Am. chem. Soc.* 81 (1959) 6428

[354] Brown, H. C. and Subba Rao, B. C. *J. Am. chem. Soc.* 81 (1959) 6434

[355] Brodskii, A. I. and Khaskin, I. G. *Dokl. Akad. Nauk SSSR* 74 (1950) 299

[356] Kaplan, L. and Wilzbach, K. E. *J. Am. chem. Soc.* 74 (1952) 6152

[357] Falk, G. J. and King, R. C. *Radiat. Res.* 20 (1963) 466

[358] Heusinger, H. and H. Rau *Kerntechnik* 3 (1961) 67

THE PREPARATION OF TRITIUM-LABELLED COMPOUNDS

358a Heusinger, H., Reinhartz, K., Rau, H. and Freitag, W. *Kerntechnik* 5 (1963) 213

359 *Brit. Patent 874,791* Gamma Ges. für Praktishe Radiologie Hartmann Futternecht and Westo G.m.b.H. Fabrik für Chemisch-Technische Erzeugnisse (10th August, 1961)

360 Smith, N. H., Wilzbach, K. E. and Brown, W. G. *J. Am. chem. Soc.* 77 (1955) 1033

361 Westfahl, J. C. and Gresham, T. L. *J. org. Chem.* 21 (1956) 1145

362 Lacassagne, A., Buu-Hoi, N. P., Dat Xuong, N., Zajdela, F. and Eckert, B. *C. r. hebd. Séanc. Acad. Sci. Paris* 235 (1952) 589

363 Steiner, B., Arnold, H., Graul, E. H., Bekel, H., Hundeshagen, H. and Wilmanns, W. *Atompraxis* 10 (1964) 358

364 Rowland, F. S. *Inorganic Isotopic Syntheses* Ed. Herber, R. H. p. 54, 1962. New York; Benjamin

365 Nyholm, R. S. *Chemy Ind.* (1963) 207

366 Isbell, H. S. and Moyer, J. D. *J. Res. Nat. Bur. Stand.* 63A (1959) 177

367 Uchida, T. *J. pharm. Soc. Japan* 85 (1965) 638

368 Brown, W. G., Kaplan, L. and Wilzbach, K. E. *J. Am. Chem. Soc.* 74 (1952) 1343

369 Staats, P. A., Morgan, H. W., Goldstein, J. H. *J. phys. Chem.* 25 (1956) 582

370 Jones, L. H. and Robinson, E. S. *J. chem. Phys.* 24 (1956) 1246

371 Burrus, C., Gordy, W., Benjamin, B. and Livingston, R. *Phys. Rev.* 97 (1955) 1661

372 Klein, F. and Wolfsberg, M. *J. chem. Phys.* 34 (1961) 1494

373 Satchell, D. P. N. *J. chem. Soc.* (1960) 4388

374 Comyns, A. E., Howald, R. A. and Willard, J. E. *J. Am. chem. Soc.* 78 (1956) 3989

375 Gutmann, J. R. and Wolfsberg, M. *J. chem. Phys.* 33 (1960) 1592

376 Landsberg, G. S., Shatenshtein, A. I., Peregudov, V., Izrailevich, E. A. and Novikova, L. A. *Izv. Akad. Nauk SSSR, Ser. Fiz.* (1954) 669; *Optika i Spektroskopiya* 1 (1956) 34

377 Kaplan, L. and Wilzbach, K. E. *J. Am. chem. Soc.* 76 (1954) 2593

378 Jenkins, W. A. and Yost, D. M. *J. inorg. nucl. Chem.* 11 (1959) 297

379 Felter, R. E. and Currie, L. A. *Proc. Symp. Tritium Phys. Biol. Sci.* I.A.E.A., Vienna 2 (1962) 61

380 Evans, C. and Wilson, E. J. *U.K.A.E.A. Res. Establ.* Harwell, *Rep.* AERE I/M 31 (1954)

381 Gow, J. D. and Pollock, H. C. *Rev. Scient. Instrum.* 31 (1960) 235

382 Arrol, W. J., Wilson, E. J. and Evans, C. *U.K.A.E.A. Res. Establ.* Harwell, *Rep.* AERE 1/R 1135 (1953)

383 Trujillo, T. T. and Langham, W. H. *Los Alamos Biol. Med. Div. Rep.* LAMS-2526 (July–Dec., 1960) 302

384 Mantescu, C. and Genunche, A. *Can. J. Chem.* 41 (1963) 3145

385 Parikh, J. R., Greenstein, J. P., Winitz, M. and Birnbaum, S. M. *J. Am. chem. Soc.* 80 (1958) 953

386 Evans, E. A., Green, R. H., Spanner, J. A. and Waterfield, W. R. *Nature, Lond.* 198 (1963) 1301

387 Friedkin, M. and Roberts, D. *J. biol. Chem.* 207 (1954) 245, 257

388 Sekiguchi, T. and Yoshikawa, H. *J. Biochem., Tokyo* 46 (1959) 1505

389 Macnutt, W. S. *Biochem. J.* 50 (1952) 384

390 Friedkin, M. and Roberts, D. *J. biol. Chem.* 207 (1954) 261

REFERENCES

[391] Abrahams, S. *Atomlight* (36) (1964) 1; *Adv. Tracer Methodol.* 2 (1965) 49

[392] Wenzel, M. and Günther, T. *Proc. Conf. on Methods of Preparing and Storing Marked Molecules*, Brussels (Nov. 1963). European Atomic Energy Community—Euratom, EUR 1625e (May, 1964) p. 971

[393] Eidinoff, M. L., Reilly, H. C., Knoll, J. E. and Marrian, D. H. *J. biol. Chem.* 199 (1952) 511

[394] Simon, H. and Trebst, A. *Z. Naturf.* 16b (1961) 285

[395] Moses, V. and Calvin, M. *Biochim. biophys. Acta* 33 (1959) 297

[396] Aronoff, S. and Choi, I. C.-S. *Archs Biochem. Biophys.* 102 (1963) 159

[397] Dutton, H. J., Jones, E. P., Scholfield, C. R., Chorney, W. and Scully, N. J. *J. Lipid Res.* 2 (1961) 63

[398] Foster, D. W. and Bloom, B. *J. biol. Chem.* 238 (1963) 888

[398a] Hulanicka, D., Erwin, J. and Block, K. *J. biol. Chem.* 239 (1964) 2778

[399] Weinberger, D. and Porter, J. W. *Hanford Works Rep.* Washington U.S.A., HW–29193 (1953)

[400] Weinberger, D. and Porter, J. W. *Science, N.Y.* 117 (1953) 636

[401] Porter, J. W. and Knauss, H. J. *Hanford Works Rep.* Washington U.S.A., HW–30252 (1953)

[401a] Porter, J. W. and Knauss, H. J. *Radiat. Res.* 1 (1954) 253

[402] Porter, J. W. and Watson, M. S. *Hanford Works Rep.* Washington U.S.A. HW–30056 (1953)

[403] Chapman-Andresen, C. *Expl Cell Res.* 4 (1953) 239

[404] Chorney, W., Scully, N. J., Crespi, H. L. and Katz, J. J. *Biochim. biophys. Acta* 37 (1960) 280

[405] Crespi, H. L., Marmur, J. and Katz, J. J. *J. Am. chem. Soc.* 84 (1962) 3489

[406] Haskell, T. H., French, J. C. and Bartz, Q. R. *J. Am. chem. Soc.* 81 (1959) 3482

[407] Ober, R. E., Fusari, S. A., Coffey, G. L., Gwynn, G. W. and Glazko, A. J. *Atomlight* (22) (1962) 3

[408] Paoletti, C. and Lamonthezie, N. *Proc. Conf. on Methods of Preparing and Storing Marked Molecules*, Brussels (Nov. 1963). European Atomic Energy Community—Euratom EUR 1625e (May, 1964) p. 855

[409] Bodmer, W. and Schildkraut, C. *Analyt. Biochem.* 8 (1964) 229

[410] Ciferri, O., Fraccaro, M., Albertini, A., Cassani, G., Mannini, A. and Tiepolo, L. *Proc. Conf. Preparation and Bio-Medical Applications of Labelled Molecules*, Venice, 23–29th Aug. 1964. European Atomic Energy Community Euratom EUR 2200e (Dec. 1964) p. 147

[411] Canfield, R. E. and Anfinsen, C. B. *Biochemistry* 2 (1963) 1073

[412] Nunez, J., Mauchamp, J., Roche, J. *Biochim. biophys. Acta* 86 (1964) 361

[413] Bauer, G. E., Lindall, A. W., and Lazarow, A. *Atomlight* (38) (1964) 1

[414] Smith, G. H., Mallory, A., Gardner, G. and Taylor, K. W. *Biochem. J.* 85 (1962) 36P

[415] Mallory, A., Smith, G. H. and Taylor, K. W. *Biochem. J.* 91 (1964) 484

[416] Taylor, K. W. and Smith, G. H. *Biochem. J.* 91 (1964) 491

[417] Taylor, K. W., Parry, D. G. and Smith, G. H. *Nature, Lond.* 203 (1964) 1144

[417a] Taylor, K. W., Gardner, G., Parry, D. G. and Jones, V. E. *Biochim. biophys. Acta* 100 (1965) 521

[418] Bernlohr, R. W., Novelli, G., D. *Archs Biochem. Biophys.* 103 (1963) 94

[419] Ayres, P. J., Pearlman, W. H., Tait, J. F. and Tait, S. A. S. *Biochem. J.* 70 (1958) 230

420 Ayres, P. J. *Proc. Symp. Tritium Phys. Biol. Sci.* I.A.E.A., Vienna 2 (1962) 131
421 Wolfgang, R., Rowland, F. S. and Turton, C. N. *Science, N.Y.* 121 (1955) 715
422 Rowland, F. S., Lee, J. K., Musgrave, B. and White, R. M. *Proc. Symp. Chemical Effects of Nuclear Transformations*, I.A.E.A., Vienna 2 (1961) 67
423 Nesmeyanov, An. N. and Pozdeev, V. V. *Usp. Khim.* 32 (1963) 773
424 El-Sayed, M. A., Estrup, P. J. and Wolfgang, R. *J. phys. Chem.* 62 (1958) 1356
425 Muschlitz, E. E. and Simons, J. H. *J. phys. Chem.* 56 (1952) 837
426 Allison, S. K. *Rev. mod. Phys.* 30 (1958) 1137
427 Bernarie, M. M. *J. inorg. nucl. Chem.* 18 (1961) 32
428 Schmidt-Bleek, F. and Rowland, F. S. *Angew. Chem. int. edn.* 3 (1964) 769
429 Wolfgang, R., Eigner, J. and Rowland, F. S. *J. phys. Chem.* 60 (1956) 1137
430 El-Sayed, M. F. A. and Wolfgang, R. *J. Am. chem. Soc.* 79 (1957) 3286
431 Rowland, F. S. and Wolfgang, R. L. *Nucleonics* 14 (8) (1956) 58
432 Elatrash, A. M., Johnsen, R. H. and Wolfgang, R. *J. phys. Chem.* 64 (1960) 785
433 Hoff, W. J. and Rowland, F. S. *J. Am. chem. Soc.* 79 (1957) 4867
434 Evans, C. C. and Maynard, J. C. *U.S. Patent* 3,210,288 (Oct. 5, 1965)
435 Kay, J. G., Malsan, R. P. and Rowland, F. S. *J. Am. chem. Soc.* 81 (1959) 5050
436 Nesmeyanov, An. N., Dzantiev, B. G., Pozdeev, V. V. and Simonov, E. F. *Radiokhimiya* 4 (1962) 116
437 Nesmeyanov, An. N., Dzantiev, B. G., Pozdeev, V. V. and Rumyantsev, Yu. M. *Proc. Conf. Use Radioisotopes Phys. Sci. and Industry*, I.A.E.A., Copenhagen, Sept., 1960, 2 (1962) 130
438 Okamoto, J. *Bull. chem. Soc. Japan* 33 (1960) 1629
439 Ciranni, E., Ciranni, G. and Guarino, A. *Gazz. chim. ital.* 93 (1963) 610
440 White, R. M. and Rowland, F. S. *J. Am. chem. Soc.* 82 (1960) 5345
441 Krizek, H., Garnett, J. and Brown, W. G. *Argonne Cancer Research Hospital ACRH–4* (Sept. 1955) p. 88
442 Topchiev, A. V., Polak, L. S., Chernyak, N. Ya., Glushev, V. E., Glazunov, P. Ya., Vereshchinskii, I. V., Syrkun, N. P., Breger, A. Kh. and Vanshtein, B. I. *Radioactive Isotopes and Nuclear Radiations in the National Economy of the USSR*, Vol. I, 1961. Moscow; Gostoptekhizdat
443 Akhtar, S. and Smith, H. A. *Rev. Scient. Instrum.* 36 (1965) 1250
444 Rowland, F. S., Turton, C. N. and Wolfgang, R. *J. Am. chem. Soc.* 78 (1956) 2354
445 Keller, H. and Rowland, F. S. *J. phys. Chem.* 62 (1958) 1373
446 Meshi, T. and Sato, Y. *Bull. chem. Soc. Japan* 36 (1963) 750
447 White, R. M. and Rowland, F. S. *J. Am. chem. Soc.* 82 (1960) 4713
448 Brown, W. G. and Garnett, J. L. *Int. J. appl. Radiat. Isotopes* 5 (1959) 114
449 Dawson, R. F., Christman, D. R., D'Adamo, A., Solt, M. L. and Wolf, A. P. *J. Am. chem. Soc.* 82 (1960) 2628
450 Elatrash, A. M. and Johnsen, R. H. *Proc. Symp. Chemical Effects of Nuclear Transformations*, I.A.E.A., Vienna 2 (1961) 123
451 Rowland, F. S. and Numerof, P. *Int. J. appl. Radiat. Isotopes* 1 (1957) 246
452 Sheppard, H., Tsien, W. H., Plummer, A. J., Peets, E. A., Giletti, B. J. and Schubert, A. R. *Proc. Soc. exp. Biol. Med.* 97 (1958) 717

REFERENCES

[453] Caffrey, J. M. and Allen, A. O. *J. phys. Chem.* 62 (1958) 33

[454] Sato, Y., Meshi, T. and Takahashi, T. *Bull. chem. Soc. Japan* 33 (1960) 1146

[455] Zifferero, M. *Energia Nucl.* 4 (1957) 479

[456] Ache, H. J., Herr, W. and Thiemann, A. *Proc. Symp. Tritium Phys. Biol. Sci.* I.A.E.A., Vienna 2 (1962) 21

[457] Kambara, T., White, R. M. and Rowland, F. S. *J. inorg. nucl. Chem.* 21 (1961) 210

[458] Rowland, F. S. *J. chem. Phys.* 30 (1959) 1098

[459] Pritchard, J., Urch, D. S. and Welch, M. J. *J. inorg. nucl. Chem.* 26 (1964) 1121

[460] Sauer, M. C. and Willard, J. E. *J. phys. Chem.* 64 (1960) 359

[461] Estrup, P. J. and Wolfgang, R. *J. Am. chem. Soc.* 82 (1960) 2661, 2665

[462] Gordus, A. A., Sauer, M. C. and Willard, J. E. *J. Am. chem. Soc.* 79 (1957) 3284

[463] Henchman, M. and Wolfgang, R. *J. Am. chem. Soc.* 83 (1961) 2991

[464] Urch, D. and Wolfgang, R. *J. Am. chem. Soc.* 83 (1961) 2997

[465] Henchman, M., Urch, D. and Wolfgang, R. *Proc. Symp. Chemical Effects of Nuclear Transformations*, I.A.E.A., Vienna 2 (1961) 83

[466] Lee, J. K., Musgrave, B. and Rowland, F. S. *Can. J. Chem.* 38 (1960) 1756

[467] Umezawa, H. and Rowland, F. S. *J. Am. chem. Soc.* 84 (1962) 3077

[468] Lee, E. K. C. and Rowland, F. S. *J. phys. Chem.* 66 (1962) 2622

[469] Wolfgang, R. *J. Am. chem. Soc.* 84 (1962) 4586

[470] Hsiung, C. and Gordus, A. A. *J. chem. Phys.* 39 (1963) 2770

[471] Lee, E. K. C. and Rowland, F. S. *J. Am. chem. Soc.* 85 (1963) 2907

[472] Breckenridge, W., Root, J. W. and Rowland, F. S. *J. chem. Phys.* 39 (1963) 2374

[473] Wolfgang, R. *J. chem. Phys.* 39 (1963) 2983

[474] Lee, E. K. C. and Rowland, F. S. *J. Am. chem. Soc.* 85 (1963) 897

[475] Jurgeleit, H. C. and Wolfgang, R. *J. Am. chem. Soc.* 85 (1963) 1057

[476] Root, J. W. and Rowland, F. S. *J. Am. chem. Soc.* 85 (1963) 1021

[477] Rosenberg, A. H. and Wolfgang, R. *J. chem. Phys.* 41 (1964) 2159

[478] Tang, Y.-N., Lee, E. K. C. and Rowland, F. S. *J. Am. chem. Soc.* 86 (1964) 1280

[479] Hsiung, C., Verosub, K. L. and Gordus, A. A. *J. chem. Phys.* 41 (1964) 1595

[480] Dzantiev, B. G. and Shvetchikov, A. P. *Radiokhimiya* 6 (1964) 371; *Soviet Radiochemistry* 6 (1964) 359

[481] Wolf, A. P. *Advances in Physical Organic Chemistry* 2 (1964) 201. Ed. Gold, V. (Academic Press, London and New York)

[482] Odum, R. A. and Wolfgang, R. *J. Am. chem. Soc.* 85 (1963) 1050

[483] Pozdeev, V. V., Nesmeyanov, An. N. and Dzantiev, B. G. *Radiokhimiya* 5 (1963) 395

[484] Pozdeev, V. V., Nesmeyanov, An. N. and Dzantiev, B. G. *Radiokhimiya* 4 (1962) 615 (*Radiochemistry* 4 (1962) 540)

[485] Erdman, K. L., Robertson, L. P., Axen, D. and MacDonald, J. R. *Rev. scient. Instrum.* 34 (1963) 1280

[486] Lee, E. K. C., Tang, Y. N. and Rowland, F. S. *J. Am. chem. Soc.* 86 (1964) 5038

[487] Henchman, M., Urch, D. and Wolfgang, R. *Can. J. Chem.* 38 (1960) 1722

[488] Nesmeyanov, An. N., Wang, L. S. and Bekker, A. *Radiokhimiya* 6 (1964) 314
[489] Nesmeyanov, An. N., Dzantiev, B. G., Pozdeev, V. V. and Simonov, E. F. *Radiokhimiya* 4 (1962) 116 (*Radiochemistry* 4 (1962) 100)
[490] Urch, D. and Wolfgang, R. *Proc. Symp. Chemical Effects of Nuclear Transformations*, I.A.E.A., Vienna 2 (1961) 99
[491] Brown, W. G. and Garnett, J. L. *Proc. Symp. peaceful Uses Atom. Energy in Australia* 1958, p. 575 (Melbourne University Press)
[492] Avdonina, E. N. *Radiokhimiya* 4 (1962) 617 (*Radiochemistry* 4 (1962) 542)
[493] Lee, E. K. C. and Rowland, F. S. *J. inorg. nucl. Chem.* 25 (1963) 132
[494] Lee, E. K. C. and Rowland, F. S. *J. chem. Phys.* 36 (1962) 554
[495] Lee, E. K. C. and Rowland, F. S. *J. Am. chem. Soc.* 84 (1962) 3085

CHAPTER 5

MEASUREMENT AND ANALYSIS OF TRITIUM COMPOUNDS

The usefulness of radioactive tracers ultimately depends upon the availability of reliable, rapid and accurate methods for radioactive measurement of the isotope, and techniques for the analysis and identification of its labelled compounds. It is only in recent years that these requirements have been fulfilled for tritium. There is no doubt that there would have been an earlier and more rapid growth in the applications of tritium and its compounds if it had been easier to measure and analyse tritium compounds.

In this chapter the various methods for the measurement of tritium are briefly described, with particular emphasis on β-liquid scintillation measurement with which the author has most experience. However, as the needs of the individual are likely to vary considerably, a bibliography is included. This is divided into four principal sections:

1. Scintillation measurement.
2. Ionization-chamber methods.
3. Geiger and proportional gas counting.
4. Windowless gas-flow methods.

References to December 1964 are included and these are arranged in order of years, alphabetically with the first author.

The importance of checking the purity of tritium compounds before use is again stressed and suitable analytical methods, including possible pitfalls, are discussed.

Autoradiographic techniques are described in some detail since many of the applications of tritium compounds are based on the use of such techniques.

It is becoming more apparent that a knowledge of the isotopic abundance of tritium at various positions within a labelled molecule is not only desirable but essential, in order to assess the probability of tritium displacement from the molecule by exchange or substitution by other atoms. The present state of knowledge and methods for establishing the intramolecular distribution of tritium are therefore included in this chapter.

MEASUREMENT

Most of the standard methods for the measurement of radioactivity, scintillation methods, ionization chamber-electrometer, Geiger and proportional counting of gases and of solids in windowless gas-flow counters, are available for the measurement of the tritium β-radiation.

Because this radiation is so weak, the tritium sample to be measured must be inside the counter in some form. End-window counting is not possible even with the ultra-thin windows now available, except for tritium Bremsstrahlung measurement and then only at relatively high activities[1-3].

The method of choice depends upon a number of factors; the form of the sample, the accuracy required, the specific activity of the sample (microcuries per gramme) and to a lesser extent on the total activity to be measured. Table 5.1 gives a summary of these various considerations.

TABLE 5.1

Measurement method	Form of sample	Minimum detectability	Accuracy	Efficiency	Uses
Beta liquid scintillation	Gas, liquid or solid dissolved in a solvent containing an organic phosphor	$10^{-4}\,\mu c$	$\pm 2\%$	10–40%	Analysis of tritiated samples of all types, particularly in biological investigations*
Ionization chamber-electrometer	Gas- usually hydrogen or lower hydrocarbon such as methane or acetylene	$10^{-4}\,\mu c$	$\pm 1\%$	70%	Air monitors, urine analyses, gas–liquid chromatography†
Geiger or proportional gas counting	Gas–hydrogen, methane and similar lower hydrocarbons or water vapour	$10^{-4}\,\mu c$	$\pm 2\%$	70%	Tritium from natural sources, gas–liquid chromatography†
Windowless gas-flow	Solid sources (a) infinitely thin	$10^{-3}\,\mu c$	$\pm 2\%$	1–5%	Paper and thin-layer chromatogram scanners†
	(b) infinitely thick	$10^{-1}\,\mu c$	$\pm 2\%$	1–5%	Tritium compound analysis‡
End-window (Bremsstrahlung or x-rays)	Solid or liquid (infinitely thin)	$1\,\mu c$	$\pm 5\%$	1%	Compound analysis§

* Much used. † Moderate use. ‡ Little used. § Seldom used.

A brief description of these various methods of measurement with some of their advantages and disadvantages, is now given, but for rather more detailed information readers should consult original papers selected from the bibliography.

Scintillation Measurement

From the bibliography it is seen that in recent years β-liquid scintillation measurement of tritium has become the method of choice for most users. The principle of the method is the conversion of the β-radiation energy into photoelectrons producing charge pulses which can be amplified and counted by a scaling circuit (see page 220).

A book [234] consisting of the papers given at a symposium on liquid scintillation counting held at Northwestern University, America, in 1957, is recommended for reading. This gives the reader a good general account of the basic principles and the applicability of β-liquid scintillation measurement, not only for tritium but for other weak β-emitters as well. The subject has also been well reviewed [4,5,365].

The requirements for the scintillation measurement of tritium are:

(a) A suitable instrument. (b) A scintillant capable of efficiently transferring the β-energy into photons.

1. *Types of Instruments*

The first task which befalls a research worker before beginning investigations with tritium (or other radioactive isotopes), is to select a suitable instrument for measurement of the samples. A number of sound commercial instruments are available for the measurement of tritium by β-liquid scintillation counting (see reference 5).

The instruments may be designed for single- or multi-channel operation. Single-channel instruments are available with or without coincidence circuitry. Non-coincidence counters with a single photomultiplier tube are normally used at temperatures around $-20°$ C to reduce the background count due to noise in the photomultiplier tube. Although the efficiency is usually as high as 40 per cent for tritium (80 per cent or more for carbon-14), disadvantages include the necessity for cooling the sample and allowing photoluminescence to decay before measurement, which may take 20 min or longer and adds greatly to the total time for sample measurement. The precipitation or crystallization of the sample from the scintillant at the low temperatures is also possible, which may produce erratic results.

Lambie [6] describes the detailed operation of sample measurement with this type of instrument.

The introduction of coincidence circuitry has revolutionized liquid scintillation measurement and enables samples to be conveniently measured at room temperature. In the single-channel coincidence type instrument, the sample is viewed by two photomultiplier tubes and only light pulses which are seen by the two tubes simultaneously are counted. Background counts are therefore quite low (usually not more than 200 c.p.m.) as the random counts from the photomultiplier tube noise or those produced by cosmic radiation are not recorded. Some events attributed to these two sources will of course be co-incident and constitute the background.

The resolving time of such instruments is about 10^{-7} sec, but the efficiency at room temperature is only about 10–15 per cent for tritium (70 per cent or more for carbon-14) depending, as with other instruments, on the scintillator system used. The time saved with this type of circuitry more than compensates for any decrease in the counting efficiency for most practical purposes, and counters with coincidence circuitry are generally to be preferred. Lambie[6] also describes the measurement of samples using a counter of this type.

Instruments with two (or more) channels and coincidence circuitry permit the determination of counting efficiency by the channels ratio technique[7, 246, 327]; while a three-channel instrument permits detection of sample quenching and the simultaneous measurement of two β-emitters of different energies (for example, tritium and carbon-14) by proper choice of energy ranges. The technique is described more fully by Bush[327, 356] and by Hendler[360].

For the routine measurement of a large number of samples, instruments are commercially available with automatic sample-changing devices[5].

2. *The Scintillation Process and Choice of Scintillant*

The scintillation process basically consists of the following simplified stages:

(*a*) The tritium β-energy is transferred to scintillant solvent (the amount transferred to solute molecules directly is negligible), where it may appear as energy of ionization, dissociation, or excitation of the solvent molecules. The electronic excitation energy of the solvent contributes most to the eventual formation of light quanta.

(*b*) The excitation energy of the solvent is now transferred to molecules of a primary solute which is a fluorescent compound. This is believed to occur within approximately 10^{-9} sec.

(*c*) The excited molecules of the fluorescent solute return to the ground state by emitting quanta of light in the visible or near ultra-violet region.

(*d*) A secondary solute (also fluorescent) is often present which may absorb this light and re-emit it at a longer wavelength. This serves to achieve a better match between the emission spectrum of the counting sample and the spectral response of the photocathode which detects the light.

The actual scintillation process as a whole is really quite inefficient, only about 5 per cent of the total energy absorbed from the β-radiation appears eventually as light. The remainder is degraded to quanta of lower energy (heat), or is consumed in chemical changes.

The scintillant normally consists of:

(*a*) A primary solvent—toluene is most widely used although xylene is just as satisfactory.

(*b*) A primary solute—2,5-diphenyloxazole ('PPO') is one of the most suitable compounds. Its maximum light emission is near 3800 Å, which is usually below the wavelength region of maximum photocathode sensitivity; therefore, it is normally used with a secondary solute as a wavelength shifter. Other fluorescent compounds such as 2-(4-biphenylyl)-5-1,3,4-oxadiazole ('PBD') or *p*-terphenyl can be used; both require a secondary solute as wavelength shifter. Although *p*-terphenyl was one of the first compounds used in liquid scintillation counting, its limited solubility at lower temperatures and in solutions containing water, has caused it to be largely superseded by 'PPO' or 'PBD'.

(*c*) A secondary solute—wavelength shifters such as 2-*p*-phenylene-bis(5-phenyloxazole) ('POPOP') or its 4,4'-dimethyl derivative ('Dimethyl-POPOP') and 2-(-naphthyl)-5-phenyloxazole ('-NPO'). Any of these compounds can be used but they tend to give concentration-quenching effects (see for example Table 5.2), and optimum concentration should be determined for a given type of scintillant.

(*d*) A solute to assist the transfer of the β-energy into light, is often included; naphthalene is commonly used for this purpose.

(*e*) Secondary solvents—In order to accommodate a wide variety of samples, scintillants usually consist of a mixture of solvents; dioxan and ethanol (and other alcohols) have proved most useful additional solvents [209, 222, 229, 233].

There is no 'best' scintillant cocktail. The choice depends to a large extent on the type of sample to be measured; the best system and optimum conditions for measurement must be decided for each need.

At the Radiochemical Centre a scintillant consisting of equal amounts (by volume) of ethanol, dioxan and xylene containing 'PPO' (5 g/l.), 'POPOP' (0·05 g/l.) and naphthalene (80 g/l.), has been used for a number of years with very satisfactory results, mainly for measurement of tritiated water samples. The naphthalene serves to increase the efficiency of the β-energy to light conversion. The effect is more marked with tritium than with carbon-14 for which there does not appear to be any great advantage in the use of naphthalene. The increase in the efficiency for tritium measurement is seen from Table 5.2 and also the chemical-quenching effect of the 'POPOP'[8].

TABLE 5.2

Scintillant composition	Background (5 ml *soln*) c.p.m.	Weight of n-hexadecane-1,2-T at 1·98 μc/g mg	Counts per minute per milligramme of hexadecane standard
A. Xylene, ethanol, dioxan (equal parts)	241	53·8	1
B. A+5 g 'PPO' per litre	460	30·5	539
C. B+0·05 g 'POPOP' per litre	570	20·6	436
D. C+80 g naphthalene per litre	651	16	841

To achieve the best performance from a scintillant the solvents used should be re-distilled but for many purposes ordinary analytical grade solvents can be used without further purification. Tanielian and colleagues[370] have studied the influence of solvent purification on the efficiency of liquid scintillators.

Background counts—Thermionic emission in the photomultiplier tube is usually the major cause of the very high background counts (several thousand per minute) observed at room temperature with single-channel, non-coincident-type instruments. Operation at lower temperatures ($-20°$ C) reduces this count, but even then this still amounts to several hundred counts per minute.

The background count with instruments having coincidence circuitry can be reduced to only a few counts per minute (often less than 40 c.p.m.) at operating temperatures around $0°$ C. In general a $12°$ C drop in temperature reduces the background count by about 50 per cent.

For low activity sample measurements a low background count is essential to achieve good counting statistics in a reasonable total measurement time, but for many investigations background counts of even a few hundred per minute are tolerable.

Problems Associated with Liquid Scintillation Measurements

Before discussing other aspects of scintillation counting it is necessary to appreciate two major problems which can arise in the measurement of tritium (and other soft β-radiation) by the liquid scintillation process. These are:

1. Quenching 2. Luminescence

which must be taken into account in the analysis of tritiated samples of any kind.

1. *Quenching*, as the name suggests, reduces the count rate being recorded for the sample and can arise, for example, from the sample being measured absorbing some of the excitation energy during the lifetime of the excited state of the scintillant, before light is emitted. Solvent molecules, which play an indispensable role in transferring energy from the β-particle to the fluorescent solute, can be quenched if their energy is transferred to solute molecules which are not fluorescent and which convert the energy into forms other than light. This type of quenching is known as chemical quenching. The absorption of the light at visible wavelengths by coloured substances also reduces the number of counts recorded, and this is known as colour quenching.

2. *Luminescence*, which results in an abnormally high count is not so easily corrected and may even escape detection. Luminescence is a general term applied to the delayed emission of light after excitation. Fluorescence, in which the lifetime of the excited state is very short (normally less than a microsecond) presents no great problem, but with phosphorescence and chemiluminescence the half-lives of the excited states may be several hours.

Phosphorescence arises from the excitations set up in the glass sample bottles on exposure to strong light[8, 306]. Strong light or even ultra-violet light does not appear to set up phosphorescence in the scintillant solution[8], although statements implying this have been made[306]. It is not necessary to keep scintillant in dark bottles, although it is advisable to keep the bottles or tubes in which the sample is to be measured, in the dark before use. Phosphorescence set up in this way usually decays fairly quickly (within 20 min), for example, a sample which had a normal count rate of 14,098 c.p.m. counted 40,782 c.p.m. immediately after being left in sunlight for 1 h. After 5 min in the counter the count rate had dropped almost to normal, being 15,342. If a sample which has been exposed to the sunlight is poured into another sample bottle which has been kept in the dark, a normal count rate is observed immediately.

Chemiluminescence arises by activation of the scintillant by chemical effects. This again results in very high counts which often decay only very slowly over a period of several hours. The only satisfactory way of overcoming this effect is to convert the sample being measured into a form which does not exhibit chemiluminescence; samples may for example be burned to tritiated water. It should be noted that alkaline solutions are particularly likely to give chemiluminescent effects.

Measurement Efficiency

The counting or measurement efficiency is defined as the ratio of the number of observed counts to the number of disintegrations occurring in the sample

$$E \text{ (efficiency)} = \frac{\text{C.P.M. (observed counts per minute)}}{\text{D.P.M. (disintegrations per minute)}}$$

The d.p.m. for any known amount of radioactive sample can be calculated; $1 \text{ c} = 3 \cdot 7 \times 10^{10}$ d.p.s. or $2 \cdot 22 \times 10^{12}$ d.p.m.

In liquid scintillation measurement of tritium, as with most other techniques for measuring radioactivity, E is normally less than 100 per cent and depends on the physico-chemical nature of the sample. It is necessary to know the value of E in order to determine the absolute activity of the sample, or to compare the activities of samples which are counted with different efficiencies. Ideally, conditions under which the measurement efficiency is constant for all types of samples are desirable, but in practice this has not been achieved; one reason being the variation in the degree of quenching for the different samples, and the efficiency for each measurement must be determined.

There are three basic methods for determining efficiency:

1. *Internal standardization*—After counting the sample, a known amount of a non-quenching radioactive standard is added and the sample recounted. The efficiency is then calculated from the equation (5.1) [9,10]

$$E = \frac{C_{s'} - C_s}{D_s} \qquad \cdots \cdots \quad (5.1)$$

where $C_{s'}$ = counts recorded for the combined standard and sample.
C_s = counts recorded for the sample.
D_s = calculated disintegration rate of the standard.

The activity of the added standard should generally be much greater than that of the sample for good counting statistics. Quenching is automatically corrected if one makes the reasonable assumption that the standard is quenched to the same extent as the sample. Note however that this procedure does not correct for other effects such as chemiluminescence.

Two other assumptions are made which must be verified for a particular system used: (1) it is assumed that if the specific activity of the standard is high enough, its addition does not significantly alter the sample volume or composition, and (2) that the counting rate is a linear function of activity over the range of activity involved.

Tritiated toluene or *n*-hexadecane are the most commonly used internal reference standards (see page 226)

2. *Channels ratio technique*—A method for the determination of efficiency has been developed for two (or more) channel coincidence counters which involves no extra manipulation of the sample[7]. By proper choice of discriminator settings, the ratio of the counting rates in two 'windows' (i.e. over two parts of the energy spectrum) can be made to vary monotonically with counting efficiency. Over small ranges of efficiency values, the ratio will vary linearly with efficiency for chemically quenched solutions or suspensions, but for large changes in quenching and for colour-quenching samples, a calibration curve must be plotted[327].

3. *Dilution method*—Two or more dilutions of the radioactive sample in a scintillation solution are counted, and a plot of count rate per millilitre against sample concentration is extrapolated to infinite dilution, where no sample quenching occurs. If the counting efficiency for the isotope in pure scintillant solution is now known, absolute activities can be calculated[263]. This method is rather longer than the internal standardization or channels ratio techniques and is probably the least used.

The method of internal standardization has certain minor disadvantages compared with the channels ratio technique, but it can be used for samples with all types of liquid scintillation counter whereas the channels ratio method does require multichannel instruments. Disadvantages include:

(*a*) Counting the sample twice is necessary.

(*b*) There is a small risk of changing the efficiency when adding the standard.

(*c*) Additional small weighing or pipetting errors are involved.

(*d*) The sample cannot be re-counted after the addition of the standard.

(*e*) There is an extra cost involved in consuming the standard compound.

On the other hand no calibration technique is required.

Standard Measurement Samples

Commercial suppliers of liquid scintillation counters normally provide standard reference sources which are sealed. It must be remembered that tritium has not a long half-life like carbon-14, and such sources must be corrected for the natural decay of the isotope. Sealed scintillation samples are also likely to become less efficient from 'age' effects, probably due to chemical decomposition of the fluorescent solutes. It is therefore advisable to check the counter efficiency at frequent intervals by the use of another standard or reference material which has not been previously mixed with a scintillant solution.

Standardized tritiated water or toluene may be obtained from the U.S. National Bureau of Standards. Tritiated *n*-hexadecane-1,2-T has been used (and supplied) by the Radiochemical Centre for a number of years. This substance has the advantage that it is a liquid at room temperature (20° C), does not quench or produce chemiluminescence, is virtually non-volatile and soluble in all the known scintillation cocktails. It is calibrated with an effective standard deviation (ESD) ± 2 per cent against the tritiated water standard of the U.S. National Bureau of Standards. The toluene standard has the disadvantage of being volatile but in other respects is just as suitable as hexadecane.

Scintillant Efficiency

The efficiency of the various scintillation cocktails varies with the solvent composition because of their different quenching characteristics. The most efficient 'cocktail' consists of toluene containing 'PPO' (6 g/l.) and 'POPOP' (0·05 g/l.)[11]. It has somewhat limited application since it is not satisfactory for the measurement of aqueous samples. On the other hand the xylene–ethanol–dioxan scintillant (page 221) is quenched (mainly by the ethanol) but can be used quite satisfactorily containing up to 7 per cent water.

A description of other combinations of solvents, primary and secondary solutes, and various other features of scintillation measurement may be found in the Nuclear Chicago liquid scintillation counting manual 1964[11].

The use of one standard scintillant cocktail greatly simplifies the routine analysis of samples but this is not always possible where a very wide variety of samples is being measured.

In general organic scintillators, such as 'PPO', have a very high speed of response (10^{-9} sec) but low efficiencies compared with the best inorganic scintillators such as ZnS(Ag), NaI(Tl) and $CdWO_4$. A good account of the scintillation processes in organic scintillators is given by Brooks[12], and is recommended for further reading.

Double Isotope Measurement

The method for the simultaneous measurement of two β-emitters is described by Bush[356] and by Hendler[360]; a two-channel instrument is required.

The Preparation of Samples for Measurement

Meticulous care is required to prevent cross-contamination during the preparation of samples for tritium measurement, especially in laboratories where multicurie amounts of tritium activity are handled in various forms; or where other isotopes are being used. Particular care must be taken to avoid contamination of the stock scintillant solution.

Sample Container

Expendable sample bottles made of low potassium-40 content glass may be used with polythene caps. Complete polythene containers have been used[13] and are said to permit higher counting efficiencies.

Tritium measurement samples can roughly be divided into two groups:

1. Purified tritium compounds.
2. Biological tritiated specimens.

1. Tritium Compounds

The measurement of purified tritiated compounds is relatively straightforward and only presents minor problems in sample preparation. They can either be burnt in oxygen to form tritiated water or measured directly by dissolving the sample in a suitable solvent such as water, dioxan, alcohol, benzene or toluene, and added to the scintillant for measurement.

Burning the sample to tritiated water is a relatively simple process and avoids chemiluminescence and colour or variable quenching. It is highly recommended where the measurement of a variety of different samples is involved, all being reduced to a standard chemical form.

For small samples (milligrammes) the simple flask-combustion method can be used. This is a modification of the method re-introduced by Schöniger[14,15] in 1955 (its analytical use has been reviewed by MacDonald[16]). The sample is burned in oxygen in a closed flask usually containing a little water, the vapour allowed to condense and the tritiated water made up to a standard volume for measurement. About 20 mg of sample can be burnt in a flask of about 1 l. capacity. Various methods have been used to handle and ignite the sample[286, 297, 328, 353]. It is convenient and simple to weigh the tritiated material into a small gelatine capsule (Parke Davis & Co., Ltd., size No. 1) (*Figure 5.1a*), which can be placed or wrapped in a paper taper (of low ash content on combustion) supported on a

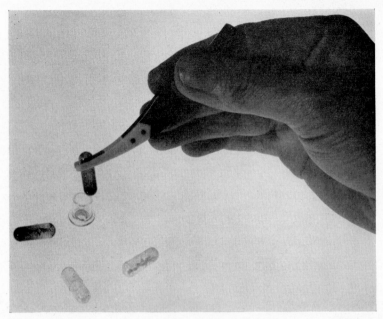

Figure 5.1 (a). Gelatine capsules containing tritiated compounds for combustion to tritiated water by the Schöniger technique

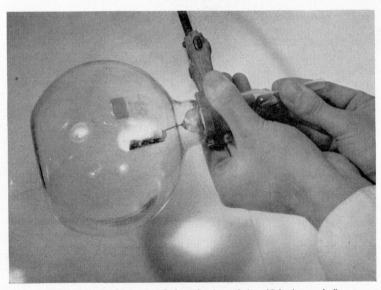

Figure 5,1 (b). The oxygen flask combustion technique (Schöniger method)

platinum boat, the taper ignited and plunged into the flask of oxygen (*Figure 5.1b*).

Paper chromatogram spots may be burned directly and by using a weighed amount of water in the combustion flask, the tritiated water can be added directly to the scintillant for measurement.

There appears to be only one reported 'serious explosion' with the oxygen flask method [307].

Wet oxidation with chromic acid or other similar oxidizing agents can also be used for converting the sample into tritiated water. For high accuracy a small correction for the fractionation of the hydrogen isotopes during any distillation process should be applied [17]. Such 'wet' methods are seldom necessary for labelled organic compounds but are often necessary when dealing with biological samples.

Direct measurement of tritiated compounds dissolved in a solvent requires a knowledge of whether the compounds cause quenching or chemiluminescence. This knowledge can only be acquired by direct experimentation. A wide variety of compounds in three different scintillants have been investigated for these two effects, by Kerr, Hayes and Ott [228]. Steroids, carbohydrates, purines, pyrimidines, nucleosides, nucleotides and simple amino acids generally present few problems of quenching or chemiluminescence; this is particularly true of course for compounds at high specific activity, i.e. at very low concentration. As a rough guide Table 5.3 (cf. Ref. 228) shows the types of aliphatic compounds which quench; compounds which do not quench and take no part in the scintillation process except to dilute the scintillant are sometimes referred to as 'diluters'.

TABLE 5.3

Diluters	Mild quenchers	Strong quenchers
R—H	R—COOH	R—SH
R—F	R—NH$_2$	R—O—COOR
R—O—R	R—CH$=$CH—R	R—CO—R
(RO)$_3$PO	R—Br	R—CO—X
R—CN	R—S—R	R—NH—R
R—OH		R—CHO
R—COOR		R$_2$N—R
R—Cl		R—I
		R—NO$_2$

However, it is best to perform a routine check for quenching for each sample under investigation using an internal standard (or channels ratio method), and plotting a quench-correction curve.

Acidic solutions have a pronounced quenching effect [247]; the quenching effects of water in a number of scintillants are discussed by

Baxter and colleagues[354], who showed that counting efficiencies are generally higher at lower temperatures ($0°$ to $-15° C$), when measuring tritiated water samples.

The advent of multi-channel instruments with their electronic refinements, enables a closer examination of quenching effects (pulse height shifts of the energy spectrum) to be made and a re-determination of the quenching characteristics of various types of compounds is then required. Alcohol for example, classified as a diluter, has quite a pronounced quenching action which is not immediately obvious using a single-channel instrument[8].

A problem sometimes encountered during the measurement of concentrated solutions of compounds in counters operating at low temperatures (below $0° C$), is crystallization of the organic compound from the scintillant. Takahashi and colleagues[350] found that a small amount of 'Hyamine' hydroxide added to a dioxan–naphthalene scintillant prevented this effect and greatly facilitated the counting of milligramme amounts of tritiated organic compounds. For example, leucine at 20 mg/ml may be counted directly. However, the channels ratio method for establishing a quench correction for tritium compounds in the 'Hyamine'–dioxan–water system was stated to be less satisfactory (variable reproducibility) than the method of internal standardization. This was not so for carbon-14 measurements.

A pitfall which has been encountered in the direct measurement of tritiated compounds at very high specific activity is the adsorption of compounds on the walls of glass vessels from dilute solutions[310]. Such compounds when measured directly (i.e. without combustion) require a very large dilution and the actual sample for measurement may only contain a few microgrammes of the compound per millilitre. It has been found[310] that the counting rate of such solutions fall on standing for some hours. This is caused by irreversible adsorption of the compound on the walls of the vessel; the addition of some inactive compound (a few milligrammes) as a 'carrier' prevents this effect.

Paper and thin-layer chromatogram samples—These can be measured by direct scintillation counting as further discussed on page 259.

2. *Tritiated Biological Samples*

Biological samples usually present special problems in tritium measurement by liquid scintillation techniques, because of the heterogeneous nature of the samples and their sparing solubility in most common solvents. They also tend to present greater problems of quenching and chemiluminescence than simple chemical compounds.

Studies with tritium-labelled compounds frequently require for example, the radioactive measurement of specimens of urine, faeces, blood and body tissues, which must be converted into a suitable form for measurement. This can be achieved in a number of ways:

(a) by direct wet or dry oxidation to tritiated water,
(b) by dissolving in a suitable solvent or mixtures of solvents,
(c) by measurement suspended in a gel.

What would appear to the beginner to be a bewildering number of variations in techniques, have been published, many of which try to avoid conversion of the sample to tritiated water. Although this may involve a little extra time, it would seem the most reproducible form for the measurement of such materials.

(a) *Oxidation*—Dry oxidation[275, 317, 341] or wet oxidation procedures of the Van Slyke–Folch type[18], can be used for biological samples. Belcher[247] oxidized tritiated biological materials with a mixture of nitric and perchloric acids. The solution was counted without distillation but required neutralization with ammonia, before measurement, to minimize quenching effects.

(b) *Solution methods*—Limited amounts of tissue may be dissolved in 'Hyamine', a method first reported by Agranoff[224]; about 40 mg (dry) or 200 mg (wet) tissue will dissolve in 1 ml of 'Hyamine' solution. 'Hyamine' homogenates of biological materials are particularly likely to produce chemiluminescence when added to the scintillant[232, 256]. Halvorsen[301] made the interesting observation that two types of chemiluminescence are present in such solutions; one decays with a short half-life of only 3–4 min producing several thousands of counts per minute, the other produces only a few hundred counts per minute but decays with a much longer half-life of 6–7 h. Acidification of the 'Hyamine' solution reduces this problem but increases the quenching effects and causes phase separation in the scintillant at lower temperatures (-20° C). Chemiluminescence is most marked with blood and blood-containing tissues or specimens[301].

Digestion with nitric acid has been used by O'Brien for dissolving rat skin and insect cuticle[364]. To increase the counting efficiency it was found necessary to mix the acid solution with tri(hydroxymethyl)aminomethane ('Tris') before adding to the dioxanethylene glycol scintillant. This method is stated to avoid the chemiluminescence problems which arise with the 'Hyamine' hydroxide digests of biological samples. However, the counting efficiency for tritiated samples was only 1 per cent.

Other methods for tissue dissolution have been reported by Herberg[256] using ethanol–potassium hydroxide, and by Kinnory[19] who found formamide a useful solvent for tissues. However, 'Hyamine' is the best of such solvents for a wide variety of tissues and also has the advantage of being readily miscible with toluene, one of the most efficient solvents for liquid scintillation measurement.

In tritiated bacterial cells most of the tritium radiation is absorbed within the cell. Suspensions of cell fractions from *Bacillus megaterium*, in water, can be solubilized by trypsin, lysozyme and 'Hyamine' hydroxide before measurement[302, 363].

The counting of urine samples by liquid scintillation is now routine in many laboratories. The results of Okita, Spratt and LeRoy[222] demonstrate the need to decolorize the urine with charcoal before counting; quenching is thereby reduced from a possible 100 per cent to perhaps a maximum of 15 per cent. Myers and Rosenblum[342] use detergent-coated anthracene crystals as the scintillant solute[20, 309]; the sensitivity of the method is high but the efficiency low (about 2 per cent) and requires a high-grade anthracene.

With all these homogenized biological samples it is important to examine the measurements carefully for inaccuracies due to chemiluminescence and phosphorescence. This is particularly so when low-activity samples are being measured. It is usually necessary to allow the samples to stand at low temperatures in the dark for several hours, to allow phosphorescence to decay before measurement.

(*c*) *Counting in suspensions*—The use of thixotropic gels for suspending tritiated (or carbon-14) samples has facilitated the measurement of samples insoluble in a suitable solvent[218, 337]. Aluminium stearate has been used as an emulsifier[21] but 'thixin' (a castor oil derivative) or 'Cab-O-sil' (finely divided silica), which form thixotropic gels with aromatic solvents, are more frequently used[22, 254]. The size of the particles and the distribution of the sample in the gel are more important factors for reproducibility with tritiated samples than with carbon-14, because of the greater self-absorption of the β-radiation with tritium.

Several workers describe the use of these gels in the measurement of biological samples. For example, Handler[335] used gel suspensions for the measurement of tritiated animal tissues, blood and faeces. These were all dried and mixed with sodium sulphate before gelling. Some problems were encountered due to phosphorescence which took several hours to decay. Halvorsen[301] dissolved the dried (lyophilized) animal tissues in 'Hyamine' and then formed a gel suspension using 'Aerosil' (finely divided silica). Samples required to be left in the dark for 24 h before measurement. Activities in mouse tissues could be followed up to 1 month following an injection of tritiated thymidine of only 1 µc/g of mouse. Similar techniques have been used by Frenkel and colleagues[299].

Table 5.4 gives some examples, necessarily selective, of the measurement of biological samples by liquid scintillation counting.

TABLE 5.4

Liquid Scintillation Measurement of Tritiated Biological Samples

Tritiated samples	Scintillant solvents	References
Animal tissues (dried blood and faeces)	Toluene–'thixin' (gel suspension)	335
Bacterial cell fractions	Dioxan–anisole-dimethoxy-ethane	302
Biological tissue (digested in nitric acid)	Dioxan–ethylene glycol	364
Biological samples (water soluble)	Toluene–methyl 'cellosolve' (ethylene glycol mono-methyl ether)	345
Biological samples (Nitric–perchloric acid oxidation)	Toluene–ethanol	247
Bone	Toluene–'Aerosil' (gel suspension)	301
Biological tissues (liver, blood, skin, intestine and muscle— in 'Hyamine')	Toluene–'Aerosil' (gel suspension)	301
Biologically important compounds (amino acids, sugars, purines, pyrimidines, nucleosides and nucleotides)	1. Toluene–'Hyamine' hydroxide 2. 'Hyamine' hydroxide–dioxan–water	350
Faeces (burnt to THO)	Toluene–ethanol–water	326
Kidney slices	Dioxan	372
Plasma and tissues (in KOH)	Methanol–toluene	251
Plasma and tissues (in hyamine)	Ethanol–toluene	235
Urine	Ethanol–toluene	222

Advantages of the Scintillation Method

In summary the chief advantages of β-scintillation techniques are:

(a) the method is rapid,

(b) quite large samples (10–50 ml) can be measured depending on the instrument used,

(c) two soft β-emitting isotopes of different energies may be measured simultaneously,

(d) an outstanding advantage is the ability to accept a very wide variety of radioactive samples without necessarily converting them to a uniform chemical composition,

(e) the method has a high sensitivity,

(f) the sample can be recovered from the scintillant if required for further investigation; for example, steroids [23],

(g) expendable sample containers may be used, minimizing contamination problems.

Disadvantages

The major disadvantages of scintillation measurement are:

(*a*) the low counting efficiency (particularly for tritium) compared with gas-counting procedures,

(*b*) the necessity to correct for quenching,

(*c*) the problems and effects due to phosphorescence and chemi-luminescence.

Of these (*c*) is the most serious.

In assessing a method for the measurement of tritium, it is the accuracy and reproducibility which are the most important factors, closely followed by considerations of sensitivity and speed of the technique. Liquid scintillation counting is by far the most practically useful method; others satisfy more limited, special needs.

Ionization Chamber—Electrometer Methods

One of the earliest procedures for the 'routine' measurement of tritium depended on the introduction of a tritium–hydrogen gas mixture into a quartz ionization chamber, the rate of charge being measured by attachment to a Lauritzen electroscope[24]. The sensitivity of the method was reported to be 10^{-4} μc/10 ml of gas sample and the accuracy of the measurement ∓ 2 per cent.

The delicate electroscopes, which usually require visual reading through a telescope, have now been replaced by the vibrating-reed electrometer, originally devised by Palevsky, Swank and Grenchik[25]. The lower limit of detectability is usually determined by the magnitude and reproducibility of the background count. It has been calculated[26] that 13 tritium d.p.s. can be determined with an accuracy of 1 per cent for a measurement time of 1 h.

Excellent descriptions and reviews relating to ionization chamber–electrometer methods for tritium measurement have been published (see References and Bibliography), and it is proposed to discuss here only the main advantages and disadvantages of the method.

Advantages

(*a*) The efficiency of counting is high.

(*b*) It can be used over a very wide range (10^8 fold) of tritium activities.

(*c*) It is relatively insensitive to trace impurities in the gas.

(*d*) It can be dismantled for decontamination without destroying the calibration.

(*e*) The apparatus is simple in design and inexpensive.

(*f*) It offers a simple method for measuring the activity of flowing gaseous systems (for example, air monitors) for weak β-radiation, which is not readily accomplished by other methods.

Disadvantages

(*a*) The principal disadvantage is the inconvenience of converting the tritiated sample into a gas and the relatively complicated gas-handling system for filling the ionization chamber. Although there is no theoretical reason why liquid or solid samples should not be measured directly, they are likely to cause trouble by contamination. The higher efficiencies and uniform geometry with gaseous samples give much better precision than non-gaseous samples.

(*b*) Ionization chambers are not cheap enough to discard at frequent intervals, unlike the bottles (sample vessels) used in β-liquid scintillation counting. There is, therefore, a greater risk of con-tamination of the ionization chamber and background measurements are essential between measurements.

(*c*) It is not possible to measure the activity of a sample containing tritium and another β-emitter (say carbon-14) simultaneously, a requirement which is now frequently arising especially with biological samples.

Ionization chamber-electrometer measurement of tritium, in spite of the listed disadvantages, is still the most precise and would seem the method of choice for gaseous samples. The precision of the ionization chamber-electrometer method is now strongly challenged by the automatic liquid scintillation counters now available. How-ever, these deal more easily with liquid or solid samples than with non-condensable tritiated gases.

Ionization chamber-electrometer methods are often used for the measurement of tritium in gas chromatograph streams where 10^{-8} c may be determined in one peak[27-29]. Other important uses are in air monitors[30].

Geiger and Proportional Gas Measurement

Like the ionization chamber-electrometer method, the measure-ment of tritium in the form of a gas by Geiger or proportional gas-counting techniques is being superseded by β-liquid scintillation methods. Again the two principal reasons for this are:

(*a*) the rather tedious and time-consuming methods required for the sample preparation,

(*b*) the frequent contamination problems encountered with the counter tubes, the so-called 'memory' effects of internal gas counters. Recent work by Hasan and Perheentupa[31] shows that tritiated gases such as hydrogen, methane or ethane do not contaminate brass cathodes in counters, but cathodes of electrolytic copper were easily contaminated by them.

At the Radiochemical Centre, before the availability of reliable commercial scintillation counters, the Glascock[32] method of tritium measurement was used. This consisted of converting tritiated water (from burning samples in oxygen) into tritiobutane which was counted in the Geiger region in tubes with stainless-steel cathodes. Dead-time losses set the upper limit for Geiger counting (about 25,000 c.p.m.), the whole process is slow and impossible to operate quickly for multiple samples. The counting tubes varied in their ability to develop 'memory' effects and could not be decontaminated by baking at high temperatures or by other means. Once contaminated they had to be discarded.

For measurement of tritium and (say) carbon-14 in the same sample, chemical separation of the isotopes before measurement is normally necessary.

The proportional counter has an advantage in its short 'dead time' which permits the use of very high count rates (above 10^5/min) and it is not so sensitive to impurities in the gas as is the Geiger counter. The size of the output pulse is proportional to the energy of the ionizing particles and it is therefore possible to count carbon-14 in the presence of tritium by making use of a suitable electronic 'gate' as a discriminator.

There is still much discussion as to the relative merits of Geiger and proportional gas-counting methods, and readers are referred to the References and bibliography for further accounts of these methods.

Windowless Gas-Flow Measurement

Here the sample is introduced inside the counter, usually a proportional counter, through which the filling gas flows continually. Argon or argon containing 10–15 per cent methane is normally the gas used. There is no window and every electron (β-particle) that escapes from the surface of the sample is measured.

This is the least-attractive method for the routine measurement of tritium, although it is relatively cheap and is still in widespread use for the measurement of carbon-14. For solid or liquid samples the method is very inefficient for tritium compared with efficiencies up to 50 per cent (or even more) obtained with carbon-14 samples.

Measurements are made with 'infinitely thick' samples (0.7 mg/cm^2 is sufficient for tritium) or 'infinitely thin' samples, their are numerous difficulties for either technique which include:

(*a*) The sample must be free from radiochemical impurities and from chemical impurities which may increase the self-absorption of the β-particles.

(*b*) Continual standardization of the instrument is required, as the field around the anode wire is easily changed, giving completely different counting characteristics.

(*c*) It is difficult to prepare small samples of substances uniformly and irregularities in the source geometry affect the results obtained.

(*d*) The very low sensitivity means that rather high tritium activities are used in the measurement samples. This, in the author's experience, usually results in severe contamination, a difficulty which may not always be foreseen from published accounts of the method.

(*e*) The method cannot be used for volatile samples; even compounds of high molecular weight such as octadecane or lauric acid, commonly regarded as being non-volatile, have been shown[515, 519] to be sufficiently volatile to contaminate the counter and to produce erratic results.

(*f*) It has been found[33], particularly with 'infinitely thick' sources, that the recorded activity appears to decrease with time, which is attributed to the build-up of electrostatic charge on the surface of the sample, thus preventing the electrons from escaping. Mixing the tritiated sample with graphite has been used to remedy the effect[507]; or a thin conducting material at earth potential may be placed between the sample and the anode wire[514]. Thin tritiated samples are normally 'plated' on metallic supports which become part of the earthed cathode.

The fact that sample preparation does not involve the time-consuming step of gas preparation and that the sample is recoverable, would seem the only advantages of the method.

Although used for the measurement of tritium samples by a number of workers including Ayres[1] (steroids), André[506] (antibiotics), Isbell and colleagues[511, 513] (carbohydrates) and Jenkins and Yost[504] (inorganic compounds—thallous hypophosphite), it is now little used as a routine method for tritium measurement.

Gas-flow methods are of course frequently used for paper and thin-layer chromatogram scanning, and here (for tritium) compete favourably with β-liquid scintillation methods.

AUTORADIOGRAPHY WITH TRITIUM

Autoradiography, the ability to detect, locate, and measure ionizing radiation by means of a photographic emulsion, was discovered by Becquerel[34] in 1896 and led him to the discovery of radioactivity.

The use of a photographic emulsion in the form of a film badge for personnel monitoring is of course well known (see page 71) but it was in 1924 that Lacassagne and Lattes[34a] first described the use of photographic emulsions for recording the distribution of radio-activity in a biological specimen. However, it was not until 1951 that high-resolution autoradiography was first used for the detection of tritium[35]. The low range of the β-particles in photographic emulsion, about 1 μ (10^{-4} cm), permits the attainment of high-resolution autoradiographs, some applications of which have already been mentioned in Chapter 2.

The principle of autoradiography is to place a specimen containing the radioactive material in contact with the photographic emulsion. The β-particles from the tritium disintegration affect the grains of silver halide in the emulsion in the same manner as light. Development and fixing of the emulsion produces a photographic image which locates the radioactivity. This method of detecting tritium qualit-atively (on paper or thin-layer chromatograms for example) is routinely used at the Radiochemical Centre. Preparations of highly active tritium compounds are most conveniently purified by paper or thin-layer chromatography and the location of the radioactivity is best made by placing the paper or thin-layer plate in physical contact with photographic x-ray film (for example, 'Kodirex' x-ray film) for a few hours. Typical autoradiographs from chromatograms are shown in *Figures 5.2* and *5.3*.

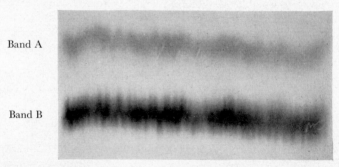

Band A

Band B

Figure 5.2. Autoradiograph of a preparation of tritiated thymidine using 'Kodirex' x-ray film with supercoat. Band A contains 25 mc Thymidine-T and Band B 10 mc of Thymine-T separated by chromatography on Whatman No. 1 paper using ethyl acetate saturated with phosphate buffer at pH 6·0. Autoradiographed for 24 h

An activity of about 1 mc/cm² is readily detected in an exposure of less than 1 h. At the other end of the scale about 5 μc/cm² as an 'infinitely thin' film will give a perceptible image on the x-ray film in 24 h. The high self-absorption of the weak tritium β-radiation by the paper severely reduces the efficiency of the process and much longer exposure times are required for smaller amounts of radio-activity. This is in contrast to other β-emitters, such as carbon-14, for which 10^{-5} μc/cm^2 can be detected in 24 h[36].

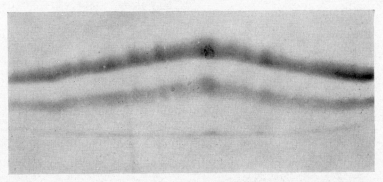

Figure 5.3. Autoradiograph of a preparation of progesterone-T (G) after thin-layer chromatography on silica gel in ethyl acetate–benzene (50:50). Exposure time 3 h using 'Kodirex' x-ray film. Total activity on plate 40 mc. Dark band is progesterone-T, others are impurities

Detection by autoradiography, in a reasonable time, is no problem for preparative chromatograms (millicurie scale) and it is not usually necessary to improve the efficiency of the process for this purpose. For lower activities (less than 5 μc/cm^2) improvement in the efficiency can be achieved by dipping or spraying the chromatogram with a scintillator; paper chromatograms may for example be sprayed with a solution of anthracene in benzene. Parups, Hoffman and Jackson[37], using Kodak Royal-X Pan sheet film, showed that better results were obtained with a scintillator than without, although an exposure of 1–2 weeks was necessary to detect approximately 0·1 μc/cm^2 using this type of film.

A toluene solution of p-diphenylbenzene (p-terphenyl) has also been used as the scintillant[38], and no doubt most of the common scintillators could be used with equal efficiency. There would seem no reason why this technique should not be applicable for thin-layer chromatograms, and similar improvements in efficiency of detection are expected.

The rather coarse autoradiographic technique described above has to be modified for the detection of tritium at low activities in analytical or biological investigations. There have been a number of newer techniques since the publication in 1955 of a book on autoradiography in biology and medicine, which deals primarily with isotopes other than tritium [39].

Analytical

Analytically an autoradiograph of a chromatogram gives a quantitative result only if there is one spot, that is if the compound is pure. It is not possible to interpret accurately, by visual means, the amount of tritium activity associated with various spots detected by autoradiography. It is only too easy either to overlook minor spots or to exaggerate their quantitative significance. Quantitative interpretation can be achieved by chromatogram scanning or by cutting up the chromatogram and counting by scintillation measurement, which is further discussed on page 259.

Biological Applications

This is by far the widest use of tritium compounds and special techniques have been developed for the autoradiographic examination of tritiated biological specimens.

It was first proposed to mount the specimen directly on a photographic plate [40]; this failed because of the lack of definition of the image and the difficulty in matching the autoradiograph with the corresponding histological detail in the specimen. In 1946 the coating method of autoradiography was developed by Belanger and Leblond [41] and consequently in nearly all high-resolution autoradiography with tritiated specimens, a wet film or liquid emulsion is applied to the specimen which is normally mounted on a glass slide.

Various techniques have been suggested for the autoradiography of microsections. Probably the most convenient suggested so far involves the use of a stripping film or stripping plate [42, 42a]. Kodak Limited manufacture two stripping plates (available from stock); these are;

1. Fine-Grain Autoradiographic Stripping Plate AR.10.
2. Fast Autoradiographic Stripping Plate AR.50.

Both these stripping plates consist of an emulsion layer attached to a very thin gelatine support. The thin support facilitates the handling of the emulsion layer, which is only a few microns thick, and renders it less prone to accidental damage. The film is stripped from a temporary glass support and transferred to the specimen. It is advisable to allow plates which have been kept in the refrigerator (4–7° C) to warm up to room temperature to avoid condensation on the film.

The film strips best from the glass plate when the relative humidity is 50–70 per cent. If the emulsion is handled it is important to have dry hands.

In the AR.10 plate the emulsion of approximately 5 μ thick is reinforced by a gelatine layer approximately 10 μ thick, whereas in the AR. 50 plates these values are 12 and 10 μ respectively. The AR.10 plate has the slower, finer-grain emulsion, while the AR.50 has a faster, coarser-grain emulsion. The relative speed obtained with

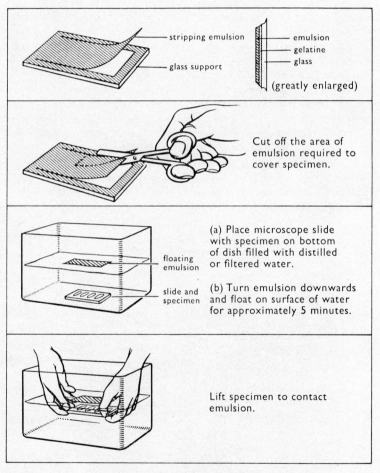

Figure 5.4. The Stripping Film Technique.
(Reproduced by kind permission of Kodak Ltd.)

241

either plate depends on the energy of the electrons, i.e. the radioisotope used. As a rough guide the AR.50 plate has about 10 times the speed of the AR.10 plate.

The emulsion may be placed in permanent contact with the specimen, as the processing solutions can permeate the gelatine. Subsequent examination can therefore be undertaken with the knowledge that specimen and image are in proper register. The procedure involved in the autoradiographic technique using stripping plates is illustrated in *Figure 5.4* and is briefly as follows:

An area of the emulsion layer is cut out (best with a scalpel), sufficient to cover the entire specimen, and with sufficient overlap to wrap completely around the slide. The microscope slide bearing the radioactive specimen is then placed on the bottom of a glass dish filled with distilled water (at about 25° C). The emulsion and its gelatine support are stripped from the plate and placed on the surface of the water with the emulsion side underneath, facing the specimen. As it swells the stripped composite first crumples and then stretches out tight and flat. It should be permitted to swell for 2 to 3 min more and may then be lifted from the water by raising the slide underneath it. If the slide is held at about 30 degrees from the horizontal, so that one edge touches the emulsion first, the emulsion will drape itself snugly over the specimen and most of the water will drain away as the slide is gradually lifted clear of the water. The specimen with its super-

TABLE 5.5

'Kodak' sensitized material	Emulsion thickness before processing (approx.) μ	Support layer and thickness (approx.) μ	Mean grain diameter μ	Per cent silver halide by weight
Fine-grain autoradiographic stripping plate AR.10	5	Gelatine 10	0·15–2	84·5
Experimental scientific plate V.1042*	2	Gelatine 10	0·15–2	84·5
Experimental scientific plate V.1055*	20	none	0·15–2	84·5
Experimental scientific plate V.1056†	5	none	0·15–2	84·5
Experimental scientific plate V.1060†	2	none	0·15–2	84·5
Experimental scientific plate V.1062*	5	none	0·15–2	84·5
Fast autoradiographic stripping plate AR.50	12	Gelatine 10	1·17	43·8

* Stripping plate.   † Non-stripping plate.

imposed emulsion layer should next be dried in a stream of clean cold air and placed in a light-tight box for exposure. The temperature within the box should not exceed about 20° C and the exposure may require from a few days to several weeks, depending on the amount of tritium activity in the specimen.

Types of Emulsions

In addition to the AR.10 and AR.50 plates, five derivatives of the AR.10 plate can be obtained (by special order from Kodak Limited). These all use the AR.10 emulsion (fine-grain) and are particularly suitable for special applications of tritium autoradiography. The basic physical properties of the plates are summarized in Table 5.5.

Experimental Scientific Plate V.1042—This stripping plate is identical with the AR.10 but the emulsion thickness is only 2 μ (approximately). Provided the specimen section is thin enough even higher resolution is obtained than with AR.10. It is particularly useful for tritium, provided the water-bath technique of application is acceptable. As the mean range of the tritium β-particles is about 1 μ, only the top layers of the grains will be utilized for recording.

Experimental Scientific Plate V.1055—Many workers prefer to use liquid emulsions which they can apply direct to the specimen. The V.1055 plate, therefore, is designed so that the emulsion layer may be stripped off and melted down to form a liquid emulsion (see page 244).

Experimental Scientific Plate V.1056—This is a *non-stripping* variety of the AR.10 plate, designed for holding in contact with the specimen. It is recommended for use when the water-bath and stripping-film technique cannot be used, as for example when using water-soluble tritium compounds and in some geological and metallurgical autoradiography. The emulsion layer is approximately 5 μ thick.

Experimental Scientific Plate V.1060—This plate is also a non-stripping variety, identical with the V.1056 plate except that it has an emulsion thickness of 2 μ (approximately), and consequently a higher resolution is attainable with thin sections.

Experimental Scientific Plate V.1062—This plate is designed for the differential autoradiography of tritium and another β-emitter by the double-stripping film technique (see page 249).

Safelighting—Until the fixing stage the materials should be handled under the light from a safelamp fitted with a 'Kodak' Safelight Filter, 'Wratten' Series 1 (red) and a 25 W bulb. When using the AR.10 or any of its derivatives for grain-counting techniques, it is recommended that as little light as possible be allowed to fall on the emulsion until fixing is completed. Similar recommendations are given for the handling of Ilford Nuclear Research Emulsions (see Ilford Limited, Technical Information Sheet Y 44.1).

Development—'Kodak' D–19 developer can be used undiluted. If sufficient exposure has been given, optimum resolution will be obtained with these emulsions by developing for not longer than 5 min at 20° C. However, when the adequacy of the exposure is doubtful, longer developing times may be needed to increase the effective emulsion speed. Developing times of up to 20 or 30 min can be used with AR.10 emulsion and its derivatives, giving a substantial increase in effective speed with some sacrifice of resolution. With the AR.50 emulsion, 10 min in D-19 developer should be taken as the maximum.

Fixing—To neutralize any excess developer, the specimen and attached emulsion or the plate, should be immersed for not less than 30 sec in a bath of clean water at 18–21° C. It should then be fixed at the same temperature in a solution of Kodak 'METAFIX' for twice the time taken to clear, washed in running water for 2 to 3 min, and dried in a dust-free atmosphere.

Liquid Emulsions

Many workers prefer to use liquid emulsions, which they can apply directly to the specimen. Liquid emulsions for the dipping technique [43, 44] are prepared by melting the bulk nuclear track emulsion with a small amount of water added. When the mixture flows readily, it is strained through a cheese cloth and placed in a water-bath at 40° C. A few drops of the melted emulsion are transferred to a warm, dry slide on which the specimen is mounted, with a glass rod or brush. The slide is then placed on a level surface for the emulsion to solidify and is finally dried as in the stripping method (*vide supra*). Alternatively, the slide (preferably wet) may be dipped into the melted emulsion, the back surface is wiped free of emulsion and the slide placed on a flat surface for the emulsion to solidify [43, 44]. The thickness of the emulsion layer can be controlled to some extent by the amount of water added to the emulsion. The dipping technique is particularly useful if large numbers of samples are being examined in batches [43].

Frequently used are the Nuclear Emulsions of the NTA, NTE and NTB series (Kodak) and Ilford Ltd., G (0.27μ), K (0.2μ) and L (0.14μ) emulsions (mean grain diameter are given in parentheses). All these emulsions are suitable for tritium and are supplied as plates, pellicles and in gel form. However, the shelf-life of all such emulsions is often an inconveniently short period and for this reason the Kodak Experimental Scientific Plate V.1055, for example, is designed so that the emulsion layer may be stripped off and melted down to form a liquid emulsion; this may then be applied by any of the usual coating methods, dipping, flowing or painting.

Special techniques are usually necessary for the autoradiography of water-soluble tritium compounds when using the stripping plate or liquid-emulsion methods, which are discussed on page 248.

Effect of Storage Conditions on Grain Density

A phenomenon which is of some importance to users of tritium autoradiographic techniques, especially when quantitative inform-ation is required, is latent image fading. Over a period of a year the rate of emission of electrons in the emulsion should be fairly constant, because of the relatively long half-life of tritium. The grain count produced should therefore increase linearly with the exposure time, but in fact the rate of image production is found to fall off with increasing exposure time, sometimes within a few days depending on the type of emulsion used and the environmental conditions. The problem has received much attention and it is generally agreed that best results are obtained if the slides are kept dry with a desiccant such as calcium sulphate or silica gel and stored at 4° C during the exposure, that is, in a refrigerator. If the amount of radioactivity in the specimen is at the lower limit of detectability, improvement in grain yield may sometimes be obtained by exposing the slides in an inert atmosphere such as argon or carbon dioxide [45] or carbon dioxide and nitrogen [46].

Differences of grain density of more than 50 per cent have been recorded even by using the optimum conditions [47]. Of particular note is the latent image fading with the nuclear emulsion Gevaert Scientia 7.15, which is greater when the slides are kept in a dry atmosphere, in contrast to all the other described nuclear emulsions [47].

Recently it has been recommended [84] that a 30 Å to 60 Å layer of carbon should be evaporated over the biological specimen before coating with photographic emulsion, to minimize oxidation (and consequently image fading) of the latent image by the biological specimen.

Luminescence—Another 'effect' which can produce false results is luminescence, actually produced within the tissues under the influence of the soft β-radiation. This effect is particularly evident at very low temperatures ($-195°$ C) which can give a distorted picture of the relative distribution of activity in the specimen. Pellerin, Fallot and colleagues [47a] found for example, that the intensity of luminescence varied greatly with the type of tissue (rat tissues containing tritiated water) and was particularly enhanced in the region of the eye.

Efficiency—The radiographic efficiency (E), the number of activated silver grains produced above the specimen per 100 disintegrations, may be calculated from the equation (5.2) [48]

$$E = \frac{100q}{DsT} \qquad \qquad \text{. . . . (5.2)}$$

where q = the average number of developed silver grains recorded above a sectional area of 100 μ^2.

s = the section thickness.

T = the exposure time.

D = the number of disintegrations per hour in a section of dimensions $1 \times 10 \times 10$ μ.

Using tritiated methyl methacrylate polymer as the section, Falk and King [48] have shown that the autoradiographic efficiency can be increased from 2 to 15·7 in decreasing a section thickness from 10 μ to 0·5 μ. In fact, best efficiencies are obtained when 's' is less than 1 μ, and with very thin sections nearly 50 per cent of the emitted β-radiation can be detected. Hence to achieve maximum sensitivity (and resolution) coating of thin sections with the emulsion is normally recommended [45a, 45b].

Readers may like to consider possible improvements in the autoradiographic efficiency by impregnating the specimen with a scintillator, such as that used for paper chromatograms [37, 38] (see page 259), but caution would be necessary to avoid misleading results from luminescence effects (see page 245).

Specimen Preparation

Sections may be prepared by smearing [54] squashing [55] or section cutting [56]. For quantitative intercomparisons the third method, namely section cutting is not usually applicable because of the difficulty in cutting several representative sections each containing the same number of cell nuclei. To minimize 'image spread', tissue sections and emulsion layers should be of minimal thickness.

Smears are often preferred as these are less time-consuming to prepare, but one has to be a little cautious in the interpretation of autoradiographic data in relation to the method of sample preparation. For example, Baserga and Kisieleski [57] found that when comparing 'sections' and 'smears' from the same specimen of cells labelled with tritiated leucine, some of the silver grains in the autoradiographic emulsion overlying the cell nuclei in the 'smears', were not due to tritiated material in the nucleus. They were in fact

246

produced by radioactivity incorporated into the thin layer of cyto-plasm interposed between the nucleus and the emulsion.

Interpretation of the Autoradiographs

It is most important to compare specimens which have been treated under the same conditions, that is with the same batch of emulsion, developed and fixed under identical conditions, otherwise differences in the results may be due to effects of temperature variations, different qualities of emulsion (ageing effects) and other similar factors[58, 59].

Emulsion-coated specimens can be used for comparing the amounts of radioactivity in different cell structures by track counting[49] (which of course is not possible for tritium), but for the analysis of most autoradiographs grain-counting methods are more usually adopted. This involves counting the number of silver grains affected by the β-radiation by visual means (microscope). There are a number of texts on the description of grain-counting instruments and their evaluation[50-53].

Although intercomparisons of samples are possible, even on a semi-quantitative basis by the use of 'standard slides'[60, 61], an accurate correlation between the grain count and the absolute amount of activity in the specimen has not yet been accomplished. An attempt has been made to correlate grain counts with the tritium concen-tration in tissue sections containing tritiated thymidine[62]. Kisieleski and colleagues[62], concluded that the number of tritium atoms that must be present in a cell nucleus of a section greater than 3 μ thick to obtain a mean grain count of 30 grains per cell was $2\cdot8 \times 10^6$ tritium atoms, which amounted to 10^{-7} μc. However, their figures differed by a factor of 8 (higher) from those estimated by Lajtha and Oliver[62a] and by Hughes[62b], who concluded that approximately 20 disinte-grations are necessary to produce 1 silver grain.

The preparation of autoradiographic reference sources containing a known amount of tritium which give a standard grain count, is still to be perfected. Ideally these should be subjected to the same pro-cedures as the specimen under examination. Beischer[63] has used tritiated stearic acid monolayers deposited on various materials as reference sources and Ilford G.5 or Kodak NTB 3 emulsions for preparing the autoradiographs. Beischer calculated that a 1 cm^2 monolayer of tritiated stearic acid at $0\cdot6$ mc/mg would contain $2\cdot31 \times 10^{-7}$ g and would give $2\cdot57 \times 10^3$ β-particles/sec from each side of the monolayer. The back-scatter from the supporting surface must also be taken into account.

Other tritiated compounds or polymer sources may be more satisfactory for reference sources but obviously the problem needs further evaluation.

Many publications present figures for the proportion of labelled cells in a cell population without mentioning the background grain count. Stillström [64, 64a] has introduced formulae for calculating the true proportion of labelled cells, their mean grain count and grain-count distribution in autoradiographs.

Autoradiography of Tritiated Water-Soluble Compounds

The severe limitation of the stripping-film technique for water-soluble compounds has already been mentioned; it is difficult to know what proportion of tritiated material is 'leached' out of the specimen.

A modification of the Pelc technique with the application of dry stripping film followed by careful moistening with a brush has been described [65], but even this is difficult with very soluble compounds. A suitable but by no means easy method consists of mounting freeze-dried sections of tissue on tape, which are then pressed onto photographic emulsion coated with a very thin film of albumin glycerin. When the tape is removed the sections remain firmly fixed to the emulsion. The albumin glycerin is apparently essential for this to be achieved. It is always a disadvantage to have an intermediate layer between the specimen and the emulsion when good resolution is required, since it increases radiation scattering, namely image spread. Even with this thin film of albumin glycerin such effects are apparent and it is also necessary to increase the exposure time.

An excellent account of this method for water-soluble compounds in particular tetracycline-T and dihydrostreptomycin-T using Ilford G.5 emulsion, is given by André [59]. In his examples exposures for as long as 9 months were conducted at $-10°$ C, but the use of a carbon dioxide atmosphere proved unsuitable in this case, as only the edges of the autoradiographs showed less image fading when the gas was used.

Another method [66] of dry-mounting specimens for the intracellular localization of water-soluble material, consists essentially of freezing the specimens in isopentane, cutting the histological sections in a cryostat, freeze-drying to dehydrate and then covering the sections with a stripping film such as the Kodak AR.10 or V. 1042 described previously.

Wilske and Ross [67] recommend vacuum embedding the freeze-dried tissues in an epoxy resin (Epon 812) and then coating with a nuclear emulsion, for the autoradiography of both lipid- and water-soluble compounds.

Canny [67a] suggests allowing the stripping film to swell on water in the usual way (see page 241), rinse in dry chloroform and apply to the section, containing the water-soluble active materials, in a bath of chloroform. The film is then dried rapidly in absolute alcohol and then in a draught of cool air. Alternatively the piece of stripping film can be suspended in a large jar containing a little water and having filter paper around the walls, i.e. to provide a moist atmosphere. After 2 to 3 h exposure to this atmosphere the film becomes limp and can then be placed over the specimen.

An apposition method for the autoradiography of cryostat sections labelled with tritiated water-soluble compounds has recently been described by Novek [68]. Appleton [68a] also describes an elegant method for the autoradiography of water-soluble labelled compounds. The method consists of cutting frozen sections in a cryostat which are mounted directly onto cover-slips coated with Kodak AR.10 stripping film with the emulsion upwards. Melting of the sections is avoided by exposing the autoradiographs at $-20°$ to $-30°$ C and no solutions that might leach out soluble compounds are used until after the exposure is complete. The technique is stated to be simple and reliable and labelled materials are immobilized in the section which remains in secure and close contact with the film. The Appleton technique overcomes some of the difficulties of previous methods (*vide supra*) and is recommended for the autoradiography of sections containing water-soluble tritium compounds.

Double Isotope Autoradiography

It may sometimes be required to make autoradiographs of specimens which contain radioisotopes emitting radiations of different energies. Successful autoradiography of specimens containing tritium and carbon-14 [69, 70, 70a] and sulphur-35 and tritium [71], has been described. The usual procedure is to apply two layers of sensitized emulsion separated by a thin layer of cellulose nitrate (collodion). The layer nearest the specimen records the radiation from both isotopes and the second layer, at a distance of greater than 3 μ from the specimen, records only the radiation from the more energetic β-emitter, the tritium β-particles not reaching this second layer.

An alternative differential autoradiographic procedure for tritium and another β-emitter, consists of superimposing two autoradiographs and to colour the silver 'grains' of one or both emulsion layers by a dye-coupling technique [72]. The use of Kodak Experimental Scientific Plate V.1062 is recommended for this procedure. The photographic properties of this material are very similar to the AR.10

but the absence of a gelatine support layer permits a second auto-radiograph to be obtained on another emulsion layer with no more than the minimum resolution loss caused by the separation of the second autoradiograph with the minimum thickness of 'Collodion' required for tritium shielding. The total stripping-film thickness is reduced about fourfold using this material (compared with AR.10), making staining and mounting of the specimens easier; the drying of the transferred emulsion is also quicker.

Autoradiography Combined with Electron Microscopy

The advantages of high-resolution autoradiography with tritium compounds can be combined with the high resolution of an electron microscope. This permits an even clearer picture and identification of labelled structures than is obtained by optical microscopes.

Best results are obtained when uniformly thin layers of emulsion (for example Kodak V.1055) on thin cells or specimen sections are used [78]. The preparation of such uniformly thin layers of photo-graphic emulsion can be achieved using a centrifugal spreading device [73]. In cases where gelatine-supported emulsion has been used, removal of this gelatine *after* exposure and development by treatment with dilute sodium hydroxide solution, has been recommended by Hay and Revel [74]. The exposed silver grains are not displaced by this treatment and the resolution of fine structure in the underlying section is greatly improved.

A combination of autoradiography and electron microscopy produces excellent results; one such investigation is the localization of tritiated noradrenaline (norepinephrine) in sympathetic axons [75]. Other publications using these combined techniques study the incor-poration of tritiated thymidine in the intestinal epithelium of mice [76], HeLa cells [71], *Tetrahymena pyriformis* [77] and bacterial DNA [78], and the incorporation of tritiated leucine into pancreatic cells of the guinea pig [79]. A combination of autoradiography (using Gevaert Scientia NUC 307 emulsion) and electron microscopy has recently been used to demonstrate that strips of chromatin are synthesizing DNA in the nucleolus of cells [80].

Kodak Nuclear Track Emulsion type NTE has recently been recommended for use in autoradiography when combined with electron microscopy [84]. This emulsion has a grain size of 300–500 Å, has a low light sensitivity and can therefore be handled relatively easily.

Recent observations on cell proliferation and metabolism of tritium compounds using autoradiographic techniques has been well reviewed by Baserga and Kisieleski[82] and by Lima-de-Faria[83]; a few other examples (necessarily selective) are given in Table 5.6. Ross[83a] briefly reviews some of the advantages and limitations of electron microscopy autoradiography using tritium compounds.

Xerography

Xerography can also be used for autoradiography[81] but the process is limited to locating high levels of activity. Prolonged exposures are ineffective because of the natural decay of charge from the xerographic plate. The method is, for example, suitable for the autoradiography of tritium sources where relatively high levels of tritium activity (millicuries) are employed.

Other Methods

A technique using a film consisting of a single layer of silver bromide crystals on a plastic film has been used for autoradiography of chemically reactive surfaces such as zinc sulphide coated with a tritiated polymer[85].

TABLE 5.6

Biological Application of Autoradiography with Tritium

Tritiated compound	Biological specimen	References
Adenine	Reticulocytes	91
DL-Adrenaline-7-T (DL-epinephrine-7-T)	Sheep (hepatic pigment)	96e
Aldosterone-1,2-T	Rat tissues	86
Aldosterone-1,2-T	Dog (distribution in kidney, heart and arteries)	96c
Amino acids (glycine, histidine, proline, lysine)	Bone and cartilage	96a
Amino acids	Mouse (cells)	96b
Aminoazo dyes (3'-Methyl-4'-dimethylaminoazobenzene and 2-methyl-4-dimethylamino-azobenzene)	Rat liver	87
3'-Methyl-dimethylaminoazo-benzene	Rat liver	88
Arginine-T	Drosophila melanogaster (histones)	96d
Biligrafin (iodipamide)	Rabbit liver	68
p-Carboxyphenylboronic acid	Gliomas	89
Cytidine-T	Mouse	90
Cytidine-T	Reticulocytes	91
Dihydromorphine	Rat tissues	92
DFP (Di-isopropylphosphoro-fluoridate)	Localization of acetylcholinesterase activity in tissue	93, 93a

TABLE 5.6 (*continued*)

Tritiated compound	Biological specimen	References
Glycine-2-T	Mouse and rat pancreatic acinar cells	94
Glycine-2-T	Rat—adrenocorticotropin-producing cells	95
Glycine-T	Rabbit	96f
Glycine-T	Mouse (femora)	96g
5-Hydroxytryptamine-T(G) (serotonin-T(G))	Blood platelets	96h
Leucine	Reticulocytes	91
Leucine-4,5-T	Mouse (with Ehrlich ascites tumour)	57
Leucine-4,5-T	Mouse and rat pancreatic acinar cells	94
Leucine-T	Rat thyroid gland	96
Leucine-T	Rabbit (lymph node cells)	96i
Leucine-T	Rat	96j
Leucine-T	Erythroblast cells	96k
DL-Methionine-T(G)	Mouse and rat pancreatic acinar cells	94
5-Methylcytosine	Reticulocytes	91
Oestradiol-6,7-T	Rat (pituitary, liver and uterus)	96l, 96m
Oestradiol-6,7-T	Rat (liver, kidney and mammary adenocarcinoma)	96n
Phenylalanine-T	Ovarian follicle	96o
Polycyclic aromatic hydrocarbons (9,10-dimethyl-1,2-benz-anthracene; 1,2,3,4-dibenz-anthracene)	Mouse skin	97
(naphthalene;1,2,3,4-DBA; 1,2,5,6-DBA; 3,4-benzpyrene; 20-methylcholanthrene and 9,10-DMBA)	Mouse skin	98
Proline	Ganglian neurons (electron-microscopy)	99
Proline	Rat [Fibroblasts]	90 [90a]
Prostaglandin E$_1$	Mouse	91a
Thymidine	Mouse (with Ehrlich ascites tumour)	57
Thymidine	Mouse brain (Gitter cells)	100
Thymidine	Eye lens epithelial cells	101
Thymidine-T	Human chromosomes	96p, 96q
Thymidine-T	Chromosomes (in chronic granulocyte leukaemia)	96r
Thymidine-T	Leukaemic marrow cells	96s
Thymidine-T	Rabbit	96f
Thymidine-T	*Alluim cepa* seedlings	96u
Thymidine-T	Heterokaryons of animal cells	96v
Thymidine-T	Man (bronchial tract)	96w
Thymidine-T	Haemolysine-producing cells	96x
Thymidine-T	Human tumour slices	96t
L-Tyrosine	Mouse	90
Tyrosine-T(G)	Rat hair	104

TABLE 5.6 (continued)

Tritiated compound	Biological specimen	References
Tyrosine	Reticulocytes	91
Tritiated water/cellulose nitrate (collodion)	Bone	102
Uridine	Reticulocytes	91
Uridine	Insect salivary gland cells	103
Uridine-T	Human tumour slices	96t
Uridine-T	Rabbit (lymph node cells)	96i
Uridine-T	Heterokaryons of animal cells	96v
Uridine-T	Erythroblast cells	96k

ANALYSIS OF TRITIUM COMPOUNDS

Many users of radioisotopes and of radioisotopically labelled compounds rely upon the integrity of the suppliers of these materials as regards the purity and analytical data recorded for them. Because of the decomposition of radioactive compounds by self-irradiation, impurities are always likely to be present (see Chapter 6). Tritium compounds are used at very high specific activities for many investigations and are much more difficult to maintain in a high state of purity than, say, carbon-14 compounds. It is therefore important to be able to perform quick and reliable checks on the purity of the labelled compounds before use. This of course is essential if impurities are likely to interfere with the experiment.

What is meant by radioisotopic and radiochemical purity? These terms are defined as follows[105]:

The RADIOISOTOPIC PURITY of a radioactive material, consisting primarily of a given isotope, is the proportion of the total radioactivity which arises from that isotope. As tritium is unlikely to be contaminated with other radioisotopes, by virtue of its method of preparation and purification, we can normally assume that all radioactive compounds of tritium are radioisotopically pure.

The RADIOCHEMICAL PURITY of a radioactive material, consisting primarily of a given radioisotope in a stated chemical form, is the proportion of the isotope that is in the stated chemical form. It is the radiochemical purity with which one is mostly concerned and the methods by which this can be established.

The methods which are available for the analysis of tritium compounds may be divided into (A) physical and (B) chemical, although there is not always a clear-cut distinction between these two divisions. Classical methods for establishing chemical purity are normally quite inadequate for obtaining a radiochemical purity and the chemical purity of the labelled compound is usually determined independently by a physical method.

(A) Physical Methods

These include all the usual methods of analysis such as a determination of the boiling point, melting or freezing point, refractive index (liquids) or the examination of the spectral property of the compound (ultra-violet and infra-red spectroscopic methods). All such methods normally provide information on the chemical purity of the substance, which is not usually critical for many tracer applications. They are not sensitive enough to detect the trace impurities with which most of the radioactivity may be associated. It is possible for example, to have a chemical purity of greater than 99 per cent and a radiochemical purity of say less than 10 per cent, most of the activity being associated with the 1 per cent impurity in the compound. An example will illustrate this point more clearly; a sample of thymidine was tritiated by the Wilzbach method (see Chapter 4) and purified by several recrystallizations from n-butanol until constant specific activity was achieved. The melting point (and mixed melting point) and ultra-violet light absorption were identical with chemically pure thymidine, but subsequent analysis by chemical methods (below) showed the presence of at least five radiochemical impurities, and in fact the radiochemical purity of the tritiated thymidine was less than 70 per cent [8]. Although these physical methods are not usually sufficiently sensitive to detect the radioactive impurities present, a tracer use of the impure compound in a biological system for example, could give very misleading results. It is most important that conclusions drawn from a tracer use of a tritium compound (or indeed from any other labelled compound) should be directly related to that compound and not due to a labelled impurity. On the other hand traces of unlabelled chemical impurities may go undetected in many investigations, although there is always the possibility that their presence could interfere with the reactions of the radioactive tracer compound.

At the low overall isotopic abundances usually in use with tritium compounds, there is no detectable change in the physical properties of the radioactive material compared with that of the unlabelled equivalent. In compounds where high tritium isotopic abundances are achieved, there are detectable differences in the physical properties, for example the maximum density of tritium oxide compared with water shown in Table 5.7 [107].

TABLE 5.7

Maximum Density of 'Heavy' Waters

Compound	Maximum density	Temperature
Tritium oxide	1·21502 g/cm³	13·4° ± 0·1° C
Deuterium oxide	1·10589 g/cm³	11·21° ± 0·05° C
Hydrogen oxide	1·00000 g/cm³	3·98° C

Spectral properties of compounds at high specific activity are also quite different. For example, *Figures 5.6(b)* and *5.7(b)* show the infra-red spectra of tritiated adipic acid and thymine compared with their unlabelled counterparts shown in *Figures 5.6(a)* and *5.7(a)* respectively. Some spectral properties have been calculated, for example the pure rotational spectrum of tritiated ammonia (NT_3)[109] and the vibrational spectra of partially deuterated and tritiated stilbenes[110], while Staats and colleagues[111] have determined the infra-red spectra of tritium oxide, THO and TDO in the vapour phase.

(B) Chemical Methods

Reverse isotope dilution analysis and chromatographic methods of all kinds are of particular value in the determination of radiochemical purity. Fortunately, labelled impurities in a radioactive compound are usually easier to detect and measure than unlabelled trace impurities.

(a) *Reverse dilution analysis*[112]—This consists essentially of diluting a small amount (usually between 100 µg and 10 mg of the radioactive compound with at least 1,000 times its weight of the corresponding inactive compound, and directly compares the radioactive material and unlabelled compound. The diluted compound is homogenized in a suitable solvent so that complete homogeneity results. The solvent is removed and the specific activity of the product measured (s_0). The compound is then put through a purification process such as several recrystallizations, and a rigorously purified sample of the compound extracted having a specific activity (s_p), then the radiochemical purity P may be calculated from the equation (5.3)

$$\%P = \frac{s_p}{s_0} \times 100 \qquad \ldots \quad (5.3)$$

This expression (5.3) only holds true if the mass of the compound, which is being analysed for, is sufficiently large in proportion to the masses of any radioactive impurities present. Other necessary conditions are:

 (i) the 'carrier' compound must be of known purity,
 (ii) there must be no isotope effect,
(iii) the activity associated with the impurities must be completely eliminated in the preparation of the pure sample,
(iv) there must be no loss of tritium by exchange reactions either with the solvent or with the impurities and,
 (v) no chemical transformations during the analysis must result in any of the activity in the impurities becoming associated with the final pure compound.

The condition (i) is perhaps obvious, although it is not uncommon to obtain a result of greater than 100 per cent implying that the 'carrier' inactive compound is impure. Being a comparative method, a pitfall can arise using reverse dilution analysis particularly for the determination of radiochemical purity of tritium compounds prepared by exchange labelling methods (see Chapter 4). If a compound selected for exchange labelling is chemically impure then all the impurities in the compound also become labelled. Some of these may be lost during the purification of the labelled compound; but suppose these are not all removed. A reverse dilution analysis carried out with the same material originally used for the exchange will give a radiochemical purity of 100 per cent or more, a reverse dilution analysis of the 'impurities' occurring side by side with the 'pure' compound; the impurities therefore go undetected. As a further safeguard in dilution analysis one usually prepares a derivative of the homogenized diluted sample and determines the specific activity of this after rigorous purification (s_d). If the original labelled compound is pure, $s_d = s_p = s_0$. Although this is excellent for carbon-14 compounds for example, greater care is required in the choice of derivative for tritium compounds in order to fulfil condition (iv); losses of tritium by exchange or displacement of tritium from the molecule under the experimental conditions required for the derivative preparation. Derivatives formed by substitution of carbon-bound hydrogen atoms are usually forbidden, for example it would be no use making a tribromo-derivative of tritiated aniline or phenol; the tritium in the ring would be displaced giving a false low radiochemical purity. In these particular examples, a derivative formed by the reactions of the amino- or hydroxyl group would be more acceptable.

Another possible pitfall which is perhaps more obvious, is the importance of knowing the exact chemical form of the compound when calculating the specific activities s_0, s_p and s_d. For example, the tritium-labelled compound and carrier may be homogenized in a non-polar solvent and purified by recrystallization from (say) aqueous alcohol. This may result in the formation of a hydrated species. One must also be on the alert for solvent of crystallization.

An interesting example in the application of the reverse isotope dilution technique is in the analysis of D-, L-, or DL-tritiated amino acids. Analysis is carried out by adding L- or D-amino acid carriers, homogenizing in a suitable solvent (usually water) and recrystallizing to a constant specific activity. By this means the radiochemical purity with respect to the optical isomer under investigation can be determined[113]. It is possible for example, to have a chemically DL-tritiated amino acid with all the activity associated with either the D- or L-form. Such is the case after treatment of DL-α-tritiated-α-amino acids with D-amino acid oxidase under conditions which *inhibit* the action of the oxidase[8]. The resulting DL-α-amino acid-T contains all the tritium activity in the D-isomer, the activity in the L-isomer being labilized under the enzymic conditions[114].

The technique is also very useful for checking the degree of racemization which occurs during the exchange labelling of optically active amino acids, and their chemical reactions. For example, no racemization occurs during benzyloxycarbonylation[115], a frequent reaction used in synthetic polypeptide chemistry.

The analysis of tritiated leucine preparations in saturated solutions of crystalline L-, DL- and D-leucine by means of a partition between solution and solid phase, described by Schneider[116], is essentially a dilution analysis.

As with carbon-14 compounds, isotope effects rarely cause significant error in dilution analysis of tritium compounds; they are discussed more fully in Chapter 6.

One of the limitations of reverse dilution analysis is failure to fulfil condition (iii). With many tritium-labelled compounds which are not extremely complex, simple methods such as recrystallization of the diluted sample normally give a satisfactory purification quite quickly. However, natural products particularly macromolecules and products from Wilzbach labelling procedures, which often contain polymeric material, can give much more trouble and other purification methods are necessary. With very rare tritiated compounds, sufficient carrier for a reverse isotope dilution analysis is not always available, and one is obliged to use other methods.

As with other methods of analysis for radioactive components, carrier dilution analysis is of course limited by the accuracy of the method of measurement used.

(b) *Chromatographic methods*—These are the methods most frequently used and probably the most convenient for the rapid analysis of labelled compounds. Three main types of chromatography are normally used. These are:

(i) paper chromatography,
(ii) chromatography on thin-layer plates,
(iii) gas–liquid chromatography.

The first two methods (i) and (ii), are restricted to analysing non-volatile compounds, while the third method (iii) can be used for the analysis of gases or volatile liquids and solids. The methods and techniques are so well known that readers are referred to textbooks dealing specifically with such procedures[117-119].

As regards the analysis of tritium compounds, methods (i) and (ii) essentially reduce to techniques for the quantitative determination of the activity on the chromatograms. This can be done by (1) auto-radiography, (2) chromatogram scanning, or (3) direct counting of the activity on the chromatogram by β-liquid scintillation measurement. In both paper and thin-layer chromatography, autoradio-graphic methods for locating the activity can really only be used for a qualitative and roughly quantitative interpretation of radiochemical purity. A visual estimation of the density of 'blackening' of the spots obtained by the autoradiograph, as with carbon-14 compounds, can be misleading; indeed, with tritium, even more misleading. Measurements of photometric density on x-ray film are stated to give results comparable with direct counting of the spots by liquid scintillation measurement[120].

TABLE 5.8

Autoradiographic technique	Minimum sensitivity $\mu c/cm^2/24$ h	References
Apposition to 'Kodirex' x-ray film	5	8
Apposition to x-ray film while immersed in scintillation fluid	0·2	121
Impregnation with photographic emulsion K2 (Ilford)	0·28	122
Impregnation with photographic emulsion G5 (Ilford)	0·3	123
Apposition to NTB emulsion (Kodak)	0·3	124
Apposition to x-ray film of paper chromatograms	0·28	120
Apposition to x-ray film of thin-layer chromatograms	0·33	120
Impregnation with Ilford x-ray emulsion XK	0·033	120
Impregnation with scintillant then apposition to fast Kodak Royal-x pan sheet film	3*	37

* By extrapolation.

A useful evaluation of the sensitivity of the available techniques for the autoradiography of tritium on chromatograms has been published[120]; a summary of the findings is presented in Table 5.8.

For very low activities the use of Ilford x-ray emulsion XK gives a sensitivity of 10 times that of direct apposition of x-ray film and other emulsions. To avoid disintegration of the thin-layer chromatograms during processing in the impregnation method, a light spraying of the plates with PVC ('Quelspray' or 'Neotan') has been recommended[120].

A much better method for the quantitative interpretation of radiochromatograms is by scanning. A windowless gas-flow proportional paper chromatogram scanner for tritium analysis was first described by Gray, Ikeda, Benson and Kritchevsky[126]. There are now a number of scanners of this type available commercially. A disadvantage for tritium is that the counting efficiency is normally only 1 to 2 per cent under the best conditions, which reduces the sensitivity to measuring a minimum of about $0 \cdot 1$ $\mu c/cm^2$ with an accuracy of about ± 5 per cent. Both paper and thin-layer chromatograms can be scanned[127], and an accuracy of ± 4 per cent is stated for some instruments and a minimum detectability of $0 \cdot 01$ μc[128].

In an alternative procedure the paper chromatograms can be sprayed with a solution of anthracene in benzene (about $0 \cdot 3$ mg of anthracene per square centimetre is required for best results with tritium compounds) and then passed over a photomultiplier tube for measurement of the light produced by the interaction of the β-particles with the anthracene crystals[244]. Similar scintillation techniques have been used by others[129]. The method cannot be used for analysing compounds which are soluble in the solvent used for spraying the chromatograms.

Even chromatogram scanning has its limitations particularly with the low sensitivity and efficiency for tritium, and the best method for achieving quantitative results from either paper or thin-layer chromatograms consists of extracting the activity from the spots and measuring with a liquid scintillation counter. The results can be compared with other spots on the chromatogram and related to the total activity present. This technique is more sensitive than the scanning techniques.

Paper chromatograms may be cut up into strips and counted by direct suspension in the liquid scintillant or alternatively burnt in oxygen to tritiated water. This is rather tedious and the suspension method is normally preferred. Because of the short range and low energy of the tritium β-particles, self-absorption of energy by the

259

paper reduces the efficiency more markedly than with more energetic betas such as carbon-14. With ordinary Whatman paper, efficiencies of about 5 per cent are obtained for tritium compounds by direct suspension of the paper strips in the scintillant[130],[131] (compared with 60 per cent or more for carbon-14[231]). However, Gill[131] has recently shown that the use of glass-fibre paper increases the efficiency to over 20 per cent for tritium; the increase for carbon-14 being from 61 to 75 per cent, substantial but much less marked than for tritium, as might be expected. The quenching factors in the use of Whatman 3 MM paper, are independent of the tritium activity per unit area[130], but naturally depend on the total activity in the sample tube. However, the solubility of the compound in the scintillant must be taken into consideration[132]; dissolution of the compound into the scintillant normally increases the efficiency and it would seem best to either have the substance completely soluble or insoluble in the scintillant. The various 'effects' associated with liquid scintillation measurement of tritium should always be borne in mind (see page 222).

Thin-layer chromatogram spots can be scraped, suspended in a thixotropic gel such as 'Cab-O-Sil' or 'thixin' and measured directly by suspending in a scintillant. Snyder[368] describes a high-resolution zonal scraper for quantitative transfer of small zones 1, 2 or 5 mm in diameter. An efficiency of 12 per cent for tritium was obtained using a dioxan–water-naphthalene scintillant. Silica, iodine, dichloro-fluorescein and rhodamine 6G had no quenching properties in this scintillant whereas elementary carbon (from spot charring with H_2SO_4) caused severe quenching.

Sources of error—There are a number of sources of error in the chromatographic methods (i) and (ii) which call for comment.

(1) Decomposition of the compound on the paper[133], or dissociation of spots due to the various ionic species which may be present (the use of buffered paper or solvents can often overcome this problem).

(2) Insufficient resolving power—failure of impurities to separate in the chosen solvent systems. It is always wise to use several different solvent systems. A recommended procedure[8] is to extract the 'pure' compound from the first chromatogram (*Figure 5.5a*) and elute this on another chromatogram in a different solvent. This can be repeated in a number of solvents until no further separation of impurities is accomplished.

This method is sometimes more convenient than two-dimensional chromatography for scanning and cutting up the chromatograms for scintillation measurement.

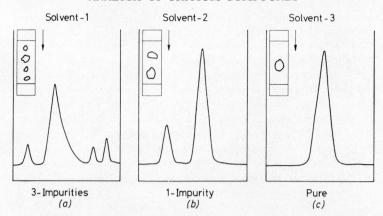

Figure 5.5. Paper chromatography in the analysis of tritium compounds. Radiochromatogram scan* showing: (a) 3-impurities detected; (b) 1-impurity detected; (c) Pure compound

* Apelgot and Duquesne[106] point out that the radioactive scan of a chromotogram of a pure substance should be a gaussian curve and that in a mixture of substances of similar R_f, the R_f properties of each substance are displaced, but the scan of the radioactivity of each substance remains gaussian. This theory has been successfully demonstrated for the behaviour of simple organic molecules such as glycine-T, for example[106].

(3) The false or 'ghost' spots, which may arise by a variety of causes, will be familiar to the many users of paper chromatography. One such effect is common in the analysis of compounds at very high specific activity. Application of the compound to the paper or thin-layer plate in such small chemical amounts, often results in some irreversible absorption[8] and subsequent analysis of the chromatogram shows a radioactive 'impurity' at the origin. If a little (100 µg or so) inactive carrier is added to the solution before applying to the chromatogram, this effect can be eliminated[8].

(4) Mass Effects. Losses of material by volatilization are important in the quantitative analysis of tritium compounds by paper or thin-layer chromatography, particularly where microgramme quantities of the compound at high specific activity are involved. It is often advantageous to add carrier. The relative distribution of activity on a chromatogram does not necessarily indicate a true picture of the radiochemical purity of the compound unless an allowance is made for any losses of the various components by volatilization or decomposition. An example gives a clearer understanding of this point. Choline-(*methyl*-T) chloride on storage is expected to decompose into trimethylamine (active) and acetaldehyde (inactive)[134]; both these

261

products are volatile and paper (or thin-layer) chromatography using neutral or alkaline solvents would always give (as indeed is observed—see Chapter 6) a radiochemical purity of 100 per cent, if no other non-volatile impurities are formed.

(5) In autoradiographic analysis of chromatograms, artefacts may also arise by chemical reactions occurring between the chromatogram and the photographic emulsion during the autoradiographic process. This is even more likely to occur in the impregnation techniques[120] where the photographic emulsion achieves very intimate contact with the chromatogram. Certain steroids for example have been found[125] to de-sensitize x-ray film and some workers have found it necessary to pre-treat the paper before use in order to remove desensitizing agents[123].

Gas–liquid or gas–solid chromatographic methods are often used for the analysis and separation of tritiated compounds, particularly the more volatile compounds to which paper or thin-layer methods cannot be applied. Even the chromatographic separation of the hydrogen isotopes on an alumina–ferric hydroxide column 24 ft. long with helium as the carrier gas, has been achieved[135]. Equipment which is designed to detect both the chemical compound and its associated radioactivity is the best[136–140]. The radioactivity of the effluent gases is usually determined by ionization chamber, proportional counting or scintillation measurement. Chemical detection by flame ionization detectors gives a measure of the chemical purity only.

A pitfall in the use of gas–liquid chromatography arises when a small amount of a highly active compound is diluted with carrier and the purity determined by gas–liquid chromatography with mass detection only. Although this may indicate over 95 per cent purity the radiochemical purity may be quite low. To illustrate this effect a sample of N-dimethylaniline-T at 10 mc/mg was diluted with 10 times its weight of carrier. Gas–liquid chromatography indicated a chemical purity of 98 per cent but reverse dilution analysis as N-dimethylaniline picrate showed the radiochemical purity to be only 70 per cent[8]. It is in such circumstances that simultaneous measurement of the activity eluted from the column is especially valuable.

In concluding this brief discussion on the analysis of tritium compounds, as with all analytical procedures no one method is infallible; the more independent checks there are, the greater the probability of an absolutely correct result[6]. A preliminary check on the radioisotopically labelled compound before use, adds that extra degree of confidence and eliminates at least one possibility of drawing the wrong conclusions from the experimental results.

SPECIFICITY OF TRITIUM LABELLING

Tritium is used much more often as a tracer for carbon structures than as a tracer for hydrogen, and for such uses it is always necessary to know the stability of the tritium label. If degradation of the labelled molecule occurs during the experiment, it is also necessary to know something at least of the position of the tritium atoms. Provided the tritium atoms are bound in non-labile positions, their intramolecular distribution is less important when studying the fate of whole molecules.

In this discussion on the specificity of tritium labelling, it must be emphasized that the distribution of tritium in compounds is likely to vary for each preparation, even though a reaction is carried out each time under apparently identical conditions. This is particularly true of compounds labelled by isotope exchange procedures as can be seen for example from Table 5.14.

Information has been collected on the distribution of tritium in various types of compounds and is classified as follows:
1. Specifically labelled compounds
   (*a*) Prepared by non-catalytic chemical synthesis.
   (*b*) Prepared by chemical synthesis involving the use of a catalyst.
2. Compounds prepared by isotope exchange reactions
   (*a*) Wilzbach-labelled compounds.
   (*b*) Modified Wilzbach-labelled compounds.
   (*c*) Compounds prepared by catalytic exchange in solution.
3. Compounds labelled by triton recoil reactions.

It would be quite impossible (and not very useful) to give a complete list of all tritium compounds with their intramolecular tritium distribution. Instead, examples in each of the groups are discussed and the methods given which are currently available for the determination of tritium distribution in molecules.

1. *Specifically Labelled Compounds*

It might seem reasonable to assume that the methods used for specific labelling with tritium (see Chapter 4) give labelled compounds in which the intramolecular distribution of tritium is known with certainty. For example, the replacement of a halogen atom by tritium or the addition of tritium to double and triple bonds might be expected to yield compounds with the tritium exclusively attached to the point of addition or replacement. It is disturbing to find that almost all of the methods which are expected to give specifically labelled tritium compounds often result in random distribution of the tritium. The reason for this is now obvious and reflects the mobility of hydrogen atoms under reaction conditions involving the use of a hydrogen transfer catalyst.

(a) *Compounds prepared by non-catalytic chemical synthesis*—Chemical reductions with tritiated sodium, potassium or lithium borohydrides and lithium aluminium tritide, all give labelled compounds in which the tritium atom is exclusively attached to the position of reduction. An example is the reduction of sugar lactones to give tritiated aldoses labelled in the 1 or 6 positions; these have been shown[141,142] to contain tritium exclusively in these positions.

There is however one reported non-specific labelling by a tritiated metal hydride[143]; this involved the reduction of 4-oxo-2,3,6-tri-*O*-methyl-D-glycopyranoside with sodium borotritide. Demethylation and degradation of the 'glucose-4-T' proved that 60 per cent of the tritium was located on carbon-4 and 40 per cent on carbon-6. No explanation for this result was put forward but in view of the specificity of tritium labelling with metal hydrides in other reductions, one might question the purity of the starting material.

Reduction of keto(oxo)-steroids with tritiated metal hydrides similarly gives specifically labelled steroid alcohols. For example, oxidation of 3β-benzoyloxy-cholest-5-en-7β-ol-7α-T (5.4), prepared by the reduction of the corresponding 7-keto-compound with sodium borohydride-T, with chromium trioxide yields inactive 3β-benzoyl-oxy-7-keto-cholest-5-ene[144].

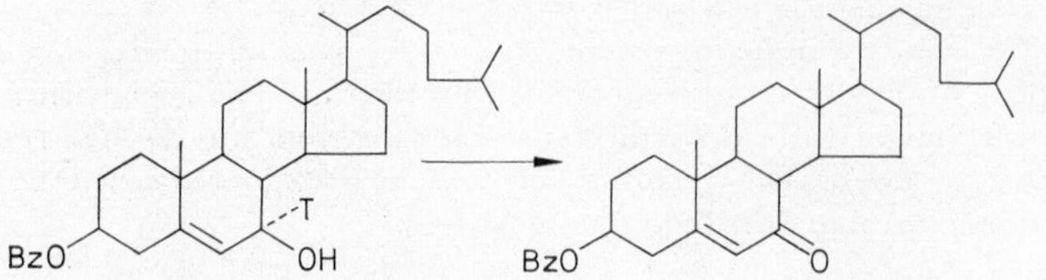

$$\dots \dots (5.4)$$

There are of course many such reactions of tritiated metal hydrides (see Chapter 4) and these are perhaps the only large class of reactions in which truly specific tritium labelling occurs. All other methods tend to give some tritium in other positions, with perhaps the exception of the newly developed hydroboration syntheses with tritium[145], and the reaction of Grignard reagents (or lithium aryls or alkyls) with tritiated water (see pages 151,153). These facts might have been deduced from work with deuterium[146] but one always has to be a little cautious in drawing inferences from corresponding reactions with deuterium; methods for the analysis of deuterium compounds, particularly at low isotopic abundances are not as sensitive as radioactive measurements and the additional effects of the β-radiation also must be taken into account with tritium.

Reductions with aluminium amalgam (or similar methods) in tritiated water can result in non-specific labelling if enolization is possible, for example in the preparation of DL-serine-2,3-T by reduction of formyl N-benzoylglycine ethyl ester (5.5)[147]:

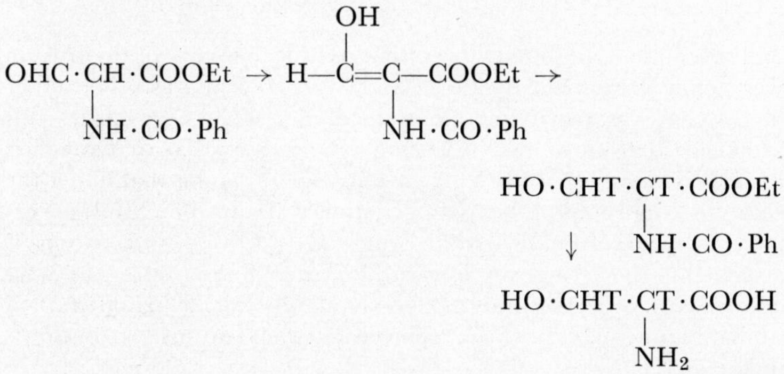

$$OHC \cdot CH \cdot COOEt \rightarrow H-\overset{\displaystyle OH}{\underset{}{C}}{=}C-COOEt \rightarrow$$

$$\underset{NH \cdot CO \cdot Ph}{|} \qquad \underset{NH \cdot CO \cdot Ph}{|}$$

$$HO \cdot CHT \cdot CT \cdot COOEt$$

$$\downarrow \quad \underset{}{|}\ NH \cdot CO \cdot Ph$$

$$HO \cdot CHT \cdot CT \cdot COOH$$

$$\underset{}{|}\ NH_2$$

$$\text{. . . . (5.5)}$$

The ratio of tritium in the 2 and 3 positions in this example was $41:47$ respectively.

(b) *Compounds prepared by chemical synthesis involving the use of a catalyst*—Many reactions of tritium enter this category, in particular the addition of tritium to unsaturated carbon–carbon bonds and halogen–tritium replacement reactions (see Chapter 4). The classical example in the non-specificity of catalytic addition of tritium to a carbon–carbon double bond is in the preparation of stearic acid-T by the catalytic hydrogenation of elaidic acid with tritium gas (5.6).

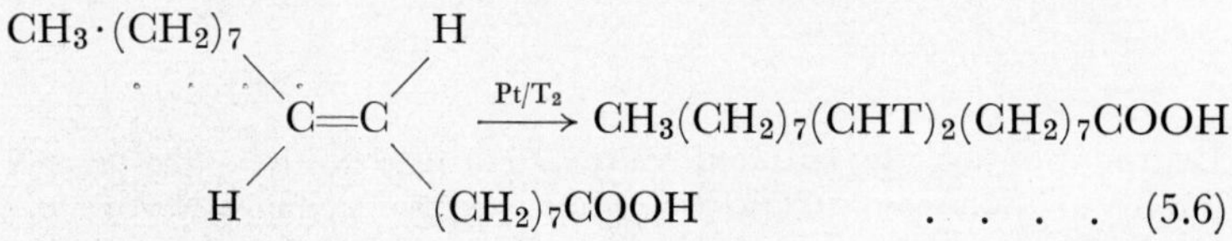

$$\underset{H}{\overset{CH_3 \cdot (CH_2)_7}{\diagdown}}C{=}C\underset{(CH_2)_7COOH}{\overset{H}{\diagup}} \xrightarrow{Pt/T_2} CH_3(CH_2)_7(CHT)_2(CH_2)_7COOH$$

$$\text{. . . . (5.6)}$$

Biochemical dehydrogenation of the stearic acid-T to oleic acid-T, which might be expected to remove at least half the tritium from the molecule, was more active than expected. Hydroxylation of the oleic acid-T double bond followed by oxidative cleavage of the diol to the aldehydes (5.7),

$$\text{Oleic acid-T} \xrightarrow[\text{H·COOH}]{\text{H}_2\text{O}_2} \text{CH}_3 \cdot (\text{CH}_2)_7 \cdot \underset{\underset{\text{OH}}{|}}{\text{CH}} - \underset{\underset{\text{OH}}{|}}{\text{CH}} \cdot (\text{CH}_2)_7 \cdot \text{COOH}$$

$$\downarrow \text{Pb}_3\text{O}_4/\text{AcOH}$$

$$\text{CH}_3 \cdot (\text{CH}_2)_7 \cdot \text{CHO} + \text{OHC} \cdot (\text{CH}_2)_7 \cdot \text{COOH} \qquad \ldots \ldots (5.7)$$

and subsequent analysis showed that only 15 per cent of the tritium was actually attached to the 9 and 10 carbon atoms. The other 85 per cent was distributed along the carbon chain with the amount attached to carbon atoms 1 to 9 being 1·68 times less than that attached to carbon atoms 10 to 18[148]. A possible explanation is that under the catalytic conditions of the hydrogenation, a double bond shift occurs prior to the addition of tritium, but exactly why so little tritium is attached to the 9,10-positions is still very much a mystery. Investigations with other saturated long-chain fatty acids tritiated in a similar manner have not been reported and their tritium distribution is unknown.

When addition of tritium across a double bond does occur, the distribution of the tritium between the two positions is likely to be uneven. An example is the tritiation of 2-phenyl-4-isopropylidene-oxazole-5-one by reduction in tetrahydrofuran in the presence of a platinum catalyst, followed by ring opening with red phosphorus and iodine to give DL-valine-$\alpha\beta$-T (5.8).

$$(\text{CH}_3)_2\text{C}=\text{C}-\overset{\displaystyle |}{\text{C}}=\text{O} \qquad \xrightarrow[\text{(ii)P / I}_2]{\text{(i) Pt /T}_2} \qquad \underset{\underset{\text{NH}_2}{|}}{\text{Me}_2\text{CT} \cdot \text{CT} \cdot \text{COOH}}$$

$$\underset{\text{Ph}}{\overset{\text{N}}{\underset{|}{\backslash}}\text{C}\diagup\text{O}}$$

$$\downarrow$$

$$\text{Me}_2\text{CT} \cdot \text{CTO} \longrightarrow \text{Me}_2\text{CT} \cdot \text{COOH} \qquad \ldots \ldots (5.8)$$

Degradation of the tritiated valine to isobutyraldehyde and isobutyric acid, showed that the α-position was favoured in the hydrogenation, about 10 times more tritium being in this position than in the β-position[149]. Further tritiations showed that the distribution of tritium between the α and β-positions varied for different experiments.

The partial catalytic hydrogenation of acetylenes to olefins with tritium is reported to give over 90 per cent of the tritium attached to the carbon atoms of the double bond[150,151]. Oleic acid-9,10-T, from stearolic acid (5.9)[150], and octene-4,5-T, from oct-4-yne (5.10)[151], are examples.

$$CH_3 \cdot (CH_2)_7 \cdot C{\equiv}C \cdot (CH_2)_7 \cdot COOH \rightarrow$$
$$CH_3 \cdot (CH_2)_7 \cdot CT{=}CT \cdot (CH_2)_7 \cdot COOH$$
$$\dots \quad (5.9)$$

$$CH_3 \cdot (CH_2)_2 \cdot C{\equiv}C \cdot CH_2 \cdot CH_2 \cdot CH_3 \rightarrow$$
$$CH_3 \cdot (CH_2)_2 \cdot CT{=}CT \cdot (CH_2)_2 \cdot CH_3$$
$$\dots \quad (5.10)$$

Hydrogenation of octadeca-9,12-diynoic acid with tritium using a Lindlar catalyst gave linoleic acid-9,10,12,13-T in which less than 5 per cent of the tritium was in positions other than those specified[152]. The degree of non-specific tritium labelling is likely to depend on the efficiency of the catalyst.

In steroid chemistry and biochemistry, it is important to know not only the position of the tritium atoms but also their stereochemistry, i.e. whether α or β-T (see page 170). The stereochemistry of the products of partial hydrogenation of acetylenes can be controlled by a suitable choice of catalyst[153], but the stereochemical course of tritiation of unsaturated steroids depends on the functional groups present in the molecule. It has been stated[154] that the reduction of $\varDelta^{1,4}$-steroids with tritium using palladium catalysts, yields predominantly $1\alpha,2\alpha$ labels. This is true in many compounds and attack usually occurs predominantly on the α-face of the molecule which is less sterically hindered by the angular 10-methyl group. However, accessibility to either face of the molecule is changed by a slight modification of the functional groups present. For example, reduction of androst-1-ene-3,17-dione with tritium gas in dioxan solution using a palladium–charcoal catalyst gives mainly (over 90 per cent) the $1\alpha,2\alpha$ labels (5.11).

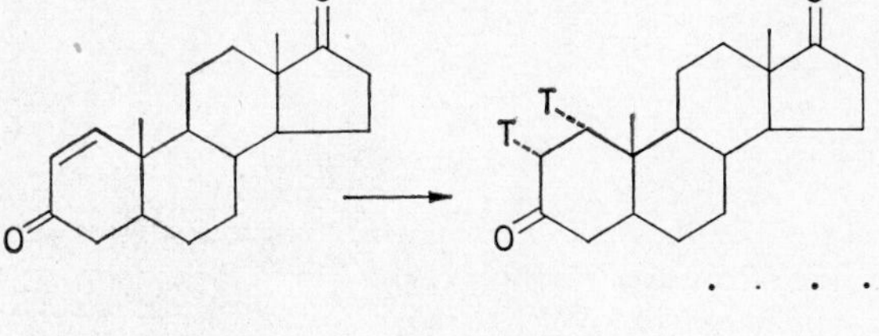

$$\dots \quad (5.11)$$

On the other hand the introduction of a 17β-hydroxyl group into the molecule results in predominantly β-reduction at carbon-1; the ratio of β- to α- reduction being about 3 to 1[155] (5.12).

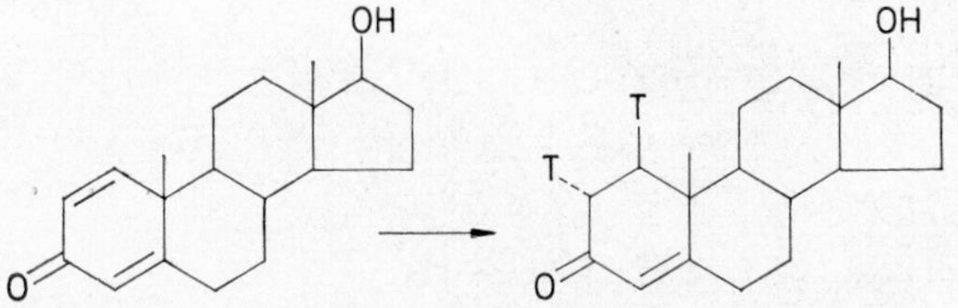

$$\dots \quad (5.12)$$

The methods for determining the stereochemical course of steroid tritiations depend on a reversal of the process, that is dehydrogenation and the re-insertion of the double bond, or by stereospecific substitution reactions. This is further discussed in Chapter 6.

Reduction of unsaturated steroids can thus give tritium atoms in α or β-positions and it is not possible to lay down simple rules at the present time, which predict with certainty to what extent α or β-addition is preferred.

The specificity of catalytic halogen–tritium exchange has been little studied; evidence from published examples suggest that catalytic replacement of halogen with tritium is not entirely specific and tritium is likely to be found in other parts of the molecule. Cholesterol-7α-T, for example, prepared from 7α-bromocholesterol was found by Clayton and Edwards[156] to have only 70 per cent of the tritium in the 7-position; Gut and Uskokovic found 80 per cent[157]. These figures represented the amount of tritium displaced from the 7-position by reforming the 7α-bromocholesterol (5.13):

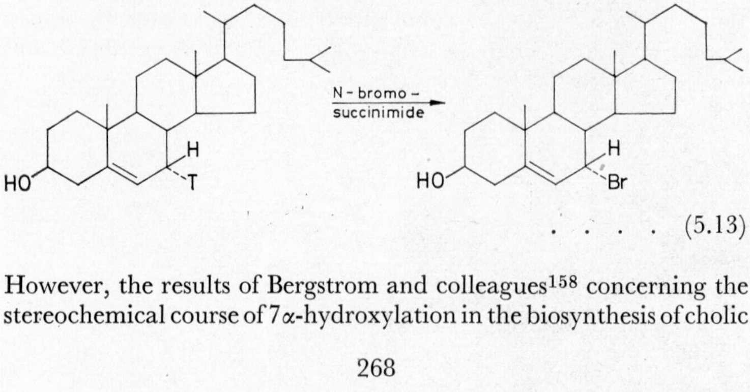

$$\dots \quad (5.13)$$

However, the results of Bergstrom and colleagues[158] concerning the stereochemical course of 7α-hydroxylation in the biosynthesis of cholic acid from cholesterol, suggest that 93 per cent of the tritium was attached at the 7α-position, in the cholesterol-7α-T used. These different degrees of specific tritium labelling might be explained by consideration of the purity of the bromo-compound. Bromine atoms situated in other positions would also be replaced and thus give the impression of non-specific labelling.

The results obtained from using L-tyrosine-3,5-T, which is prepared by the palladium-catalysed replacement of halogen from 3,5-di-iodo-L-tyrosine with tritium gas, for tyrosine hydroxylase estimation[159], suggests that the halogen replacement was not completely specific.

One must always be aware that under the catalytic conditions of hydrogenation or dehalogenation with tritium, exchange reactions can occur in hydrogen positions in the molecule which would normally be reckoned 'non-labile'. It is a rather disturbing feature of such 'specific' labelling reactions and no simple solution to the problem is apparent. It is perhaps fortunate that for many of the uses of tritium compounds a few per cent tritium in unspecified positions does not matter, but for others it might be very important. The possibility must always be borne in mind.

2. Compounds Prepared by Isotope Exchange Reactions

(a) Wilzbach-labelled compounds—Some examples of the tritium distribution which is obtained when compounds are labelled by exposure to tritium gas, are shown in Table 5.9. The results may be summarized by saying that 'random but not uniform distribution of the tritium can be expected'. Isolated examples of specific labelling by the Wilzbach method have been published. For example, coenzyme-Q_0 (5.14) after purification, was found to contain 99 per cent of the tritium in the 6-position[160].

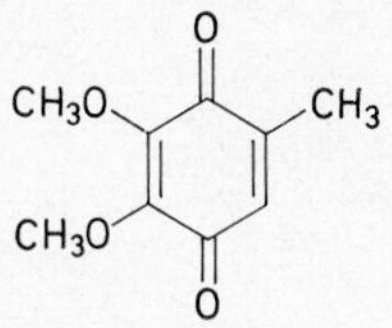

. . . . (5.14)

Another example is *myo*inositol-T isolated as one of the products from the exposure of inositol to the tritium gas, which was found to contain tritium only at the carbon-1 position (5.15)[161].

269

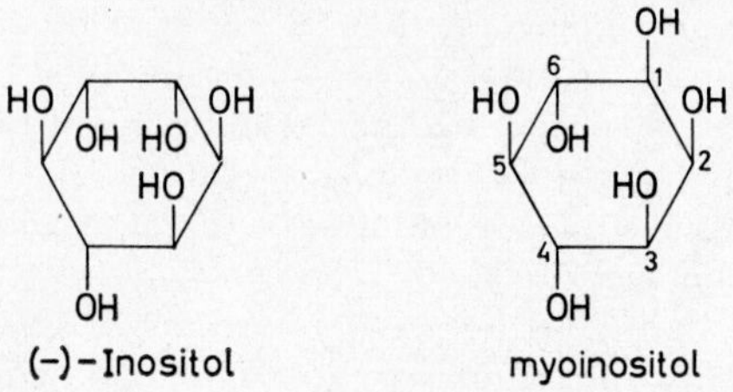

(−)−Inositol   myoinositol

. . . . (5.15)

TABLE 5.9

Intramolecular Distribution of Tritium in Wilzbach Labelling

Tritiated compound	Position of tritium label	Tritium %	References
Anisole	Methyl	0·2	163
	Ortho	40	
	Meta	33	
	Para	26·9	
Atropine	Tropine	43	164
	Tropic acid	32	
	not located	25	
Benzpyrene	4,5	27	166
Chlorobenzene	Ortho	50	163
	Meta	33·2	
	Para	15·4	
Cholesterol	3	6·4	165
	6	10	
	2,4	5·6	
	16	4·1	
	17–27	27	
Co-enzyme Q_0	6	99	160
Deoxyribosenucleic acid	Ratio in bases:		167
	Adenine	1	
	Thymine	9·8	
	Guanine	1·4	
	Cytosine	2·4	
9,10-Dimethyl-1,2- benzanthracene	3,4	16	166
	9,10	39	
	1′,2′,3′,4′	56	
Ethyl benzoate	Methyl	2·1	163
	Methylene	12·0	
	Ortho	40	
	Meta	12·4	
	Para	33·4	
Folic acid	2-Amino-4-hydroxy-6-methyl pteridine (position-9)	22·1	168
	p-Aminobenzoic acid	28·4	
	Glutamic acid	47·3	
Furan	Alpha	63·2	163
	Beta	36·8	

TABLE 5.9 (*continued*)

Tritiated compound	Position of tritium label	Tritium %	References
Human albumin	Acid hydrolysate amino acids		169
	Leucine	8·5	
	Phenylalanine	8·3	
	Valine	9·9	
	Proline	18·0	
	Aspartic acid	0·9	
	Glutamic acid	4·6	
	Glycine	3·8	
	Threonine	0·9	
	Alanine	2·6	
	β-Alanine	4·2	
	Tyrosine	6·6	
	Glutamine	1·4	
	Arginine	1·3	
	Lysine	1·2	
	Unknown	27·8	
Insulin	Ratio in amino acids		170
	Aspartic acid	1	
	Serine	2·2	
	Leucine	8·7	
	Isoleucine	16·5	
	Tyrosine	24·5	
	Phenylalanine	52·1	
Mandelic acid	α-Position; Phenyl ring	57; 43	171
20-Methylcholanthrene	6,7	29	166
Nitrobenzene	Ortho	57·4	163
	Meta	33·4	
	Para	9	
Phenol	Ortho	35·8	163
	Meta	38·4	
	Para	25·8	
Selenomethionine	Methyl	29	163a
Thiophene	Alpha	55·2	163
	Beta	45	
Toluene	Methyl	5	172
	Ortho	53·6	
	Meta	27·8	
	Para	13·5	
Toluene	Methyl	9·6	163
	Ortho	50·6	
	Meta	25·8	
	Para	13·3	
Uridine diphosphate-*N*-acetylglucosamine	*N*-Acetylglucosamine	63	173
	Uridine diphosphate	37	
L-Valyl-L-leucine	Valine	35	174
	Leucine	72	

These two examples are the results from one labelling of each compound. It would be rash to infer that repetition of the exchange, perhaps at a different level of activity, necessarily produces the same degree of specificity of labelling.

271

Distribution of the tritium in the compound does not depend upon the length of the exposure. Results obtained by Thieman[162] for toluene are shown in Table 5.10.

TABLE 5.10

Position of Tritium	Exposure times Days					
	5	7	10	15	18	28
Side-chain (Me) %	7·0	8·3	6·9	8·0	7·9	7·3
o-Positions %	57·0	55·8	56·0	56·2	55·6	56·0
m-Positions %	21·6	21·0	20·8	21·2	21·4	21·0
p-Position %	14·3	14·9	16·3	14·6	15·1	15·7

Volume of flask: 2,000 cm³   Pressure: 0·3 mmHg
Tritium activity: 2 c   Toluene pressure: 14–18 mmHg = 150–200 mg

From Table 5.11 it is seen that the tritium labelling of sugars by the Wilzbach method does not result in uniform labelling, which is perhaps only to be expected. An interesting feature however is the widely different labelling pattern observed for glucose-6-phosphate compared with glucose. The results are not readily explained; the difference may be due to a number of factors including crystal shape, hydrogen bonding and the influence of the phosphate group on the excitation energy distribution throughout the excited states of the glucose molecule. Similar differences are observed between the labelling of ribose and ribose-5-phosphate.

TABLE 5.11
Intramolecular Tritium Distribution in Various Sugars Labelled by the Wilzbach Method [206a]

Compound	Labelling conditions	% Tritium distribution				
		C–1	C–2	C–3	C–4 C–5 or C–4+C–5	C–6
D-Glucose	31 days; 200 mmHg T₂	2·1	—	89·0	0·7 | 0·6	6·4
D-Glucose	31 days; 200 mmHg T₂	2·0	1·0	88·0	1·0	5·2
D-Glucose	6 days; 200 mmHg T₂	0·3	—	92	2·6	4·0
D-Glucose	1 day; 200 mmHg T₂	0·3	—	95	2·8	4·3
D-Glucose	by New England Nuclear Corporation, U.S.A. (N.E.N.C.)	0·3	—	89	4·5	4·3
		5·3	21·5	13·6	12·3 | 25·0	17·8
D-Glucose-6-phosphate	6 weeks; 750 mc	2·0	4·0	2·0	85	6·0
D-Mannose	30 days; 160 mm T₂	0·1	3·2	0·1	50 | 43	6·6
D-Mannose	30 days; 160 mm T₂/H₂	15·1	—	42	5·3 | 29·7	4·0
D-Fructose	by N.E.N.C., U.S.A.					
D-Fructose-6-phosphate	6 weeks; 750 mc	39·9	—	7·6	14·3 | 7·8	40·3
Tetraacetyl-D-ribofuranoside	—	0·5	7·6	0·7	93·0	6·3	—
D-Ribose (cryst.)	7 days; 20 mc	0·1	1·0	95·0	0·3 | 1·4	—
D-Ribose-5-phosphate	6 weeks; 1 c	10·7	40·0	15·8	12·2 | 19·5	—
Mannitol	21 days; 200 mc	C–1+C–6 15·8		C–2+C–5 53·0		C–3+C–4 30

(b) *Compounds labelled by modified Wilzbach conditions*—If the conditions for the tritium gas exposure are changed, for example by Tesla discharge, ultra-violet light irradiation or similar activation processes, then the distribution of the tritium in the purified products can be expected to be different from the labelling pattern observed for the normal Wilzbach procedure. This effect is illustrated by the results obtained by Ache, Herr and Thiemann[172] for toluene labelled under different conditions, which are summarized in Table 5.12. Labelling in the methyl group is particularly influenced by the conditions used.

TABLE 5.12

Gas-Exposure Labelling of Toluene under Different Conditions[172]

Position of the tritium label in the toluene molecule	Tritium gas (Wilzbach) %	Tritium + hydrogen (Wilzbach) %	Tritium gas (Tesla discharge) %	Tritium gas (u.v.-irradiation) %	Tritium gas (γ-irradiation) %
Methyl group	5	31	28·5	16	6·7
Ortho	53·6	30·8	28·4	41·6	51·6
Meta	27·8	25·4	29·2	28	27·6
Para	13·5	13·8	13·9	13·9	15·1

Quite large differences in the distribution of tritium are observed between compounds labelled under Wilzbach conditions and the platinum-catalysed gas-exposure technique. A summary of some examples obtained by Meshi and Sato[175] are shown in Table 5.13.

TABLE 5.13

Compound	Labelling method	Distribution of tritium				
		Labile μc/mg	Non-labile μc/mg	ortho %	meta %	para %
Benzoic acid	Wilzbach	62·5	0·47	58·3	21·3	20·4
Benzoic acid	Catalysed gas-exposure (Pt)	382·3	18·9	5·0	72·5	22·5
Salicylic acid	Wilzbach	115·6	0·17	39·0	48·4	13·6
Salicylic acid	Catalysed gas-exposure (Pt)	792·0	102·0	16·9	31·7	51·4
				(positions relative to —OH group)		
Benzoylvaline	Wilzbach	77·8	0·15	92·5 (in ring)		
				7·5 (in side-chain)		
Benzoylvaline	Catalysed gas-exposure (Pt)	286·3	0·27	60·2 (in ring)		
				39·8 (in side-chain)		

It is suggested[175] that the hydrogen–tritium exchange in the aromatic ring under the platinum-catalysed procedure, may follow the substitution rules for electrophilic aromatic exchange; further investigations may be expected to test these conclusions.

(c) *Compounds prepared by catalytic exchange in solution*—Few workers have investigated the distribution of the tritium atoms in compounds labelled by catalytic exchange reactions in solution. Table 5.14 shows the distribution of tritium in generally labelled thymidine.

TABLE 5.14

Experiment No.	1	2	3	4	5
Tritiated solvent (platinum catalyst)	THO	THO	THO	70% AcOT	70% AcOT
% Tritium in thymine moiety	37·5	37	70	60	28

The tritium distribution between the thymine and deoxyribose parts of the thymidine molecule was quite unpredictable [176] and the exclusive labelling in the thymine moiety, which had been reported by others[177,178], could not be obtained. Some examples of the tritium distribution in other compounds is shown in Table 5.15.

TABLE 5.15

Distribution of Tritium in Compounds Labelled by Catalysed Exchange in Solution

Tritiated compound	Labelling method	Position of tritium label	Tritium %	References
Cholesterol	Tritiated acetic acid-Pt	Alicyclic rings Side-chain	60·8 36·5	179
Cortisone (from 3α-acetoxy-pregnane-11,20-dione)	Tritiated acetic acid-Pt	16 21 4 not located	70 5 20 4	180, 181
Folic acid	Tritiated water-Pt	2-Amino-4-hydroxy-6-methylpteridine p-Aminobenzoyl-glutamic acid	50 [15] 50	182 [8]
Methotrexate	Tritiated acetic acid-Pt	Pteridine N10-methyl-p-amino-benzoylglutamic acid	62 [30] 38	183 [183a]
Toluene	Tritiated sulphuric acid	Methyl Ortho Meta Para	0·1 60 10 30	184
Uracil	Tritiated acetic acid-Pt	5 6	34 66	8
Methyl p-amino-benzoate	Tritiated water-Pt	Methyl Phenyl ring	10 90	8

TABLE 5.15 (continued)

Tritiated compound	Labelling method	Position of tritium label	Tritium %	References
Phenol	Tritiated water-Pt	Ortho	40	8
		Meta	40	
		Para	20	
Thymine	Tritiated acetic acid-Pt	Methyl	15	8
		6	85	

Exchange of tritium into the aromatic ring occurs more readily than with aliphatic hydrogen positions. It is not possible to draw other generalizations from the few examples where the distribution of the tritium is known.

3. Compounds Labelled by Triton Recoil Reactions

Although the recoil method of labelling (see Chapter 4) is not normally used for the preparation of tritium compounds, the intramolecular distribution of tritium in some compounds labelled by this technique, has been examined principally with the expectation that it may help to elucidate the mechanism of recoil triton reactions.

Some examples are listed in Table 5.16. No examples appear to have been reported in which uniform labelling occurs and even compounds in which the replacement of a specific group might be expected to lead to specific labelling, such as deiodination, were accompanied by exchange and produced generally labelled molecules[188].

TABLE 5.16

Intramolecular Distribution of Tritium in Recoil Labelling

Labelled compound	Position of label	Tritium %	References
Acetanilide	Alkyl group	13·2	186
	Ortho	42·4	
	Meta	31·6	
	Para	12·9	
DL-Alanine	1	20	185
	Methyl	80	
Benzoic acid	Ortho	7·2	187
	Meta	94·0	
	Para	2·2	
Benzoic acid (by irradiation of p-hydroxybenzoic acid)	Ortho	11	188
	Meta	12	
	Para	77	
Benzoic acid (by irradiation of o-iodobenzoic acid)	Ortho	84	188
	Meta	9	
	Para	7	

TABLE 5.16 (*continued*)

Labelled compound	Position of label	Tritium %	References
Benzoic acid	Ortho	7	188
(by irradiation of	Meta	86	
m-aminobenzoic acid)	Para	7	
Benzoic acid	Ortho	2	188
(by irradiation of	Meta	22	
p-chlorobenzoic acid)	Para	76	
n-Butylanilide	Alkyl group	31·1	186
	Ortho	28·6	
	Meta	24·2	
	Para	16·3	
isoButylanilide	Alkyl group	45·4	186
	Ortho	19·4	
	Meta	21·8	
	Para	15·6	
Trans-Cinnamic acid	Alpha	12	189
(Ph·CH=CH·COOH)	Beta	7	
	Ortho	33	
	Meta	31	
	Para	17	
D-Glucose	1	3 (3)	190 (191)
	2	6 (6)	
	3	29 (50)	
	4	14 (2)	
	5	0 (23)	
	6	24 (0)	
Galactose	1	8	190
	2	5	
	3	22	
	4	32	
	5	11	
	6	11	
Methyl cholate	11		
	20	mainly	191a
	22		
Phenylacetic acid	Methylene	0·75	192
	Labile	22	
	Ortho	29	
	Meta	29·4	
	Para	18·3	
Propionanilide	Alkyl group	31·7	186
	Ortho	32·6	
	Meta	22·4	
	Para	13·1	
isoPropylbenzoate	Methyl groups	20	193, 194
	Methine group	26·4	
	Aromatic ring	53·6	
Reserpine	Trimethoxybenzoic acid	35	195
	Methyl reserpate	65	
Toluene	Methyl	22	172
	Ortho	34	
	Meta	28	
	Para	16	

Determination of the Intramolecular Distribution of Tritium in Labelled Compounds

The methods which are at present available for the determination of the intramolecular distribution of tritium in a labelled compound normally involve a degradation of the molecule or the substitution of hydrogen atoms (and any tritium occupying its place) at a particular position within the molecule. These procedures are rather wasteful if valuable material is involved, and the process of degradation is often difficult to perform without unpredictable or uncertain loss of tritium by exchange, particularly with the more complex molecules.

The substitution method is rather limited but it is particularly useful in the aromatic series where the replacement of tritium atoms in the ring by substituents is relatively easy to achieve. The intramolecular distribution of the tritium is then established by difference. There are many examples and an illustration of the method is the determination of labelling in tritiated benzoic acid produced by a recoil reaction[187] (5.16).

Conversion of the benzoic acid-T into *m*-dinitrobenzoic acid (step I) establishes the tritium displaced at both meta positions, while mono-

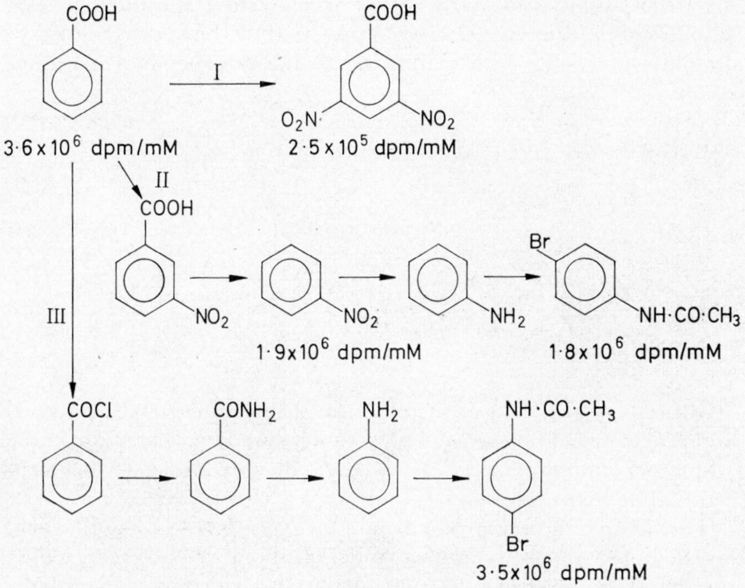

$$\dots\dots\quad(5.16)$$

nitration (step II), followed by decarboxylation, reduction to aniline and bromination of the anilide, serves to establish the tritium in the ortho-position. Tritium in the para-position is determined by the reaction sequence, benzoyl chloride, benzamide, aniline and bromoacetanilide (step III).

The results show that 94 per cent of the tritium is associated with the meta positions and only 7 per cent and 2 per cent with the ortho and para positions respectively.

It would be a very tedious task to determine the tritium distribution for every preparation of a labelled compound, even for the simplest molecules such as uracil. However, this information is becoming more necessary, and simple, rapid and reliable methods for determining the intramolecular distribution of tritium in molecules must be sought. Methods in which the sample is not destroyed would be ideal and this directs attention to the physical methods of analysis, in particular spectroscopic methods.

Absorption spectra of tritiated compounds in the ultra-violet region do not usually exhibit significant differences from the unlabelled material, but quite large differences are evident in the infra-red spectral region. For example, *Figures 5.6a* and *5.6b* show the infra-red spectra of adipic acid and tritiated adipic acid respectively[8]. The adipic acid-T (dimethyl ester) was prepared by the hydrogenation of dimethyl muconate with tritium gas in the presence of a platinum catalyst (5.17).

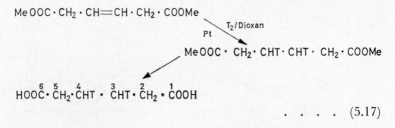

$$Me\,OOC \cdot CH_2 \cdot CH = CH \cdot CH_2 \cdot COOMe$$

$$\xrightarrow[\;Pt\;]{\;T_2/Dioxan\;}$$

$$Me\,OOC \cdot CH_2 \cdot CHT \cdot CHT \cdot CH_2 \cdot COOMe$$

$$\overset{6}{HOOC} \cdot \overset{5}{CH_2} \cdot \overset{4}{CHT} \cdot \overset{3}{CHT} \cdot \overset{2}{CH_2} \cdot \overset{1}{COOH}$$

$$\cdots \quad (5.17)$$

Hydrolysis of the ester with potassium hydroxide yielded tritiated adipic acid on acidification. The isotopic abundance of tritium in the adipic acid molecule was in this particular example, 25 per cent (non-labile hydrogen positions only).

The method of preparation would be expected to give adipic acid labelled predominantly in the 3 and 4 positions. This is reflected by the almost complete disappearance of the CH-deformation band of the 3,4-methylene groups at 6·84 μ in the tritiated compound, also the

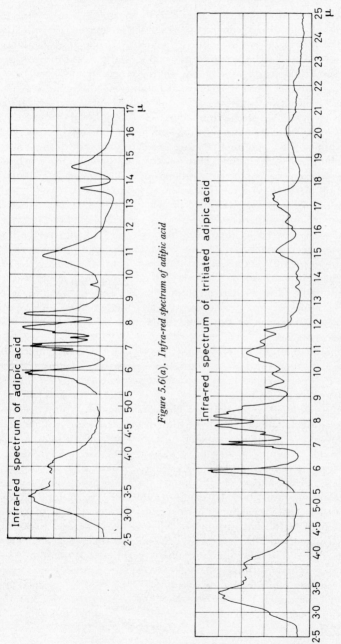

Figure 5.6(a). Infra-red spectrum of adipic acid

Figure 5.6(b). Infra-red spectrum of tritiated adipic acid

279

CH-deformation band at 7·0 μ, due to the methylene groups at positions 2 and 5[196], is reduced but to a much less marked extent. This suggests that some tritium is also attached to carbon atoms 2 and 5, which is what one might expect under the catalytic conditions of the tritiation. The band at 13·62 μ characteristic of methylene vibrations of all the —CH₂— groups in the labelled compound (usually termed methylene 'wagging')[197,198], is only about 10 per cent of its intensity in the labelled adipic acid. This is due to the 'damping' effect of the heavier tritium atoms attached to the chain. The CH stretching region observed in adipic acid is obscured by the —OH stretching; in addition the whole spectrum is altered, particularly in the 9 to 12 μ region, of the tritiated material. The —OH deformation band of the carboxyl group is shown at 10·8 μ.

Another interesting example[8] is that of unlabelled and tritiated thymine shown in *Figures 5.7a* and *5.7b* respectively. Tritiated thymine was prepared by the platinum-catalysed exchange method in tritiated acetic acid (see Chapter 4). The isotopic abundance of tritium at the 6-position was about 54 per cent in this example.

The CH-deformation band of the methyl group at 7·25 μ is slightly reduced in the active compound. A rough estimate suggests that about 10 per cent of the tritium is in the methyl group. Above 8 μ the whole spectrum of the tritiated thymine is different from the carrier material.

Among other publications on the spectra of tritium compounds are isotope shifts in the Balmer (emission) spectrum of tritium[199], the infra-red spectrum of tritiated water[111] and two examples mentioned on page 255.

Infra-red analysis is essentially one of comparison; in this instance between the unlabelled and the tritiated compound and a qualitative and perhaps semi-quantitative picture of tritium distribution, is only attainable in simple molecules containing a relatively high (say 10 per cent) isotopic abundance of tritium. However, it is not satisfactory, nor is it likely to be, for an accurate interpretation of tritium distribution, particularly for complex molecules.

Tritium has a nuclear spin quantum number of $\frac{1}{2}$, a magnetic moment of 2·9788 and a triton frequency of 45·414 Mc/s at 10,000 G; the isotope lends itself to study by nuclear magnetic resonance (n.m.r.)[200]. The potential usefulness of n.m.r. for 'pin-pointing' proton positions in molecules has been demonstrated many times with investigations using deuterium[201-205]. N.M.R. permits the direct (non-destructive) estimation of the exact number and the position of the deuterium atoms introduced into molecules by

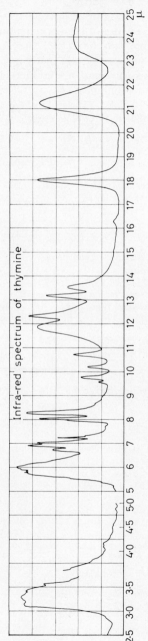

Figure 5.7(a). Infra-red spectrum of thymine

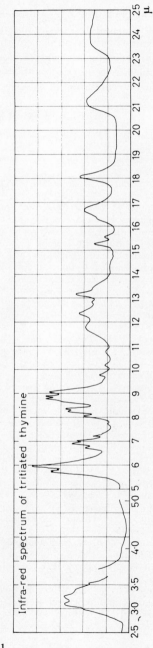

Figure 5.7(b). Infra-red spectrum of tritiated thymine

281

exchange reactions [204]. A similar use of n.m.r. can be envisaged for tritiation reactions. So far the n.m.r. spectrum of only one tritium compound has been published; that of ethyl benzene (*ethyl*-T) having a tritium isotopic abundance of about 1 per cent [206] and many more examples are required to fully explore this potentially useful method for the determination of tritium distribution in molecules.

REFERENCES AND BIBLIOGRAPHY

[1] Ayres, P. J. *Proc. Symp. Tritium Phys. Biol. Sci.* I.A.E.A., Vienna 2 (1962) 131

[2] Westermark, T., Devell, L. and Ghanem, N. A. *Nucl. Instrum. Meth.* 9 (1960) 141

[3] Kannuna, M. M. and Cameron, J. F. *Int. J. appl. Radiat. Isotopes* 2 (1957) 76

[4] Funt, B. L. *Can. J. Chem.* 39 (1961) 711

[5] Forsberg, H. G. *Svensk kem. Tidskr.* 74 (1962) 144

[6] Lambie, D. A. *Techniques for the Use of Radioisotopes in Analysis.* A Laboratory Manual. 1964. E. & F. N. Spon

[7] Bruno, G. A. and Christian, J. E. *Analyt. Chem.* 33 (1961) 650

[8] Radiochemical Centre—Unpublished results

[9] Hayes, F. N. *Int. J. appl. Radiat. Isotopes* 1 (1956) 46

[10] Davidson, J. D. and Feigelson, P. *Int. J. appl. Radiat. Isotopes* 2 (1957) 1

[11] *Nuclear Chicago Corp. Liquid Scintillation Counting Manual* (Feb. 1964) and Pub. 711580 (Nov. 1963). Nuclear Chicago Corp. Des Plaines, Illinois, U.S.A.

[12] Brooks, F. D. *Prog. nucl. Phys.* 5 (1956) 252

[13] Kasida, Y., Yamazaki, M. and Iwakura, T. *Radio-Isotopes Tokyo*, 10 (1961) 36

[14] Schöniger, W. *Mikrochim. Acta* (1955) 123; (1956) 869

[15] Schöniger, W. *Proc. Int. Symp. Microchemistry, Birmingham*, 1958. p. 93, 1960. Oxford; Pergamon Press

[16] MacDonald, A. M. G. *Analyst* 86 (1961) 3

[17] Riley, C. J. and Brooks, H. *Talanta* 11 (1964) 897

[18] Van Slyke, D. D. and Folch, J. *J. biol. Chem.* 136 (1940) 509

[19] Kinnory, D. S., Kanabrocki, E. L., Greco, J., Veatch, R. L., Kaplan, E. and Oester, Y. T. *Liquid Scintillation Counting* Ed. Bell, C. G. and Hayes, F. N. p. 223, 1958. New York; Pergamon Press

[20] Steinberg, D. *Nature, Lond.* 183 (1959) 1253; *Analyt. Biochem.* 1 (1960) 23

[21] Funt, B. L. *Nucleonics* 14 (8) (1956) 83

[22] White, C. G. and Helf, S. *Nucleonics* 14 (10) (1956) 46

[23] Ichii, S., Forchielli, E., Perloff, W. H. and Dorfman, R. I. *Analyt. Biochem.* 5 (1963) 422

[24] Henriques, F. C. and Margnetti, C. *Ind. Engng Chem. Anal. Edn* 18 (1946) 420

[25] Palevsky, H., Swank, R. K. and Grenchik, G. *Rev. scient. Instrum.* 18 (1947) 298

[26] Janney, C. D. and Moyer, B. J. *Rev. scient. Instrum.* 19 (1948) 667

[27] Riesz, P. and Wilzbach, K. E. *J. phys. Chem.* 62 (1958) 6

[28] Mason, L. H., Dutton, H. J. and Bair, L. R. *J. Chromat.* 2 (1959) 322

[29] Cacace, F. *Nucleonics* 19 (5) (1961) 45

[30] Howes, J. H. *A.E.R.E. Harwell, Rep.* AERE–M839 (April, 1961)

[31] Hasan, J. and Perheentupa, J. *Rep. Inst. Occupational Health*, Helsinki, Finland, 9 (1963) 1

[32] Glascock, R. F. *Nature, Lond.* 168 (1951) 121 (see also Ref. 434)

[33] Verly, W. G. *CEN–R1426* (1959)

[34] Becquerel, H. *C. r. hebd. Séanc. Acad. Sci., Paris* 122 (1896) 420, 501

[34a] Lacassagne, A. and Lattes, J. *C. r. Séanc. Soc. Biol.* 90 (1924) 352

[35] Fitzgerald, P. J., Eidinoff, M. L., Knoll, J. E. and Simmel, E. B. *Science, N.Y.* 114 (1951) 494

[36] Catch, J. R. *Carbon-14 Compounds* 1961. London; Butterworths

[37] Parups, E. V., Hoffman, I. and Jackson, H. R. *Talanta* 5 (1960) 75

[38] Wilson, A. T. *Nature, Lond.* 182 (1958) 524

[39] Boyd, G. A. *Autoradiography in Biology and Medicine* 1955. New York; Academic Press

[40] Evans, T. C. *Proc. Soc. exp. Biol. Med.* 64 (1947) 313

[41] Belanger, L. F. and Leblond, C. P. *Endocrinology* 39 (1946) 8

[42] Pelc, S. R. *Nature, Lond.* 160 (1947) 749

[42a] Berriman, R. W., Herz, R. H. and Stevens, G. W. W. *Brit. J. Radiol.* 23 (1950) 472

[43] Messier, B. and Leblond, C. P. *Proc. Soc. exp. Biol. Med.* 96 (1957) 7

[44] Joftes, D. L. *Lab. Invest.* 8 (1959) 131

[45] Herz, R. H. *Lab. Invest.* 8 (1959) 71

[45a] Doniach, I. and Pelc, S. R. *Brit. J. Radiol.* 23 (1950) 184

[45b] Stevens, G. W. W. *Nature, Lond.* 161 (1948) 432; *Brit. J. Radiol.* 23 (1950) 723

[46] Ray, R. C. and Stevens, G. W. W. *Brit. J. Radiol.* 26 (1953) 362

[47] Lord, B. I. *J. photogr. Sci.* 11 (1963) 342

[47a] Pellerin, P., Fallot, P., Laine-Boszormenyi, M. and Serrel, F. *Nature, Lond.* 184 (1959) 1385

[48] Falk, G. J. and King, R. C. *Radiat. Res.* 20 (1963) 466

[49] Ficq, A. *Lab. Invest.* 8 (1959) 237

[50] Pelc, S. R. *Lab. Invest.* 8 (1959) 127

[51] Gullberg, J. E. *Lab. Invest.* 8 (1959) 94

[52] Tolles, W. E. *Lab. Invest.* 8 (1959) 99

[53] Dendy, P. P. *Physics. Med. Biol.* 5 (1960) 131

[54] Edwards, J. L., Koch, A. L., Youcis, P., Freese, H. L., Laite, M. B. and Donaldson, J. T. *J. biophys. biochem. Cytol.* 7 (1960) 273

[55] Wimber, D. E., Quastler, H., Stein, O. L. and Wimber, D. R. *J. biophys. biochem. Cytol.* 8 (1960) 327

[56] Hughes, W. L., Bond, V. P., Brecher, G., Cronkite, E. P., Painter, R. B., Quastler, H. and Sherman, F. G. *Proc. natn. Acad. Sci. U.S.A.* 44 (1958) 476

[57] Baserga, R. and Kisieleski, W. E. *Lab. Invest.* 12 (1963) 648

[58] Baserga, R. and Nemeroff, K. *Stain Technol.* 37 (1962) 21

[59] André, T. *Acta Radiologica* (Suppl.) 142 (1956) 26

[60] Baserga, R. and Nemeroff, K. *Stain. Technol.* 38 (1963) 111

[61] Bleecken, S. *Atompraxis* 10 (1964) 376

[62] Kisieleski, W. E., Baserga, E. and Vaupotic, J. *Argonne Natn. Lab., Biol. Med. Res. Div. Rep.*, Jan.–Dec., 1960, ANL–6368 (May, 1961) 181; *Radiat. Res.* 15 (1961) 341

[62a] Lajtha, L. G. and Oliver, R. *Lab. Invest.* 8 (1959) 214
[62b] Hughes, W. L. *Adv. Tracer Methodol.*
[63] Beischer, D. E. *Nucleonics* 11 (12) 1953) 24
[64] Stillström, J. *Int. J. appl. Radiat. Isotopes* 14 (1963) 113
[64a] Stillström, J. *Int. J. appl. Radiat. Isotopes* 16 (1965) 357
[65] Winteringham, F. P. W., Harrison, A. and Hammond, J. H. *Nature, Lond.* 165 (1950) 149
[66] Fitzgerald, P. J. *Lab. Invest.* 10 (1961) 846
[67] Wilske, K. R. and Ross, R. *J. Cell Biol.* 19 (1963) 75A
[67a] Canny, M. J. *Nature, Lond.* 175 (1955) 857
[68] Novek, J., *Int. J. appl. Radiat. Isotopes* 15 (1964) 485
[68a] Appleton, T. C. *Jl. R. microsc. Soc.* 83 (1964) 277
[69] Baserga, R. *J. Cell Biol.* 12 (1962) 633
[70] Krause, M. and Plaut, W. *Nature, Lond.* 188 (1960) 511
[70a] Owen, M. *J. Cell Biol.* 19 (1963) 33
[71] Harford, C. G. and Hamlin, A. *Lab. Invest.* 10 (1961) 627
[72] Dawson, K. B., Field, E. O. and Stevens, C. W. W. *Nature, Lond.* 195 (1962) 310
[73] Koehler, J. K., Muhlethaler, K. and Freywyssling, A. *J. Cell. Biol.* 16 (1963) 73
[74] Hay, E. D. and Revel, J. P. *J. Cell Biol.* 16 (1963) 29
[75] Wolfe, D. E., Potter, L. T., Richardson, K. C. and Axelrod, J. *Science, N.Y.* 138 (1962) 440
[76] Hampton, J. C. and Quastler, H. *J. biophys. biochem. Cytol.* 10 (1961) 140
[77] Przybylski, R. J. *Expl. Cell Res.* 24 (1961) 181
[78] Van Tubergen, R. P. *J. biophys. biochem. Cytol.* 9 (1961) 219
[79] Caro, L. G. *J. biophys. biochem. Cytol.* 10 (1961) 37
[80] Granboulan, N. and Granboulan, P. *Expl Cell Res.* 34 (1964) 71
[81] Dobbs, H. E. *Int. J. appl. Radiat. Isotopes* 14 (1963) 285
[82] Baserga, R. and Kisieleski, W. E. *Atompraxis* 8 (1962) 386
[83] Lima-de-Faria, A. *Hereditas* 45 (1959) 632; *Prog. Biophys. biophys. Chem.* 12 (1962) 281
[83a] Ross, R. *Atomlight* 46 (1965) 1
[84] Salpeter, M. M. and Bachmann, L. *J. Cell Biol.* 22 (1964) 469
[85] Rogers, G. T. and Hughes, J. D. H. *Nature, Lond.* 199 (1963) 566
[86] Sulya, L. L., McCaa, C. S., Read, V. H. and Bomer, D. *Nature, Lond.* 200 (1963) 788; *Physiologist* 6 (1963) 230
[87] Hughes, P. E. *Expl Cell Res.* 29 (1963) 327
[88] Spain, J. D. and Brouillard, J. *Proc. Am. Ass. Cancer Res.* 4 (1963) 65
[89] Zervas, N. T. and Soloway, A. H. *J. Neuropath. exp. Neurol.* 22 (1963) 352
[90] Maurer, W. and Primbsch, E. *Expl Cell Res.* 33 (1964) 8
[90a] Ross, R. and Benditt, E. P. *J. cell Biol.* 27 (1965) 83
[91] Pinheiro, P., Leblond, C. P. and Droz, B. *Expl Cell Res.* 31 (1963) 517
[91a] Hansson, E. and Samuelsson, B. *Biochim. biophys. Acta* 106 (1965) 379
[92] Hug, C. C. and Mellett, L. B. *Univ. Mich. med. Bull.* 29 (1963) 165
[93] Ostrowski, K., Barnard, E. A., Stocka, Z. and Darzynkiewicz, Z. *Expl Cell Res.* 31 (1963) 89
[93a] Barnard, E. A. and Ostrowski, K. *Biochem. J.* 85 (1962) 27P
[94] Warshawsky, H., Leblond, C. P. and Droz, B. *J. Cell Biol.* 16 (1963) 1
[95] Siperstein, E. R. *J. Cell Biol.* 17 (1963) 521

[96] Young, B. A. *Anat. Rec.* 145 (1963) 304 (Abstract)

[96a] Tonna, E. A. *Med. Res. Centre, Brookhaven Natn. Lab.*, BNL–7917 (April, 1964)

[96b] Gerbaulet, K., Maurer, W. and Brueckner, J. *Biochim. biophys. Acta* 68 (1963) 462

[96c] Hollander, W., Kramsch, D. M., Chobanian, A. V. and Melby, J. C. *J. clin. Invest.* 44 (1965) 1060 (Abstract only)

[96d] Das, C. C., Kaufmann, B. P. and Gay, H. *Nature, Lond.* 204 (1964) 1008

[96e] Arias, I. M., Bernstein, L., Toffler, R. and Ben-Ezzer, J. *J. Clin. Invest.* 44 (1965) 1026 (Abstract only)

[96f] Owen, M. *J. Cell Biol.* 19 (1963) 19

[96g] Tonna, E. A., Cronkite, E. P. and Pavelec, R. *J. Histochem. Cytochem.* 11 (1963) 720

[96h] Davis, R. B. and Kay, D. *Nature, Lond.* 207 (1965) 650

[96i] Kornguth, S. E., Anderson, J. W., Ladinsky, J. and Thompson, H. G. *Expl Cell Res.* 37 (1965) 650

[96j] Altman, J. *Nature, Lond.* 199 (1963) 777

[96k] Torelli, U., Artusi, T., Grossi, G., Emilia, G. and Mauri, C. *Nature, Lond.* 207 (1965) 755

[96l] King, R. J. B., Gordon, J. and Inman, D. R. *J. Endocrin.* 32 (1965) 9

[96m] Inman, D. R., Banfield, R. E. W. and King, R. J. B. *J. Endocrin.* 32 (1965) 17

[96n] King, R. J. B., Cowan, D. M. and Inman, D. R. *J. Endocrin.* 32 (1965) 83

[96o] Roversi, G. D. and Silvestrini, R. *Expl Cell Res.* 31 (1963) 484

[96p] Teixeira Pinto, A. A. *Lab. De Fisica-Sacavem Portugal* LFEN–N1. 11 (1964)

[96q] Frøland, A. *Stain Technol.* 40 (1965) 41

[96r] Haines, M. *Nature, Lond.* 207 (1965) 552

[96s] Clarkson, B., Ohkita, T., Ota, K. and O'Connor, A. *J. clin. Invest.* 44 (1965) 1035

[96t] Wolberg, W. H. and Brown, R. R. *Cancer Res.* 22 (1962) 1113

[96u] Budd, G. C. and Mills, G. M. *Nature, Lond.* 205 (1965) 524

[96v] Harris, H. *Nature, Lond.* 205 (1965) 583

[96w] Lesch, R., Schiessle, W. and Oehlert, W. *Beitr. path. Anat.* 129 (1963) 296

[96x] Berglund, K. *Nature, Lond.* 204 (1964) 89

[97] Giovanella, B. C. and Heidelberger, C. *Proc. Am. Ass. Cancer Res.* 4 (1963) 23

[98] Brookes, P. and Lawley, P. D. *Nature, Lond.* 202 (1964) 781

[99] Bunge, R. P. and Bunge, M. B. *Anat. Rec.* 145 (1963) 213

[100] Konigsmark, B. W. *J. Neuropath. exp. Neurol.* 22 (1963) 327

[101] Hanna, C. and O'Brien, J. E. *Radiat. Res.* 19 (1963) 1

[102] Barreira, F., Brito Carvalho, A. and Vidal Sobral, J. M. *Int. J. appl. Radiat. Isotopes* 14 (1963) 428

[103] Jacob, J. and Sirlin, J. L. *Nature, Lond.* 202 (1964) 622

[104] Sims, R. T. *Nature, Lond.* 199 (1963) 395

[105] Radiochemical Centre. *The Radiochemical Manual Part 2. Radioactive Chemicals* 1963. The Radiochemical Centre; Amersham

[106] Apelgot, S. and Duquesne, M. *J. Chromatog.* In the press. (1965)

[107] Goldblatt, M. *J. phys. Chem.* 68 (1964) 147

[108] Chang, T. L. and Chien, J. Y. *J. Am. chem. Soc.* 63 (1941) 1709

[109] McDowell, R. S. and Jones, L. H. *J. molec. Spectrosc.* 9 (1962) 79

[110] Daykin, P. N. and Sundaram, S. *Z. phys. Chem., Frankf. Ausg.* 32 (1962) 222
[111] Staats, P. A., Morgan, H. W. and Goldstein, J. H. *J. chem. Phys.* 24 (1956) 916
[112] The Radiochemical Centre, *Radioactive Isotope Dilution Analysis* R.C.C. Review No. 2 (April, 1964)
[113] Bayly, R. J. *Proc. Symp. Radioisotopes Phys. Sci. Ind.*, I.A.E.A. Vienna 2 (1962) 305
[114] Evans, E. A., Green, R. H., Spanner, J. A. and Waterfield, W. R. *Nature, Lond.* 198 (1963) 1301
[115] Waterfield, W. R. *J. chem. Soc.* (1963) 2731; (1964) 541
[116] Schneider, C. H. *Biochim. biophys. Acta* 65 (1962) 521
[117] Block, R. J., Durrum, E. L. and Zweig, G. *A Manual of Paper Chromatography and Paper Electrophoresis* 1955. Academic Press; New York
[118] Randerath, K. *Thin-layer Chromatography* (Trans. from German by Libman, D. D.) 1963. Academic Press; New York
[118a] Truter, E. V. *Thin film Chromatography* 1963. London; Cleaver-Hume Press
[119] Ambrose, D. and Ambrose, B. A. *Gas Chromatography* 1961. London; George Newnes
[120] Chamberlain, J., Hughes, A., Rogers, A. W. and Thomas, G. H. *Nature, Lond.* 201 (1964) 774
[120a] cf. Narath, A. and Gundlach, D. *Angew. Chem.* 72 (1960) 707
[121] Wilson, A. T. *Biochim. biophys. Acta* 40 (1960) 522 (see also ref. 38)
[122] Rogers, A. W. *Nature, Lond.* 184 (1959) 721
[123] Markman, B. *J. Chromat.* 11 (1963) 118
[124] Sheppard, H. and Tsien, W. H. *Analyt. Chem.* 35 (1963) 1992
[125] Richardson, G. S., Weliky, I., Batchelder, W., Griffith, M. and Engel, L. L. *J. Chromat.* 12 (1963) 115
[126] Gray, I., Ikeda, S., Benson, A. A. and Kritchevsky, D. *Univ. Calif. Radiat. Lab. Rep.* UCRL–743 (June, 5th 1950)
[127] Carleton, F. J. and Roberts, H. R. *Int. J. appl. Radiat. Isotopes* 10 (1961) 79
[128] Wenzel, M. *Atompraxis* 7 (1961) 86
[129] Apelgot, S., Ekert, B. and Tisne, M. R. *Proc. Conf. on Methods of Preparing and Storing Marked Molecules*, Brussels (Nov. 1963). European Atomic Energy Community, Euratom EUR 1625e (May, 1964) p. 939
[130] Fecher, R., Chanley, J. D. and Rosenblatt, S. *Analyt. Biochem.* 9 (1964) 54
[131] Gill, D. M. *Nature, Lond.* 202 (1964) 626
[132] Willenbrink, J. *Int. J. appl. Radiat. Isotopes* 14 (1963) 237
[133] Moses, V. *J. Chromat.* 9 (1962) 241
[134] Lemmon, R. M. and Smith, M. A. *J. Am. chem. Soc.* 85 (1963) 1395
[135] King, J. *J. phys. Chem.* 67 (1963) 1397
[136] Scharpenseel, H. W. *Angew. Chem.* 73 (1961) 615
[136a] Scharpenseel, H. W. and Menke, K. H. *Proc. Symp. Tritium Phys. Biol. Sci.* I.A.E.A., Vienna 1 (1962) 281
[137] Dobbs, H. E. *J. Chromat.* 5 (1961) 32
[138] Karmen, A., McCaffrey, I., Winkelman, J. W. and Bowman, R. L. *Analyt. Chem.* 35 (1963) 536
[139] Wolfgang, R. and Rowland, F. S. *Analyt. Chem.* 30 (1958) 903
[140] Lee, J. K., Lee, E. K. C., Musgrave, B., Tang, Yi-N., Root, J. W. and Rowland, F. S. *Analyt. Chem.* 34 (1962) 741

[141] Isbell, H. S., Frush, H. L., Holt, N. B. and Moyer, J. D. *J. Res. Nat. Bur. Stand.* 64A (1960) 177

[142] Sniegoski, L. T. and Isbell, H. S. *J. Res. Nat. Bur. Stand.* 64A (1962) 29

[143] Bevill, R. D., Nordin, J. H., Smith, F. and Kirkwood, S. *Biochem. biophys. Res. Commun.* 12 (1963) 152

[144] Thompson, G. A., Medical Research Council, National Institute for Medical Research, Mill Hill, London. *Ph.D. Thesis*, University of London, 1964

[145] Levisalles, J. and Pete, J-P. *Proc. Conf. Methods Preparing and Storing Marked Molecules*, Brussels (Nov. 1963). European Atomic Energy Community, Euratom EUR 1625e (May, 1964) page 663

[147] Weiss, B. *J. biol. Chem.* 238 (1963) 1953

[148] Glascock, R. F. and Reinius, L. R. *Biochem. J.* 62 (1956) 529

[149] Crawhall, J. C. and Smith, D. G. *Biochem. J.* 69 (1958) 280

[150] Tenny, K. S., Gupta, S. C., Nystrom, R. F. and Kummerow, F. A. *J. Am. Oil Chem. Soc.* 40 (1963) 172

[151] Borcic, S., Strelkov, T. and Sunko, D. E. *Croat. chem. Acta* 34 (1962) 243

[152] Sgoutas, D. S. and Kummerow, F. A. *Biochemistry* 3 (1964) 406

[153] Raphael, R. A. *Acetylenic Compounds in Organic Synthesis* 1955. London; Butterworths

[154] Axelrod, L. R., Goodzieher, J. W. *J. clin. Endocr. Metab.* 22 (1962) 537

[155] Brodie, H., Hayano, M. and Gut, M. *J. Am. chem. Soc.* 84 (1962) 3766

[156] Clayton, R. B. and Edwards, A. M. *J. biol. Chem.* 238 (1963) 1966

[157] Gut, M. and Uskokovic, M. *J. org. Chem.* 25 (1960) 792

[158] Bergstrom, S., Linstredt, S., Samuelson, B., Corey, E. J. and Gregoriou, G. A. *J. Am. chem. Soc.* 80 (1958) 2337

[159] Nagatsu, T., Levitt, M. and Udenfriend, S. *Analyt. Biochem.* 9 (1964) 122

[160] Wagner, A. F., Lusi, A., Folkers, K. *Arch. Biochem. Biophys.* 101 (1963) 316

[161] Angyal, S. J. and Fernandez, C. *Nature, Lond.* 202 (1964) 176

[162] Thieman, A. *Kernforschungsanlage Jülich*, JÜL–27–RC (Oct. 1961)

[163] Cacace, F. *Proc. Symp. Chem. Effects Nucl. Transformations*, I.A.E.A., Vienna 2 (1961) 155

[163a] Bremer, J. and Natori, Y. *Biochim. biophys. Acta* 44 (1960) 367

[164] Evans, E. A. *Chemy Ind.* (1961) 2097

[165] Schwenk, E. and Joachim, E. *Experientia* 18 (1962) 360

[166] Lijinsky, W. and Garcia, H. *Nature, Lond.* 197 (1963) 688

[167] Borenfreund, E., Rosenkranz, H. S. and Bendlich, A. *J. Molec. biol.* 1 (1959) 195

[168] Johns, D. G., Sperti, S. and Burgen, A. S. V. *J. clin. Invest.* 40 (1961) 1684

[169] Jeejeebhoy, K. N., Stewart, J. H., Evans, E. A. and Booth, C. C. *Gut* 5 (1964) 346

[170] Holt, C. V., Nolte, I. and Holt, L. V. *2nd U.N. Conf. Peaceful Uses Atom. Energy*, Geneva 25 (1955) 230

[171] Riesz, P. and Wilzbach, K. E. *134th Meeting Am. Chem. Soc.*, Chicago, Sept. 1958, Abstracts of Papers 27P.

[172] Ache, H. J., Herr, W. and Thiemann, A. *Proc. Symp. Chem. Effects Nucl. Transformations*, I.A.E.A., Vienna 2 (1961) 111

[173] Markovitz, A., Cifonelli, J. A. and Gross, J. I. *Atomlight* (16) (1961) 1

[174] Burnett, J. P., Haurowitz, F. *Hoppe-Seyler's Z. physiol. Chem.* 331 (1963) 67

[175] Meshi, T. and Sato, Y. *Bull. chem. Soc. Japan* 37 (1964) 683

[176] Crowter, D. G., Evans, E. A. and Lambert, R. W. *Chemy Ind.* (1960) 899

[177] Verly, W. G. and Hunebelle, G. *Bull. Socs. chim. belg.* 66 (1957) 640
[178] Taylor, J. H., Woods, P. S. and Hughes, W. L. *Proc. Natn. Acad. Sci. U.S.A.* 43 (1957) 122
[179] Werbin, H., Chaikoff, I. L. and Jones, E. E. *J. biol. Chem.* 234 (1959) 282
[180] Fukushima, D. K., Kritchevsky, T. H., Eidinoff, M. L. and Gallagher, T. F. *J. Am. chem. Soc.* 74 (1952) 487
[181] Kritchevsky, T. H., Garmaise, D. L. and Gallagher, T. F. *J. Am. chem. Soc.* 74 (1952) 483
[182] Anderson, B., Belcher, E. H., Chanarin, I. and Mollin, D. L. *Br. J. Haemat.* 6 (1960) 439
[183] Johns, D. G., Hollingsworth, J. W., Cashmore, A. R., Plender-Leith, I. H. and Bertino, J. R. *J. clin. Invest.* 43 (1964) 621
[183a] Henderson, E. S., Adamson, R. H. and Oliverio, V. T. *Cancer Res.* 25 (1965) 1018
[184] Ache, H. J., Herr, W. and Thiemann, A. *Proc. Symp. Tritium Phys. Biol. Sci.*, I.A.E.A. Vienna 2 (1962) 21
[185] Kay, J. G., Malsan, R. P., Rowland, F. S. *J. Am. chem. Soc.* 81 (1959) 5050
[186] Okamoto, J. and Tsuchihashi, G. *Radio-Isotopes Tokyo* 10 (1961) 414
[187] Okamoto, J. *Bull. chem. Soc. Japan* 33 (1960) 1629
[188] White, R. M. and Rowland, F. S. *J. Am. chem. Soc.* 82 (1960) 4713
[189] White, R. M. and Rowland, F. S. *J. Am. chem. Soc.* 82 (1960) 5345
[190] Rowland, F. S., Turton, C. N. and Wolfgang, R. *J. Am. Chem. Soc.* 78 (1956) 2354
[191] Keller, H. and Rowland, F. S. *J. phys. Chem.* 62 (1958) 1373
[191a] Bradlow, H. L., Fukushima, D. K. and Tsutsui, M. *Chemy Ind.* 36 (1959) 1124
[192] Elatrash, A. M. and Johnsen, R. H. *Proc. Symp. Chem. Effects Nucl. Transformations*, I.A.E.A. Vienna 2 (1961) 123
[193] Krizek, H., Garnett, J. and Brown, W. G. *Argonne Cancer Research Hospital Rep.* ACRH–4 (Sept. 1955) 88
[194] Brown, W. G. and Garnett, J. *Int. J. appl. Radiat. Isotopes* 5 (1959) 114
[195] Sheppard, H., Tsien, W. H., Plummer, A. J., Peets, E. A., Giletti, B. J. and Schulert, A. R. *Proc. Soc. exp. Biol. Med.* 97 (1958) 717
[196] Hadzi, D. and Sheppard, N. *Proc. R. Soc.* A216 (1953) 247
[197] Sheppard, N. and Sutherland, G. B. B. M. *Nature, Lond.* 159 (1947) 739
[198] Sutherland, G. B. B. M., Vallance Jones, A. *Nature, Lond.* 160 (1947) 567
[199] Pomerance, H. and Terranova, D. *Am. J. Phys.* 18 (1950) 466
[200] Pople, J. A., Schneider, W. G. and Berstein, H. J. *High Resolution Nuclear Magnetic Resonance* 1959. New York; McGraw-Hill
[201] Garnett, J. L., Henderson, L. J., Sollich, W. A. and Tiers, G. V. D. *Tetrahedron Lett.* (1961) 516
[202] Schulze, J. and Long, F. A. *Proc. chem. Soc.* (1962) 364
[203] Katz, J. J., Thomas, M. R. and Strain, H. H. *J. Am. chem. Soc.* 84 (1962) 3587
[204] Buu-Hoi, N. P., van Bac, N., dat Xuong, N. and Parello, J. *Bull. Soc. chim. Fr.* (8–9) (1962) 1747
[205] MacDonald, C. G., Shannon, J. S. and Sternhell, S. *Aust. J. Chem.* 17 (1964) 38
[206] Tiers, G. V. D., Brown, C. A., Jackson, R. A. and Lahr, T. N. *J. Am. chem. Soc.* 86 (1964) 2526
[206a] Simon, H., Müllhofer, G. and Dorrer, H. D. *Proc. Symp. Methods Pre-*

paring Storing Marked Molecules, European Atomic Energy Community, Euratom, EUR 1625e (May, 1964) p. 997

BIBLIOGRAPHY OF TRITIUM MEASUREMENT

Scintillation Measurement

1952

[207] Hayes, F. N., Hiebert, R. D. and Schuch, R. L. *Science, N.Y.* 116 (1952) 140. Low energy counting with a new liquid scintillation solute (2,5-diphenyloxazole)

1953

[208] Farmer, E. C. and Berstein, I. A. *Science, N.Y.* 117 (1953) 279. Determination of specific activities of tritium-labeled compounds with liquid scintillators

[209] Hayes, F. N. and Gould, R. G. *Science, N.Y.* 117 (1953) 480. Liquid scintillation counting of tritium-labeled water and organic compounds

1954

[210] Rosenthal, D. J. and Anger, H. O. *Rev. scient. Instrum.* 25 (1954) 670, and *Univ. Calif. Radiat. Lab. Rep.*, UCRL–2320 (1953). Liquid scintillation counting of tritium and C^{14}-labeled compounds

1955

[211] Anderson, E. E. *Tracerlog* 69 (1955) 5. Notes on liquid scintillation counting

[212] Baker, E. M. *Univ. Calif. Radiat. Lab. Chem. Div. Quart. Rep.*, UCRL–2841 (1955) 17. A liquid scintillation counter for tritium measurement

[213] Baker, E. M. and Vogelsberg, F. *Univ. Calif. Radiat. Lab., Chem. Div. Quart. Rep.*, UCRL–3240 (1955) 28. Liquid scintillation counting of tritium by means of coincidence techniques

[214] Hayes, F. N., Ott, D. G., Kerr, V. N. and Rogers, B. S. *Nucleonics* 13 (12) (1955) 38. Pulse height comparison of primary solutes

[215] Okita, G. T., Spratt, J. and Leroy, G. V. *Semiannual Rep. Argonne Cancer Research Hospital*, ACRH–4 (1955) 85

[216] Wagner, C. D. and Guinn, V. P. *Nucleonics* 13 (10) (1955) 56. For low specific activity: use scintillation counting

1956

[217] Anderson, E. C. and Hayes, F. N. A. *Rev. nucl. Sci.* 6 (1956) 303. Recent advances in low level counting techniques

[218] Hayes, F. N., Rogers, B. S. and Langham, W. H. *Nucleonics* 14 (3) (1956) 48. Counting suspensions in liquid scintillators

[219] Kinard, F. E. *Du Pont de Nemours, E.I. & Co. Rep.* DP–190 (1956). A liquid scintillator for the analysis of tritium in water

[220] Langham, W. H., Eversole, W. J., Hayes, F. N. and Trujillo, T. T. *J. Lab. clin. Med.* 47 (1956) 819. Assay of tritium activity in body fluids with the use of a liquid scintillation system

[221] Matsukawa, E. and Eaborn, C. *Res. Correspondence Suppl. to Research* 9 (1956) S37. Simple measurement of the relative activities of samples of tritiated materials

[222] Okita, G. T., Spratt, J. and Leroy, G. V. *Nucleonics* 14 (3) (1956) 76. Liquid-scintillation counting for assay of tritium in urine

[223] Selinger, H. H. and Ziegler, C. A. *Nucleonics* 14 (4) (1956) 49. Liquid-scintillator temperature effects

1957

224 Agranoff, B. W. *Nucleonics* 15 (10) (1957) 106. Silica vials improve low-level counting

225 Blau, M. *Nucleonics* 15 (4) (1957) 90. Separated channels improve liquid scintillation counting

226 Eaborn, C., Matsukawa, E. and Taylor, R. *Rev. scient. Instrum.* 28 (1957) 725. Measurement of tritium

227 Hayes, F. N. and Ott, D. G. *Los Alamos Scient. Lab. Rep.* LA–2095 (1957). The small-volume internal sample scintillation counter: instrumentation, performance characteristics and capabilities

228 Kerr, V. N., Hayes, F. N. and Ott, D. G. *Int. J. appl. Radiat. Isotopes* 1 (1957) 284. Liquid Scintillators III. The quenching of liquid-scintillator solutions by organic compounds

229 Kinard, F. E. *Rev. scient. Instrum.* 28 (1957) 293. Liquid scintillator for the analysis of tritium in water

230 Okita, G. T., Kabara, J. J., Richardson, F. and Leroy, G. V. *Nucleonics* 15 (6) (1957) 111. Assaying compounds containing H^3 and C^{14}

231 Roucayrol, J. C., Oberhauser, E. and Schussler, R. *Nucleonics* 15 (11) (1957) 104. Liquid scintillators in filter paper—a new detector

232 Vaughan, M., Steinberg, D., Logan, J. *Science, N.Y.* 126 (1957) 446. Liquid scintillation counting of C^{14}- and H^3-labeled amino acids and proteins

233 Ziegler, C. A., Chleck, D. J. and Brinkerhoff, J. *Analyt. Chem.* 29 (1957) 1774. Radioassay of low activity tritiated water by improved liquid scintillation techniques

1958–1959

234 Bell, C. G. and Hayes, F. N. (Eds.) *Liquid Scintillation Counting* 1958. New York; Pergamon Press

235 Chen, P. S. *Proc. Soc. exp. Biol. Med.* 98 (1958) 546. Liquid scintillation counting of C^{14} and H^3 in plasma and serum

236 Duncombe, W. G. *Biochem. J.* 69 (1958) 6P. Scintillation counting of tritium in solid samples

237 Haigh, C. P. *Nuclear Power* 3 (1958) 585. Liquid scintillation counting for tritium and carbon-14

238 Hodgson, T. S., Gordon, B. E. and Ackerman, M. E. *Nucleonics* 16 (7) (1958) 89. Single-channel counter for carbon-14 and tritium

239 Protopopov, Kh. V., Arslanov, Kh. A., Butomo, S. V. and Timofeeva, T. V. *Instrums exp. Tech., Wash.* 2 (1958) 200. New Liquid Scintillators

240 Bibron, R. *Onde élec.* 39 (1959) 40. Measurement of weak activities in carbon-14 and tritium by a scintillation method. (In French)

241 Bibron, R., Delibrias, G. and Léger, C. Société Francaise des Radio-electriciens, Nuclear Electronics II, p. 157. (*Proc. Int. Symp. Nucl. Electronics*, Paris, 1958), I.A.E.A., Vienna, 1959. Apparatus for the detection of carbon-14 and tritium. (In French)

242 Forte, M. and Anzani, A. *Hlth Phys. Nucl. Installations Symp.*, Risö, May 25–29th, 1959. Paris, France. Organisation for European Economic Co-operation, 1959, p. 193. A method for scintillation counting of very low-energy particles

242a Hours, R. M. and Kaufman, W. J. *U.S.A.E.C. Rep.* TID–13910 (1959). Low-level tritium measurement with liquid scintillation spectrometer

243 Scharpenseel, H. W. *Angew. Chem.* 71 (1959) 640. Tritium and carbon-14 direct labelling and liquid scintillation spectrometry (In German)

REFERENCES AND BIBLIOGRAPHY

244 Seliger, H. H., Agranoff, B. W. *Analyt. Chem.* 31 (1959) 1607. Solid scintillation counting of hydrogen-3 and carbon-14 in paper chromatograms

245 Werbin, H., Chaikoff, I. L. and Imada, M. R. *Proc. Soc. exp. Biol. Med.* 102 (1959) 8. Rapid sensitive method for determining H^3-water in body fluids by liquid scintillation spectrometry

1960

246 Baillie, L. A. *Int. J. appl. Radiat. Isotopes* 8 (1960) 1. Determination of liquid scintillation counting efficiency by pulse height shift

247 Belcher, E. H. *Phys. Med. Biol.* 5 (1960) 49. The assay of tritium in biological material by wet oxidation with perchloric acid followed by liquid scintillation counting

248 Boyce, I. S., Cameron, J. F. and Taylor, K. J. *Int. J. appl. Radiat. Isotopes* 9 (1960) 122. A simple plastic scintillation counter for tritiated hydrogen

249 Bray, G. A. *Analyt. Biochem.* 1 (1960) 279. A simple efficient liquid scintillator for counting aqueous solutions in a liquid scintillation counter

250 Bruno, G. A. and Christian, J. E. *J. Am. pharm. Ass. Scient. Edn* 49 (1960) 560. Note on suitable solvent systems usable in the liquid scintillation counting of animal tissue

251 Gjone, E., Vance, H. G. and Turner, D. A. *Int. J. appl. Radiat. Isotopes* 8 (1960) 95. Direct liquid scintillation counting of plasma and tissue

252 Gruber, G. H. AECL–801 (1960) 73. *Proc. 6th Tripartite Instrum. Conf.* Chalk River, Ontario, April 20–24th, 1959. Detection of D_2O leakage in heat exchangers

253 Guinn, V. P. and Wagner, C. D. *Atomlight* No. 12 (1960) 1. A comparison of ionization chamber and liquid scintillation methods for measurement of beta emitters

254 Helf, S., White, C. G. and Shelley, R. N. *Analyt. Chem.* 32 (1960) 238. Radioassay of finely divided solids by suspension in a gel scintillator

255 Herberg, R. J. *Analyt. Chem.* 32 (1960) 1468. Backgrounds for liquid scintillation counting of colored solutions

256 Herberg, R. J. *Analyt. Chem.* 32 (1960) 42. Determination of carbon-14 and tritium in blood and other whole tissues. Liquid scintillation counting of tissues

257 Hutchinson, W. P., *A.E.R.E., Harwell Rep.*, AERE–R 3238 (Jan. 1960). Liquid scintillation counting of tritium at 22°C

258 Hutchinson, W. P. *A.E.R.E., Harwell Rep.*, AERE–R 3425 (Aug. 1960). The determination of tritiated water in urine by liquid scintillation counting

259 Hutchinson, W. P. *A.E.R.E., Harwell Rep.*, AERE–R 3605 (Oct. 1960). The identification of beta-emitting isotopes by liquid scintillation counting

260 Jones, E., Mallard, J. R. and Peachey, C. J. *Physics Med. Biol.* 4 (1960) 253. A tritium counter designed for routine laboratory use

261 Overman, R. T. and Clark, H. M. *Radioisotope Techniques* p. 185, 1960. New York; McGraw-Hill

262 Peets, E. A., Florini, J. R. and Buyske, D. A. *Analyt. Chem.* 32 (1960) 1465. Tritium radioactivity determination of biological materials by a rapid dry combustion technique

263 Peng, C. T. *Analyt. Chem.* 32 (1960) 1292. Quenching of fluorescence in liquid scintillation counting of labeled organic compounds

291

264 Shapira, J. and Perkins, W. H. *Science, N.Y.* 131 (1960) 414. Liquid scintillation counting of aqueous solutions of carbon-14 and tritium

265 Steel, G. G. *Int. J. appl. Radiat. Isotopes* 9 (1960) 94. A simple method of estimating the tritium content of biological samples

266 *U.K.A.E.A. Rep. P.G. Rep.*–162 (1960). Analytical method for the determination of tritium in urine (Liquid scintillation method)

267 Trusov, G. N. and Aladzhalova, N. A. *J. analyt. Chem. USSR* 15 (1960) 271. The determination of tritium

268 Westermark, T., Grapengiesser, B., Lindroth, H. and Ghanem, N. *Nucl. Instrum. Meth.* 9 (1960) 357. Note on the determination of tritium by means of liquid scintillators and DC-measurements of photomultiplier currents

269 Whisman, M. L., Eccleston, B. H. and Armstrong, F. E. *Analyt. Chem.* 32 (1960) 484. Liquid scintillation counting of tritiated organic compounds

270 Whisman, M. L., Eccleston, B. H. and Armstrong, F. E. *U.S. Dept. Interior Bureau Mines Rep.* BM–RI 5801 (July, 1960). Reproducibility of tritium analysis of organic compounds using a liquid scintillation spectrometer

271 Yavorsky, P. M. and Gorin, E. *Consolidation Coal Co. Rep.* NYO–9139 (1960). Utilization of radioactive isotopes in coal process research. *Quart. Tech. Status Rep.* No. 5, May 1st, 1960, to July 31st, 1960

1961

272 Apelgot, S. and Duquesne, M. *J. Chim. phys.* 58 (1961) 774. Liquid scintillation counting applied to the quantitative measurement of tritium in bacteria. (In French)

273 Baillie, L. A. *Atomlight* No. 19 (1961) 1. Determination of liquid scintillation counting efficiency by pulse height shift

274 Butler, F. E. *Analyt. Chem.* 33 (1961) 409. Determination of tritium in water and urine: Liquid scintillation counting and rate-of-drift determination

275 Buyske, D. A., Kelly, R., Florini, J., Gordon, S. and Peets, E. *Atomlight* No. 20 (1961) 1. Determination of tritium and carbon-14 in biological samples by rapid combustion techniques

276 Christman, D. R. *Nucleonics* 19 (3) (1961) 51. Choosing a method for counting soft betas

277 Dobbs, H. E. *J. Chromat.* 5 (1961) 32. Detection of tritium labelled compounds in vapour phase chromatography

277a Foskett, A. C. *A.E.R.E., Harwell Rep.*, AERE–Bib. 132 (1961). Tritium measurement

278 Gibson, J. A. B. *Physics Med. Biol.* 6 (1961) 55. Liquid scintillation counting of tritium in urine

279 Hamada, T. *Radio-Isotopes Tokyo* 10 (1) (1961) 8. Liquid scintillation counting. (In Japanese)

280 Hamada, T. *Radio-Isotopes Tokyo* 10 (1) (1961) 79. Liquid scintillation counter. Assembly for carbon-14 and tritium counting—NE 8301 (Nuclear Enterprises Co.). (In Japanese)

281 Horrocks, D. L. and Studier, M. H. *Analyt. Chem.* 33 (1961) 615. Determination of the absolute disintegration rates of low energy beta emitters in a liquid scintillation spectrometer

282 Iwakura, T. *Radio-Isotopes Tokyo* 10 (1) (1961) 64. Detail on liquid

scintillation counter 'Tri-carb Model 314X' (Packard Instrument Co. U.S.A.) (In Japanese)

283 Kalberer, F. and Rutschmann, J. *Helv. chim. Acta* 44 (1961) 1956. Rapid determination of tritium, radiocarbon, and radiosulphur in random organic specimens by liquid scintillation counting

284 Kasida, Y., Yamazaki, M. and Iwakura, T. *Radio-Isotopes Tokyo* 10 (1) (1961) 27. ^{14}C and ^{3}H measurement with the use of liquid scintillation counters. (In Japanese, English Summary)

285 Kawai, H. and Nishiwaki, Y. *Radio-Isotopes Tokyo* 10 (1) (1961) 19. Basic consideration on the method of counting low energy β-particles with liquid scintillation. (In Japanese, English Summary)

286 Kelly, R. G., Peets, E. A., Gordon, S. and Buyske, D. A. *Analyt. Biochem.* 2 (1961) 267. Determination of C^{14} and H^{3} in biological samples by Schöniger combustion and liquid scintillation techniques

287 Okano, M. *Radio-Isotopes Tokyo* 10 (1) (1961) 38. Liquid scintillation counting method of tritium. (In Japanese)

288 Sandalls, J. *A.E.R.E., Harwell Rep.* AERE—R 3716 (1961). A method for routine determinations of tritium in urine using a coincidence liquid scintillation counter

289 Shimojima, H. *Radio-Isotopes Tokyo* 10 (1) (1961) 70. Tracerlab liquid scintillation counter. (In Japanese)

290 Sidei, T. and Higashimura, T. *Radio-Isotopes Tokyo* 10 (1) (1961) 1. Tritium measurement with liquid scintillation counters. (In Japanese)

291 Ueno, K., Yabe, A., Tsurumaki, I. and Chang, C. *J. atom. Energy Soc. Japan* 3 (1961) 688. Determination of tritium in human urine

292 Vaughan, B. E. and Boling, E. A. *J. Lab. clin. Med.* 57 (1961) 159. Rapid assay procedures for tritium-labeled water in body fluids

1962

293 Anbar, M., Neta, P. and Heller, A. *Int. J. appl. Radiat. Isotopes* 13 (1962) 310. The radioassay of tritium in water in liquid scintillation counters— the isotopic exchange of *cyclo*hexene with water

294 Benson, R. H. and Maute, R. L. *Analyt. Chem.* 34 (1962) 1122. (also *Trans. Am. Nucl. Soc.* 5 (1962) 203). Liquid scintillation counting of tritium: Improvements in sensitivity by efficient light collection

295 Boyce, I. S. and Cameron, J. F. *Proc. Symp. Tritium Phys. Biol. Sci.*, I.A.E.A., Vienna 1 (1962) 231. A low-background liquid-scintillation counter for the assay of low-specific-activity tritiated water

296 Dobbs, H. E. *A.E.R.E. Rep.* AERE—M 1075 (1962). Quenching and adsorption in liquid scintillation counting

297 Eastham, J. F., Westbrook, H. L. and Gonzales, D. *Proc. Symp. Tritium Phys. Biol. Sci.*, I.A.E.A., Vienna 1 (1962) 203. Liquid scintillation detection of tritium and other radioisotopes in insoluble or quenching organic compounds

298 Feldman, M. S. *Du Pont de Nemours, E.I. and Co., Rep.* DP–511 (June, (1962). Techniques for the determination of tritium. A literature search

299 Frenkel, E. P., Whalley, B. E., Knorpp, C. T. and Korst, D. R. *J. Lab. clin. Med.* 59 (1962) 174. On counting of tritiated thymidine in tissues

300 Funt, B. L. and Hetherington, A. *Int. J. appl. Radiat. Isotopes* 13 (1962) 215. The kinetics of quenching in liquid scintillators

301 Halvorsen, K. *Proc. Symp. Tritium Phys. Biol. Sci.*, I.A.E.A., Vienna 1

(1962) 313. Direct measurement of tritium in biological materials with the liquid scintillation counter

302 Hash, J. H. *Analyt. Biochem.* 4 (1962) 257. Determination of tritium in whole cells and cellular fractions of *Bacillus megaterium* using liquid scintillation techniques

303 Higashimura, T., Yamada, O., Nohara, N. and Shidei, T. *Int. J. appl. Radiat. Isotopes* 13 (1962) 308. External standard method for the determination of the efficiency in liquid scintillation counting

304 Jones, J. R. and Monk, C. B. *Lab. Pract.* 11 (1962) 675. Some aspects of liquid scintillation counting of tritiated compounds

305 Kaufman, W. J., Nir, A., Parks, G. and Hours, R. M. *Proc. Symp. Tritium Phys. Biol. Sci.*, I.A.E.A., Vienna 1 (1962) 249. Recent advances in low-level scintillation counting of tritium

306 Lloyd, R. A., Ellis, S. C. and Hallowes, K. H. *Proc. Symp. Tritium Phys. Biol. Sci.*, I.A.E.A., Vienna 1 (1962) 263. Phosphorescence in liquid scintillation counting

307 Martin, L. and Harrison, C. *Biochem. J.* 82 (1962) 18P. The determination of ^{14}C- and tritium-labelled compounds in biological materials

308 Meade, R. C. and Stiglitz, R. A. *Int. J. appl. Radiat. Isotopes* 13 (1962) 11. Improved solvent systems for liquid scintillation counting of body fluids and tissues

309 Myers, L. S. and Brush. A. H. *Analyt. Chem.* 34 (1962) 342. Counting of alpha- and beta-radiation in aqueous solutions by the detergent-anthracene scintillation method

310 Peyser, P. *Atomlight* No. 22 (1962) 7. Assay of high specific activity compounds

311 Piez, K. A. *Analyt. Biochem.* 4 (1962) 444. Continuous scintillation counting of carbon-14 and tritium in effluent of the automatic amino acid analyser

312 Popjak, G., Lowe, A. E. and Moore, D. *J. Lipid. Res.* 3 (1962) 364. Scintillation counter for simultaneous assay of H^3 and C^{14} in gas–liquid chromatographic vapors

313 Radoszewski, T. *Polish Acad. Sci., Inst. Nucl. Res.*, Warsaw, PAN–IBJ 330/XIII (1962). Carbon-14 and tritium measurements using liquid scintillation counter

314 Scharpenseel, H. W. and Menke, K. H. *Proc. Symp. Tritium Phys. Biol. Sci.*, I.A.E.A., Vienna 1 (1962) 281. Radio column chromatographic assay of H^3-labelled substances

315 Schram, E. and Lombaert, R. *Analyt. Biochem.* 3 (1962) 68. Determination of tritium and carbon-14 in aqueous solution with anthracene powder

316 Sharpe, J. and Stanley, V. A. *Proc. Symp. Tritium Phys. Biol. Sci.*, I.A.E.A., Vienna 1 (1962) 211. Photomultipliers for tritium counting

317 Sheppard, H. and Rodegker, W. *Atomlight* No. 22 (1962) 1. Parr bomb combustion of tissues for carbon-14 and tritium analysis

318 Shneour, E. A., Aronoff, S. and Kirk, M. R. *Int. J. appl. Radiat. Isotopes* 13 (1962) 623. Liquid scintillation counting of solutions containing carotenoids and chlorophylls

319 Snyder, F. and Stephens, N. *Analyt. Biochem.* 4 (1962) 128. Quantitative carbon-14 and tritium assay of thin-layer chromatography plates

[320] Tamers, M., Bibron, R. and Delibrias, G. *Proc. Symp. Tritium Phys. Biol. Sci.*, I.A.E.A., Vienna 1 (1962) 303. A new method for measuring low level tritium using a benzene liquid scintillator

[321] Tkachuk, R. *Can. J. Chem.* 40 (1962) 2348. A continuous flow beta scintillation detector for aqueous solutions

[322] Weg, M. W. *Nature, Lond.* 194 (1962) 180. Beta-scintillation counting of radioactive tracers insoluble in toluene

1963

[323] Bersaques, de, J. *Int. J. appl. Radiat. Isotopes* 14 (1963) 173. Relation between the absorption and the quenching of liquid scintillation samples

[324] Blanchard, F. A. *Int. J. appl. Radiat. Isotopes* 14 (1963) 213. A computer program for automated testing and reduction of liquid scintillation counting data

[325] Bloom, B. *Analyt. Biochem.* 6 (1963) 359. Use of internal scintillation standards in heterogenous counting systems

[326] Burns, H. G. and Glass, H. I. *Int. J. appl. Radiat. Isotopes* 14 (1963) 627. The assay of tritium-labelled compounds in faeces

[327] Bush, E. T. *Analyt. Chem.* 35 (1963) 1024. General applicability of the channels ratio method of measuring liquid scintillation counting efficiencies

[328] Dobbs, H. E. *Analyt. Chem.* 35 (1963) 783. Oxygen flask method for the assay of tritium-, carbon-14,- and sulfur- 35 labeled compounds

[329] Dobbs, H. E. *Nature, Lond.* 197 (1963) 788. Effect of naphthalene on the quenching of liquid scintillation solutions

[330] Downes, A. M. and Till, A. R. *Nature, Lond.* 197 (1963) 449. Assay of tritium, carbon-14 and sulphur-35 in wool by liquid-scintillation counting

[331] Erdtmann, G. and Herrmann, G. *Radiochim. Acta* 1 (1963) 98. High water content emulsions for the scintillation counting of aqueous solutions of β-emitters. (In German)

[332] Dulcino, J., Bosco, R., Verly, W. G. and Maisin, J. R. *Clinica chim. Acta* 8 (1963) 58. Assay of tritium and carbon-14 in animal tissues by liquid scintillation

[333] Erdtmann, G. and Herrmann, G. *Radiochim. Acta* 1 (1963) 103. Tritium counting in liquid scintillators with *p*-oligophenylene. (In German)

[334] Feine, U. *Atompraxis* 9 (1963) 357. Determination of tritium in tissue and other biological samples. (In German)

[335] Handler, J. A. *Analyst* 88 (1963) 47. A liquid-scintillation method for determining tritium in the tissues of animals dosed with tritium-labelled vitamin A

[336] Hattori, T., Takahashi, H. and Maruo, B. *Abstr. 5th Japan Conf. Radioisotopes* (1963) p. 59. Liquid scintillation counting of tritium in aqueous solution

[337] Hoffmann, W. *Radiochim. Acta* 1 (1963) 216. Method for the activity determination of tritium labelled polymers. (In German)

[339] Kasida, Y., Iwakura, T. and Morisaki, N. *Abstr. 5th Japan Conf. Radioisotopes* (1963) p. 57. ^{14}C and ^{3}H measurement by the use of a liquid scintillation spectrometer IV. Determination of counting efficiency by the discriminator ratio method

[340] Karmen, A., McCaffrey, I., Winkelman, J. W. and Bowman, R. L. *Analyt.*

Chem. 35 (1963) 536. Measurement of tritium in the effluent of a gas chromatography column

341 McFarlane, A. S. and Murray, K. *Analyt. Biochem.* 6 (1963) 284. ^{14}C and ^{3}H specific activities by bomb combustion and scintillation counting (Bomb combustion of ^{14}C and ^{3}H)

342 Myers, L. S. and Rosenblum, C. *Hlth Phys.* 9 (1963) 345. A rapid method for determination of tritium water in urine following acute exposure

343 Petrozzi, E. *Minerva nucl.* 7 (1963) 91. Measurement of tritium and carbon-14 with liquid scintillators. (In Italian)

344 Popjak, G., Lowe, A. E. and Moore, D. *Adv. Tracer Methodol.* 1 (1963) 127. Plenum Press, New York. (*5th Symp. Adv. Tracer Methodol.* 1961.) Simultaneous measurement of C^{14} and H^3 during gas–liquid chromatography

345 Prockop, D. J. and Ebert, P. S. *Analyt. Biochem.* 6 (1963) 263. A simple method for the differential assay of tritium and carbon-14 in water-soluble biological materials

346 Scales, B. *Analyt. Biochem.* 5 (1963) 489. Liquid scintillation counting: The determination of background counts of samples containing quenching substances

347 Schmidt, H.-L. *Atompraxis* 9 (1963) 349. Determination of ^{14}C and ^{3}H in biological material. (In German)

348 Snell, J. F. *Adv. Tracer Methodol.* 1 (1963) 106. Plenum Press, New York. (*5th Symp. Adv. Tracer Methodol.* 1961.) Liquid scintillation counting of tritium in suspended materials

349 Tamers, M. A. and Bibron, R. *Nucleonics* 21 (6) (1963) 90. Benzene method measures tritium in rain without isotope enrichment

350 Takahashi, H., Hattori, T. and Maruo, B. *Analyt. Chem.* 35 (1963) 1982. Liquid scintillation counting of biological compounds in aqueous solution

351 Weltman, J. K. and Talmage, D. W. *Int. J. appl. Radiat. Isotopes* 14 (1963) 541. A method for the simultaneous determination of H^3 and S^{35} in samples with variable quenching

352 Willenbrink, J. *Int. J. appl. Radiat. Isotopes* 14 (1963) 237. On the quantitative assay of radiochromatograms by liquid scintillation counting

1964

353 Baden, H. P. *Analyt. Chem.* 36 (1964) 960. Improved technique for determination of C^{14} and H^3 by flask combustion

354 Baxter, J. A., Fanning, L. E. and Swartz, H. A. *Int. J. appl. Radiat. Isotopes* 15 (1964) 415. Liquid scintillation solvent systems: water content and related counting efficiencies

355 Burt, A. K. and Gibson, J. A. B. *A.E.R.E., Harwell, Hlth Phys. Med. Div. Rep.* AERE–R 4638 (May 1964). Scintillation counting of tritiated water and other beta-active solutions

356 Bush, E. T. *Analyt. Chem.* 36 (1964) 1082. Liquid scintillation counting of doubly-labelled samples: choice of counting conditions for best precision in two-channel counting

356a Conway, W. D. and Grace, A. J. *Analyt. Biochem.* 9 (1964) 487. Liquid scintillation-counting errors due to oxygen-quenching of samples prepared by the oxygen-flask combustion procedure

357 Gill, D. M. *Nature, Lond.* 202 (1964) 626. Use of glass fibre paper in liquid scintillation counting

358 Goldstein, G. and Lyon, W. S. *Int. J. appl. Radiat. Isotopes* 15 (1964) 133. Liquid scintillators using 1-methylnaphthalene

359 Hempel, K. *Atompraxis* 10 (1964) 148. The simultaneous measurement of tritium and carbon-14 in biological material with the liquid scintillation counter. (In German)

360 Hendler, R. W. *Analyt. Biochem.* 7 (1964) 110. Procedure for simultaneous assay of two β-emitting isotopes with the liquid scintillation counting technique

361 Herberg, R. J. *Analyt. Chem.* 36 (1964) 1079 Statistical aspects of double isotope liquid scintillation counting by internal standard technique

362 Moghissi, A. and Hogrebe, K. *Int. J. appl. Radiat. Isotopes* 15 (1964) 165. The qualitative determination of tritiated water in the hydrocarbons. (In German)

363 Neujahr, H. Y. and Ewaldsson, B. *Analyt. Biochem.* 8 (1964) 487. Counting of weak β-emitters in bacterial cells by means of the liquid scintillation method

364 O'Brien, R. D. *Analyt. Biochem.* 7 (1964) 251. Nitric acid digestion of tissues for liquid scintillation counting

365 Rapkin, E. *Int. J. appl. Radiat. Isotopes* 15 (1964) 69. Liquid scintillation counting 1957–1963: A review

366 Ritzl, F., Janz, I. and Höschler, G. *Atomkernenergie* 9 (1964) 199. Measurement of weak β-rays by means of a liquid scintillation spectrometer. (In German)

367 Shapiro, I. L. and Kritchevsky, D. *Int. J. appl. Radiat. Isotopes* 15 (1964) 325. The quenching of carbon-14 and tritium by organic solvents in two common liquid scintillation solutions

368 Snyder, F. *Analyt. Biochem.* 9 (1964) 183. Radioassay of thin-layer chromatograms: A high-resolution zonal scraper for quantitative C^{14} and H^3 scanning of thin-layer chromatograms

369 Tamers, M. A. *Packard Techn. Bull.* No. 12 (1964) 1. Liquid scintillation counting of low level tritium

370 Tanielian, C., Coche, A., Deluzarche, A., Laustriat, G. and Maillard, A. *Int. J. appl. Radiat. Isotopes* 15 (1964) 11, 17. Influence of the purification of solvents on the efficiency of the liquid scintillators—Parts I and II. (In French)

371 Träger, L. *Atompraxis* 10 (1964) 472. Simultaneous measurement of tritium and ^{14}C in aqueous solutions with a liquid scintillation counter

372 Tamers, M. A. and Diez, M. *Int. J. appl. Radiat. Isotopes* 15 (1964) 697. Determination of C^{14} and tritium in blood and other biological materials

373 Wu, R. *Analyt. Biochem.* 7 (1964) 207. Simultaneous studies of phosphate transport and glycolysis by a simple liquid scintillation counting procedure with P^{32}, C^{14} and H^3 compounds

374 Pethe, V. A. and Sangodkar, D. B. *Nucl. Instrum. Meth.* 30 (1964) 306. Dependence of efficiency of a coincidence tritium counter on photocathode sensitivity

Ionization Chamber Methods
1946
375 Henriques, F. C. and Margnetti, C. *J. ind. Engng Chem. Analyt. edn* 18 (1946) 420. Analytical procedure for measurement of radioactive hydrogen (tritium)
1947
376 Libby, W. F. *Analyt. Chem.* 19 (1947) 2. Measurement of radioactive tracers, particularly C^{14}, S^{35}, T and other long-lived low-energy activities

1949
377 Healy, J. W. *G.E.C. Nucleonics Div. Rep.* HW–13949 (July, 1949). Urine analysis for tritium oxide
1950
378 Wilzbach, K. E. and Van Dyken, A. *Argonne Natn. Lab. Rep.* AECD–2998 (Oct. 1950) (see also ANL–WMM–708). The determination of tritium and carbon-14 in organic compounds
1951
379 Calvin, M., Tolbert, B., Adams, P., Bartsch, R., Chiado, P., Fry, A., Ikeda, S., Kritchevsky, D., Noller, R., Ostwald, R. and Zeitschel, R. *Univ. Calif. Radiat. Lab.* (June, 1951). *Chemistry Div. Quart. Rep.;* March, April and May, 1951. UCRL–1365. Synthetic and experimental chemistry, p. 16
380 Deal, J. B. *Los Alamos Scient. Lab., Rep.* LA–1270 (Feb. 1951). Continuous tritium monitor
381 Finnigan, J. W. *G.E.C. Hanford Atomic Products Operation, Rep.* AECD–4199 (Sept. 1950, Declass. Dec. 1955). The Regnault method as applied to tritium purity determinations
382 Mattraw, H. C. *Knolls Atomic Power Lab. Rep.*, AECD–3821 (May, 1951). An ion chamber for the determination of small amounts of tritium in other gases
383 Winteringham, F. P. W. *Analyst* 76 (1951) 362. Radiometric assay in tracer experiments
1953
384 Jeffries, T. O. and Owen, M. E. *J. scient. Instrum.* 30 (1953) 387. A tritium monitor
385 Pittendrigh, L. W. D. *A.E.R.E., Harwell Rep.* AERE–HP/M 48 (March, 1953). Continuous flow tritium in air monitor
386 Wilzbach, K. E., Kaplan, L. and Brown, W. G. *Science, N.Y.* 118 (1953) 522. (See also *Argonne Natn. Lab.* ANL–5056 (June, 1953).) The preparation of gas for assay of tritium in organic compounds
1954
387 Booker, D. V., Megaw, W. J. and Pittendrigh, L. W. D. *A.E.R.E., Harwell Rep.* AERE–HP/M 74 (April, 1954). A monitor for estimating tritium in urine
388 *Massachusetts Inst. Tech., Lab. Nucl. Science,* Chemistry of the Fission Elements Group; Inorganic and Nuclear Chemistry (Organic) Group. *Prog. Rep.* No. 33 for Period June 1, 1953, to May 31, 1954, AECU–2943. (LNSE/PR 33)
389 McClelland, J., Eutsler, B. C., Milligan, M. F. and Wilson, W. E. *Los Alamos Scient. Lab., Rep.* LA–1678 (May, 1954). A portable apparatus for the determination of tritium in liquid samples
390 Pittendrigh, L. W. D. *A.E.R.E., Harwell Rep.* AERE–HP/M 84 (Nov. 1954). A continuous flow, tritium in air, warning monitor for use with a Van der Graaff generator
391 Pittendrigh, L. W. D. and Vousden, J. E. *A.E.R.E., Harwell Rep.* AERE–HP/R 1585 (Dec. 1954). A differential ionisation chamber method for continuous flow monitoring of tritium in air in the presence of a significant gamma background and with occasional traces of radon in the sampled air
392 Robbins, M. C., Eutsler, B. C. and Mitchell, R. N. *Los Alamos Scient. Lab.,*

Rep. LA–1683 (June, 1954). The calibration of tritium monitoring devices

393 Wilzbach, K. E., Van Dyken, A. R. and Kaplan, L. *Analyt. Chem.* 26 (1954) 880. Determination of tritium by ion current measurement

1955

394 Eutsler, B. C., Evans, G. L., Hiebert, R. D., Mitchell, R. N., Robbins, C. and Watts, R. J. *Los Alamos Scient. Lab., Rep.* LA–1909 (April, 1955). Instruments for the monitoring of tritium in the atmosphere

395 Eutsler, B. C., Robbins, M., Hiebert, R. and Larkins, J. *Los Alamos Scient. Lab., Rep.* LA–1894 (April, 1955). A portable apparatus for the determination of tritium in body fluids and aqueous solutions

396 Finkelstein, A. and Lesimple, M. *J. nucl. Energy* 2 (1955) 101. Determination of tritium in tritiated water. (In French)

397 Shaw, D. F. *J. scient. Instrum.* 32 (1955) 178. Automatic monitor for measuring tritium contamination in air

398 Swain, C. G., Kreiter, V. P. and Sheppard, W. A. *Analyt. Chem.* 27 (1955) 1157. Procedure for routine assay of tritium in water

1956

399 Rieck, H. G., Myers, I. T. and Palmer, R. F. *Radiat. Res.* 4 (1956) 451. A tritiated water standard

400 Ryder, F. D. *Du Pont, E. I. de Nemours & Co., Rep.* DP–150 (March 1956). An explosion-resistant ion chamber for the measurement of tritium

401 Tolbert, B. M. *Univ. Calif. Radiat. Lab. Rep.,* UCRL–3499 (March, 1956). Ionization chamber assay of radioactive gases

1957

402 Colvin, D. W. *Du Pont E. I. de Nemours & Co., Rep.* DP–198 (Jan. 1957). A simple leak detector for tritium

403 Colvin, D. W. *Du Pont E. I. de Nemours & Co., Rep.* DP–242 (Oct. 1957). A simple monitor for tritium contamination on surfaces

404 Fallot, P., Aeberhardt, A. and Masson, J. *Int. J. appl. Radiat. Isotopes* 1 (1957) 237. Determination of tritium in water and its clinical applications. (In French)

405 Gracheva, E. G. and Khusainova, Sh. G. *Soviet J. atom. Energy* 2 (1957) 74. Determination of tritium content in liquids

406 Jesse, W. P. and Sadauskis, J. *Phys. Rev.* 107 (1957) 766. Absolute energy to produce an ion pair by beta particles from S^{35}

407 Ziegler, C. A. and Schwebel, A. *Nucleonics* 15 (1) (1957) 64. Technique for monitoring tritiated-water vapor in air

1958

408 Briere, M. *Centre d'Etudes Nucleaires de Saclay, Rep.* CEA–942 (1958) (see also HW-tr-22). Limit to the measurement of low activities with ionization chambers

409 Tolbert, B. M. *Adv. Tracer Methodol.* 1 (1963) 167. Plenum Press, New York. (*Symp. Adv. Tracer Applications of Tritium* New York City, Oct. 1958.) Tritium measurement using ionization chambers

1959

410 Anthony, J. D. *Nucleonics* 17 (4) (1959) 110. Portable tritium monitor has gamma compensation

411 Brinkerhoff, J., Ziegler, A., Bersin, R. and Chleck, D. J. *Nucleonics* 17 (2) (1959) 76. Continuous air monitor for H^3

[412] Fry, R. M. *A.E.R.E., Harwell Rep.* AERE–HP/R 2858 (July, 1959). Tritium in urine monitoring by the acetylene flow ion chamber method

[413] Fry, R. M. *A.E.R.E., Harwell Rep.* AERE–M–428 (July, 1959). Monitoring of D_2O for tritium contamination

[414] Fry, R. M. *A.E.R.E., Harwell Rep.* AERE–M–429 (August, 1959). The calibration of flow ionisation chambers for tritium monitoring in air

[415] *U.K.A.E.A., Rep.* IGO–AM/W–112 (Feb. 1958). The determination of tritium in urine

[415a] Lobunez, W. and Karush, F. *J. Am. chem. Soc.* 81 (1959) 795. The assay of tritium in the form of ammonia and the measurement of exchangeable hydrogen

1960

[416] Brooks, R. O. R. *A.E.R.E., Harwell Rep.* AERE–AM 60 (August, 1960). Collected laboratory procedures for the determination of radioelements, in urine

[417] Cowper, G. and Simpson, S. D. *Atomic Energy of Canada Ltd., Rep.* CRRD–858 (July, 1960). A monitor for airborne tritium

[418] Guinn, V. P. and Wagner, C. D. *Atomlight* No. 12 (1960) 1. A comparison of ionisation chamber and liquid scintillation methods for measurement of beta emitters (see ref. 253)

1961

[419] Howes, J. H. *A.E.R.E., Harwell Rep.* AERE–M 839 (April, 1961). A gamma compensated ionisation chamber for measuring tritium concentration in air

1963

[420] Ballard, L. F. and Ely, R. L. *Oak Ridge Natn. Lab. Rep.* (Final) ORO–491 (1963). A sensitive tritium monitor

1964

[421] *Nucleonics* 22 (1) (1964) 76. A sensitive tritium monitor

[422] Langer, H. *Kerntechnik* 6 (1964) 404. Measurement of the specific activity of tritiated water and tritiated watery solutions by means of a heated ionization chamber. (In German)

Geiger and Proportional Gas Counting

1943

[423] Black, J. F. and Taylor, H. S. *J. chem. Phys.* 11 (1943) 395. Equilibrium in hydrogen–water systems containing tritium

1947

[424] Eidinoff, M. L. *J. Am. chem. Soc.* 69 (1947) 2504. The quantitative measurement of tritium: hydrogen–alcohol–argon mixtures

[425] Libby, W. F. *Analyt. Chem.* 19 (1947) 2. Measurement of radioactive tracers, particularly C^{14}, S^{35}, T, and other longer-lived low-energy activities

1948

[426] Melander, L. *Acta chem. scand.* 2 (1948) 440. On the determination of radioactive hydrogen

1949

[427] Schubert, J. *Argonne Natn. Lab. Biol. Med. Div. Quart. Prog. Rep.* November, December 1949, and January 1950. ANL–4401, p. 171

REFERENCES AND BIBLIOGRAPHY

1950

428 Bernstein, W. and Ballentine, R. *Brookhaven Nat. Lab. Rep.* AECU–680 (1950) (*see also Rev. scient. Instrum.* 21 (1950) 158). Gas phase counting of low energy beta-emitters

429 White, D. F., Campbell, I. G. and Payne, P. R. *Nature, Lond.* 166 (1950) 628. Estimation of radioactive hydrogen (tritium)

430 Wu, Chien-Shiung *Rev. mod. Phys.* 22 (1950) 386. Recent investigation of the shapes of β-ray spectra

1951

431 Bouton, R. Z., Houston, R. W. and Van der Grinten, W. *Knolls Atomic Power Lab., Rep.* KAPL–492 (Jan. 1951). Development Activities in the Health Physics Division. Semi-Annual Progress Report for the Period Ending Dec. 31 1950

432 Frisby, J. H. and Roaf, D. *Proc. Phys. Soc. Lond.* 64B (1951) 169. Quantitative measurement of samples of tritium

433 Glascock, R. F. *Nucleonics* 9 (5) (1951) 28. Estimation of tritium and some preliminary experiments on its use as a label for water

434 Glascock, R. F. *Nature, Lond.* 168 (1951) 121. Estimation of radioactive hydrogen as tritiobutane in the Geiger counter

435 Grosse, A. V., Johnston, W. M., Wolfgang, R. L. and Libby, W. F. *Science, N.Y.* 113 (1951) 1. Tritium in nature

436 Jones, W. M. *Phys. Rev.* 83 (1951) 537 (see also AECU–1055 (1951)). The half-life of tritium by absolute counting

437 Robinson, C. V. *Harvard Med. School.* AECU–1033 (see also *Rev. scient. Instrum.* 22 (1951) 353). A methane, proportional counting method for the assay of tritium

438 Schubert, J., Myers, L. S. and Jackson, J. A. *Argonne Natn. Lab. Rep.* ANL–4509 (March, 1951). The analytical procedures of the bioassay group at the Argonne *Nat. Lab.*

1952

439 Glascock, R. F. *Biochem. J.* 52 (1952) 699. A combustion technique for the assay of tritium, ^{13}C and ^{14}C in a single 10 mg sample of biological material

440 Grenon, M. and Viallard, R. *J. Phys. Radium, Paris* 13 (1952) 310. Counters with internal filling for numeration of low-energy β-particles. (In French)

441 Payne, P. R., Campbell, I. G. and White, D. F. *Biochem. J.* 50 (1952) 500. The combustion of tritium-labelled organic compounds

442 Wolfgang, R. L. and Libby, W. F. *Phys. Rev.* 85 (1952) 437. Absolute excitation function of the $Be^9(d,t)$ reaction

1953

443 Faltings, V. *Naturwissenschaften* 40 (1953) 409. Tritium counter with hydrogen filling and toluene addition. (In German)

444 Hiebert, R. D. and Watts, R. J. *Nucleonics* 11 (12) (1953) 38. Fast-coincidence circuit for H^3 and C^{14} measurements

1954

445 Bayhurst, B. P., Eutsler, B. C., Foreman, W. W., Head, B. M., Hiebert, R. D., McClelland, J., Milligan, M. F., Watts, R. J. and Wilson, W. E. *Los Alamos Scient. Lab. Rep.* LA–1645 (March, 1954). Determination of tritium in urine and water

[446] Glascock, R. F. *Isotopic Gas Analysis for Biochemists* 1954. New York; Academic Press

[447] Grosse, A. V., Kirshenbaum, A. D., Kulp, J. L. and Broecker, W. S. *Phys. Rev.* 93 (1954) 250. The natural tritium content of atmospheric hydrogen

[448] Kaufman, S. and Libby, W. F. *Phys. Rev.* 93 (1954) 1337. The natural distribution of tritium

[449] Viallard, R., Corval, M., Dreyfus-Alain, B., Grenon, M. and Hermann, J. *Chim. analyt.* 36 (1954) 102. Determination of tritium in tritiated organic compounds. (In French)

1955

[450] Butler, E. B. *Nature, Lond.* 176 (1955) 1262. Counting tritiated water at high humidities in the Geiger region

[451] Cameron, J. F. *Nature, Lond.* 176 (1955) 1264. Measurement of tritium in water samples

[452] Glascock, R. F. *Atomics* 6 (1955) 363. Gas counting techniques in biochemistry. II. The determination of tritium and some applications of gas counting to biochemical research

[453] Meunier, R., Bonpas, M. and Legrand, J. P. *J. Phys. Radium, Paris* 16 (1955) 148. Geiger counters with internal electrodes containing tritiated water vapour. (In French)

[454] Robinson, C. V. *Nucleonics* 13 (11) (1955) 90. Improved methane proportional counting method for tritium assay

[455] Wing, J. and Johnston, W. H. *Science, N.Y.* 121 (1955) 674. Method for counting tritium in tritiated water

1956

[456] Bradley, J. E. S. and Bush, D. J. *Int. J. appl. Radiat. Isotopes* 1 (1956) 233. A simple method for the assay of tritium in water samples

[457] Brown, R. M. and Grummitt, W. E. *Can. J. Chem.* 34 (1956) 220. The determination of tritium in natural waters

[458] Healy, J. W. and Schwendiman, L. C. *Radiat. Res.* 4 (1956) 278. Hydrogen counter for analysis of dilute tritium oxide

[459] Weinstein, A. I. and Bonner, F. T., *U.S. Patent 2,736,812* (Feb. 28, 1956). Radioactivity measuring apparatus

1957

[460] Christman, D. R. *Chemist Analyst* 46 (1957) 5. Tritium counting in glass proportional counting tubes

1958

[461] Merritt, W. F. *Analyt. Chem.* 30 (1958) 1745. System for counting tritium as water vapor

[462] Milligan, M. F., Campbell, E. E., Eutsler, B. C., McClelland, J. and Moss, W. D. *Los Alamos Scient. Lab. Rep.* LA–1858 (2nd Edn) (August, 1958). Analytical procedures of the industrial hygiene group

[463] Monfeuga, S. *Mikrochim. Acta* (1958) 177. Use of external Geiger counters to determine tritium. (In French)

[464] Payne, P. R. and Done, J. *Physics Med. Biol.* 3 (1958) 16. The routine assay of tritium in water and labelled substances in the range 20 to $10^4 \mu\mu c$

[465] Puri, S. P. and Gill, P. S. *Proc. natn. Inst. Sci. India* Pt. A 24 (1958) 66. Firing characteristics of halogen-quenched Geiger–Müller counters

1959

[466] Ciccarone, P. S., Thomas, G. and Verly, W. G. *Nukleonik* 1 (1959) 329.

Tritium measurement in a proportional counter. II. Preparation of the samples. (In French)

[467] Herczynska, E. *Nukleonika* 4 (1959) 381. Estimation of tritium in the gas phase. (In Polish, English Summary)

[468] Herczyriska, E. *Naturwissenschaften* 46 (1959) 169. Estimation of tritio-methane in GM counters

[469] Petukhov, G. G. and Suloev, Yu, N. *Trudy Khim. i Khim. Tekhnol* 1 (1959) 194. Radiometric analysis of tritium-containing organic substances

[470] Verly, W. G., Hunebelle, G. and Thomas, G. *Nukleonik* 1 (1959) 325. Determination of tritium in a proportional counter. (In French)

1960

[471] Cameron, J. F. and Puckett, B. J. *A.E.R.E., Harwell Rep.* AERE–R 3092 (Jan. 1960). Geiger gas counting methods of assaying tritiated hydrogen and tritiated water

[472] Fry, R. M. *A.E.R.E., Harwell Rep.* AERE–R 2867 (July, 1959). The determination of tritium as water vapour in a Geiger–Müller counter

[473] Melhuish, W. H. *N.Z. Jl. Sci.* 3 (1960) 549. The measurement of carbon-14 and tritium activities in gas-filled Geiger counters

[474] Rowland, F. S., Lee, J. K. and White, R. M. *Oklahoma Conf. Radioisotopes in Agriculture*, April 2 and 3, 1959. *U.S.A.E.C. Rep.* TID–7578 (Oklahoma State University, March 1960) p. 39

[475] Simon, H. Berlin-Charlottenberg, Germany: *Technische Universität*, (1960) 67p. Contributions to methods for working with radioactive isotopes in Organic Chemistry and Biochemistry

[476] Trusov, G. N. and Aladzhalova, N. A. *J. analyt. Chem. USSR* 15 (1960) 271 On the determination of tritium

1961

[477] Bainbridge, A. E., Sandoval, P. and Suess, H. E. *Science, N.Y.* 134 (1961) 552. Natural tritium measurements by ethane counting

[478] Kigoshi, K. and Tomikura, Y. *Bull. chem. Soc. Japan* 34 (1961) 1738. Tritium and Carbon-14 in the tree rings

[479] Scharpenseel, H. W. *Angew. Chem.* 73 (1961) 615. The combined gas chromatography and activity measurement of ^{14}C and ^3H labelled sub-stances

[480] Sepall, O., Lang, A. R. G. and Mason, S. G. *Can. J. Chem.* 39 (1961) 827. A counter for measurement of tritium exchange in solids

1962

[481] von Buttlar, H. and Stahl, W. *Proc. Symp. Tritium Phys. Biol. Sci.*, I.A.E.A., Vienna 1 (1962) 325. A low-level Geiger-counter for tritium

[482] Hasan, J. *Proc. Symp. Tritium Phys. Biol. Sci.*, I.A.E.A., Vienna 1 (1962) 361. A zinc fusion method for the determination of tritium in biological material by gas counting

[483] Lee, J. K., Lee, E. K. C., Musgrave, B., Tang, Yi-Noo, Root, J. W. and Rowland, F. S. *Analyt. Chem.* 34 (1962) 741. Proportional counter assay of tritium in gas chromatographic streams

[484] O'Brien, B. J. *Proc. Symp. Tritium Phys. Biol. Sci.*, I.A.E.A., Vienna 1 (1962) 343. The measurement of natural tritium levels in Geiger-counters

[485] Östlund, G. *Proc. Symp. Tritium Phys. Biol. Sci.*, I.A.E.A., Vienna 1 (1962) 333. A hydrogen gas counting system for natural tritium measure-ments

[406] Tykva, R. and Grünberger, D. *Proc. Symp. Tritium Phys. Biol. Sci.*, I.A.E.A.,

Vienna 1 (1962) 353. Rapid assay of tritium-labelled substances in Geiger–Müller gas counting tubes

[487] Zielinski, M. and Zlotowski, I. *Isotopen Tech.* 2 (1962) 281. The use of esters of formic acid for activity measurements both of tritium and carbon-14. (In German)

1963

[488] Charalambus, St. and Goebel, K. *Nucl. Instrum. Meth.* 25 (1963) 109 (see also *Rep.: CERN–63–4*, European Organisation for Nuclear Research, Geneva, Feb. 10, 1963, 29). Low level proportional counter for tritium

[489] Eulitz, G. W. *Rev. scient. Instrum.* 34 (1963) 1010. Sensitive tritium counting with a propane proportional counting system

[490] Karmen, A., McCaffrey, I., Winkelman, J. W. and Bowman, R. L. *Analyt. Chem.* 35 (1963) 536. Measurement of tritium in the effluent of a gas chromatography column.

[491] Mlinko, S. and Szarvas, T. *Int. J. appl. Radiat. Isotopes* 14 (1963) 197. Gas analysis of tritium in the form of ethane.

[492] Takahashi, T., Ohno, S. and Hamada, T. *Abstr. 5th Japan Conf. Radio-isotopes* (1963) p. 51. Measurement of low level tritium

1964

[493] Anand, J. S. and Lal, D. *Nature, Lond.* 201 (1964) 775. Synthesis of methane from water for tritium measurement

[494] Curtis, M. L. and Rook, H. L. *Analyt. Chem.* 36 (1964) 2047. Improved techniques for routinely counting low levels of tritium and krypton-85

[495] Mann, W. B., Medlock, R. W. and Yura, O. *Int. J. appl. Radiat. Isotopes,* 15 (1964) 351. A recalibration of the National Bureau of Standards tritiated water standards by gas counting

[496] Mann, W. B. and Spernol, A. *Int. J. appl. Radiat. Isotopes* 15 (1964) 628. The National Bureau of Standards tritiated water standards

[497] Spernol, A. and Denecke, B. *Int. J. appl. Radiat. Isotopes* 15 (1964) 139. High precision absolute gas counting of tritium I. Preparation of hydrogen and counting gas. (In German)

[498] Spernol, A. and Denecke, B. *Int. J. appl. Radiat. Isotopes* 15 (1964) 195. High precision absolute gas counting of tritium II. Characteristics and construction of internal gas counters. especially for hydrogen–methane mixtures

[499] Spernol, A. and Denecke, B. *Int. J. appl. Radiat. Isotopes* 15 (1964) 241. High precision absolute gas counting of tritium III. Absolute measurement of tritium in the internal gas counters. (In German)

[500] Koch, H. and Dermietzel, J. *Z. Naturf.* 19b (1964) 960. The catalytic decomposition of tritium labelled compounds in sealed tubes. (Conversion to gas for measurement). (In German)

[501] Lindeman, H. and Shamir, J. *Nucl. Instrum. Meth.* 30 (1964) 348. A twin counter for low-level beta detecting

Windowless Gas-Flow Methods
1950

[502] Eidinoff, M. L. and Knoll, J. E. *Science, N.Y.* 112 (1950) 250. The measurement of radioactive hydrogen in solid samples—comparison with gas counting

[503] Gray, I., Ikeda, S., Benson, A. A. and Kritchevsky, D. *Univ. Calif., Lawrence Radiat. Lab. Rep.* UCRL–743 (June, 1950). Detection of tritiated compounds in paper chromatography

REFERENCES AND BIBLIOGRAPHY

1952

[504] Jenkins, W. A. and Yost, D. M. *J. chem. Phys.* 20 (1952) 538. The kinetics of the exchange of tritium between hypophosphoric acid and water

1953

[505] Karraker, D. G., *Du Pont, E. I. de Nemours & Co., Savannah River Lab., Aiken, S.C. Rep.* DP–34 (Dec. 1953). A monitor for surface adsorbed tritium

1956

[506] André, T. *Acta radiol.*, Supp. 142 (1956) 35. Studies on the distribution of tritium-labelled dihydrostreptomycin and tetracycline in the body

[507] Banks, T. E., Crawhall, J. C. and Smyth, D. G. *Biochem. J.* 64 (1956) 411. Some techniques in the assay of tritium

[508] Driver, G. E. *Rev. scient. Instrum.* 27 (1956) 300. Tritium survey instruments

[509] Jackson, F. L. and Lampe, H. W. *Analyt. Chem.* 28 (1956) 1735. Direct counting of tritium-tagged solid and liquid samples

1958

[510] Rydberg, J. *Acta chem. scand.* 12 (1958) 399. Determination of the absolute activity of solid tritium samples

1959

[511] Isbell, H. S., Frush, H. L. and Peterson, R. A. *J. Res. Nat. Bur. Stand.* 63A (1959) 171. Tritium-labeled compounds I. Radioassay of tritium-labeled compounds in 'infinitely thick' films with a windowless, gas-flow, proportional counter

[512] Yaffe, L. and Fishman, J. B. *Proc. Symp. Metrology Radionuclides*, Vienna, Oct. 14–16, 1959, I.A.E.A., Vienna, 1960, p. 185. Self-absorption studies with $4\pi\beta$-proportional flow counter

1960

[512a] Alpen, E. L. and Mandel, H. G. *Biochim. biophys. Acta* 43 (1960) 317. A rapid assay method for tritium in bacterial cells

[513] Isbell, H. S., Frush, H. L. and Holt, N. B. *J. Res. Nat. Bur. Stand.* 64A (1960) 363. Tritium-labeled compounds V. Radioassay of both carbon-14 and tritium in films with a proportional counter

[514] Lang, A. R. G. and Mason, S. G. *Int. J. appl. Radiat. Isotopes* 7 (1960) 251. A counter for solid samples containing labile tritium

[515] Muramatsu, M. and Sasaki, T. *Science, N.Y.* 131 (1960) 302. Solid counting of octadecane-1-H^3

1961

[516] Mizuno, S., Takahashi, T. and Maruo, B. *Radio-Isotopes Tokyo* 10 (1) (1961) 61. Tritium counting with a windowless gas flow counter. (In Japanese)

[517] Sato, Y. and Takahashi, T. *Bull. chem. Soc. Japan* 34 (1961) 169. Studies on tritium labeled compounds IV. Preparation of tritium labeled alanine by means of electric discharge.

[518] Sato, Y., Meshi, T. and Takahashi, T. *Bull. chem. Soc. Japan* 34 (1961) 167. Studies on tritium labeled compounds II. Preparation of tritium labeled stearic acid

1963

[519] Tajima, K., Sasaki, T. and Muramatsu, M. *Bull. chem. Soc. Japan* 36 (1963) 700. Anomalies in the counting rate of the solid thin film of tritiated lauric acid in relation to its film structure

CHAPTER 6

PROPERTIES PECULIAR TO TRITIUM COMPOUNDS

All radioisotopically labelled compounds have some properties which are peculiar to them, by virtue of their radioactivity or because of mass difference between the radioisotope and its more abundant natural stable analogue. Tritium and its compounds are no exception, and in this concluding chapter the properties peculiar to them are discussed under the following headings:

1. Nomenclature.
2. Isotope effects.
3. Decomposition by self-irradiation.
4. Stability of tritium atoms in molecules.

Of these four, perhaps the two most important are the decomposition of tritium compounds by self-irradiation and the stability of the tritium label under the various experimental conditions. For both self-decomposition and stability a great deal of information is already available, but much more is required to enable tritium compounds to be used with the same degree of confidence experienced with compounds labelled with other radioisotopes, for example, carbon-14, sulphur-35 and phosphorus-32.

Tritium having a mass three times that of hydrogen exhibits large effects due to this mass difference; these are reviewed briefly under the general heading of 'Isotope effects'.

1. NOMENCLATURE

The isotope of hydrogen having a mass of three, was originally referred to as triterium[1] to conform with the name given to the stable isotope of mass two, deuterium. This soon became shortened to tritium[2], the preferred American nomenclature, and the more recently discovered hydrogen isotopes of masses 4 and 5 might well be named tetrium and pentium respectively.

The recognized symbol for tritium is ^3H which is sometimes written H-3, but some publications and catalogues of commercial organizations adopt the letter 'T' for simplicity. The small letter 't' has also been used[3,4]. The use of capital 'T' would seem to avoid confusion with 'tertiary' and the introduction of additional numbers. There are no formal rules published for the nomenclature of tritium compounds and the position is rather unsatisfactory, as it is for carbon-14 compounds[5]. A few general comments only are presented here mainly to clarify the system adopted for the presentation of information in this book.

The capital letter 'T' is mainly used throughout to distinguish a tritium atom in a molecule, and the position of the isotope within the molecule follows the numbering of the atom to which it is attached. For example, consider the three possible positions in labelled ethanol (6.1):

$$\overset{2}{C}H_3 \cdot \overset{1}{C}HT \cdot OH \qquad \overset{2}{C}H_2T \cdot \overset{1}{C}H_2 \cdot OH \qquad \overset{2}{C}H_3 \cdot \overset{1}{C}H_2 \cdot OT$$
$$(a) \qquad\qquad\qquad (b) \qquad\qquad\qquad (c)$$

$$\cdot \quad \cdot \quad \cdot \quad \cdot \quad (6.1)$$

Compound (a) is ethanol-1-T, or ethanol-(*methylene*-T) but the former shorter version is usually preferred. Compound (b) is ethanol-2-T or ethanol-(*methyl*-T) and compound (c) is ethanol-(*hydroxyl*-T). Where the tritium atom is attached to an atom other than carbon, the group to which it is attached is normally described. For example, glycine labelled with tritium on the nitrogen atom is referred to as glycine-(*amino*-T) (6.2):

$$HTN \cdot CH_2 \cdot COOH \qquad \cdot \quad \cdot \quad \cdot \quad (6.2)$$

In cyclic compounds the numbering generally used is that recommended by the International Union of Pure and Applied Chemistry (I.U.P.A.C.)[6]. Thus adenine-2,8-T is as shown in (6.3):

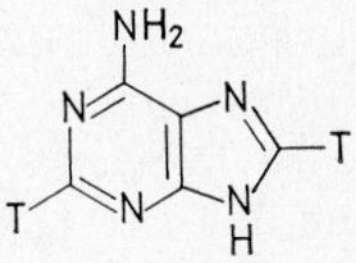

$$\cdot \quad \cdot \quad \cdot \quad \cdot \quad (6.3)$$

Compounds which are uniformly labelled are designated by a 'U' after the compound. In the case of tritium compounds this is usually done to denote uniform labelling in non-labile positions in the molecule only. Stearic acid-T(U) for example, means that the tritium atoms are uniformly spread over the whole molecule with the exception of the hydrogen of the carboxyl group (6.4):

$$CH_2T \cdot CHT \cdot CHT \cdot CHT \cdot CHT \cdot CHT \cdot CHT \cdot$$
$$CHT \cdot CHT \cdot CHT \cdot (CHT)_7 \cdot COOH$$
$$\qquad \qquad \cdots \cdots \quad (6.4)$$

Degradation of such a molecule would result in the same loss of tritium as each carbon atom is removed. As uniform labelling with tritium is seldom achieved and is more the rare exception than the rule, a letter 'G' is frequently used instead. This is used to denote that labelling is likely to be present in all non-labile hydrogen positions, but the exact distribution of tritium is not known and is probably not uniform. Thus cholesterol-T(G) implies that tritium atoms may be present in the rings, angular methyl groups, and in the side-chain but the distribution is not uniform.

Multiple Labelling

Most tritium-labelled compounds, particularly those at low specific activity containing a large number of hydrogen atoms, will contain very few molecules which actually have more than 1 atom of tritium present in the molecule. Sometimes it is necessary to have a molecular species which contains 2 or more tritium atoms per molecule, or a tritium atom and another radioactive atom such as carbon-14.

It has been shown in Chapter 1 that the specific activity of a compound in which one hydrogen atom is completely replaced by tritium is $29 \cdot 12$ c/mM. If the compound has only one hydrogen atom in the molecule then complete replacement with tritium results in 100 per cent isotopic abundance as tritium at the position substituted. If the compound contains two hydrogen atoms attached to the same atom, the isotopic abundance is halved if only one is replaced with tritium, the specific activity being $29 \cdot 12$ c/mM. It is not difficult to see that if the two hydrogen atoms are attached to two different atoms, each bearing two hydrogen atoms of which all forms are strictly equivalent, the proportion of doubly labelled molecules is only 25 per cent. The proportion of doubly labelled molecules in a compound may be calculated from the equation (6.5)

$$P = \frac{S}{29 \cdot 12 \times H_n} \qquad \cdots \cdots \quad (6.5)$$

where P = proportion of doubly labelled molecules,
H_n = number of hydrogen atoms in the molecule directly involved in the labelling,
S = specific activity of the compound in curies per millimole.

This simple equation applies only when all the hydrogen atoms H_n are strictly equivalent, each with an equal probability of labelling.

In practice very few compounds satisfy this requirement namely, have all hydrogen positions equivalent, and it is not possible to determine the proportion of multiple-labelled molecules unless one knows the fraction of tritium associated with each position in the molecule; knowing the relative ease of labelling in the various positions within the molecule can enable approximate values to be calculated. The actual proportion of multiple-labelled molecules in a compound depends basically upon:

1. the method used for the preparation of the compound, and,
2. the specific activity of the compound *as prepared*.

A few simple examples will illustrate these points more clearly. If tritium at 100 per cent isotopic abundance adds across a carbon–carbon double bond (6.6), then all the molecules will be doubly labelled.

$$—CH=CH— + T—T \rightarrow —CHT—CHT—$$

$$. \quad . \quad . \quad . \quad (6.6)$$

On the other hand if a mixture of tritium and hydrogen is used for the reduction, the proportion of doubly labelled molecules will depend on the proportions and relative rates of reaction of T_2, HT, and H_2 molecules present in the gas, and the calculations (as with exchange reactions) become very complicated indeed.

Consideration of multiple labelling must be given to the compound *as prepared* and not after dilution with carrier. For example, 2-methyl-naphthalene-6,7-T at only 100 mc/mM could have all its radioactive molecular species doubly labelled if carrier inactive 2-methyl-naphthalene was added to the tritiated compound prepared by the replacement of halogen atoms in positions 6 and 7 with tritium at 100 per cent isotopic abundance. However, if the dihalogen compound had been reduced with a tritium–hydrogen mixture to yield a product at 100 mc/mM only a small fraction of the molecules present would be doubly labelled. Assuming only the 6 and 7 positions are labelled and that these positions are equivalent, i.e. have an equal probability of labelling, then the proportion of doubly labelled molecules calculated from equation (6.5) is:

$$P = \frac{0·1}{29·12 \times 2}$$

$$= 0·17 \text{ per cent}$$

For the majority of uses of tritium compounds statistical multiple labelling only is required, i.e. a tritiated compound comprising unlabelled molecules, singly labelled molecules with tritium atoms attached to different positions, and perhaps a fractional percentage of molecules with tritium atoms in two or more positions within a single molecule.

There are perhaps only a few investigations in which multiple tritium-labelled molecules are necessary. These include:

1. the study of primary (internal) decomposition (see page 319),
2. in the study of ion-molecule reactions at atmospheric pressure[7],
3. in biochemical or chemical transformations multiply labelled molecules may be more (or less) reactive than singly labelled ones[9]. This possibility of molecular selection should be borne in mind particularly in checking the validity of tritium as an ancilliary tracer for carbon-14.

To determine whether two parts of a molecule remain associated during a chemical or biochemical process usually requires only statistical multiple labelling and the same even applies for the determination of molecular weights by the Wenzel and Schulze method[8].

Labelling with Two Different Isotopes

Many experiments are performed with multiple labelling techniques using two or more radioisotopes. The combination of carbon-14 and tritium is often ideal (see page 356). Such experiments are usually carried out by mixing the carbon-14-labelled compound with the tritium compound before use. In this mixture there are of course no molecules which are labelled with both these radioisotopes, assuming there is no hydrogen isotope exchange. These are intermolecular doubly labelled molecules and to obtain molecules which contain both radioisotopes, i.e. intramolecular double labelling, it is necessary to use a carbon-14-labelled compound in the synthesis involving tritium, or vice versa.

The fraction of the molecules containing both carbon-14 and tritium can be calculated from the equation (6.7)

$$P_{CT} = \frac{S_T}{T_A} \times \frac{S_C}{C_A} \qquad \cdots \quad (6.7)$$

where S_T = specific activity of the compound due to tritium in millicuries per millimole, T_A = number of millicuries of tritium per milliatom (29120), S_C = specific activity of the compound due to carbon-14 in millicuries per millimole, C_A = number of millicuries of carbon-14 per milliatom (64).

Consider a specific example where say thymine-2-C14 at 8 mc/mM

310

is used to prepare thymine-2-C14-6-T at 10 c/mM. The fraction of molecules containing both carbon-14 and tritium is

$$P_{CT} = \frac{10,000}{29,120} \times \frac{8}{64}$$

$$= 0\cdot043$$

Thus only 4·3 per cent of the thymine molecules will contain both radioisotopes.

At present most applications of tritium compounds do not require the use of multiple-labelled *molecules* but the presence of such molecules should be borne in mind when interpreting results.

2. ISOTOPE EFFECTS

An isotope effect may be broadly defined as any difference in the chemical or physical behaviour between two compounds which differ only in isotopic composition. The large mass difference between hydrogen (protium) and tritium favours isotopic fractionation and many examples are described in the literature[10-13]. The significance of isotope effects in the general utilization of tritium and its compounds depends on whether one is studying isotope effects using tritium as a tracer or merely regarding them as possible additional effects in an experimental investigation. The reader's attention is drawn particularly to isotope effects in the preparation and use of tritium compounds.

Isotope effects are usually most apparent when the isotope is directly involved in the rate-determining step of a reaction. Many organic chemical and biological reactions involve carbon–hydrogen bonds either directly or indirectly; the possible applications of tritium for the study of isotope effects is therefore almost limitless. There are many publications relating to isotope effects observed using deuterium compounds; similar effects are to be expected using tritium for all such observations. Some reviews have been published on the reaction kinetics of deuterium and tritium compounds[14], in fact most studies in this field have been concerned with establishing differences in specific reaction rate constants for two isotopically different species of the same compound. These intermolecular rate differences may be classified into primary or secondary isotope effects.

Primary Isotope Effects

This is the difference in the reaction rates of two different isotopic species of the same compound, due to the breaking or formation of

311

isotopically different bonds. Examples here include the quite large isotope effect observed in the hydrolysis of Grignard reagents, when excess of the reagent is used (6.8)

$$R \cdot MgX + THO \rightarrow R \cdot T + R \cdot H + MgXOH + MgXOT$$

. . . . (6.8)

Frequent use is made of this reaction for the preparation of tritiated hydrocarbons (see Chapter 4). The differences one can expect between the calculated and observed specific activities of the resulting tritiated hydrocarbons are illustrated in Table 6.1. The reaction of the tritiated water 'lags' behind that of ordinary water[15].

TABLE 6.1
Grignard Reactions with Tritiated Water

Grignard reagent	Tritiated water specific activity mc/mM	Product	Specific activity mc/mM	
			Calc.	Obs.
Phenylmagnesium bromide	100	Benzene-T	50	20
Phenylmagnesium bromide	200	Benzene-T	100	68
p-Tolylmagnesium bromide	100	Toluene-4-T	50	20
p-Tolylmagnesium bromide	360	Toluene-4-T	180	115
1-Naphthylmagnesium bromide	100	Naphthalene-T	50	20
9-Phenanthrylmagnesium bromide	100	Phenanthrene-T	50	17

Similar effects have been reported for deuterium-labelled hydrocarbons prepared in this way[16].

Assarson[17] has shown that the rates of hydrolysis of Grignard reagents are slower with tritiated water than with ordinary water. At $20°$ C the rate-constant ratios for the preparation of methane k_T/k_H was 0·67 and for benzene k_T/k_H was 0·61. No isotopic exchange occurs between the alkyl or aryl group and the tritiated water during the hydrolysis reaction[18].

Another example of a large primary isotope effect is observed in the mercuration of benzene with mercuric acetate in acetic acid in the presence of a perchloric acid catalyst[19]. The overall reaction is shown in equation (6.9).

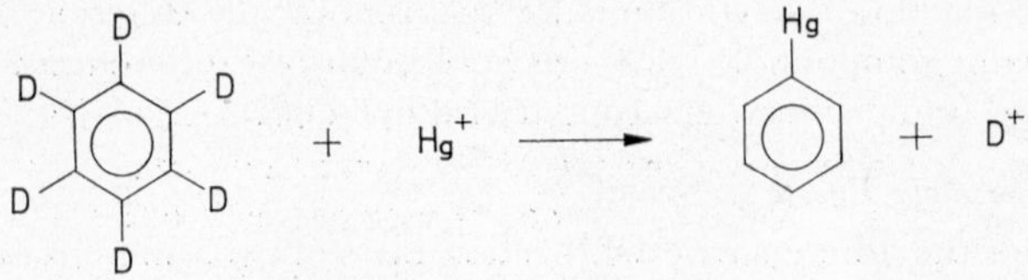

. . . . (6.9)

The rate observed for the mercuration of benzene was considerably faster than for hexadeuterobenzene; the ratio of the rates k_H/k_D being 6 at 25° C. This example is in fact the first instance of a primary isotope effect for the reaction of benzene itself.

The absence of isotopic fractionation in a reaction may, in some instances, serve in eliminating a particular step as rate determining. For example, carbon–hydrogen bond breaking is not the rate-determining step in the nitration of aromatic compounds [20].

Quite large isotope effects have also been reported for reductions with tritiated sodium borohydride [21, 22], a reagent frequently used in the preparation of tritium compounds.

Secondary Isotope Effects

These effects are those in which isotopically different chemical bonds are not broken or formed during the rate process being studied. Thus tritium-element bonds are not broken. One example is the rate of hydrolysis of methyl p-methyl-T benzoate, which is slower in alkaline solution but the same as the unlabelled compound in acid solution [23].

Methods for the Determination of Isotope Effects

There are three general methods:

1. the kinetic method,
2. the method of competing reactions,
3. the method of product analysis.

The techniques involved in these methods have been adequately reviewed by Collins [10] and some examples of each type are given in Table 6.2.

Double-labelling techniques with say carbon-14 are often used in the determination of isotope effects with tritium compounds [24, 25]. This procedure requires that the isotope effects (if any) caused by the 'tracer' isotope (carbon-14) itself are known.

In preparative work such as the author's at the Radiochemical Centre it is unlikely that very small primary or secondary isotope effects would be observed, because of the complex nature of the labelling techniques involved. In such work most reactions are taken to completion and intermediate changes in the isotopic composition of the product and residual reactants are not measured, so that isotope effects are therefore not apparent, although they may occur in the reaction. Care is necessary when measuring small effects, particularly if trace impurities are present at high specific activity, as

Zollinger[11] has justly observed that 'no conclusions should be drawn from a single measurement of one isotope effect alone.'

Some of the isotope effects observed with tritium compounds are:

1. the fractionation of hydrogen isotopes between hydrogen ions and water[26, 27],
2. the distillation of tritiated water[28-31] and of aqueous solutions of tritiated formaldehyde[32],
3. tritium recoil reactions[33],
4. the oxidation of aldoses-1-T with iodine[34] or the oxidation of D-mannitol-T[35, 36],
5. the Hofmann degradation of quaternary ammonium bases[37, 38],
6. ion-exchange chromatography[39] and the adsorption chromatography of multiple-labelled compounds[40, 45],
7. gas–liquid chromatography[41, 42] and gas–solid chromatography[43],
8. the crystallization of D-glucose-1-T[44] and sugar phenylhydrazones[46-47],
9. the decomposition of tritium compounds by self-irradiation[48],
10. the radiolysis of compounds containing tritium and deuterium[49].

Particularly important are the isotope effects which may be observed by the use of tritium compounds as tracers in biological systems. Enzyme reactions are often even more selective than chemical reactions in the choice of an isotopically labelled species. Some examples will help to clarify this point.

Suppose a tritium-labelled methyl group, $-CH_2T$, is subjected to an enzymic transformation (say oxidation); hydrogen atoms may be more readily oxidized than tritium atoms so that the product of the reaction, formed of methylene groups, is enriched with tritium. This is an *intramolecular* isotope selection. If a mixture containing the species $-{}^{14}CH_3$ and $-CT_3$ is oxidized, the hydrogen-containing methyl group (carbon-14 labelled) may be more readily oxidized than the one containing tritium. This is *intermolecular* isotope selection and results in the relative enrichment of $-CT_3$ in the starting material. Such an example is the biosynthesis of choline and creatinine from methanol labelled with carbon-14, deuterium and tritium in the methyl group, in the rat[9, 50]; another is the utilization of labelled formate in the rat[52].

The use of the double-labelling technique is certainly useful for studying isotope effects in biological systems but requires caution. Care must be taken not to confuse isotope effects for instability of the tritium label and vice versa (see page 356). It can be seen that an intermolecular multiple labelling of the methyl groups (for example a mixture of CT_3OH and $^{14}CH_3OH$) gives no indication of the degree of oxidation reached by the methanol before it is utilized for choline synthesis in say the rat. In order to do this it is necessary to have intra-molecular multiple labelling, that is *molecules* which contain both isotopes, $^{14}CH_2T \cdot OH$. It is of course very difficult to separate, singly, doubly and multiply labelled molecular species of the same compound. In fact this has only been achieved with very simple molecules; Gant and Yang[174] for example separated four species of tritiated methane, CT_4, CHT_3, CH_2T_2 and CH_3T, by solid–gas chromatography on charcoal using helium as the carrier gas. Other workers have separated the hydrogen isotopes[175,176], and the positional isomers of tritiated propylene (and butene), CH_2T—$CH{=}CH_2$, CH_3—$CT{=}CH_2$ and CH_3—$CH{=}CHT$, were separated on a 160 ft. silver nitrate–ethylene glycol column[177].

An interesting example of isotopic fractionation in a biological system is demonstrated by the work of Siri and Evers[53]. The specific activity of the expired water from the pigeon following an intake of tritiated water, was less than the specific activity of tritium in the blood and urine; the ratio being respectively 0·35–0·55 compared with 0·78–0·96 for the human. The pigeon seems to have a respiratory system capable of efficiently concentrating the tritium in the bird, fortunately this concentration isotope effect is small in the human.

TABLE 6.2
Determination of Isotope Effects

Method*	Examples†	References
1. Kinetic method	Rate of racemization	55 , 56
	Rate of oxidation of benz-aldehyde	57
2. Method of competing reactions		
(a) cumulative	Crystallization of sugar phenylhydrazones	45—47
	Hydrolysis of Grignard reagents	15—17
(b) differential	Conversion of ketones to dinitrophenylhydrazones	10
3. Product analysis	Pinacol-type rearrangements	58
	Deamination or dehydro-halogenation of 3-amino- or 3-chloro-isopentane respectively	59
	Oxidation of alditols-T	60
	Oxidation of aldoses-1-T	25
	Addition of THO to 5,6-position in pyrimidines under u.v.-light	61

* See reference 10 for description of methods.
† Examples also include those of deuterium compounds.

The quantum statistical mechanics of isotope effects is described by Oppenheim and Friedman [54], while the subject of isotope effects, particularly in chemical kinetics has been well reviewed [12,13] Isotope effects are always likely in the use of tritium compounds and the cautious experimentalist will bear this in mind.

3. DECOMPOSITION OF TRITIUM COMPOUNDS BY SELF-IRRADIATION

The need to use radiochemically pure tritium compounds for tracer investigations has been emphasized. Users should therefore be aware of the risk of decomposition on storage. Decomposition by self-irradiation is an unwelcome property which is peculiar to all compounds labelled with radioisotopes, although its magnitude varies widely with the circumstances.

The radiation chemistry of organic compounds is currently an important and widely studied subject of research [62], but (for reasons which will become apparent) theoretical knowledge is still inadequate to explain all the phenomena of self-irradiation decomposition, except in a general or qualitative way.

Modes of Decomposition

There are four modes by which a labelled compound can undergo self-decomposition. The simple classification adopted is that proposed by Bayly and Weigel [63] in 1960, which consists of:

(*a*) Primary internal radiation effects—the decomposition or transformation of a molecule caused by the disintegration of one of its unstable atomic nuclei.

(*b*) Primary external radiation effects—caused by the interaction of a molecule with a nuclear particle giving rise to a radioactive decomposition product if the interacting molecule is a labelled one.

(*c*) Secondary radiation decomposition—which results from the interaction of molecules with, for example, free radicals or other excited species produced by the radiation.

(*d*) Chemical effects—which would occur in some degree even in the absence of ionizing radiation.

(*a*) *Primary internal decomposition*—Isotopes of very long half-life contribute a very small percentage decomposition from natural decay and for most practical purposes can be neglected for simple molecules. In compounds labelled with carbon-14 (half-life over 5,600 years) for example, less than 0·01 per cent decomposition per annum occurs by natural decay to nitrogen in a one carbon compound. On the other hand, for isotopes of short half-life such as phosphorus-32 (14·3 days)[63a], the decomposition due to primary decay can be the major contributing factor. Tritium compounds are in between these two extremes.

The spontaneous disintegration of a tritium atom into helium (6.10) is beyond our control, but it is interesting, from both theoretical and practical points of view, to know exactly what effect this decay ultimately has on the labelled compound.

$$T \rightarrow \beta^- + {}^3He^+ \qquad \ldots \quad (6.10)$$

One of the more obvious effects is of course a decrease in the molar specific activity of the compound with time which can be calculated from the normal decay law equation (6.11):

$$N_t = N_0 (1 - e^{-\lambda t}) \qquad \ldots \quad (6.11)$$

where N_t represents the number of labelled molecules present at time t,

N_0 is the number of labelled molecules originally present and,

λ is the disintegration constant for tritium (see page 2).

For tritium-labelled compounds the molar specific activity is reduced by about 5 per cent per annum on storage.

In practice, if a tritium compound is stored for a number of years and then re-purified, the specific activity of the pure compound is often found to be much lower than expected by calculation of natural decay, indicating that other modes of decomposition must also be taken into consideration.

When a β-particle is ejected from the tritium compound, helium and a recoil fragment are produced. The kinetic energy of the recoil fragment may be calculated from the equation[64] (6.12):

$$E_r = \frac{E_\beta^2}{1862\ M_r} + \frac{E_\beta\ M_0}{1848\ M_r} \qquad \ldots \quad (6.12)$$

where E_r = recoil kinetic energy,

M_r = mass of the recoil atom,

E_β = energy of the β-particle $= (M_\beta - M_0)\,c^2$,

M_β = relativistic mass of the β-particle,

M_0 = rest mass of the β-particle, and

c = velocity of light.

In mono-tritiated molecules, the recoil fragment will be non-radioactive and will therefore not contribute a radiochemical impurity.

Such a nuclear process gives rise to chemical impurities only, which can normally be tolerated. If the original molecule contained two or more tritium atoms the recoil fragment will be labelled, and a radio-chemical impurity will be produced. At low isotopic abundances, i.e. low specific activity, the proportion of multiply labelled molecules is small (see page 308), and hence it can reasonably be assumed that primary internal natural decay of tritiated compounds produces predominantly non-radioactive recoil fragments, the net result being only a reduction in the molar specific activity of the compound. Consider for example the tritiated amino acid glycine-2-T (6.13):

$$NH_2 \cdot CHT \cdot COOH \qquad NH_2 \cdot CT_2 \cdot COOH \qquad NH_2 \cdot CH_2 \cdot COOH$$
$$(a) \qquad\qquad (b) \qquad\qquad (c)$$

$$. \quad . \quad . \quad . \quad (6.13)$$

This will consist of a mixture of singly (a), doubly (b) and unlabelled (c) molecules. Assuming that both the hydrogen atoms attached to the 2-position are strictly equivalent, the proportion of doubly labelled molecules is only about 1 per cent at 500 mc/mM. Primary internal decomposition would not therefore be expected to give rise to significant radioactive impurities at this specific activity. This is seen from the figures given in Table 6.4, the glycine-2-T (at 176 mc/mM) remaining pure even after 2 years.

The atomic and molecular consequences of primary radioactive decay have been studied only for tritium [65] and one or two tritiated hydrocarbons [66, 67]. For the simple tritiated hydrocarbon methane, the predominant process is one in which neutral helium-3 separates leaving a positively charged methyl group, and less frequently other hydrogen atoms are also split off leaving positively charged units shown (6.14):

$$CH_3\text{---}T \; \rightarrow \; \beta^- + CH_3He^+ \; \rightarrow \; CH_3^+ + {}^3He$$
$$\downarrow$$
$$CH_2^+ \; \rightarrow \; CH^+ \; \rightarrow \; C^+$$

$$. \quad . \quad . \quad . \quad (6.14)$$

These effects can all be seen by mass spectrographic [67a] analysis. Similar results are reported with tritiated ethane [67] giving rise to helium and a positively charged ethyl group (6.15):

$$C_2H_5\text{---}T \; \rightarrow \; \beta^- + C_2H_5He^+ \; \rightarrow \; C_2H_5^+ + {}^3He$$

$$. \quad . \quad . \quad . \quad (6.15)$$

In molecules of hydrogen tritide (HT), the pure β-emission fails to dissociate which remains as $(^3HeH)^+$ [65].

Nothing is known about the primary decay processes occurring in more complex molecules, but it is reasonable to suppose that neutral helium-3 will be produced and positively charged recoil fragments, which may lose further hydrogen atoms, will be formed [68]. The maximum energy available for bond rupture in consequence of the recoil from the tritium β-emission in ethane-T, for example, is estimated at 3·3 eV and the bond energy for the carbon–helium bond at 2 eV. It is not surprising that the primary decay does not appear to cause the breaking of carbon–carbon bonds where normally about 4 eV are required to break such a bond. Unlike the decay product of carbon-14 (nitrogen), helium-3 is unlikely to produce a helium-containing compound, i.e. to form a stable bond with carbon. Primary decay products of carbon-14 have been identified; the nitrogen atom forming a stable bond with carbon. Examples are the formation of methylamine-^{14}C from ethane-1,2-^{14}C [69] and glycine-^{14}C from succinic acid-2,3-^{14}C (6.16) [70]:

$$
\begin{array}{ccccc}
^{14}CH_2 \cdot COOH & & ^{14}CH_2 \cdot COOH & & ^{14}CH_2 \cdot COOH \\
| & \to & | & \to & | \qquad + CO_2 + H^+ \\
^{14}CH_2 \cdot COOH & & ^+NH_2 \cdot COOH & & NH_2
\end{array}
$$

$$\cdots \cdots (6.16)$$

The nature of the more complex recoil fragments from tritium compounds could be conveniently studied by using doubly labelled molecules with say carbon-14. The proportion of the breakdown fragments labelled with carbon-14 could then be detected. However, unless the specific activity with respect to both isotopes were very high, the recoil fragments would have to be carefully sorted from the singly labelled molecules remaining. It is of interest to note that Manning and Monk [64] used doubly labelled (carbon-14 and tritium) toluene and ethylbenzene for their investigations of bond rupture in the primary decay of carbon-14.

Although in general the effects produced by natural decay of tritium are too small to be troublesome with small molecules, there is one situation in which a high proportion of radioactive impurities could be produced, even at quite low isotopic abundances, and this is with macromolecules. To illustrate this point diagrammatically, consider a labelled compound '(T)' having only one tritium atom per molecule.

Primary decay of (T) gives an unlabelled decomposition product (), as discussed on page 317. If the molecules of Ⓣ are polymerized to say five units of Ⓣ, then primary decay now results in the formation of

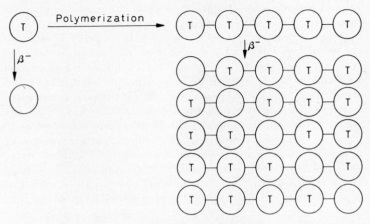

Figure 6.1. Decomposition of tritiated polymers

three radioactive impurities (five if the molecules of Ⓣ were not identical). The percentage of the radioactive impurity formed in a given time depends on the molecular weight, and of course will fall exponentially with time, as nuclei in the resultant impurities themselves disintegrate. If the molecules of Ⓣ are multiply labelled it is easy to see that the polymer will produce radioactive impurities much faster than the monomer, at the same isotopic abundance of tritium. Dilution of the tritiated polymer with carrier (unlabelled) polymer would not reduce the formation of labelled impurities by primary (internal) decomposition (although it may well reduce the decomposition by other modes). Bayly and Weigel[63] have pointed out that such effects in macromolecules can only be reduced, at low isotopic abundance, by diluting the isotope first and then preparing the macromolecule. Those working with nucleic acids and proteins should bear this point in mind, in fact Person[71, 71a] has attributed a high proportion of cell deaths in *E. coli* treated with tritiated thymidine, to the tritium decay in the labelled macromolecular nucleic acid, i.e. by direct nuclear transmutation, rather than by radiation effects.

(*b*) *Primary external radiation*—A much more serious radiation decomposition is that produced by the direct action of the β-radiation on the compound molecules. If the molecule changed is a radioactive one then a radiochemical impurity is produced. The magnitude of this effect can be calculated from the empirical formula [63] (6.17):

$$\% \text{ Decomposition} = (1 - e^{-FEASt \cdot 6 \cdot 14 \times 10^{-16}})100$$

$$\cdots \cdots (6.17)$$

where F = fraction of its own radiation energy absorbed by the compound,

E = mean energy of the tritium radiation (5,700 eV),

S = specific activity of the compound in curies per mole,

t = time in seconds,

A = number of molecules *irreversibly* damaged per 100 eV of absorbed energy. This is also called the $G(-M)$ value [72].

For more accurate values t should be replaced by $(1/\lambda)(1-e^{-\lambda t})$ where λ is the radioactive decay constant. However, for tritium this makes little difference for most practical purposes during one year storage.

It is clear that decomposition will increase as the specific activity of the compound is increased. The term A or $G(-M)$ value is determined experimentally and depends on the type of compound, temperature and other conditions of storage. The fraction of the radiation energy absorbed, F, depends on the geometry of the system. The tritium β-radiation being very weak and of low penetrating power results in almost complete self-absorption of the energy. For labelling molecules intended to deliver large radiation doses to small, localized areas, tritium is the isotope *par excellence*, and this has suggested its possible use in radiotherapy (page 53).

Calculation of absorbed energy—The radiation energy absorbed by solid tritium compounds (making the valid assumption that all the radiation energy is absorbed) can be calculated from equation [72] (6.18):

$$F = \frac{NE(1 \cdot 602 \times 10^{-12})}{100 \, M} \quad \cdots \cdots (6.18)$$

where N = number of nuclear particles, i.e. disintegrations,

E = mean energy of the tritium β-particles (5,700 eV),

M = weight of compound in grammes, and

F = energy absorbed in rads.

Consider a tritium compound at a specific activity 1 mc/mg.

Number of disintegrations per day = $3 \cdot 7 \times 10^7 \times 3,600 \times 24$

$$= 3 \cdot 2 \times 10^{12}$$

Mean energy of the tritium β-particles = $5 \cdot 7 \times 10^3$ eV.

11   321

$$\text{Total energy available per millicurie per day} = 3 \cdot 2 \times 5 \cdot 7 \times 10^{15} \text{ eV}$$
$$= 1 \cdot 82 \times 10^{16} \text{ eV}$$
$$1 \text{ eV} = 1 \cdot 602 \times 10^{-12} \text{ ergs}$$
$$\text{Hence total energy per millicurie per day} = 1 \cdot 82 \times 1 \cdot 602 \times 10^{4}$$
$$\text{ergs}$$
$$= 2 \cdot 9 \times 10^{4} \text{ ergs}$$
$$1 \text{ rad} = 93 \text{ ergs/g}$$
$$= 6 \cdot 24 \times 10^{13} \text{ eV/g}$$

Thus for a tritium compound at 1 mc/mg the absorbed energy per day is approximately 3×10^{5} rads or $1 \cdot 1 \times 10^{8}$ rads/year. If the compound is in solution, the energy absorbed by 1 g of the solution containing 1 mc is approximately 300 rads/day.

Although one cannot prevent natural radioactive decay, one can alleviate primary external radiation by shielding the labelled molecules from the nuclear particles.

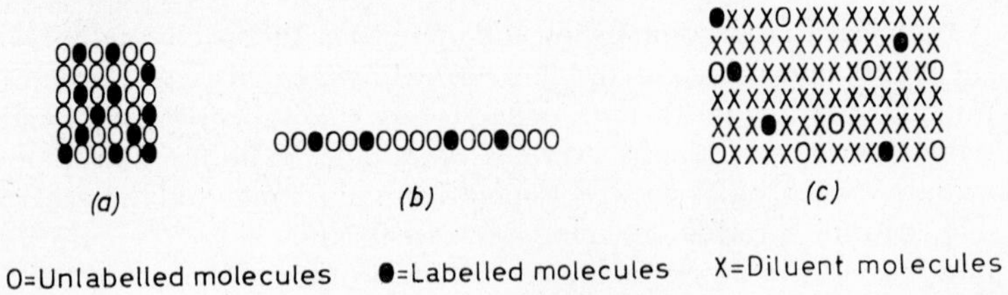

(a)   (b)   (c)

O=Unlabelled molecules   ●=Labelled molecules   X=Diluent molecules

Figure 6.2. Distribution of labelled molecules

Figures 6.2a, b and *c* represent diagrammatically the absorption effects of tritium β-radiation. From *Figure 6.2a* where the labelled compound is in the form of a solid, one immediately sees that the self-absorbed energy increases as the number of labelled molecules is increased, i.e. the molar specific activity is raised. All the molecules are close together and the self-absorption of radiation energy is maximal. In *Figure 6.2b* the molecules are spread out over a large area, ideally in the form of a mono-molecular layer. Here the chance of a β-particle interacting with a labelled molecule is much reduced; only the beta decays in the plane of the layer can cause decomposition. Almost all molecular dimensions (several angströms, i.e. 10^{-8} cm) are much smaller than the penetration of the tritium β-particles (a few microns, i.e. 10^{-4} cm) so that a large fraction of the total energy will escape from the sample. Thus one method by which primary external decomposition can be minimized is by distributing the compound in a layer which is thin enough to give negligible self-absorption of the β-energy. Although this dispersal technique often affords a high

322

degree of protection for carbon-14 compounds for example[73], it is of little use for tritium compounds. The high self-absorption of the tritium β-particles coupled with the difficulty of producing and maintaining very thin (ideally mono-molecular) layers, eliminates this method as a practical one for the storage of tritium compounds. The most effective and practical segregation of the labelled molecules is seen from *Figure 6.2c* where the compound is diluted with a solvent or a diluent of some kind which interposes unlabelled molecules between the β-particle and the labelled molecules under bombardment. These diluent molecules are themselves damaged, but being unlabelled do not contribute directly to the radioactive impurity.

Primary external radiation damage can therefore be minimized by dispersal of the labelled molecules in a suitable medium. From Tables 6.5–6.9 it can be seen that water, benzene and alcohol are effective solvents for such dispersal. Dispersal in paper is also another useful method but it is clearly seen from Table 6·4 that in the solid state, even freeze-dried as a film, tritium compounds decompose severely.

As with primary internal effects it will be evident that compounds of high molecular weight are more susceptible to self-decomposition than their constituent moieties, if the molecule is considered as an entity. This may be important in biological systems although there would not appear to be any direct evidence to suggest this at present.

(c) *Secondary radiation decomposition*—Absorption of nuclear radiation may produce ions, free radicals, high-energy electrons, positions, free sub-excitation electrons or x-rays; decomposition or transformation due to the reaction of a labelled molecule with such reactive species, or the excited products of primary decay, presents the most serious problems in the storage of tritium compounds.

Secondary radiation effects are related to the same general factors as those described for primary external effects and it is not always possible to distinguish between the products which are produced by the two modes of decomposition. The important factor in this type of decomposition when one considers the whole range of tritium-labelled compounds, is the $G(-M)$ value (defined on page 321). This parameter varies over a wide range for pure compounds and depends upon the storage conditions used. Tolbert[72] has calculated the percentage decomposition of organic compounds which *may* be expected to occur for various radiation doses and $G(-M)$ values. These are summarized in Table 6.3.

The figures in Table 6.3 were calculated for a compound of molecular weight 125 on the basis of a 'hit' theory[72].

323

TABLE 6.3

Absorbed energy Rads	$G(-M) = 5$	$G(-M) = 10$	$G(-M) = 20$
		% Decomposition	
10^6	0·06	0·12	0·24
10^7	0·59	1·19	2·38
10^8	5·8	11·3	21·4
10^9	45·0	70·2	90·9

Complete absorption of the tritium β-radiation energy from 1 mc of a compound having $G(-M) = 1$, in one year results in the destruction of $6·6 \times 10^{16}$ molecules. This would mean a loss in purity of about 10 per cent per year at 1 c/mM. For $G(-M) = 10$ and a specific activity of 10 c/mM, most of the compound would be destroyed within 12 months.

Unfortunately $G(-M)$ values are known for relatively few compounds and these have not been determined under the conditions for the storage of tritium compounds. They vary considerably with the type and energy of the radiation [62, 74, 77] and it must be emphasized that the $G(-M)$ values obtained with γ-irradiation (for example) cannot simply be applied to self-irradiation with tritium. The published $G(-M)$ values however do act as a rough guide for the more sensitive compounds.

In principle the same measures can be taken to minimize both secondary decomposition and primary external radiation effects. Dispersal in a suitable medium is essential for nearly all compounds above 500 mc/mM although a number of the less radiation-sensitive compounds, such as aromatic hydrocarbons, may be stored as solids at the lower specific activities. Being a chemical and not a nuclear effect, secondary decomposition is temperature dependent, and can often be reduced by storing the compound at low temperatures. The various methods of storage are discussed later.

In solutions of tritiated compounds (as with solid compounds) the percentage decomposition depends on the total energy absorbed by the solution, which can be calculated as shown on page 322. Over a fairly wide range of specific activities the decomposition is practically independent of the specific activity of the compound provided the number of solvent molecules is very large compared with the number of molecules of the compound. The degree of protection by the solution does depend on the nature of the compound studied, i.e. on its $G(-M)$ value for the storage conditions.

(d) Chemical effects—From thermodynamic considerations organic chemical compounds are unstable. The degree of instability varies considerably from one class of compound to another but as a general rule compounds are more stable at lower temperatures. For most compounds chemical decomposition at ordinary temperatures is so slow that only the most sensitive techniques can observe it[75, 76], but most organic chemists have to deal at times with compounds requiring special care to check decomposition; examples are vitamin-A, unsaturated long-chain fatty acids, allylic halides, nitrosomethylurea, benzaldehyde and numerous other compounds.

Purely chemical decomposition (or, more generally, decomposition from causes other than ionizing radiation) can be troublesome with labelled compounds and is indeed often overlooked. Labelled compounds (particularly those labelled with tritium) are used at high specific activity and are necessarily handled in small quantities and at low (chemical) concentrations. Under these conditions chemical reactions become apparent which would not be observed without a sensitive method for their detection. With a non-radioactive reagent in say a tracer experiment, chemical decomposition merely reduces the potency, which may not matter; with a radioactive reagent it produces labelled impurities, which are likely to be much more serious. Trace impurities can greatly affect the yield of radiation decomposition products by reacting (for example) with the excited products of primary decomposition.

The various modes by which tritium compounds can decompose and some of the methods which can be adopted to minimize the decomposition, have been discussed in general terms. It is now proposed to describe in more detail the behaviour of tritium compounds on storage and where possible the best methods for keeping them.

Storage Conditions and Observations on the Decomposition of Tritium Compounds

Few publications[68, 78-82] have dealt specifically with the problems associated with the self-irradiation decomposition of tritium-labelled compounds. The very high specific activities at which these are now used present complex problems of storage for both the supplier and user. For the user a knowledge of the rate of decomposition of the compound (under recommended storage conditions) and the nature of the decomposition fragments are probably the two most important considerations. This enables a realistic shelf-life to be ascribed to the material under given conditions, while a knowledge of the decomposition fragments enables an assessment of the extent of interference to be expected from them, in a tracer investigation. An attempt has been made to collect all information on this very important topic concerning tritium compounds.

A tritium compound may be stored (*a*) in its natural physical form (solid, liquid or gas) or (*b*) with a diluent, which may be solid, liquid or a gas depending on the compound to be protected. Any method of storage selected is aimed at reducing the total amount of radiation energy absorbed by the tritiated compound.

(*a*) *Storage of compounds in their normal physical form*—If the tritiated compound must be stored as a solid, liquid or gas, without dilution, low temperatures of storage are generally to be preferred even down to −196° C (liquid nitrogen) if this is conveniently possible. Most compounds are best stored in the absence of oxygen, i.e. *in vacuo* or in ampoules filled with an inert gas (nitrogen or argon).

(*b*) *Storage of compounds with a diluent*—At present this technique of diluting the labelled molecules with unlabelled ones is the best. Numerous diluents have been investigated including paper, powdered cellulose, charcoal, benzanthracene, clathrates[81] and various solvents.

The use of filter paper as a means of affording protection from self-irradiation, i.e. as the dispersal medium, has been used frequently, and is particularly useful for radioactive sugars[63]. The degree of protection is independent of the specific activity of the compound but depends on the actual weight of compound and just how it is dispersed in the paper. Investigations of only a few tritium compounds stored in this manner have been reported; di-iodothyronines labelled with tritium at 100 mc/mM are reported to be stable for 3 years when stored on paper in the dark[83], on the other hand DL-lysine-4,5-T at 32 c/mM does not keep any better when stored on paper than in the solid state[81]. The $G(-M)$ value for D-glucose-6-T at 468 mc/mM is reduced from 4·5, when stored as a solid at −40° C to only 0·3 when stored on paper under identical conditions (see Table 6.4).

In general, results would indicate that storage on paper for tritium compounds does not afford the same degree of protection experienced with carbon-14 compounds (for example), which is what one might expect from the high self-absorption and short range of the tritium β-particles. This can be seen from the examples given in Table 6.4.

Guarino[48, 82], *et al.* have studied the decomposition of tritiated cyclohexane (248 mc/mM) and found negligible decomposition when absorbed on charcoal $(G(-M) = 0)$ but on cellulose and benzanthracene the $G(-M)$ values were 4·8 and 3·7 respectively; little better than storage in air $G(-M) = 5·5$. *n*-Propanol-2,3-T at 136 mc/mM was better stored on a mixture of iron oxides $(G-M) = 2·4)$ than sealed *in vacuo* $(G(-M) = 7·6)$. The decomposition of methyl stearate-T at 1·29 c/mM and methyl butyrate-2,3-T at 244 mc/mM stored as choleic acid and cycloveratryl adducts, i.e. as a molecular complex, was observed to be better than storage in air or *in vacuo*[82]. The $G(-M)$ values were not stated in these examples.

In summary, undoubtedly most of these absorption methods give some extra degree of protection from self-radiolysis over storage in the natural form, but they are inconvenient for the many users of tritium compounds. Recovery of the compound and separation from the supporting medium is not always quantitative resulting in the loss of expensive material. It is also difficult when handling very small chemical amounts of the labelled compound. The recovery of a compound from paper is relatively simple and the technique is self-evident from *Figure 6.3*.

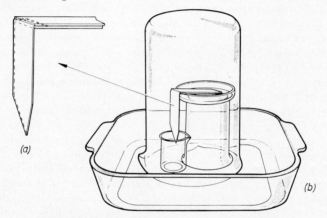

(a)

(b)

Figure 6.3. Recovery of labelled compounds dispensed on paper

A NOTE ON THE RECOVERY OF LABELLED COMPOUNDS DISPENSED ON PAPER

The following method of recovering a labelled compound from paper is based on a procedure described by C. E. Dent, *Biochem. J.* 41 (1947) 245

Open the tube by marking it with a glass-knife about 1–2 cm from the pointed end and touching this scratch mark with a glass rod that has been heated in an oxygen/coal gas flame. Remove the roll of paper from the tube (forceps may be used if necessary). The amount of activity remaining in the empty tube is usually negligible but this should be checked and if necessary the tube washed out. Wearing surgical gloves unroll the paper and place about 3–4 mm of the square-shaped end between two microscope slides (a). The slides will cohere by capillary attraction when they are wetted, but a clip or rubber band may be used if desired.

Place the other ends of the slides in a shallow Petri dish containing distilled water (about 5 ml) and cover the arrangement with a large beaker to prevent evaporation (b).

Over 99 per cent of the activity will, in general, be eluted from the point of the paper in a volume of water of less than 1 ml in 1 h.

327

In practice over 90 per cent of the labelled compound is usually eluted with a suitable solvent.

A more convenient technique for reducing decomposition by self-irradiation is by dissolving the compound in a suitable solvent. The solvent selected depends of course on the solubility of the compound. Solvents which readily produce free radicals on irradiation with γ-rays or other forms of radiation should be avoided where possible. Methylene dichloride for example would produce halogen radicals but aromatic hydrocarbons have a low radical yield, and are therefore frequently used. Unfortunately many compounds, particularly those of interest to biologists and biochemists, are only soluble in hydroxylic solvents and one is obliged to use water, aqueous alcohol and similar mixtures for their storage.

In solution ionization occurs along the paths of the β-particles [84]. If a labelled molecule is in the track of a β-particle or near enough to react with any energized species produced, then a radioactive decomposition product results. Relatively little is known about the loss of energy by the β-particle per unit path length (known as the linear energy transfer effect, LET effect) during autoradiolysis of tritium compounds. The percentage decomposition is related to the total energy absorbed by the solution; much of this energy is expended in reactions with inactive molecules and producing radicals or ions in yields depending on the solvent. The possibility of reducing decomposition due to radical-labelled molecule interaction by introducing a free radical scavenger into the solution, would seem the next obvious move. However, the free radical scavenger must be carefully chosen as many of the solutions of tritiated compounds are used directly for biological investigation in which the scavenger must have no adverse effect. Benzyl alcohol has been shown to reduce decomposition by scavenging hydroxyl radicals [78] and its beneficial effects on the storage of uridine-T (for example) are seen from Table 6.7. Benzyl alcohol is also a bacteriostat and is therefore advantageous in preserving sterility in solutions. Experiments by Bayly [73] indicate that even small amounts of ethanol (less than 1 per cent) also reduce decomposition in aqueous solution (compare reference 81); the mechanism is at present unknown.

At the Radiochemical Centre benzene, alcohols and aqueous solutions are used as the main solvents for the storage of tritium compounds, and have been found satisfactory. However, this does not necessarily mean they are the best solvents as much more investigation is really required.

Effect of temperature on storage—As a general rule compounds, particularly organic compounds, keep better at a low temperature. If the tritiated compound is stored at low temperature in a solvent, temperature gradients along the storage vessel can cause the solvent to sublime to the cooler end of the tube leaving the compound unprotected (shown diagrammatically in *Figures 6.4a* and *6.4b*); regular inspection is therefore advisable. This effect is particularly noticeable in evacuated sealed ampoules.

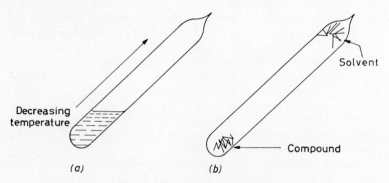

Figure 6.4. Storage at low temperatures

The possibility of crystallization of the compound at low storage temperatures must also be borne in mind. This again would severely reduce the protective action of the solvent. Frequent warming and cooling of a bulk solution of a tritiated compound during intermittent sampling is bad practice and accelerates decomposition; constant temperature conditions are recommended. If frequent sampling is necessary it is preferable to sub-divide the bulk solution into smaller quantities, each forming one sample. Many compounds are conveniently and satisfactorily stored in aqueous solution at $+2°$ C, in benzene at room temperature $(15°$ C) and in aqueous alcohol or alcohol–benzene solutions at $-20°$ C or perhaps lower temperatures. (See Tables 6.5–6.9).

When solutions of tritiated compounds are stored at very low temperatures there is always the possibility of prolonging the life of any free radicals which are formed[85], and upon warming the solution very rapid decomposition may result. In this respect the investigations of Henriksen[86, 87] and colleagues[88, 89], on the effect of temperature on the irradiation yield of radicals in frozen aqueous solutions, are of considerable importance. Although experiments were conducted with x-rays, the deductions are relevant to the storage of tritium compounds in frozen aqueous solutions. Henriksen found [89] that at temperatures of 77° K ($-196°$ C) or lower, there is little or no interaction between the solvent radicals and solute molecules. When the frozen aqueous solutions are heated after irradiation, the radicals induced in the water disappear in the temperature range 100° to 130° K ($-173°$ to $-143°$ C). Some of the radicals will, however, interact with the solute molecules and if these are labelled will produce a radiation decomposition product. The extent of radical-solute molecule interaction in frozen aqueous solutions irradiated at $-196°$ C was small compared to that observed after irradiation in the liquid state [87]. From these experiments it may be deduced that secondary radiation decomposition of tritiated compounds in solution should be considerably reduced on storing at $-196°$ C. Such a deduction seems justified by the fact that the stability of uridine-T stored in aqueous solution at $-196°$ C is not improved by the presence of benzyl alcohol (see Table 6.6). This suggests that secondary decomposition, i.e. radical-solute interaction is minimal, perhaps eliminated, at this low temperature.

Apelgot, Ekert and Tisne [80] published the first information on the storage of a tritium compound at $-196°$ C. They found that the decomposition of tritiated thymidine in aqueous solution at $-196°$ C was only 5 per cent for 198,000 rads. At a concentration of 1 mc/ml this amounts to less than 3 per cent per annum. In Table 6.6 the advantage of storing solutions of tritiated compounds at $-196°$ C is clearly seen [73].

It is perhaps only the inconvenience which prevents all solutions of tritiated (and other) compounds to be stored at $-196°$ C, but the possibility should be borne in mind.

Calculation of G($-M$) Values

The number of radioactive molecules irreversibly changed per 100 eV of absorbed energy, the G($-M$) value, recorded in Tables 6.4–6.6 was calculated from the specific activity and percentage decomposition per annum as follows:

The total energy absorbed by a tritiated compound

$$= 1.82 \times 10^{16} \text{ eV/day/mc}$$
$$= 6.6 \times 10^{18} \text{ eV/year/mc}.$$

For a compound at a specific activity S mc/mM the energy absorbed per annum per millimole

$$= 6.6 \times 10^{18} \times S \text{ eV}$$

1 mM of a compound contains 6.02×10^{20} molecules (Avogadro's number).

Hence,

$$\text{Fraction of the molecules decomposing per annum} = \frac{G(-M) \times 6.6 \times 10^{18} \times S}{100 \times 6.02 \times 10^{20}}$$

$$\text{Percentage decomposition per annum} \quad P_a = \frac{G(-M) \times 6.6 \times 10^{18} \times S \times 100}{100 \times 6.02 \times 10^{20}}$$

$$P_a = G(-M) \times S \times 1.1 \times 10^{-2}$$

or

$$G(-M) = 91 \times P_a/S \quad \dots \quad (6.19)$$

No correction has been made for the energy lost by natural decay of the tritium. To calculate the degree of decomposition for a particular time the equation (6.19) can be used in its simple linear form providing the magnitude of the decomposition is small (say 10 per cent), otherwise the exponential form (equation 6.17, page 321) is used.

TABLE 6.4

Self-decomposition of Tritium Compounds Stored in their Normal State [68,73]

Compound	Specific activity mc/mM	Absorbed energy Rads	G(—M)	Age months	Temp. °C	Decomposition %
Acetic anhydride-T	100	2.7×10^7	4	3	20	1
Acetic anhydride-T	102	4.6×10^8	3	51	—40	14
Acetic acid-(methyl-T)	133	1×10^9	0.7	51	0	4
Adenine-2,8-T	82	1.9×10^8	0	36	20	0
Adenine-2,8-T	439	3.2×10^8	0	11	—40	0
Adenine-2,8-T	439	8.4×10^8	0.1	29	—40	1
Adipic acid-T	58,400	9.0×10^9	1.5	2.5	0	86
DL-Alanine-T(G)	1,130	1.4×10^9	0.8	12	0	10
5-Aminouracil-6-T	16	1.3×10^7	6	11	0	1
Δ^4-Androstene-3,17-dione-T(G)	3,400	2.1×10^9	1.2	20	20	24
Δ^4-Androstene-3,17-dione-7α-T	1,158	2.0×10^8	7	5.5	20	34 (ref. 90)
Aniline-T (ring-G)	40	2.0×10^8	0.5	50.5	20	1
DL-Aspartic acid-T(G)	465	5.8×10^8	1.3	18	—40	10
DL-Aspartic acid-T(G)	465	8.5×10^8	1.4	27	—40	15
DL-Aspartic acid-T(G)	465	1.1×10^9	1.5	34	—40	20
Atropine-T(G)	136	4.6×10^7	16	11	—40	20
Atropine-T(G)	246	2.2×10^8	2.3	29	20	15
Atropine-T(G)	246	2.8×10^8	0.7	36	20	6
Benzene-1-T	252	8.1×10^8	0.2	27	—40	1
1,2-Benzanthracene-T(G)	655	2.6×10^8	3.7	10	—40	20
Benzimidazole-T(G)	268	5.4×10^8	1.6	26	—40	10

TABLE 6.4 (*continued*)

Compound	Specific activity mc/mM	Absorbed energy Rads	G(—M)	Age months	Temp. °C	Decomposition %
Benzoic acid-T (*ring*-G)	174	3.2×10^8	3	25	20	12
3,4-Benzpyrene-T(G)	451	5.8×10^8	0·2	36	−40	3
3,4-Benzpyrene-T(G)	660	2.5×10^8	1·2	11	0	8
Benzylpenicillin- (*benzyl*-T(G)	112	2.4×10^7	24	9	−40	20
	189	2.3×10^7	5·7	5	−40	5
Benzylpenicillin-T	128	4.0×10^7	19	13	−196	25
Bromoacetic acid-2-T	130	9.2×10^7	6·8	11	−40	9
Bromobenzene-T	71	1.3×10^8	7·5	31	20	14
Caffeine-T(G)	1,280	5.3×10^8	0·1	9	0	1
Choline chloride- (*methyl*-T)	103	3.7×10^7	115	5·5	0	45*
Choline chloride- (*methyl*-T)	102	1.3×10^8	20	19	0	30
DL-Citrulline-T(G)	14	2.6×10^7	19	36	20	12
Cortisol-1,2-T	4,530	6.8×10^8	1·1	6	0	24 (ref. 79)
Cortisol-1,2-T	4,530	6.8×10^8	1·4	6	−25	29
Cortisone-T(G)	259	3.8×10^7	16	6	−40	20
Cortisone-T(G)	259	9.5×10^7	14	15	−40	40
Corticosterone-1,2-T	2,210	3.5×10^8	2	6	0	24 (ref. 79)
Corticosterone-1,2-T	2,210	3.5×10^8	1·2	6	−25	14
Coumarin-T(G)	1,900	8.2×10^8	2·9	7	0	30
Cyclohexane-1,2-T	248	1.1×10^8	5·5	4	20	5 (in air) (ref. 82)
Cyclohexane-1,2-T	248	1.1×10^8	5	4	20	4·6 (*in vacuo*)
Cytidine-T(G)	159	4.1×10^7	1	7	0	1
Cytosine-T(G)	117	1.8×10^8	0·5	20	20	1
Cytosine-T(G)	117	3.4×10^8	0·2	38	−40	1
n-Decane-1,2-T	210	3.8×10^8	2	28	20	10
α,ε-Diaminopimelic acid	40	5.7×10^7	15	30	20	15
Diethylstilboestrol- T(G)	297	4.2×10^8	0·1	42	0	1
DL-Dihydroxyphenyl- alanine-T(G)	223	6.3×10^7	0·7	7	0	1
DL-Dihydroxyphenyl- alanine-T(G)	223	1.4×10^8	1	15	−40	3
Di-(isopropyl-1,3-T)- phosphorofluoridate	2,560	8.8×10^8	>25	7	0	100
9,10-Dimethylbenz- anthracene-T(G)	14,500	3.3×10^8	0·6	0·75	0	7
9,10-Dimethylbenz- anthracene-T(G)	189	3.2×10^7	0	4·5	−80	0
9,10-Dimethylbenz- anthracene-T(G)	14,500	1.8×10^9	0·2	4	−40	12
	15,100	2.5×10^9	0·8	4·5	−80	40
9,10-Dimethyl-1,2- benzanthracene- T(G)	14,500	1.3×10^9	0·7	2·5	−196	40
	15,100	1.1×10^9	0·5	2	−80	12
	15,100	1.6×10^9	0·45	3	−80	17
DL-Ethionine-T(G)	41	4.2×10^7	72	19	0	40

* Decomposition products included 27 per cent trimethylamine and three unidentified impurities of 8 per cent, 6 per cent and 4 per cent.

TABLE 6.4 (*continued*)

Compound	Specific activity mc/mM	Absorbed energy Rads	G(—M)	Age months	Temp. °C	Decomposition %
DL-Ethionine-T(G)	41	$2 \cdot 5 \times 10^7$	14	11	−40	6
Ethyl iodide-2-T	25	$4 \cdot 9 \times 10^7$	4	34	−40	6
Folic acid-T(G)	154	$1 \cdot 6 \times 10^7$	6	6	0	5
(K salt)	270	$5 \cdot 5 \times 10^7$	0·8	10	−196	2
Folic acid-T(G)	1,720	$3 \cdot 2 \times 10^8$	0·7	9	−40	10
(K salt)						
Folic acid-3′-T	4,450	$2 \cdot 7 \times 10^8$	1·8	3	−40	20
(K salt)						
Folic acid-3′-T	4,450	$5 \cdot 4 \times 10^8$	0·9	6	−40	20
(K salt)						
Folic acid-3′-T	4,450	$1 \cdot 2 \times 10^9$	1·3	13	−40	50
(K salt)						
Folic acid-3′,5′-T	5,420	$7 \cdot 6 \times 10^8$	0·6	7	−40	20
(K salt)						
Folic acid-3′,5′-T	5,420	$1 \cdot 1 \times 10^9$	0·04	10	−196	2
(K salt)						
Folic acid-3′,5′-T	5,420	$5 \cdot 5 \times 10^8$	1·4	5	−40	30
potassium salt	5,420	$5 \cdot 5 \times 10^8$	0·4	5	−196	10
(0·25 mc ampoule)						
Folic acid-3′,5′-T	25,900	$7 \cdot 1 \times 10^7$	> 0·6	4 days	20	2
potassium salt	25,900	$3 \cdot 2 \times 10^9$	0·03	6	−196	4
	400	$5 \cdot 4 \times 10^7$	3	6	−80	6
Folic acid-3′,5′-T	5,420	$2 \cdot 2 \times 10^8$	1	2	−40	10
(potassium salt)	5,420	$5 \cdot 5 \times 10^8$	1·5	5	−40	35
(1 mc ampoule)	5,420	$5 \cdot 5 \times 10^8$	0·9	5	−196	20
D-Glucose-6-T	260	$5 \cdot 2 \times 10^7$	13	4	−40	12
D-Glucose-6-T	324	$1 \cdot 1 \times 10^8$	1·9	7	0	4
D-Glucose-6-T	324	$1 \cdot 8 \times 10^8$	9	11	0	25
D-Glucose-6-T	468	$2 \cdot 6 \times 10^8$	0	11	0	0
D-Glucose-6-T	468	$8 \cdot 4 \times 10^8$	4·5	36	−40	60
D-Glucose-6-T	468	$3 \cdot 5 \times 10^8$	2·5	15	0	15
D-Glucose-6-T	468	$8 \cdot 4 \times 10^8$	0·3	36	−40	36 (on paper)
D-Glucose-6-T	260	$1 \cdot 0 \times 10^8$	9	10	−40	20
D-Glucose-6-T-6-phos-	244	$5 \cdot 8 \times 10^7$	5	5·5	2	6
phate	244	$5 \cdot 8 \times 10^7$	6	5·5	−196	7
Glycerol-2-T	71	$2 \cdot 3 \times 10^8$	< 1·1	33	2	< 2
Glycine-2-T	176	$3 \cdot 5 \times 10^8$	0	17	0	0
Glycine-2-T	1,130	$8 \cdot 1 \times 10^8$	1·1	6	−40	7
Glycine-2-T	1,130	$1 \cdot 6 \times 10^9$	0·8	12	−40	10
Guanine-8-T	750	$1 \cdot 0 \times 10^9$	< 0·3	22	−40	< 4
Guanine-8-T HCl	750	$1 \cdot 4 \times 10^9$	0·07	42	20	2
Guanosine-T(G)	89	$1 \cdot 6 \times 10^7$	4	6	−40	2
Guanosine-T(G)	240	6×10^7	1·9	8	−40	3
n-Hexadecane-1,2-T	207	$3 \cdot 4 \times 10^8$	7	45	20	44
n-Hexadecane-1,2-T	316	$1 \cdot 0 \times 10^8$	5·5	8	20	12
L-Histidine-2,5-T	1,000	$1 \cdot 4 \times 10^8$	0·9	2·5	−196	2
L-Histidine-2,5-T	1,000	$3 \cdot 9 \times 10^8$	1·6	7	−40	10
Histamine-T(G)-	51	$3 \cdot 5 \times 10^7$	3·3	13	−40	2
dihydrochloride						
Hypoxanthine-2,8-T	630	$2 \cdot 0 \times 10^9$	0·8	46	20	2

TABLE 6.4 (*continued*)

Compound	Specific activity mc/mM	Absorbed energy Rads	G(—M)	Age months	Temp. °C	Decomposition %
Hypoxanthine-2,8-T	630	1.3×10^9	0.1	30	−40	1
Isonicotinic hydrazide-T(G)	603	7.1×10^8	0.7	18	−40	7
Isonicotinic hydrazide-T(G)	918	6.0×10^8	1.9	10	−196	15 (on paper)
Isopropanol-1,3-T	990	2.1×10^9	4.2	14	+2	40
5-Iodouracil-6-T	167	1.9×10^7	35	3	0	15
L-Leucine-T(G)	197	1.2×10^8	2	12	0	4
DL-Leucine-T(G)	105	1.3×10^8	4.4	18	20	7
DL-Leucine-T(G)	105	2.6×10^8	0.6	36	20	2
DL-Leucine-4,5-T	10,900	8×10^9	2	12	+2	93
DL-Leucine-4,5-T	10,900	8×10^9	0.05	12	+2	6 (on paper)
DL-Lysine-T(G)	201	7.9×10^7	3	8	0	5
DL-Lysine-4,5-T	32,000	2.4×10^{10}	0.07	12	20	20 (on paper) (ref. 79)
DL-Lysine-4,5-T	32,000	2.4×10^{10}	0.07	12	20	22 (ref. 79)
Methanol-T	50	6.9×10^8	5	48	20	10
DL-Methionine-T(G)	209	7.6×10^7	14	6	0	15
DL-Methionine-T(G)	145	1.4×10^8	0.9	16	−40	2
DL-Methionine-T(G)	145	1.2×10^8	1.2	13	−40	2
L-Methionine-	232	1.1×10^8	21	8	−40	30
(*methyl*-T)	232	3.2×10^8	3.3	23	−80	15 (on paper)
Methotrexate-3′,5′-T	9,170	3.6×10^8	0.4	2	−40	6
Methotrexate-3′,5′-T	9,170	7×10^8	0.1	4	−196	5
Methyl iodide-T	135	3.3×10^8	4.4	39	−40	19
Methyl δ-amino-levulinate-T(G) hydrochloride	672	3.3×10^7	7	1	+2	4
2-Naphthylamine-T(G)	1,660	4.8×10^9	0.3	36	−40	15
Nicotine-T(G)	41	2.9×10^7	20	13	−40	10
Nicotine-T(G)	41	8.3×10^7	4	37	−40	5
Nicotine-T(G)	761	6×10^8	3.7	14	−196	30
Nicotine-T(G)	761	6×10^8	6.3	14	−40	45
Nicotinic acid-T(G)	320	4.0×10^8	0.2	17	−40	1
Nicotinic acid-T(G)	320	3.7×10^8	0.2	16	−40	1
Nicotinic acid-T(G)	320	7.7×10^8	0.2	33	0	2
DL-Noradrenaline-7-T hydrochloride	880	2.8×10^8	4.6	6	−80	20 (on paper)
Oestradiol-T(G)	100	6.1×10^7	0.6	17	20	1
Phenylacetic acid-T(G)	12,104	9.4×10^9	0.9	12	0	70
L-β-Phenylalanine-2,3-T	1,600	5.2×10^8	12	6	−30	64 (ref. 186)
DL-β-Phenylalanine-T(G)	1,800	2.4×10^9	1.3	24	−40	40
	441	3.9×10^8	1.2	16	−40	8

TABLE 6.4 (*continued*)

Compound	Specific activity mc/mM	Absorbed energy Rads	G(—M)	Age months	Temp. °C	Decomposition %
DL-β-Phenylalanine-4-T	5,600	$9 \cdot 2 \times 10^8$	45	3	0	50
Progesterone-6,7-T	754	$1 \cdot 7 \times 10^8$	8	8	20	36 (ref. 90)
Progesterone-7α-T	524	$1 \cdot 2 \times 10^8$	14	8	20	41 (ref. 90)
L-Proline-T(G)	141	$2 \cdot 9 \times 10^8$	$2 \cdot 4$	27	−40	8
L-Proline-T(G)	196	2×10^8	$6 \cdot 8$	$13 \cdot 5$	−40	15
L-Proline-T(G)	224	$9 \cdot 6 \times 10^7$	4	6	−40	5
n-Propanol-2,3-T	136	2×10^7	6	3	20	$2 \cdot 2$ (ref. 82)
Pyridine-T(G)	280	$7 \cdot 6 \times 10^8$	5	28	−40	30
Pyridoxine-T(G) HCl	331	$3 \cdot 6 \times 10^8$	2	26	−40	15
DL-Serine-T(G)	138	$1 \cdot 6 \times 10^8$	$2 \cdot 2$	14	0	4
Serotonin-T(G)	365	$1 \cdot 6 \times 10^7$	$7 \cdot 5$	2	−40	5
Sodium butyrate-2,3-T	374	$5 \cdot 7 \times 10^8$	5	19	20	28
Sodium butyrate-2,3-T	374	9×10^8	7	30	20	50
Sodium pyruvate-T	83	$2 \cdot 6 \times 10^8$	$5 \cdot 7$	$37 \cdot 5$	−40	15
Stearic acid-9,10-T(n)	171	$1 \cdot 9 \times 10^8$	6	36	0	30
Thymidine-T(G)	261	$3 \cdot 5 \times 10^8$	5	39	0	35
Thymidine-T(G)	82	$1 \cdot 1 \times 10^8$	13	36	0	30
Thymidine-T(G)	82	$1 \cdot 1 \times 10^8$	13	36	−40	30
Thymidine-6-T	9,500	$2 \cdot 1 \times 10^9$	$0 \cdot 7$	6	−80	30
Thymidine-6-T	9,500	$2 \cdot 1 \times 10^9$	$0 \cdot 2$	6	20	10
Thymine-T(G)	125	$3 \cdot 3 \times 10^8$	$0 \cdot 2$	36	20	1
Thymine-T(G)	2,520	$9 \cdot 0 \times 10^8$	$0 \cdot 3$	5	−40	4
Thymine-T(G)	3,528	$4 \cdot 5 \times 10^9$	$0 \cdot 4$	18	−40	20
Thymine-T(G)	15,750	$5 \cdot 6 \times 10^9$	$0 \cdot 2$	5	−40	14
Thymine-T(G)	17,000	$6 \cdot 1 \times 10^9$	$0 \cdot 2$	5	−40	14
DL-Threonine-T(G)	32	$6 \cdot 6 \times 10^7$	13	27	0	10
DL-Threonine-T(G)	32	$8 \cdot 7 \times 10^7$	9	38	20	10
DL-Threonine-T(G)	32	$9 \cdot 7 \times 10^7$	13	42	20	15
Tryptamine-T(G) HCl	453	$1 \cdot 45 \times 10^8$	$1 \cdot 4$	7	0	4
Tryptamine-T(G) hydrochloride	453	$4 \cdot 8 \times 10^8$	$0 \cdot 4$	23	2	4
L-Tryptophan-T(G)	1,630	$1 \cdot 4 \times 10^9$	$0 \cdot 5$	20	−40	15
DL-Tyrosine-T(G)	69	$9 \cdot 5 \times 10^7$	$0 \cdot 6$	28	20	1
DL-Tyrosine-T(G)	428	$7 \cdot 8 \times 10^8$	$0 \cdot 2$	36	20	3
L-Tyrosine-T(G)	163	$1 \cdot 9 \times 10^8$	$0 \cdot 2$	23	20	1
L-Tyrosine-T(G)	670	$4 \cdot 3 \times 10^8$	$1 \cdot 3$	13	0	10
L-Tyrosine-T(G)	163	$1 \cdot 9 \times 10^8$	$0 \cdot 6$	23	0	2
L-Tyrosine-T(G)	670	$6 \cdot 6 \times 10^8$	$0 \cdot 7$	19	2	8
Uridine-T(G)	2,440	$7 \cdot 2 \times 10^8$	2	7	0	30
Uridine-T(G)	2,440	$8 \cdot 1 \times 10^8$	$0 \cdot 6$	9	−196	11
Uridine-T(G)	2,440	$8 \cdot 1 \times 10^8$	$0 \cdot 8$	9	−196	15
Uridine-5-T	1,100	$8 \cdot 2 \times 10^7$	3	2	0	6 (on paper)
Vitamin-B$_{12}$-T(G)	2,570	$1 \cdot 3 \times 10^8$	$0 \cdot 06$	7	−40	1
Vitamin-B$_{12}$-T(G)	2,570	$3 \cdot 8 \times 10^8$	$0 \cdot 08$	21	−40	4
Vitamin-B$_{12}$-T(G)	2,570	$4 \cdot 1 \times 10^8$	$0 \cdot 04$	23	0	2

TABLE 6.5

Decomposition of Tritium Compounds on Storage in Solvents

Compound	Specific activity mc/mM	Solvent	Concn. mc/g	Age months	Temp. °C	Energy absorbed Rads	G(—M)	Decomp. %
Adenine-2,8-T	2,360	Water (N/100-	2·8	8	+2	$2·0 \times 10^5$	0·23	4
Adenine-2,8-T	2,900	NH₃)	1	9	+2	$8·1 \times 10^4$	1	22
Adenosine-T(G)	680	Water	10	28	+2	$2·5 \times 10^6$	0·12	2
Adenosine-T(G)	2,880	Water	4·9	4·5	2	$2·0 \times 10^5$	1·3	14
Adenosine-T(G)	2,900	Water	1	6	+2	$5·4 \times 10^4$	0·3	5
Adenosine-T(G)	2,900	Water	10·3	10	+2	$9·3 \times 10^5$	1·3	30
Adrenaline-(ring-GT)	139	Water	2	1	+2	$1·8 \times 10^4$	40	5
DL-Adrenaline-7-T	990	Water	0·94	8	+2	$6·8 \times 10^5$	0·7	5
DL-Alanine-T(G)	1,130	Water	6·6	21	20	$1·2 \times 10^6$	0·05	1
DL-Alanine-T(G)	1,130	Water	6·6	36	20	$2·1 \times 10^6$	0·1	2
D(+)-Aldo-sterone-1,2-T	443	Benzene–EtOH (95:5)	0·11	15	0	$1·5 \times 10^4$	0·5	3
D(+)-Aldo-sterone-1,2-T	443	Benzene–EtOH (95:5)	0·11	14	0	$1·4 \times 10^4$	0·9	5
D(+)-Aldo-sterone-1,2-T	1,970	Benzene–EtOH (95:5)	0·22	15	0	$3·0 \times 10^4$	0·4	10
2-Aminoisobutyric acid-T(G)	1,280	Water	1·25	8	+2	9×10^4	0·1	1
Δ⁴-Androstene-3,17-dione-7α-T	841	Benzene	2·3	12	0	$2·5 \times 10^5$	1·5	13
Δ⁴-Androstene-3,17-dione-7α-T	670	Benzene	2·2	10	20	$2·0 \times 10^5$	0·16	1
L-Arginine-T(G) HCl	247	Water	2	10	+2	$1·8 \times 10^5$	2·6	6
1,2-Benzpyrene-T(G)	242	Benzene	2·3	7·5	20	$1·6 \times 10^5$	1·2	2
3,4-Benzpyrene-T(G)	451	Benzene	11·3	36	20	$3·7 \times 10^6$	0·2	3
3,4-Benzpyrene-T(G)	520	Benzene	7·6	7·5	20	$5·1 \times 10^5$	0·6	2
1-Bromo-2,4-dinitrobenzene-3,5,6-T	95	Benzene	7·1	24	20	$1·5 \times 10^6$	7·8	15
1-Bromo-2,4-dinitrobenzene-3,5,6-T	156	Benzene–EtOH (1:1)	5·7	11	0	$5·6 \times 10^5$	6	10
5-Bromo-2′-deoxyuridine-6-T	552	Water	0·4	4·5	−40	$1·6 \times 10^4$	2·2	5
5-Bromo-2′-deoxyuridine-6-T	588	Water	2·3	14	−40	$3·0 \times 10^5$	3	20
5-Bromo-2′-deoxyuridine-6-T	588	Water	0·4	7	+2	$2·5 \times 10^4$	0·3	1
5-Bromouracil-6-T	655	Water	1·2	5	+2	$5·4 \times 10^4$	1·7	5
5-Bromouracil-6-T	764	Water	11	7	+2	$6·9 \times 10^5$	6	25
5-Bromouracil-6-T	1,300	Water	1	5	+2	$4·5 \times 10^4$	2·7	15
5-Bromouracil-6-T	2,340	Water	1	3	+2	$2·7 \times 10^4$	0·8	5
Caffeine-T(G)	1,280	Water	5	15	−40	$6·8 \times 10^5$	0·6	10
Cholesterol-T(G)	150	Benzene	2·2	40	20	$7·9 \times 10^6$	1·5	8
Cholesterol-T(G)	465	Benzene	2·2	24	20	$4·8 \times 10^6$	1	10
Cholesterol-T(G)	465	Benzene	3·2	1·5	20	$4·3 \times 10^4$	4·7	3
Cholesterol-T(G)	465	Benzene	3·2	7	0	$2·0 \times 10^5$	1·7	5
Cholesterol-T(G)	1,060	Benzene	5·7	5	20	$2·6 \times 10^5$	0·4	2
Cholesterol-7α-T	1,550	Benzene	2·3	18	20	$3·7 \times 10^5$	0·27	7
Cholesterol-7α-T	1,970	Benzene	1·1	17	20	$1·7 \times 10^5$	0·06	2
Cholesterol-7α-T	3,000	Benzene	2·2	6	20	$1·2 \times 10^5$	0·06	1
Cholesteryl pal-mitate-9,10-T	273	Benzene	5·7	11	20	$5·6 \times 10^5$	0·7	2
Cholesteryl-7α-T palmitate	919	Benzene	2	11	20	$2·0 \times 10^5$	0·2	2

TABLE 6.5 (*continued*)

Compound	Specific activity mc/mM	Solvent	Concn. mc/g	Age months	Temp. °C	Energy absorbed Rads	G(—M)	Decomp. %
Choline chloride-(*methyl*-T)	102	Water	3·5	2	+2	$6·3 \times 10^4$	5·4	1
Corticosterone-1,2-T	30,000	Methanol	1·25	8	0	$9·0 \times 10^4$	0·01	2
Cortisol-1,2-T	2,000	Benzene–methanol (1:1)	1·6	4	0	$5·7 \times 10^4$	0·7	5
Cortisol-1,2-T	2,000	Benzene–MeOH (1:1)	1·6	6	−20	$8·6 \times 10^4$	1·1	12
Cortisol-1,2-T	23,000	Benzene–	1·5	6	−20	$8·1 \times 10^4$	0·2	25
Cortisol-1,2-T	38,400	MeOH (1:1)	6·4	32	2	$1·8 \times 10^6$	0·01	12
Cortisol-1,2-T	38,400	Benzene	2	11	20	$2·0 \times 10^5$	0·01	3
Cortisol-1,2-T	38,400	Benzene–MeOH (1:1)	6	19	20	$1·0 \times 10^6$	0·04	23
Cytidine-T	1,500	Water	1	8	+2	$7·2 \times 10^4$	1	11 (ref. 51)
Cytidine-T monophosphate	1,200	Water ethanol (1:1)	1	5	+2	$4·5 \times 10^4$	0·2	1 (ref. 51)
Cytidine-T(G)	2,300	Water*	1	2·5	+2	$2·3 \times 10^4$	0·4	2
Cytidine-T(G)	1,620	Water	0·6	10	2	$5·4 \times 10^4$	0·7	10
Cytidine-T(G)	2,020	Water	1·1	12	+2	$1·2 \times 10^5$	1	20
Cytidine-T(G)	2,020	Water	1·1	4	+2	$4·0 \times 10^4$	0·13	1
Cytidine-T(G)	2,300	Water*	1·2	9	2	$9·7 \times 10^4$	0·1	2
Cytidine-T(G)	2,500	Water	1	8	2	$7·2 \times 10^4$	0·3	5
Cytidine-5-T	1,060	Water	0·5	1	+2	$4·5 \times 10^3$	2	2
Cytidine-5-T	1,060	Water	0·5	5	2	$2·2 \times 10^4$	2	10
Cytidine-5-T	9,400	Water	1	10·5	2	$9·5 \times 10^5$	0·25	20
Cytidine-5-T	15,000	Water	2·2	14	+2	$2·8 \times 10^5$	0·15	25
Cytidine-5-T	15,000	Water	2·2	3	+2	$5·9 \times 10^4$	0·05	2
Cytidine-5-T	14,600	Water*	1·2	5	2	$5·4 \times 10^4$	0·02	1
Dehydroepiandro-sterone-7α-T acetate	1,460	Benzene	2	7	20	$1·3 \times 10^5$	0·04	4
Dehydroepiandro-sterone-7α-T acetate	18,300	Benzene	2·5	6	20	$1·4 \times 10^5$	0·01	1
Dehydroepiandro-sterone-7α-T acetate	1,800	Benzene	7·5	33	20	$2·2 \times 10^6$	1	40
Dehydroepiandro-sterone-7α-T acetate	1,800	Benzene	7·5	19	20	$1·3 \times 10^6$	0·3	10
Dehydroepiandro-sterone-7α-T	3,460	Methanol	1·2	9	0	$9·7 \times 10^4$	0·1	3
Dehydroepiandro-sterone-7α-T	4,960	Benzene	2·3	11	20	$2·3 \times 10^5$	0·7	30
Deoxyadenosine-T(G)	1,100	Water	0·4	20	2	$7·2 \times 10^4$	11	90
2′-Deoxycytidine-5-T	2,800	Water	0·3	11	+2	$3·0 \times 10^4$	0·6	16
Deoxyuridine-5,6-T	1,340	Water	0·7	10	+2	$6·3 \times 10^4$	2	23
2′-Deoxyuridine-T(G)	385	Water	2·5	42	−40	$9·5 \times 10^5$	4	45
1,2,3,4-Dibenz-anthracene-T(G)	151	Benzene	2·5	12	20	$2·7 \times 10^5$	1·2	2
1,2,5,6-Dibenz-anthracene-T(G)	834	Benzene	5·7	8	20	$4·1 \times 10^5$	0·3	2
1,2,5,6-Dibenz-anthracene-T(G)	834	Benzene	5·7	12	20	$3·6 \times 10^6$	0·8	7
Diethylstil-boestrol-T(G)	1,400	Benzene	11	14	20	$1·4 \times 10^6$	0·4	7
L-3(3,4-dihydroxy-phenyl)alanine-ring-2,5,6-T	2,000	Water	1	7	2	$6·3 \times 10^4$	1·7	20
	2,000	Water	1	7	2	$6·3 \times 10^4$	2·2	25
	12,800	Water	1	7	2	$6·3 \times 10^4$	1·5	70
L-Dihydroxy-phenylalanine-2,5,6-T	5,600	Water	2	3	+2	$5·4 \times 10^4$	0·3	4
9,10-Dimethyl-1,2-benzan-thracene-T(G)	14,500	CCl₄	2,500	0·75	20	$1·7 \times 10^7$	160	80

* Containing 1 per cent benzyl alcohol.

TABLE 6.5 (continued)

Compound	Specific activity mc/mM	Solvent	Concn. mc/g	Age months	Temp. °C	Energy absorbed Rads	G(—M)	Decomp. %
9,10-Dimethyl-1,2-benzan-thracene-T(G)	3,250	Benzene	16	14	20	2.0×10^6	0.85	30
	3,250	Benzene	16	14	20	2.0×10^6	1.1	37
9,10-Dimethyl-1,2-benzan-thracene-T(G)	904	Hexane	1.4	2	−40	2.5×10^4	14	20
5-Fluorouracil-6-T	494	Water	3.7	16	−40	4.4×10^5	1.8	12
5-Fluorouracil-6-T	624	Water	0.8	2	+2	1.4×10^5	1.7	2
5-Fluorodeoxy-uridine-6-T	1,000	Water	0.5	11	+2	5.0×10^4	2.4	20
Folic acid-T(G) (potassium salt)	1,720	Water	0.5	9	+2	4.1×10^4	4.9	50
Glucose-6-T	225	Water	1.7	11	+2	1.7×10^5	0.9	2
Glucose-6-T	260	Water	1	4	+2	3.6×10^4	6	6
Glucose-6-T	441	Water	1.7	10	+2	1.5×10^5	1.7	7
Glucose-6-T	1,300	Water	1	9	+2	8.1×10^4	1	11
Glucose-6-T	1,400	Water	1	5	+2	4.5×10^4	1.1	7
Glucose-6-T	1,300	Water	1	15	2	1.4×10^5	0.6	10
Glucose-6-T	1,400	Water	1	11	2	9.9×10^4	0.4	5
D-Glucose-6-T	450	Water	10	12	+2	1.1×10^6	3.3	15
D-Glucose-6-T	450	Water	10	12	+2	1.1×10^6	5.8	25
D-Glucose-6-T	450	Water	10	8	+2	7.2×10^5	5	15
D-Glucose-6-T	468	Water	12.5	7	−40	7.9×10^5	0.3	1
D-Glucose-6-T	468	Water	12.5	15	+2	1.7×10^6	0.6	4
D-Glucose-6-T	1,300	Water	12.5	7	+2	7.9×10^5	2	15
D-Glucose-6-T	1,300	Water	12.5	11	+2	1.2×10^6	2.7	30
Glucose-6-T-6-phosphate	244	Water	1	4.5	+2	4.1×10^4	2.9	25
	244	Water	1	5.5	−196	5.0×10^4	0.3	4
Glycerol-2-T	71	MeOH	7	9	−40	5.7×10^5	1.7	1
Glyceryl-2-T trioleate	104	Benzene	4.5	13	20	5.3×10^5	4	5
Glyceryl tri-(oleate-9,10-T)	354	Benzene	28.4	12	20	3.1×10^6	4.8	17
	341	Benzene	9.6	3.5	20	3.0×10^5	4.6	<5
Glyceryl tri-(stearate-9,10-T)	4,000	Benzene	57	4.5	20	2.3×10^6	0.6	10
Guanosine-8-T	500	Water	0.7	8	2	5.0×10^4	0.5	2
Guanosine-8-T	4,000	Water	0.7	9	2	5.7×10^4	0.3	10
Hexoestrol-T	810	Benzene	1.6	14	20	2.0×10^5	0.1	1
L-Histidine-2,5-T	1,000	Water	1	7	2	6.3×10^4	3.9	20
L-Histidine-2,5-T	2,000	Water	1	6	+2	5.4×10^4	1.5	15
L-Histidine-2,5-T	5,000	Water	2.5	4	+2	9.0×10^4	0.9	15
L-Histidine-2,5-T	6,500	Water	1	3	+2	2.7×10^4	4	50
L-Histidine-2,5-T	6,500	Water*	4	4	+2	1.4×10^5	0.4	10
L-Histidine-2,5-T	7,000	Water	1	2	2	1.8×10^4	1.0	6†
DL-5-Hydroxy-tryptophan-T(G)	220	Water	1	5	+2	4.5×10^4	10	10
DL-5-Hydroxy-tryptophan-T(G)	927	Water	6	3	+2	1.6×10^5	2.4	6
DL-5-Hydroxy-tryptophan-T(G)	927	Water	6	17	−40	9.2×10^5	2.5	30
DL-5-Hydroxy-tryptophan-T(G)	927	Water	6	18	−40	9.7×10^5	3.4	40
DL-5-Hydroxy-tryptophan-T(G)	1,450	Water	3	3	+2	8.1×10^4	2.5	10
DL-5-Hydroxy-tryptophan-T(G)	3,630	Water	1	5	+2	4.5×10^4	2.6	35
5-Iododeoxy-uridine-6-T	744	Water	1	9	+2	8.1×10^4	5.8	30
5-Iodo-2′-deoxy-uridine-6-T	195	Water	0.12	7	+2	7.6×10^3	6.5	8
DL-isoLeucine-T(G)	315	Water	5	18	+2	8.1×10^5	0.4	2
Isonicotinic hydrazide-T(G)	603	Ethanol	25	18	−40	4.1×10^6	0.8	8
DL-Leucine-4,5-T	576	Water	1.1	30	−40	3.0×10^5	1.4	20
DL-Leucine-4,5-T	576	Water	10	35	+2	3.2×10^6	1.2	20
DL-Leucine-4,5-T	5,100	Water	23	11	+2	2.3×10^6	0.7	30

* Containing 1 per cent benzyl alcohol.
† Solution contained 63 per cent labile tritium.

TABLE 6.5 (*continued*)

Compound	Specific activity mc/mM	Solvent	Concn. mc/g	Age months	Temp. °C	Energy absorbed Rads	G(—M)	Decomp. %
DL-Leucine-4,5-T	5,400	Water	4	6	−40	$2 \cdot 2 \times 10^5$	4	70
DL-Leucine-4,5-T	5,400	Water	4	3·5	−40	$1 \cdot 3 \times 10^5$	2	30
DL-Leucine-4,5-T	7,600	Water	1·1	3	2	$3 \cdot 0 \times 10^4$	0·8	15
DL-Leucine-4,5-T	7,860	Water	6	8	+2	$4 \cdot 3 \times 10^5$	0·6	30
DL-Leucine-4,5-T	10,000	Water	1	5·5	2	$5 \cdot 0 \times 10^4$	0·4	15
DL-Leucine-4,5-T	10,900	0·01N–HCl–	1	12	+2	$1 \cdot 1 \times 10^5$	0·02	2
DL-Leucine-4,5-T*	10,900	EtOH (20:80)	1	12	+2	$1 \cdot 1 \times 10^5$	0·02	2
DL-Leucine-4,5-T	10,900	Water	6·4	12	+2	7×10^5	0·1	10
DL-Leucine-4,5-T*	10,900	Water	6·4	12	+2	7×10^5	0·1	10
L-Leucine-4,5-T	7,600	Water	4·8	13·5	−196	$5 \cdot 8 \times 10^6$	0·3	25
L-Leucine-4,5-T	7,600	Water	4·8	5·5	−196	$2 \cdot 4 \times 10^5$	0·3	10
DL-Lysine-T(G)	476	Water	1	6·5	+2	$5 \cdot 9 \times 10^4$	4	10
L-Lysine-T(G)	91	Water	7	7	+2	$4 \cdot 4 \times 10^5$	61	30
HCl	210	Water	1	6·5	+2	$5 \cdot 9 \times 10^4$	1·6	2
L-Methionine-T(G)	160	Water	1	12	+2	$1 \cdot 1 \times 10^5$	13	20
DL-Methionine-T(G)	209	Water	8·3	23	−40	$1 \cdot 7 \times 10^6$	1·4	6
L-Methionine-(*methyl*-T)	232	Water	1	8	+2	$7 \cdot 2 \times 10^4$	6	10
20-Methylchol-anthrene-T(G)	346	Benzene	2·3	26	20	$5 \cdot 4 \times 10^5$	0·8	7
20-Methylchol-anthrene-T(G)	346	Benzene	2·3	12	20	$2 \cdot 5 \times 10^5$	1·3	5
20-Methylchol-anthrene (TG)	3,150	Benzene	1·1	11	20	$1 \cdot 1 \times 10^5$	0·16	5
5-Methyl-cytosine-T(G)	15,300	Water (0·1% Na formate)	1·1	7	+2	$6 \cdot 9 \times 10^4$	0·04	4
DL-Mevalonic acid-2-T lactone	85	Benzene	2·3	7	0	$1 \cdot 5 \times 10^5$	3·7	2
DL-Mevalonic acid-2-T lactone	85	Benzene	2·3	19	0	$3 \cdot 9 \times 10^5$	0·7	1
Nicotinic acid-T(G)	320	EtOH/H₂O (75:25)	9	16	−40	$1 \cdot 3 \times 10^6$	0·2	1
Nicotinic acid-T(G)	320	Ethanol–Water (1:3)	10	33	2	$3 \cdot 0 \times 10^6$	0·2	2
DL-norAdren-aline-7-T	1,250	Water	1	3	+2	$2 \cdot 7 \times 10^4$	3	10
DL-norAdren-aline-7-T	1,400	Water	2	1·5	2	$2 \cdot 7 \times 10^4$	1	2
DL-Noradren-aline-7-T hydrochloride	1,400	Water	0·5	6	+2	$2 \cdot 7 \times 10^4$	7	43
Oestradiol-6,7-T	300	Ethanol	2·5	3	−20	$6 \cdot 8 \times 10^4$	4	3
Oestradiol-6,7-T	653	Benzene–EtOH (1:1)	1·5	12	20	$1 \cdot 6 \times 10^5$	0·3	2
Oestradiol-6,7-T 17-acetate	2,300	Ethanol	0·9	7	20	$5 \cdot 6 \times 10^4$	0·7	1
Oestradiol-6,7-T 17β-acetate	3,200	Benzene–EtOH (1:1)	5·3	20	−40	$9 \cdot 5 \times 10^5$	0·1	6
Oestradiol-6,7-T 17β-acetate	3,200	Benzene	1·1	36	20	$3 \cdot 6 \times 10^5$	0·4	35
Oestradiol-6,7-T	14,800	Ethanol	0·7	2	−30	$1 \cdot 3 \times 10^4$	0·04	1
Oestradiol-6,7-T	17,000	Benzene–EtOH (1:1)	1·5	5	−20	$6 \cdot 6 \times 10^4$	0·1	11
Oestrone-T(G)	188	Benzene	2·3	53	20	$1 \cdot 1 \times 10^6$	0·5	5
Oestrone-6,7-T	1,200	Benzene	2·2	22	20	$4 \cdot 4 \times 10^5$	0·13	3
Oestrone-6,7-T	1,200	Benzene	2·2	22	20	$4 \cdot 4 \times 10^5$	0·13	3
Oestrone-6,7-T	18,600	Benzene	1·1	6	20	$5 \cdot 9 \times 10^4$	0·1	9
Oleic acid-9,10-T	730	Benzene	2·8	9	20	$2 \cdot 3 \times 10^5$	1·4	8
Oleic acid-9,10-T	930	Benzene	18	18	−40	$4 \cdot 5 \times 10^6$	4·5	50
Oleic acid-9,10-T	930	Benzene	28	10	−40	$2 \cdot 5 \times 10^6$	4·2	30
Oleic acid-9,10-T	930	Benzene	28	18	−40	$4 \cdot 5 \times 10^6$	4·5	50
Oleic acid-9,10-T	2,480	Benzene	2·8	5	20	$1 \cdot 3 \times 10^5$	0·4	4
Orotic acid-5-T†	4,400	Water	3·8	21	+2	$7 \cdot 2 \times 10^6$	0·2	15
Orotic acid-5-T	4,600	Water	1	3	+2	$2 \cdot 7 \times 10^4$	0·4	5

* Containing 1 per cent benzyl alcohol.
† Solution contained 64 per cent labile tritium and only 14 per cent of the original orotic acid-5-T was left in the solution.

TABLE 6.5 (*continued*)

Compound	Specific activity mc/mM	Solvent	Concn. mc/g	Age months	Temp. °C	Energy absorbed Rads	G(—M)	Decomp. %
Palmitic acid-9,10-T	256	Benzene	5·6	8	0	$4·0 \times 10^6$	8·6	15
Palmitic acid-9,10-T	389	Benzene	31	11	20	$3·1 \times 10^6$	8	25
L-3-Phenyl-alanine-T(G)	825	Water	1	6	−40	$5·4 \times 10^4$	0·4	2
L-3-Phenyl-alanine-T(G)	825	Water	1	10	2	$9·0 \times 10^4$	1·1	8
L-3-Phenyl-alanine-T(G)	825	Water	1	6·5	−40	$5·9 \times 10^4$	1·2	6
L-3-Phenyl-alanine-*ring*-4-T	2,000	Water	1	7	2	$6·3 \times 10^4$	1·3	15
	2,000	Water	1	4	2	$3·6 \times 10^4$	0·7	5
	7,950	Water	1	4	2	$3·6 \times 10^4$	0·6	15
L-β-Phenylalanine-2,3-T	1,600	Water	1	8	−30	$7·2 \times 10^4$	1·6	17 (ref. 186)
DL-β-Phenyl-alanine-T(G)	441	Water	5	16	−40	$7·2 \times 10^5$	1·2	8
DL-β-Phenyl-alanine-T(G)	1,800	Water	10	24	−40	$2·2 \times 10^6$	0·25	10
DL-β-Phenyl-alanine-4-T	5,600	Water	3·9	3	+2	$1·1 \times 10^5$	0·7	10
Prednisolone-T(G)	650	Benzene	1·1	6	20	$5·9 \times 10^4$	1·4	5
Prednisolone-T(G)	650	Methanol	1·2	6	−40	$6·5 \times 10^4$	2	7
Prednisolone-T(G)	810	Methanol	1·2	12	−40	$1·3 \times 10^5$	1·1	10
Prednisolone-T(G)	810	Benzene	1·1	12	20	$1·2 \times 10^5$	2	17
Pregnenolone-7α-T	1,030	Benzene	2·3	12	20	$2·5 \times 10^5$	0·2	2
Pregnenolone-7α-T	1,030	Benzene	1·1	18	20	$1·8 \times 10^5$	0·2	3
Pregnenolone-7α-T	1,100	Benzene	7·5	10	20	$7·1 \times 10^5$	0·3	3
Progesterone-7α-T	1,160	Benzene	2·3	18	20	$3·7 \times 10^5$	0·2	4
Progesterone-7α-T	1,160	Benzene	3·4	13	20	$4·0 \times 10^5$	0·7	10
L-Proline-T(G)	224	Water	5	6	+2	$2·7 \times 10^5$	4	5
L-Proline-T(G)	403	Water	1	5	2	$4·5 \times 10^4$	3·8	7
Pyridoxine-T(G)	163	Water	4	8	+2	$2·9 \times 10^5$	2·5	3
Pyridoxine-T(G)	163	Water	4	24	+2	$8·6 \times 10^5$	3	10
Serotonin-T(G)	365	Water	1	2·5	+2	$2·3 \times 10^4$	6	5
Serotonin-T(G)	7,700	Water	1	2·5	+2	$2·3 \times 10^4$	2	30
Sodium propion-ate-2,3-T	538	Water	50	14	+2	$6·3 \times 10^6$	23	80
Stearic acid-9,10-T	457	Benzene	27	11	20	$2·7 \times 10^6$	8	30
Stearic acid-9,10-T	662	Benzene	2·8	6	20	$1·5 \times 10^6$	0·8	<3
	1,200	Benzene	11·4	11	20	$1·1 \times 10^6$	0·1	<2
Testosterone-7α-T	850	Benzene	2·5	20	20	$4·5 \times 10^5$	0·3	5
Testosterone-1,2-T	17,900	Benzene	2	7	20	$1·3 \times 10^5$	0·02	3
Tetrasodium 2-methyl-1,4-napthaquinol-6-T diphosphate	27,000	Water	390	10	+2	$3·5 \times 10^7$	0·6	75
Tetrasodium 2-methyl-1,4-naphthaquinol-5,6,7-T diphosphate	87,000	Water	560	6	+2	$3·0 \times 10^7$	0·6	95
	65,000	Water	344	0·5	−80	$1·6 \times 10^6$	2	45
Tetrasodium 2-methyl-1,4-naphthaquinol-6,7-T diphosphate	54,000	Water	300	1	−40	$2·7 \times 10^6$	1·5	50
Theophylline-T(G)	398	Water	3·3	11	+2	$3·3 \times 10^5$	0·9	3
Thymidine-(*methyl*-T)	1,900	Water	1	4	+5	$3·6 \times 10^4$	0·4	3 (ref. 51)
Thymidine-(*methyl*-T)	3,000	Water	1	3	+5	$2·7 \times 10^4$	0·5	4 (ref. 51)

(TABLE 6.5 (*continued*))

Compound	Specific activity mc/mM	Solvent	Concn. mc/g	Age months	Temp. °C	Energy absorbed Rads	G(—M)	Decomp. %
Thymidine-(*methyl*-T)	4,000	Water	1	7	+2	$6\cdot3\times10^4$	0·08	2
Thymidine-(*methyl*-T)	4,200	Water	1	5	−40	$4\cdot5\times10^4$	0·2	4
Thymidine-(*methyl*-T)	4,200	Water	0·4	22	+2	$7\cdot9\times10^5$	0·6	40
Thymidine-(*methyl*-T)	6,000	Water	1	1	+5	9×10^3	0·4	2 (ref. 51)
Thymidine-(*methyl*-T)	6,000	Water	1	4	+5	$3\cdot6\times10^4$	0·8	15 (ref. 51)
Thymidine-(*methyl*-T)	8,000	Water	1	7	+2	$6\cdot3\times10^4$	0·6	25
Thymidine-(*methyl*-T)	13,760	Water	6·3	2·5	+2	$1\cdot4\times10^5$	1·1	30
Thymidine-(*methyl*-T)	18,750	Water	1	4	+2	$3\cdot6\times10^4$	0·4	25
Thymidine-6-T	3,000	Water	1	6	+2	$5\cdot4\times10^4$	1·5	22
Thymidine-6-T	3,000	Water*	1	6	+2	$5\cdot4\times10^4$	0·85	13
Thymidine-6-T	3,000	Water*	1	2	+2	$1\cdot8\times10^4$	0·7	4
Thymidine-6-T	4,000	Water	2	7	+2	$1\cdot3\times10^5$	0·2	5
Thymidine-6-T	5,000	Water	1	6	+2	$5\cdot4\times10^4$	1·6	35
Thymidine-6-T	11,600	Water	3·6	3·5	+2	$1\cdot1\times10^5$	1·4	40
Thymidine-6-T	13,500	Water	1	31	+2	$3\cdot7\times10^6$	0·3	65
Thymine-(*methyl*-T)	4,200	Water	5	4	+2	$1\cdot8\times10^5$	1·3	18
Thymine-T(G)	2,600	Water	8·2	11	−40	$8\cdot1\times10^5$	0·9	20
Thymine-T(G)	3,730	Water	1·5	9	+2	$1\cdot2\times10^5$	0·6	18
Thymine-T(G)	12,600	Water	1	6·5	+2	$5\cdot9\times10^4$	0·3	20
Thymine-T(G)	12,700	Water	1	5	+2	$4\cdot5\times10^4$	0·7	35
Tryptamine-T(G) hydrochloride	453	Water	1	23	2	$2\cdot1\times10^5$	2·4	20
DL-Tryptophan-T(G)	1,460	Water	1·8	8	2	$1\cdot3\times10^5$	0·9	10
DL-Tryptophan-T(G)	1,460	Water	1·8	8	−20	$1\cdot3\times10^5$	0·5	5
DL-Tryptophan-T(G)	1,460	Water	1·8	8	−40	$1\cdot3\times10^5$	0·5	5
L-Tryptophan-T(G)	1,630	Water	7·7	20	−40	$1\cdot4\times10^6$	1·2	30
L-Tryptophan-T(G)	4,700	Water	1	9	+2	$8\cdot1\times10^4$	0·7	25
L-Tyrosine-3,5-T	1,220	Water	2·4	4·5	+2	$9\cdot7\times10^4$	1·4	7
L-Tyrosine-3,5-T	2,000	Water	1	7	+2	$6\cdot3\times10^4$	0·5	6
L-Tyrosine-3,5-T	30,000	Water	1	7	+2	$6\cdot3\times10^4$	0·01	2
L-Tyrosine-3,5-T	30,000	Water	2·4	2	+2	$4\cdot3\times10^4$	0·02	1
L-Tyrosine-3,5-T	32,600	Water	1	3·5	+2	$3\cdot2\times10^4$	0·1	10
L-Tyrosine-3,5-T	39,600	Water	4·3	5	+2	$1\cdot9\times10^5$	0·2	30
L-Tyrosine-3,5-T	48,000	Water	1	3	2	$2\cdot7\times10^4$	0·2	25
Uracil-5,6-T	560	Water	1	2	+2	$1\cdot8\times10^4$	4	4
Uracil-5,6-T	870	Water	3	13	−40	$3\cdot5\times10^5$	0·5	5
Uracil-5,6-T	870	Water	3	21	+2	$5\cdot7\times10^5$	0·4	6
Uracil-5,6-T	4,700	Water	1	7	2	$6\cdot3\times10^4$	1·2	30
Uracil-5,6-T	4,800	Water	1	7	+2	$6\cdot3\times10^4$	0·26	8
Uridine-T(G)	500	Water	2	6	+2	$1\cdot1\times10^5$	3·3	9
Uridine-T(G)	500	Water	2	10	+2	$1\cdot8\times10^5$	6·7	27
Uridine-T(G)	500	Water	2	31	+2	$5\cdot6\times10^5$	0·8	
Uridine-T(G)	1,080	Water	31	2	+2	$5\cdot6\times10^5$	1·0	2
Uridine-T(G)	1,080	Water	31	5	+2	$1\cdot4\times10^6$	2	9
Uridine-T(G)	1,080	Water	31	10	−40	$2\cdot8\times10^6$	3·2	27
Uridine-T(G)	1,440	Water	1	4·5	2	$4\cdot1\times10^4$	2·2	12
Uridine-T(G)	1,570	Water	4	6	+2	$2\cdot2\times10^5$	2·6	20
Uridine-T(G)	1,570	Water	4	9	+2	$3\cdot2\times10^5$	2·2	25
Uridine-T(G)	1,570	Water	4	2	−40	$7\cdot2\times10^4$	1·7	5
Uridine-T(G)	3,000	Water	20	12	+2	$2\cdot2\times10^6$	0·6	17
Uridine-T(G)	3,000	Water	20	2	−40	$3\cdot6\times10^5$	3	15
Uridine-T(G)	3,000	Water	20	10	−40	$1\cdot8\times10^6$	1	25
Uridine-5-T	2,900	Water	1	6	+2	$5\cdot4\times10^4$	1·2	17
Uridine-5-T	5,000	Water	1	8·5	+2	$7\cdot7\times10^4$	0·9	25
Uridine-5-T	11,100	Water	6·1	9	+2	$4\cdot9\times10^5$	0·3	25
Uridine-5-T	13,000	Water	1	10	+2	$9\cdot0\times10^4$	0.14	15
Uridine-5-T	13,000	Water	3·6	4	+2	$1\cdot3\times10^5$	0·6	25
Uridine-5-T	13,000	Water	5	0·75	+2	$3\cdot4\times10^4$	0·8	7
Uridine-5-T	21,500	Water	1	4	+2	$3\cdot6\times10^4$	0·3	20
Uridine-5-T	24,400	Water	1	2·5	+2	$5\cdot4\times10^4$	0·5	25
Uridine-5-T	24,400	Water	1	2·5	+2	$5\cdot4\times10^4$	0·6	28
DL-Valine-T(G)	480	Water	12·5	28	−40	$3\cdot2\times10^6$	1	12

* Containing 1 per cent benzyl alcohol.
In Table 6.5, compounds stored in benzene were sealed under nitrogen or *in vacuo*.

TABLE 6.6

Decomposition of Tritium Compounds in Aqueous Solution at $-196°$ C

Compound	Specific activity mc/mM	Concn. mc/g	Age months	Energy absorbed Rads	G(—M)	De-comp. %
Benzyl-T(G) penicillin	128	2	6	1.1×10^5	9	6
Isonicotinic hydra-zide-T(G)	918	20	10	1.8×10^6	0.6	5
DL-Leucine-4,5-T	786	4	8.5	3.1×10^5	0.3	2
L-Leucine-4,5-T	7,100	1	6	5.4×10^4	0.1	5
L-Leucine-4,5-T	7,100	1	6.5	5.9×10^4	0.1	5
Tetrasodium	27,000	2	6	1.1×10^5	0.07	10
2-methyl-1,4-	27,000	240	6	1.3×10^7	0.07	10
naphthaquinol-6-T	27,000	2	6	1.1×10^5	0.03	5
diphosphate*	27,000	266	6	1.4×10^7	0.09	12
Tetrasodium	59,000	655	2.75	1.6×10^7	0.07	10
2-methyl-1,4-	55,000	360	3	9.7×10^6	0.06	9
naphthaquinol-6,7-T diphosphate*	20,000	247	3.5	7.8×10^6	0.14	9
Thymidine-(methyl-T)	4,200	1.3	7	8.2×10^4	0.07	2
Uridine-5-T	13,000	5	6	2.7×10^5	0.07	5
Uridine-T(G)	2,440	2	9	1.6×10^5	0.15	3
Uridine-T(G)†	2,440	2	9	1.6×10^5	0.25	5
Uridine-T(G)	2,440	6.9	9	5.6×10^5	0.4	8
Uridine-T(G)†	2,440	6.9	9	5.6×10^5	0.25	5

* Containing 1 per cent NaCl.
† Containing 1 per cent benzyl alcohol.

TABLE 6.7

Effect of Benzyl Alcohol on the Decomposition of Tritiated Uridine in Aqueous Solution at $+2°$

Compound	Specific activity mc/mM	Concn. mc/g	Age months	Energy absorbed Rads	G(—M)	De-comp. %
Uridine-T(G)	1,100	1.5	5	6.8×10^4	0.8	4
Uridine-T(G)*	1,100	1.5	5	6.8×10^4	0.6	3
Uridine-T(G)	2,440	2	8	1.4×10^5	2.7	35
Uridine-T(G)*	2,440	2	8	1.4×10^5	0.3	5
Uridine-T(G)*	2,440	6.9	9	5.6×10^5	0.5	10
Uridine-5-T*	11,100	6.1	2	1.1×10^5	0.3	6
Uridine-5-T	11,100	6.1	9	4.9×10^5	0.3	25

* Containing 1 per cent benzyl alcohol.

At 20° C

Uridine-T(G)	2,440	2	13	2.3×10^5	1.2	30
Uridine-T(G)*	2,440	2	13	2.3×10^5	0.3	8
Uridine-T(G)	2,440	6.9	13	8.1×10^5	1.5	35
Uridine-T(G)*	2,440	6.9	13	8.1×10^5	0.6	17

* Containing 1 per cent benzyl alcohol.

One of the first compounds to be examined in detail was tritiated water, which even at low isotopic abundance (2–19 per cent) decomposes into the elements hydrogen tritide and oxygen[91,92]. The decomposition continues when the water is frozen, even at liquid nitrogen temperature ($-196°$ C). In sealed tubes the decomposition reaches an equilibrium as a result of the back reaction. This occurs when the pressure of the gaseous products reaches values which vary from 20 to 600 cm of mercury, and depend largely on the catalytic action of any impurities (particularly metallic impurities) which may be present in the tubes (6.20):

$$2\,THO \rightleftharpoons 2\,TH + O_2 \quad . \quad . \quad . \quad . \quad (6.20)$$

Hydrogen peroxide is formed in the reaction which was first detected by measuring the oxygen content of the gaseous products. These showed a deficiency in the oxygen content expected from the reaction (6.20); there is also spectroscopic evidence for peroxide formation[93] and reported to be about 10^{-3} moles/l. in 98 per cent tritium oxide[93]. Pure tritiated water, 1 g containing about 2,700 c, irradiates itself at the rate of 10^9 rads/day. The measurements of hydrogen peroxide concentration have established the existence of a stationary state of H_2O_2 formation and decomposition in the self-radiolysis of tritiated water[94].

There are many published papers concerning the radiolysis of water by various forms of radiation, including a recent review by Brustad[95]. The effect of the tritium β-particles upon water is intermediate in character possessing certain features both of penetrating rays from cobalt-60 and of heavy-particle radiation from (say) polonium α-particles. One important difference is that the steady-state concentration of hydrogen peroxide is much larger in the case of tritium radiolysis than in γ-radiolysis[94]. Storage of aqueous solutions of tritium compounds are therefore expected to give decomposition products by oxidation; hydroxylation or peroxidation of carbon–carbon double bonds are other reactions which can be expected.

Observations with tritiated thymidine—Because of the importance of tritiated thymidine as a DNA label in cytological investigations, its decomposition by self-irradiation has been studied by a number of workers[51,78,80,96].

A major proportion of the decomposition fragments of thymidine-(*methyl*-T) or thymidine-6-T are *cis*- and *trans*-thymidine glycols (6.21) or peroxides (6.22) together with smaller amounts of *cis*- and *trans*-thymine glycols[96].

343

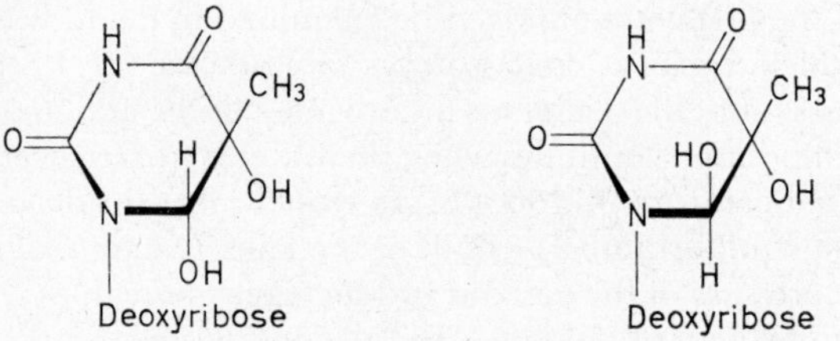

$$\dots \quad (6.21)$$

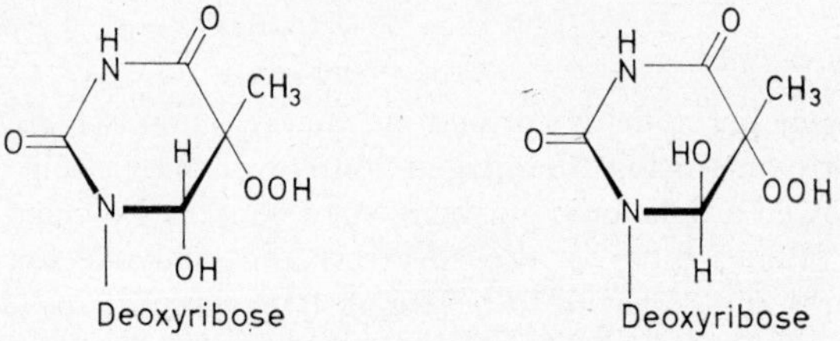

$$\dots \quad (6.22)$$

In this respect the decomposition of tritiated thymidine by self-irradiation resembles the effects of x-rays or γ-rays on aqueous solutions of inactive thymidine. The formation of dimers[97], similar to those formed on irradiation of frozen aqueous solutions of thymine with ultra-violet light (6.23), has not been reported in self-irradiation decomposition.

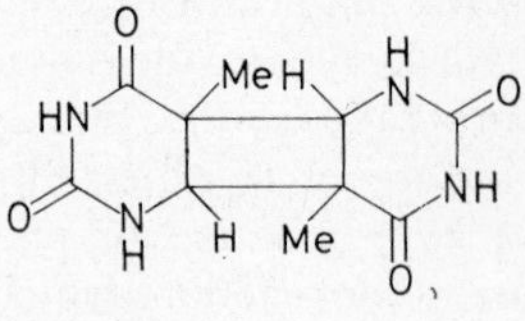

$$\dots \quad (6.23)$$

When generally labelled thymidine is stored in aqueous solution at $+4°$ C for a number of months, the observed decomposition products are mainly thymine-T and 2-deoxy-D-ribose-T[78, 98]. These products probably arise by radiolytic fission of the N-glycoside bond (bond energy 73 kcal/mole) through constant irradiation of the C–N bond.

By comparison, relatively little thymine-T is produced when thymidine-6-T or thymidine-*methyl*-T is stored in aqueous solution under the same conditions. In these cases there are marked secondary effects involving the carbon–carbon double bond in the 5,6-position, as mentioned (*vide supra*). One therefore has to recognize that the composition (chemical structure and concentrations) of the decomposition products is likely to depend, not only on the solvent in which the compound is stored, but also on the position of the tritium atoms in the molecule.

Decomposition of thymidine-T in aqueous solution is greater at $-20°$ C[80] or $-40°$ C[78] than at $0°$ C or $-75°$ C. The reason for this peculiar effect is now known. Apelgot, Ekert and colleagues[181,182] studied this phenomenon in detail and they discovered that slowly frozen solutions of tritiated thymidine were not homogeneous. The thymidine-T concentrated in 'pockets' and the consequent increased localized radiation dose to the compound resulted in an increase in the rate of decomposition. This effect may not be confined only to solutions of thymidine[185] and, in general, aqueous solutions of tritiated compounds should not be kept frozen except of course when these are stored at $-196°$ C.

Following the investigations of Henriksen (*vide supra*) it is also possible that the life of the free radicals is prolonged at low temperatures and that between $-20°$ and $-40°$ C radical thymidine-T interaction is more favourable than radical recombination. As the temperature is lowered from $-40°$ C down to $-196°$ C the thermal activation energy is insufficient for radical–thymidine interaction.

Although not identified, the decomposition products of similar tritiated nucleosides such as uridine, deoxyuridine, 5-halogenated uridines and deoxyuridines are likely to include hydroxylated compounds.

It is perhaps of interest to note by comparison the stability of thymidine-2-C14 (specific activity $18 \cdot 3$ mc/mM) even stored as a freeze-dried solid at $-40°$ C. Less than 2 per cent decomposition was detected after 5 years' storage[183]. The stability of thymidine and rather surprisingly other deoxynucleosides, bromo- and iodo-deoxyuridine, to x-irradiation (10^8 rads) has been noted by Tanovka[184] and confirms previous results[78] concerning the irradiation of freeze-dried thymidine by γ-rays. Tanovka[184] also found that in solution the pyrimidine ring structures of thymidine, bromo- and iodo-deoxyuridine are equally sensitive to radical attack and the rate of decomposition increased as the x-ray dose to the solutions was increased.

Uracil-6-T has been identified as one of the principal products from the decomposition of 5-bromo-uracil-6-T by self-irradiation when stored in aqueous solution at $+2^\circ$ C[73]. However, 5-fluoro-uracil-6-T stored under the same conditions did not apparently give uracil-6-T as a principal decomposition product, which does suggest that the decomposition of the 5-halogenated uracil-6-T derivatives may be a function of the carbon–halogen bond energy in which case the order of dehalogenation be self-irradiation will be $F < Cl < Br < I$. The liberation of iodine from 5-iodo-uracil-6-T was clearly visible on storing this compound as a solid at $+2^\circ$ C and uracil-6-T was again identified as the principal decomposition product[73].

Observed effects of solvent variation on the storage of tritiated steroids— Osinski and Deconinck[79] found that at low temperatures there are only small differences in the rate of decomposition of cortisol-1,2-T and corticosterone-1,2-T when stored in dioxan, benzene, methanol or water. Temperature plays a very important role and quite different results were obtained when the storage temperature was raised above 0° C as seen from Table 6.8[79].

TABLE 6.8

Steroid	Cortisol-1,2-T			Corticosterone-1,2-T		
Specific activity	4·53 c/mM			2·21 c/mM		
Activity concentration	0·1 mc/ml			0·1 mc/ml		
Temperature of storage	37° C	0° C	−25° C	37° C	0° C	−25° C
Solvent: Dioxan	100% (8)	20% (0·5)	6% (0·1)	96% (13)	28% (1·3)	8% (0·3)
Benzene	92% (5)	44% (1·2)	40% (1·0)	70% (5)	22% (1·0)	1% (0·04)
Methanol	100% (8)	26% (0·6)	4% (0·08)	100% (17)	40% (2·1)	24% (1·1)
Water	100% (8)	30% (0·7)	12% (0·3)	100% (17)	6% (0·25)	18% (0·8)

The percentage decomposition per annum is given in the table and the $G(-M)$ values in parentheses (calculated from equation (6.19) on page 331 with exponential correction for decomposition > 10 per cent).

Particularly striking is the relatively poor observed protection afforded by benzene, even at the lower temperatures. Similarly the observed rate of decomposition of the corticosterone-1,2-T in methanol is quite rapid. These results contrast with those shown in Table 6.5[73] where the rate of decomposition of corticosterone-1,2-T at 30 c/mM in methanol at 1·25 mc/g at 0° C is only 4 per cent per annum. Similarly cortisol-1,2-T stored in methanol–benzene at 6 mc/g at 20° C also showed less than 10 per cent decomposition per annum. The differences observed between the results of workers in this field of study are not readily explained, although there are many possible explanations; for example, sublimation of the solvent at low temperatures (page 329) or crystallization, trace impurities in the product which may catalyse chemical decomposition, purity of the solvent and other similar considerations.

Although decomposition products have not been identified, chromatographic analysis showed that quite different products were formed in the four solvents investigated by Osinski and Deconinck[79].

Observations with tritiated amino acids—A number of tritiated amino acids at very high specific activity have been examined by Hempel[81] and the results are shown in Table 6.9:

TABLE 6.9

Storage of Tritiated Amino Acids in Solution at Specific Activities above 12 c/mM

Storage conditions			Rate of decomposition % per annum			
Solvent	Tritium concn.	Temp.	Phenyl-alanine	Lysine	DOPA*	α-Aminoadipic acid
80% ethanol ⎱ 20% water ⎰	3 mc/ml	−15° +20°	3 5	6 6	100 100	15 100
80% ethanol ⎱ 20% water ⎬ 0·1N-HCl ⎰	3 mc/ml	−15° +20°	2 30	7 45	70 100	50 100
80% ethanol ⎱ 20% water ⎬ 0·1N-NaOH ⎰	3 mc/ml	−15° +20°	3 5	4 14	— —	26 50
Physiological saline	6 mc/ml	−15°	3	30	100	30

* 3,4-Dihydroxyphenylalanine.

Storage of DL-lysine-4,5-T in the dry state even on paper results in a decomposition rate of about 20 per cent per annum[81]. The beneficial effects of dispersal in a suitable solvent will be apparent; storage in aqueous ethanol produces only about 5 per cent decomposition per annum. The main products of decomposition on storage of four amino acids are summarized in Table 6.10[81].

The storage of tritiated L-amino acids in solution at $+2°$ C may result in racemization. This has been observed[73] with solutions of tritiated L-methionine-T(G), L-phenylalanine-(ring-4-T), and L-leucine-4,5-T. It is not yet known whether this is due to radiation or arises by chemical effects.

Decomposition of inorganic tritiated compounds—Apart from tritiated water, the decomposition of which has already been discussed (page 343), few inorganic compounds have been tritiated at high specific activity. One compound however is tritium cyanide (TCN) which at maximum isotopic abundance polymerizes almost completely

TABLE 6.10

Radioactive Impurities on Storing Tritiated Amino Acids at High Specific Activity in Solution [81]

Amino acid	Labelled impurity
Phenylalanine	Phenylalanine ethyl ester (2,3)
	2 acids (4)
	1 neutral compound (1)
Lysine	Lysine ethyl ester (2, 3, 4)
	1 acid (4)
	3 bases (1)
	2 neutral substances (1, 2, 4)
α-Aminoadipic acid	Piperidine carboxylic acid (1, 2, 3, 4)
	3 ethyl esters of α-Aminoadipic acid (2, 3)
	1 acid (1, 4)
Leucine	Leucine ethyl ester (3)

1. Physiological saline. 2. 80 per cent aqueous ethanol. 3. 80 per cent aqueous ethanol:0·1N-HCl. 4. 80 per cent aqueous ethanol:0·1N-NaOH.

(>80 per cent) within 12 h of preparation[178]. Another is tritiated ammonia, NT_3, which is reported to decompose at the rate of a few per cent per day into nitrogen and tritium[179].

Miscellaneous observations—Hempel[81] observed that the addition of vitamin-C to a solution of tritiated dihydroxyphenylalanine actually increased the rate of decomposition by self-irradiation.

Pichat[180] reported that stearic acid-9,10-T at 35 c/mM stored as a solid at room temperature polymerizes in less than 1 month producing a dark brown material which is insoluble in most organic solvents. This result is perhaps not very surprising when one considers that the compound is irradiating itself at about $3·7 \times 10^7$ rads/day.

In the analysis of the tritiated compounds listed in Tables 6.4 to 6.7, readily volatile decomposition products would not normally be detected because the methods used were paper or thin-layer chromatography[68, 73]. This may account (in part) for some of the rather erratic results recorded. Although the tritiated compounds should not exchange their tritium atoms with the hydrogen atoms of the solvent in which they may be dissolved, there is the possibility of tritium atoms in the excited decomposition fragments exchanging with the solvent hydrogen atoms. Less than 5 per cent of such 'labile' tritium was detected on storage of tritiated thymidine in solution over a period of one year[78]; about 10 per cent has been found with uridine-T stored in aqueous solution[73], about 60 per cent with solutions of L-histidine-2,5-T, and as much as 64 per cent in some samples of orotic acid-5-T (see page 339) but note that this is accompanied by almost complete breakdown of the orotic acid molecule.

Conclusions

In concluding the discussion on the decomposition of tritium compounds by self-irradiation the results of the experimental observations may be summarized as follows:

1. Compounds are in general best stored dispersed in a solvent; notable exceptions are tritiated folic acid, 9,10-dimethyl-1,2-benzanthracene and methotrexate at high specific activity.

2. Compounds can be further protected, particularly those in aqueous solvents, by the presence of a free radical scavenger; for example, benzyl alcohol[78] or cysteamine[80] can be used. Note however that the protective ation of the free radical scavenger depends on the mechanism of the decomposition. For example, benzyl alcohol offers additional protection for uridine-T in aqueous solution but not for DL-leucine-4,5-T, indicating different mechanisms for the decomposition of these compounds, which might be expected.

3. Storage on paper may be satisfactory with a few compounds, examples are glucose-6-T and DL-leucine-4,5-T, but in general the method offers much less protection than for (say) carbon-14 compounds.

4. Care should be taken to avoid bacterial contamination, particularly in solutions containing low chemical concentrations, and in general these should be stored below 20° C. Decomposition (particularly secondary effects) can be minimized by storage at −196° C.

5. Solutions of tritiated compounds should not be subjected to rapidly changing conditions of temperature, especially to those above 20° C.

6. Solutions should not be exposed to external radiation. For example, exposure to bright sunlight or ultra-violet irradiation should be avoided; remember there may be only a few microgrammes of compound in the solution.

There is obviously much more to be learned about the self-decomposition of tritium compounds, particularly the identification of the decomposition fragments, and this may help to shed further light on the mechanisms by which they arise. The ease of destruction of tritium compounds especially those at high specific activity, is a property (regrettably) not always realized by many users of these compounds.

4. STABILITY OF TRITIUM ATOMS IN MOLECULES

The most important factor in appraising the usefulness of tritium compounds as radioactive tracers is the stability of the tritium label under the experimental conditions. These conditions can vary from simple chemical states to more complex biological environments where relatively little is known about the mechanism of hydrogen (or tritium) transfer reactions.

The correct interpretation of the results obtained from a tracer use of a tritium compound, largely depends on an understanding of the stability of the tritium atoms, occupying various positions within the molecule, under the experimental conditions. For many compounds there are no general rules for predicting the stability of the tritium label and this applies particularly to their use in biological investigations.

Unfortunately there is little published work dealing specifically with this problem and the limited information available has tended to get 'buried' in the many papers which describe the use of tritium tracers. An attempt has therefore been made to extract such information and (where possible) to classify it into the groups of compounds to which it is related.

Labile Tritium

Differences between the rates of loss of tritium from attachment to other atoms such as carbon, oxygen, nitrogen or sulphur (for example), are not due to any differences in physical parameters such as bond energy, force constants, polarizability or bond length, but depend upon the structure of the electron cloud surrounding the atom directly attached to the tritium atom.

The presence of a free electron pair on the atom attached to the tritium atom facilitates protonation and consequently hydrogen isotope exchange. This is admirably illustrated by tritiated ammonia with its free electron pair (6.25):

$$\begin{matrix} H & & H \\ T:\ddot{N}:+H^+ & \rightleftharpoons & :\ddot{N}:H+T^+ \\ \ddot{H} & & \ddot{H} \end{matrix}$$

. . . . (6.25)

If the ammonia is held in solution as the ammonium ion with the free electron pair already protonated, the exchange is very much suppressed, although still occurring through the equilibrium in equation (6.26).

It would be expected that a slower exchange between tritium and hydrogen occurs in acid solution of ammonia in agreement with experimental observations [99,100].

$$NH_4^+ + H_2O \rightleftharpoons NH_3 + H_3O^+$$
$$H_3O^+ + T^+ \rightleftharpoons H_2TO^+ + H^+$$
$$\overline{NH_4^+ + H_2O + T^+ \rightleftharpoons NH_3T^+ + H^+}$$

$$. \quad . \quad . \quad . \quad (6.26)$$

Another interesting example is that of hydrogen–tritium exchange in phosphorous acid. With the phosphorus atom in the pentavalent state with no free electron pair, only two hydrogen atoms are exchanged (6.27):

$$
\begin{array}{c}
\text{O} \\
\parallel \\
\text{H}-\text{P}-\text{OH} \\
\mid \\
\text{OH}
\end{array}
+ \text{T}_2\text{O}
\rightleftharpoons
\begin{array}{c}
\text{O} \\
\parallel \\
\text{H}-\text{P}-\text{OT} \\
\mid \\
\text{OT}
\end{array}
$$

$$. \quad . \quad . \quad . \quad (6.27)$$

When tautomerism to the trivalent form of the phosphorus atom occurs as with hypophosphorous acid, then all the hydrogen atoms are exchangeable (6.28):

$$
\begin{array}{c}
\text{H} \quad \text{O} \\
\diagdown\!\diagup \\
\text{P} \\
\diagup\!\diagdown \\
\text{H} \quad \text{OH}
\end{array}
\rightleftharpoons
\text{H}-\text{P}\!\!\begin{array}{c}\diagup \text{OH} \\ \diagdown \text{OH}\end{array}
+ \text{T}_2\text{O}
\rightleftharpoons
\text{T}-\text{P}\!\!\begin{array}{c}\diagup \text{OT} \\ \diagdown \text{OT}\end{array}
$$

$$. \quad . \quad . \quad . \quad (6.28)$$

These simple exchange reactions were investigated fully by Brodskii using deuterium and an excellent review of this work has been published[101]. The tritium atoms attached to such atoms or groups which can readily dissociate into ions are termed 'labile'. This is rather an arbitrary term and is commonly applied to tritium which is readily exchangeable in polar (hydroxylic) solvents. It is therefore necessarily related to the conditions under which the compound is being used.

Tritium atoms directly attached to oxygen, nitrogen or sulphur atoms are labile and are readily exchanged with other hydrogen atoms because of their acidic or basic nature (6.29).

Other examples include hydroxyl groups and imino groups.

$$—COOT \rightleftharpoons —COO^- + T^+$$
$$—NHT + H^+ \rightleftharpoons —NH_2T^+ \rightleftharpoons —NH_2 + T^+$$
$$—ST \rightleftharpoons S^- + T^+ \qquad \ldots \ldots \quad (6.29)$$

For tritium compounds to be useful as radioactive tracers it is normally necessary for all labile tritium to be removed from the molecule. This is because tritium compounds are more often used as tracers for carbon structures (as explained in Chapter 2) than for tracing hydrogen. The user of tritium compounds is therefore mainly interested in the stability of tritium attached to carbon atoms.

If tritium compounds are compared with say those labelled with carbon-14, a difference between them becomes immediately apparent. With carbon-14 compounds the radioactive carbon atoms in the molecule are fixed and the loss of one of these carbon atoms cannot occur without changing the molecular structure. With tritium compounds this is not so; although carbon–hydrogen or carbon–tritium bonds are stronger than carbon–carbon bonds (in so far as their bond energies are concerned—see page 120), they often break under certain conditions resulting in the exchange or migration of the tritium atoms with other hydrogen atoms, either within the molecule itself (intramolecular exchange) or with the hydrogen atoms of neighbouring molecules (intermolecular exchange). The consequence of such an exchange is perhaps best illustrated by an example. Consider thymine labelled in the 2-position with carbon-14 and in the 5-methyl group and 6-position with tritium (6.30):

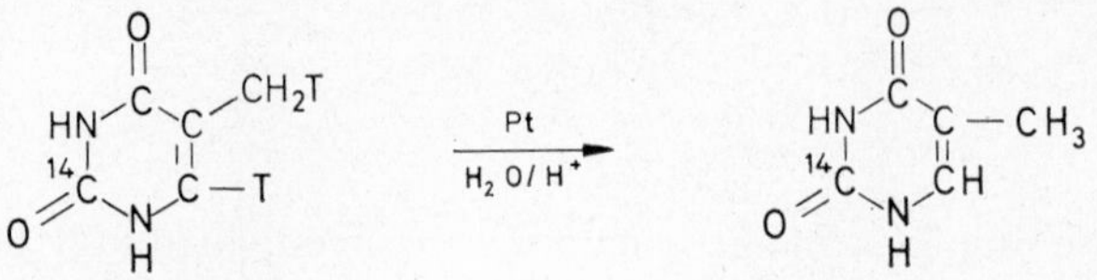

$$\ldots \ldots \quad (6.30)$$

If the compound is heated in water or acetic acid in the presence of a hydrogen transfer catalyst (such as platinum), the molecules of thymine lose their tritium by intermolecular exchange with the hydrogen atoms of the solvent, but the carbon-14 labelling is not affected as only disruption of the molecule can alter the function of the carbon atom at the 2-position.

The important point to observe is that such exchange reactions are not usually associated with any overall change in molecular structure or physical properties of the compound, but generally lead to a loss of radioactivity from the compound. This of course reduces the molar specific activity of the compound. The ease with which this exchange or migration of tritium takes place obviously depends on the ease of rupture of the hydrogen or tritium bonds and is directly related to the structure of the compound and the position of the tritium atoms within the molecule.

Carbon-bound tritium atoms can also be 'labilized' without a hydrogen transfer catalyst, for example if the tritium atoms in the molecule are in positions which may undergo tautomerism. Such an example is tritium attached to a carbon atom next to a keto group, tautomerism to the enol form occurs under alkaline conditions and the tritium atoms are lost by exchange with the hydrogen ions in the solvent (6.31):

$$R\text{—}CHT\text{—}\underset{\underset{O}{\|}}{C}\text{—}R' \; \rightleftharpoons \; R\text{—}CH\text{=}\underset{\underset{OT}{|}}{C}\text{—}R' + H^+ \; \rightleftharpoons$$

$$R\text{—}CH\text{=}\underset{\underset{OH}{|}}{C}\text{—}R' + T^+$$

$$. \quad . \quad . \quad . \quad (6.31)$$

Another good example is tritiated diazomethane in which all the tritium atoms are labile[102] through the equilibria in the equation (6.32):

$$\overset{\delta-}{C}T_2\text{—}\overset{\delta+}{N}\text{≡}N \; \rightleftharpoons \; T\overset{\delta+}{C}\text{≡}\overset{\delta-}{N}\text{—}NT \; \rightleftharpoons \; C T_2\text{=}\overset{\delta+}{N}\text{=}\overset{\delta-}{N}$$

$$. \quad . \quad . \quad . \quad (6.32)$$

Some hydrogen-containing carbon compounds cannot be labelled with tritium for use as carbon tracers because they contain only labile hydrogen positions. Uric acid (6.33), 8-aza-guanine (6.34) and urea (6.35) are examples of such compounds.

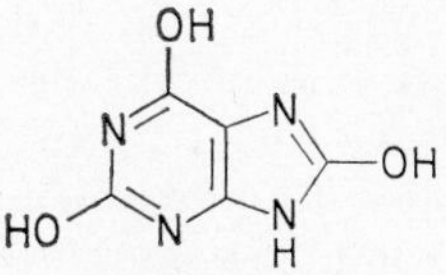

(6.33) 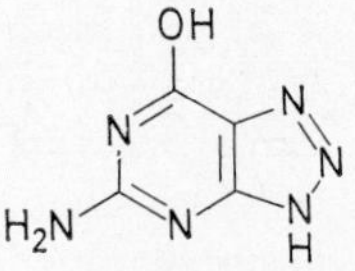   (6.34)   (6.35)

Removal and detection of labile tritium—Labile tritium is easily and rapidly removed by equilibrating the compound several times with water, aqueous alcohol and other hydroxylic solvents, sometimes in the presence of a proton donor or proton acceptor, i.e. under acid or alkaline conditions to accelerate the rate of exchange and to remove tritium in tautomeric forms of the compound. The process is repeated until a constant specific activity is achieved.

The most sensitive test for the detection of labile tritium in non-volatile compounds is to shake the compound with water or aqueous alcohol, distil off the solvent and measure the activity in the distillate. This is much more sensitive than following very small changes in the molar specific activity of the compound. For testing a volatile compound for labile tritium, the compound should be distilled from a non-volatile hydroxylic compound such as mannitol, and the activity of the residual compound determined; alternatively water or alcohol may then be distilled from the residual compound and the activity of the distillate determined.

Labile tritium is usually completely removed during the isolation and purification of the tracer compound by the methods required to achieve a pure compound, such as recrystallization from an aqueous solvent, or by washing an ether extract of the compound with water.

Chemical Stability of Tritium Compounds

The stability of the tritium label under chemical conditions is usually determined by a simple experiment. For example, if tritium does not 'leak' from the compound in solution over a wide range of pH values, this is often taken as sufficient evidence of chemical stability. Illustrative examples are given later.

Stability under Biological Conditions

Anyone using a tritium-labelled compound in a biological tracer experiment must be aware of the risk of exchange. Chemical exchange, for the compound itself, can be excluded by removing all labile tritium; but unless the metabolic pathway is fully known there is always the possibility that it will involve intermediates in which the tritium atoms become placed in chemically labile positions. When attack by enzymes comes into question, there are other possibilities of hydrogen exchange, and little enough is known about them. It should not be assumed that chemically stable tritium atoms in a compound will remain stable under biological conditions or even vice versa.

At the present time it is not possible to lay down even the simplest rules as a guide to the stability of the tritium label under biological conditions. The experimentalist cannot as a rule know the answers, but must judge the probabilities as best he can. For this reason a knowledge of the position of tritium labelling is needed, and this aspect of the problem is discussed more fully in Chapter 5.

Determination of Biological Stability of Tritium Compounds

Our knowledge of the behaviour of tritium atoms in labelled molecules is very incomplete. Under chemical conditions it can sometimes be predicted with confidence, but under biological conditions the only safe guide is experimental verification. There are four methods by which biological stability of tritium labelling can be tested:

1. *Retention of Specific Activity*

The first method involves a comparison of the specific activity of the recovered material having passed through the biological system, with that of the administered compound. The method is particularly suitable for testing drugs and makes the assumption that unknown isotopic dilution by endogenous synthesis does not occur. This approach has been successfully used for testing the stability of the tritium label in morphine[103] labelled by the Wilzbach technique. The morphine-T isolated from rat urine has the same specific activity as the morphine-T administered interperitoneally.

This test fails of course if the biological system already has a pool of the compound under test, i.e. the compound must be exogenous. The resulting isolated compound would have a lower specific activity but may well be biologically stable so far as the tritium label is concerned. Readers will particularly note that trace impurities at high specific activity (such as one often encounters with the Wilzbach labelling of complex molecules) would give very misleading results and again emphasizes the importance of using radiochemically pure tracer compounds.

2. *Measurement of Biological Half-life (Effective Half-life in the System)*

A method which can be used if endogenous dilution eliminates Method (1) depends on measuring the biological (effective) half-life of the tritium compound in the system. This is then compared with the biological half-life of the same compound labelled with carbon-14, for it is known that labelled carbon atoms are not exchanged under such conditions. If the biological half-times are identical for the two labelled compounds, it can be deduced that no tritium is lost by exchange *in vivo*. An example of the use of this technique is in the testing of the biological stability of tritiated cholesterol[104]. The same criterion of high radiochemical purity of the tracer compound again applies. The method is limited by the availability of the compound labelled with carbon-14.

3. *Urinary Tritium*

The absence of tritium as tritiated water from the urinary distillate following administration of the compound, has been suggested as another possible test for the stability of the tritium label in biological systems[105]. This is quite a good method for testing the biological stability of the tritium label which may even be applicable when the compound is metabolized. For example, no tritium could be found as tritiated water in urine following the administration of DL-adrenaline-7-T to humans; all the tritium could be accounted for in the metabolic products. However, one must bear in mind the possibility of intermolecular tritium (hydrogen) transfer without actual exchange with body water. The classical examples here are the transfer of tritium atoms by the di- and tri-phosphopyridine nucleotide co-enzymes[106]. In this method the need to use labelled compounds free from any chemically 'labile' tritium is essential.

4. *Double Isotope Technique*

The most popular method for testing the stability of the tritium label in biological systems involves the double isotope technique. The compound is labelled with tritium and (for example) carbon-14 and the ratio of tritium to carbon-14 is measured before and after administration of the sample. Identical isotope ratios demonstrate the stability of the tritium label. An application of this method was the testing of the cardiac glycoside, digitoxin-T labelled by the Wilzbach method. Injection of the compound labelled with tritium and carbon-14 intravenously into rats gave the same isotopic ratio in digitoxin isolated from the urine and the faeces[107]. The stability of the tritium in the metabolic products can also be tested by examining their tritium to carbon-14 ratios. The stability of generally labelled progesterone-T and its urinary metabolites following injection into the rabbit, has recently been demonstrated using this method[108]. Although validity of the tritium label under biological conditions is not quite the same as stability, a change in the isotopic ratio of tritium to carbon-14 will be apparent if there is isotopic fractionation. Such changes must be carefully interpreted before the stability of the tritium label is challenged. However, if the tritium atoms do in fact occupy stable positions it is doubtful whether isotopic fractionation will occur very often.

When using compounds which are generally labelled with tritium by exchange procedures (see Chapter 4) it is wise to test the biological stability of *each batch* because the distribution of tritium throughout the molecule can vary markedly from batch to batch (see Chapter 5). For this reason specifically labelled tritium compounds are usually preferred for biological investigations. Once a compound has been tested in the biological system and proved to be satisfactory, it can be used with the same confidence experienced with the use of carbon-14 compounds.

Having briefly discussed the methods for testing the stability of the tritium label under biological conditions, let us now examine the behaviour of the tritium atoms in the various classes of compounds mostly used. These include (*a*) amino acids (*b*) steroids (*c*) carbohydrates (*d*) aromatic compounds (*e*) aliphatic compounds (*f*) heterocyclic compounds (*g*) organometallic compounds and (*h*) the metal hydrides.

(*a*) *Stability of the tritium atoms in tritiated amino acids*—Biologically the group of compounds comprising the amino acids is one of the most important. Chemically the tritium atoms attached to any carbon atom in the amino acid molecule are fairly firmly bound and these compounds can be recrystallized as the free amino acid or as salts (for example the hydrochloride) from hydroxylic solvents without loss of tritium. The chemical stability of a number of tritiated amino acids upon heating under reflux in 5 per cent hydrochloric acid, has been examined by Hempel[81]. Glycine-2-T, serine-2-T, 3,4-dihydroxy-phenylalanine-(*side-chain*-αβ-T), leucine-4,5-T, lysine-4,5-T, phenyl-alanine-2,4-T and 3-nitro-tyrosine-5-T did not exchange their tritium atoms even when the refluxing time was 15 h. The observed stability of the ring tritium atoms of phenylalanine-T under these acidic conditions, is in agreement with earlier work by Schoenheimer[109]. Note however, that the ring tritium atoms are exchanged if the compound is heated in strong sulphuric acid (> 80 per cent)[110].

The presence of electron-donating substituents in the aromatic ring (see pages 126 and 367) facilitate the exchange of tritium atoms; tyrosine-5-T and 3,4-dihydroxyphenylalanine-2,5,6-T rapidly exchange their tritium atoms on heating in acid solutions[81]. Conversely electron-attracting substituents in the aromatic ring (see pages 125 and 367) stabilize the tritium atoms attached to ring positions. For example, if tyrosine-5-T is converted into 3-nitro-tyrosine-5-T, the electron-attracting properties of the nitro-group are stronger than the electron-donating properties of the hydroxyl-group[111] with the result that upon refluxing 3-nitro-tyrosine-5-T in 5 per cent hydrochloric acid no loss of tritium occurs by exchange[81]; tyrosine-3,5-T loses some tritium by exchange on storage even in 0·01N-hydrochloric acid[113].

The α-hydrogen atom of α-amino acids is labilized by heating the compound under reflux with a mixture of acetic acid and acetic anhydride. Labilization and exchange occurs through the lactam tautomer[112] (6.36):

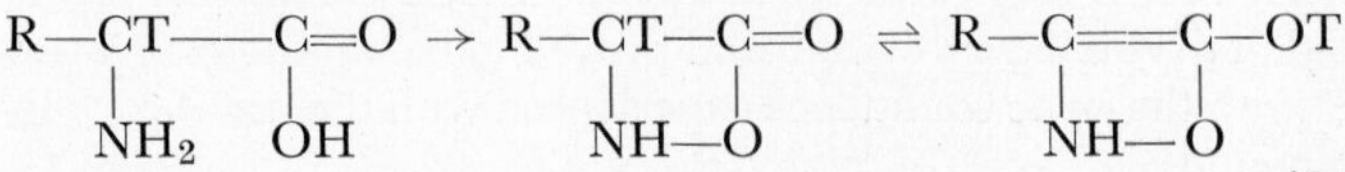

$$\underset{\substack{| \\ NH_2}}{R—CT}\underset{\substack{| \\ OH}}{—C=O} \rightarrow \underset{\substack{| \\ NH—O}}{R—CT—C=O} \rightleftharpoons \underset{\substack{| \\ NH—O}}{R—C=\!\!=C—OT}$$

. . . . (6.36)

Thus acetylation of amino acids containing tritium in the α-position is accompanied by exchange with the solvent resulting in a reduction in specific activity. Alternatively, tritium can be introduced into the α-position by refluxing the unlabelled amino acid in a mixture of tritiated acetic acid-(*carboxyl*-T) and acetic anhydride[112].

Analysis of amino acids frequently involves their reaction with ninhydrin when degradation to the corresponding aldehyde occurs. The mechanism of this reaction has already been discussed in Chapter 2 and it has been shown that the α-hydrogen atom is not involved[112, 114]. Amino acids labelled with tritium in the α-position upon oxidation with ninhydrin will therefore give aldehydes of the same molar specific activity (6.37):

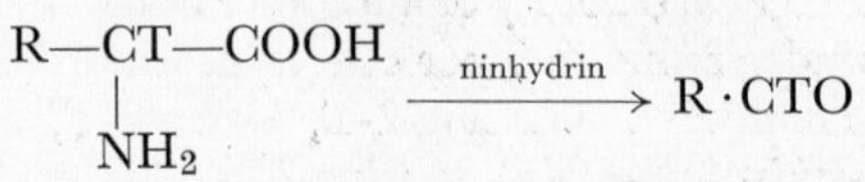

$$\underset{\substack{| \\ NH_2}}{R—CT—COOH} \xrightarrow{\text{ninhydrin}} R \cdot CTO$$

. . . . (6.37)

The stability of the tritium atoms in labelled amino acids under alkaline conditions, has not been studied systematically. Observations [73] suggest that their behaviour is similar to that in acid solution unless the tritium is attached to carbon in an enolisable position.

The biological stability of the α-hydrogen atom of lysine has been determined using deuterium[115]. Labilization of this α-deuterium atom in the intact animal is slight in comparison with the α-hydrogen atom of leucine or glycine from which it was concluded that lysine is not involved in any transaminase system[116].

An interesting observation was made during experiments on the preparation of tritiated L-amino acids from generally labelled DL-amino acids[117]. Treatment of these generally tritiated α-amino acids with renal D-amino acid oxidase (hog kidney extract) or with L-amino acid oxidase (rattlesnake venom), resulted in the loss of tritium from the molecules. The isolated L- or D-amino acids respectively after such treatment have a considerably lower specific activity than the starting DL-compound. The losses experienced[117,118] with a number of tritiated DL-α-amino acids upon treatment with amino acid oxidase are shown in Table 6.11.

TABLE 6.11

Tritiated α-amino acid	Specific activity mc/mg	L-Amino acid activity mc/mg	D-Amino acid activity mc/mg	Tritium loss %
DL-Alanine-T(G)	5·0	2·14	—	57
DL-Alanine-T(G)	0·66	0·022	—	97
DL-Alanine-T(G)	17·3	0·23	—	98
Glycine-2-T	1·23	0·64	—	48
Glycine-2-T	0·2	0·08	—	60
Glycine-2-T (2nd treatment with D-oxidase	0·08	0·06	—	25
DL-Leucine-T(G)	1·3	0·73	—	44
DL-Leucine-2-T	0·063	0·0017	—	97
DL-Methionine-T(G)	0·44	0·22	—	50
DL-Methionine-T(G)	0·73	0·26	—	64
DL-β-Phenylalanine-T(G)	5·0	3·4	—	32
DL-β-Phenylalanine-T(G)	5·0	—	3·4	32
DL-Tyrosine-T(G)	0·56	0·34	—	39

The activity associated with the D- and L-components of the tritiated DL-amino acids was determined by reverse dilution analysis with D- and L-carriers (see page 257). In all cases the distribution of tritium was 50 per cent in each isomer indicating that no differentiation between the two forms occurs during the tritiation processes used (see Chapter 4). This is also confirmed (for example) by the results obtained on treatment of DL-phenylalanine-T(G) with D- or L-amino acid oxidases; the same amount of tritium is lost in either case.

The reason for the observed loss of tritium from the resulting optically active acid, is not yet clear. It has been assumed that the L-component (for example) under the conditions of the D-amino acid oxidase remains unaffected, while the D-component is oxidized to the corresponding keto acid[119]. It is well known that the α-hydrogen atom is labilized in the presence of aminopherase[120] and the losses of tritium may be due to transaminations rather than a specific function of the oxidases. Further evidence which suggests this might be the case was provided by studies on the D-amino acid oxidation of DL-alanine-T(G), where it was observed that all the tritium atoms in the L-component could be removed by prolonged shaking in the reaction medium. Tritium loss from the β-position of L-alanine-T could be explained by the following equilibria (6.38):

$$
\begin{array}{ccc}
\begin{array}{c} CH_2T \\ | \\ CH\cdot NH_2 \\ | \\ COOH \end{array}
& + &
\begin{array}{c} CH_3 \\ | \\ OC \\ | \\ COOH \end{array}
& \longrightarrow &
\begin{array}{c} CH_2T \quad CH_3 \\ | \qquad | \\ CH-N=C \\ | \qquad | \\ COOH \quad COOH \end{array}
\end{array}
$$

$$
\begin{array}{c} CH_2 \\ \| \\ C-OT \\ | \\ COOH \end{array}
\;\rightleftharpoons\;
\begin{array}{c} CH_2T \\ | \\ C=O \\ | \\ COOH \end{array}
\; + \;
\begin{array}{c} CH_3 \\ | \\ CH\cdot NH_2 \\ | \\ COOH \end{array}
\;\longleftarrow\;
\begin{array}{c} CH_2T \quad CH_3 \\ | \qquad | \\ C=N-CH \\ | \qquad | \\ COOH \; COOH \end{array}
$$

$$\text{. . . . (6.38)}$$

Transamination with the pyruvate produced during the oxidation of the D-component results in tritium atoms being placed in an enolisable position[121]. Proof that such a transamination did occur was obtained by injecting pyruvate-3-C14 into the reaction mixture; L-alanine-C14 was isolated[118]. Another observation suggests that transamination may not be the only cause of tritium loss; if the action of the D-amino acid oxidase is inhibited, by the presence of benzoic acid for example, the tritium in the L-component of the DL-alanine-T(G) is lost (over 95 per cent and one obtains DL-alanine-T containing all the tritium radioactivity in the D-component.

The results obtained with glycine-2-T lead to the speculation of the existence of D- and L-forms of tritiated glycine (6.39):

$$
\begin{array}{cc}
\begin{array}{c} COOH \\ | \\ T-C-H \\ | \\ NH_2 \end{array}
&
\begin{array}{c} COOH \\ | \\ H-C-T \\ | \\ NH_2 \end{array} \\
\text{L-Glycine-2-T(?)} & \text{D-Glycine-2-T(?)}
\end{array}
$$

$$\text{. . . . (6.39)}$$

When the tritium atoms are situated further from the optical centre, for example in DL-leucine-4,5-T; no loss of tritium occurs during the reaction with D- or L-amino acid oxidases[118].

This type of biological labilization of tritium atoms is a good example of what one must look out for and for biological investigations it would seem better to use amino acids labelled in positions other than alpha or beta to optically active centres.

Hempel[81] investigated the stability of 3,4-dihydroxyphenyl-alanine-2,5,6-T in the mouse. Mice were given dihydroxyphenyl-alanine, labelled with tritium and carbon-14 in the ring, by intraperitoneal injection. After two days, measurement of the tritium and carbon-14 activity of the suprarenal capsule showed the ratio of tritium to carbon-14 in the products (unstated) was the same as in the administered DOPA. This experiment suggests that the hydrogen atoms of the benzene ring of DOPA, which are chemically rather labile in acid conditions, are stable *in vivo*. This is one of the few known cases for which biological stability appears better than chemical stability, a fact one could not have predicted.

It is sometimes important to know both the position and stereo-specificity of the tritium label in certain amino acids[173]. For example, Witkop, Udenfriend and colleagues recognized the importance of knowing these factors when studying the mechanism of enzymatic hydroxylation of proline in chick embryos[167]. Use of *cis*-L-proline-4-T resulted in the complete retention of the tritium label during the hydroxylation process (6.40) while complete loss of tritium was observed when using *trans*-L-proline-4-T (6.41).

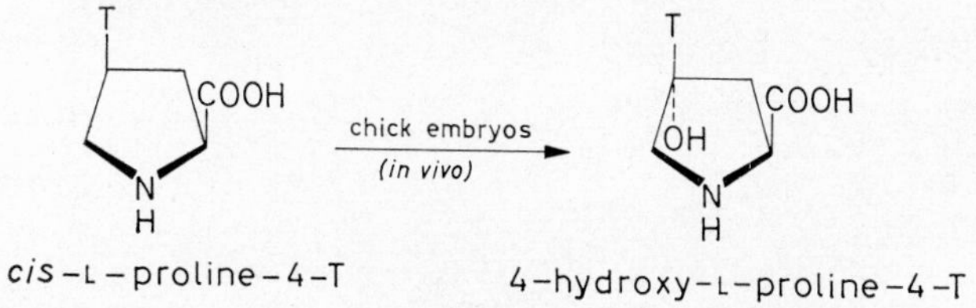

cis –L – proline – 4 –T   4–hydroxy–L–proline–4 –T

. . . . (6.40)

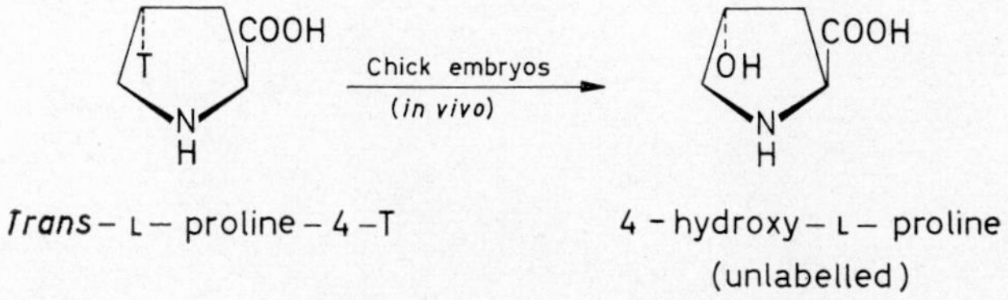

Trans – L – proline – 4 –T   4 – hydroxy – L – proline
(unlabelled)

. . . . (6.41)

The mechanism of hydroxy proline biosynthesis in some respects resembles the mode of hydroxylation of steroids, in that it is not accompanied by isotope effects[168,169]. On the other hand, whereas

12*   361

steroid hydroxylases attack both the equatorial and axial positions[170] (see page 364), biological hydroxylation of proline results in the *trans*-diastereoisomer only[171,172].

(*b*) *Stability of the tritium atoms in tritiated steroids*—Tritium atoms in the steroid molecule which are attached to carbon atoms adjacent to a carbonyl (keto or oxo) group are usually labilized in alkaline solutions by enolisation. For example, in the preparation of androstane-3,17-dione-1-T use is made of this labilization effect to remove tritium from the 2-position[122] (6.42):

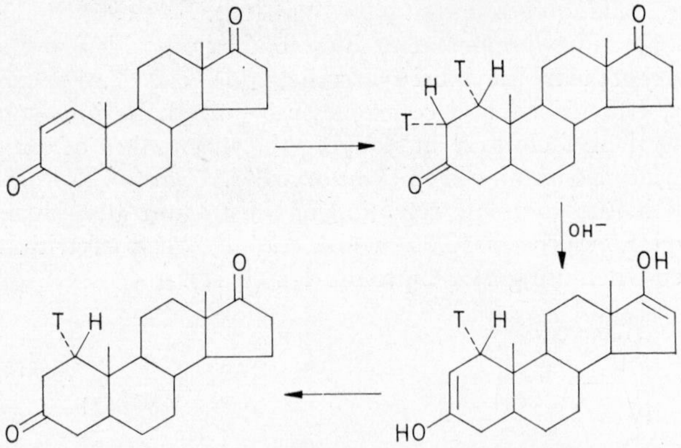

. . . . (6.42)

Similarly alkali treatment is used to remove tritium from the 17-position of Δ^5-pregnenolone-16,17-T by enolisation of the 20-oxo group[123] (6.43):

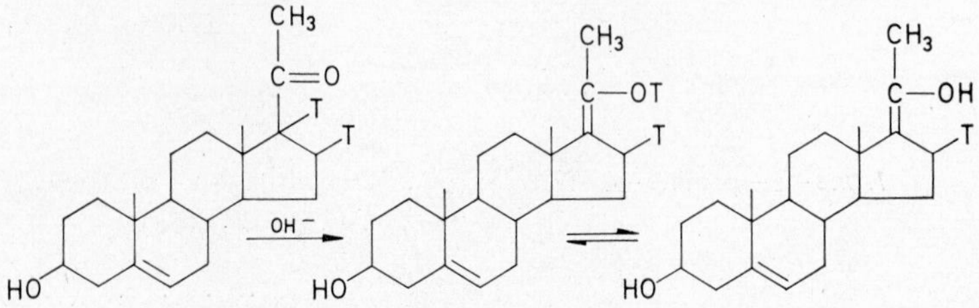

. . . (6.43)

In contrast, cortisol-1,2-T does not lose tritium from the 2-position under alkaline conditions although adjacent to an oxo group. In this case the direction of enolisation is influenced by the carbon–carbon double bond in the 4,5-position and occurs exclusively in the opposite direction to what one might expect[124] (6.44):

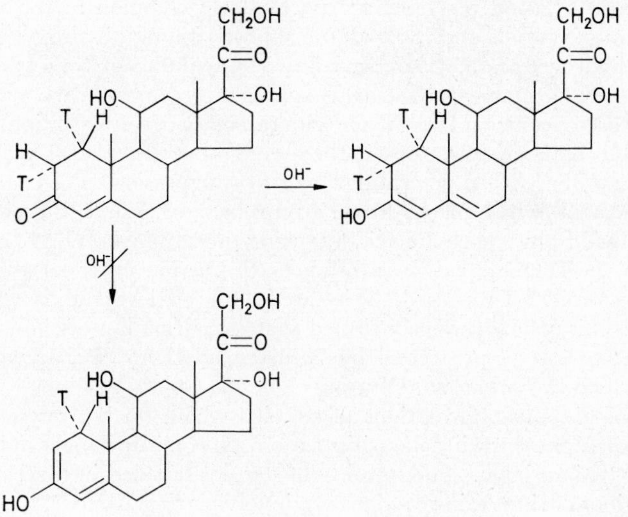

. . . . (6.44)

The introduction of tritium atoms into the steroid molecule by the saturation of a carbon–carbon double bond for example, can give rise to conformational isomers (see Chapter 4). In many cases, the tritium atoms occupy the α-configuration because steric effects prevent reduction from the top or β-side of the molecule[125]. The position and configuration (whether α- or β-) become very important in assessing the stability of the tritium atoms in the molecule, under both chemical and biological conditions.

The introduction of a double bond in the 1,2-position by dehydrogenation of the steroid with dichloro-dicyano-o-benzoquinone (DDQ) is known to involve loss of the 1α-hydrogen atom, hence a tritium atom in this position would be eliminated.

Biochemical dehydrogenations can also involve the α- or β-hydrogen atoms and some illustrative examples have been published[122]. For example, the biochemical introduction of the double bond in the 1,2-position of steroids by *Bacillus sphaericus* is brought about by the elimination of the axial 1α- and 2β-hydrogen atoms[126]. A tritiated

363

steroid produced by saturation of the Δ^1-compound which yields the $1\alpha,2\alpha$-tritiosteroid will lose the tritium from the 1α-position by the biochemical dehydrogenation giving a steroid specifically labelled in the 2α-position.

Hydroxylation reactions are particularly common in the metabolism of steroids and involves the substitution of a hydroxyl group for a hydrogen atom. It has been shown by a number of workers[127–134] that these enzyme-catalysed hydroxylations at saturated carbon atoms are stereospecific and take place with retention of configuration. The stability of the tritium atoms in the steroid molecule towards hydroxylation will again be determined by its configuration. For example, cholic acid (which has hydroxyl groups in the 3, 7 and 12 positions) obtained from bile cholic acid following the administration of cholesterol-7α-T to the rat, was unlabelled. On the other hand when cholesterol-7β-T was used, the isolated cholic acid was radioactive[130]. From this result it was concluded that the formation of cholic acid from cholesterol proceeded by 7α-hydroxylation. Similar work is described by Samuelsson[131] using cholesterol-6-T.

Biological transformations of steroids which do not involve the carbon atoms carrying the tritium atoms, have little danger in losing their tritium label. The stability of steroids labelled in the 1 and 2 positions of ring A, in reactions not involving ring A[187,189], has been established by enzymatic transformation of the 11-hydroxy to the 11-keto compound[132]. The 7-position is also regarded as a suitable position for the tritium label for much biological work, in contradistinction to the 16-position where oxidation at C-17 would labilize the 16-position by enolisation[133].

Other positions of interest in steroid molecules are the 11- and 12-position, where stereospecific hydroxylations can be performed by various organisms (6.45).

The 11α-hydroxylation of pregnane-3,20-dione-$11\alpha,12\alpha$-T (prepared by the catalytic reduction of pregn-11-ene-3,20-dione with tritium gas) is carried out with *Rhizopus nigricans* with a loss of 69 per cent of the tritium. Hydroxylation at the 11β-position by adrenal perfusion results in only 3 per cent loss of tritium while 12β-hydroxylation with *Calonectria decora* also results in about 3 per cent loss of tritium. Oxidation of the hydroxylated products with chromium trioxide establishes conclusively the proportions of tritium at the 11α and 11β-positions[127,134]. The unequal distribution of tritium in the hydrogenation of carbon–carbon double bonds has been discussed in Chapter 5.

Proof that degradation of the side-chain of progesterone to testo-

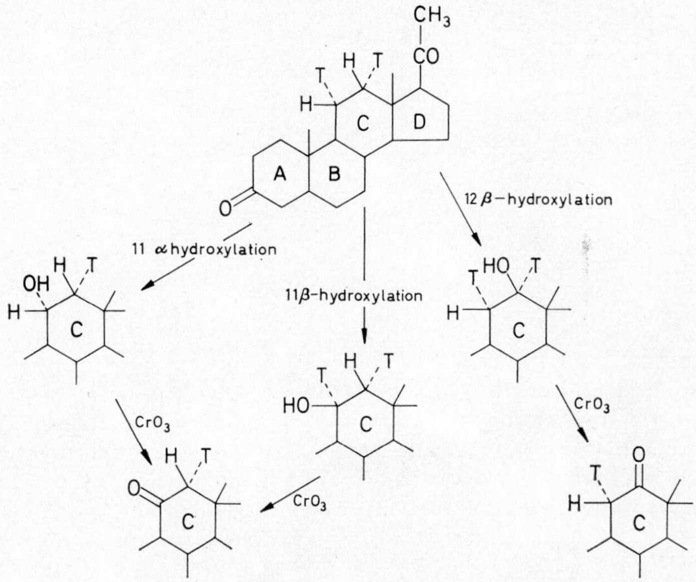

$$\cdots \quad (6.45)$$

sterone in the rat testis does not proceed via oxidative scission of a 17,20-ketol or glycol, is obtained by using progesterone-17α-T. The testosterone isolated retains tritium activity[122].

These few examples illustrate undeniably the usefulness of stereo-specifically labelled steroids, but unless one is aware of such reactions, losses of tritium under the biological conditions might be taken as instability of the tritium label whereas the correct choice of stereo-specific label would have provided a stable tracer.

(c) *Stability of the tritium atoms in tritiated carbohydrates*—The stability of tritium in D-glucose-1-T on repeated recrystallization from organic solvents has been demonstrated[135]. There is little or no tendency for cleavage of the carbon-bound tritium atom under neutral conditions, or in slightly acidic solutions. However, in alkaline solution enolis-ation readily occurs with tritium–hydrogen exchange and subsequent loss of the label (6.46). A similar loss of tritium can be expected with other aldoses labelled on the C_1-portion.

Tritium atoms attached to carbon-6 in glucose are stable in acid, neutral and alkaline solution as enolisation cannot result in tritium exchange from this position.

Relatively little is published on the biological stability of the

$$
\begin{array}{ccc}
\underset{\text{C}}{\overset{\text{O}}{\diagdown}}\,^{\text{T}} & \text{HO}-\text{C}-\text{T} & \text{HO}-\text{C}-\text{H} \\
\text{H}-\text{C}-\text{OH} & \parallel & \parallel \\
\text{HO}-\text{C}-\text{H} \quad \xrightarrow{\text{OH}^{-}} & \text{C}-\text{OH} & \text{C}-\text{OT} \\
\text{H}-\text{C}-\text{OH} & \text{HO}-\text{C}-\text{H} \quad \rightleftharpoons & \text{HO}-\text{C}-\text{H} \\
\text{H}-\text{C}-\text{OH} & \text{H}-\text{C}-\text{OH} & \text{H}-\text{C}-\text{OH} \\
\text{CH}_2\,\text{OH} & \text{H}-\text{C}-\text{OH} & \text{H}-\text{C}-\text{OH} \\
& \text{CH}_2\,\text{OH} & \text{CH}_2\,\text{OH}
\end{array}
$$

. . . . (6.46)

tritium label in carbohydrates. Transfer of the tritium atom from the 1-position of glucose to fatty acids is known to occur in slices of normal rat liver or of lactating mammary glands[136]. This observation is interesting from a radiological point of view. It perhaps suggests that tritiated carbohydrates are potentially more toxic than simple tritiated fatty acids, which are not built up into stored fats[137].

Dunn and Strahs[137a] found that glucose-6-T could not be used as a *quantitative* tracer for the glucose–carbon chain *in vivo* (rat). Apparent values obtained for the size of the body glucose pool, glucose space and the rates of glucose production and utilization using glucose-6-T were much larger than values obtained when using glucose-C14(U). After inter-arterial injection of 'doubly' labelled glucose-C14(U)-6-T into the rat, the tritium to carbon-14 ratio decreased with time which is opposite to that expected for an isotope effect[137b] and indicated that cleavage of the C_6-hydrogen bond occurs and not the C_5—C_6 bond. Dunn and Strahs speculate on a hydrogen transfer mechanism involving the C_6-hydrogen bond of glucose and that the observed loss of tritium may reflect an important physiological event in the *in vivo* metabolism of glucose. Such results clearly show the value and frequently the necessity, for comparing results using both carbon-14 and tritium as tracers.

(*d*) *Stability of tritium atoms in aromatic compounds*—Increasing use is made of de-tritiation of aromatic compounds under acidic conditions as a means of studying aromatic reactivity[138,139]. This type of work also gives information on the stability of the tritium atoms in the aromatic rings under such conditions. Normally, substituents in the ring which abstract electrons (electrophiles) deactivate the ring for exchange, that is the tritium atoms in the ring are firmly bound, while electron-donating substituents (nucleophiles) facilitate tritium exchange by activation of the ring.

Electrophilic reagents or groups include NO_2—, —SO_3H, —CN, —COOH, —CO·CH_3 and —COCl, while nucleophilic reagents or groups include —OH, —OCH_3, —NH_2 and —PO_4^{3-}. If two or more groups are attached to the aromatic ring the stability of the tritium atoms will depend upon which group exerts the greater influence. An example is given on page 357.

The ease of exchange of the tritium from an aromatic ring is also influenced by the strength of the acid, for example o-acetamido-acetophenone (6.47) exchanges its ring tritium on suspension in dilute mineral acids but repeated suspension in 0·4N-acetic acid for periods of 18 h causes no exchange of the tritium from the ring positions[140].

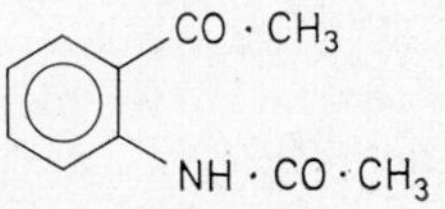

$$\ldots \ldots (6.47)$$

The tritiated vitamin-K analogue, tetrasodium 2-methyl-1,4-naphthaquinol diphosphate labelled with tritium in the 5, 6 and 7 positions does not exchange its tritium even under the hot, strongly acidic, conditions of a ceric sulphate oxidation[141].

Substituents in the benzene ring can sometimes influence the stability of the tritium atoms in the side-chain of aromatic compounds. An example is the lability of tritium in N-carbobenzyloxy-2-methoxy-4,5-dihydroxylphenylethylamine-β-T quinone [142] (6.48):

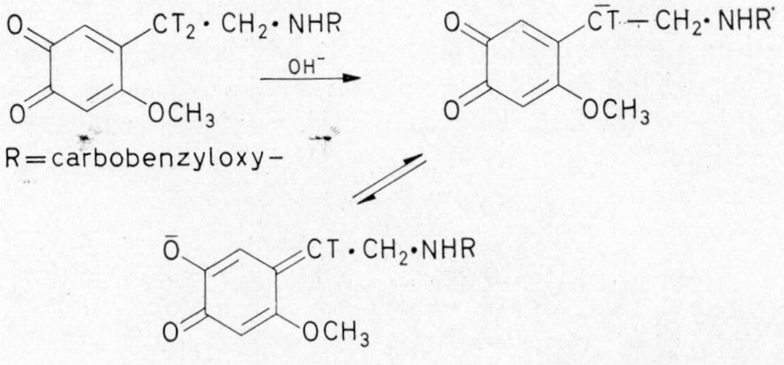

$$\ldots \ldots (6.48)$$

No significant loss of tritium from the molecule is observed in acid solution but up to 30 per cent of the tritium is lost by exchange in alkaline solution which can be explained by the formation of a resonance stabilized anion as shown (6.48).

A comprehensive review of the effects of substituents on the hydrogen (deuterium) exchange is given by Shatenshtein[101] and the conclusions are applicable to tritium–hydrogen exchange. In considerations of lability there is no reason for believing that the exchange of the tritium from aromatic systems is influenced by radiation, especially at low molar specific activity.

Little is known concerning the stability of the tritium atoms in aromatic compounds under biological conditions.

(*e*) *Stability of the tritium atoms in aliphatic compounds*—The tritium atoms in aliphatic compounds are stable unless they are attached to a carbon atom which has a deficiency of electrons, which can facilitate exchange. The electron density around a carbon atom is of course dependent on the groups attached to the molecule. To take a simple example; consider a nitrile (6.49):

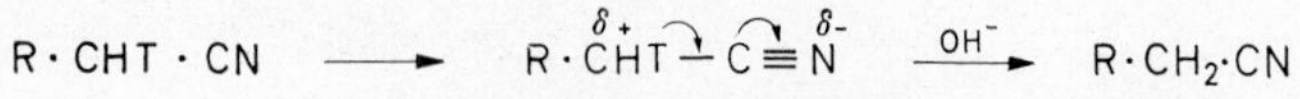

$$R \cdot CHT \cdot CN \longrightarrow R \cdot \overset{\delta+}{C}HT \overset{\frown}{\underset{}{\longrightarrow}} \overset{\delta-}{C \equiv N} \xrightarrow{OH^-} R \cdot CH_2 \cdot CN$$

$$\cdots \cdots (6.49)$$

In alkaline solution the alpha tritium atom exchanges rapidly with the hydrogen atoms (ions) of the solvent. This is admirably demonstrated using deuterium oxide; under alkaline conditions β-hydroxypropionitrile exchanges its α-hydrogen atoms only which can be followed by nuclear magnetic resonance studies on the solution[143]. Note however, that acetonitrile (6.47; R = H) does not exchange tritium atoms in the methyl group on alkali treatment at room temperature[73].

Tritium atoms of labelled acetone are perfectly stable under acidic conditions[114] but in alkaline solution enolisation occurs with subsequent loss of the label by exchange[144]. Sodium pyruvate labelled with tritium loses activity from the methyl group under alkaline conditions for the same reasons (6.50):

$$CH_3 \cdot CO \cdot COONa \xrightarrow{OH^-} CH_2 = \underset{\underset{OH}{|}}{C} - COO^-$$

$$\cdots \cdots (6.50)$$

At room temperature enolisation and exchange occurs at a measurable rate under weakly alkaline (pH 7–8) conditions[73].

Under biological conditions oxidation at various positions in the molecule may give rise to direct loss of tritium at the point of oxidation or by secondary effects. The beta oxidation of fatty acids is an example[137]. The introduction of a keto group into the molecule can enhance loss of tritium from the adjacent positions by enolisation. Consider for example the beta oxidation of n-butyric acid (6.51):

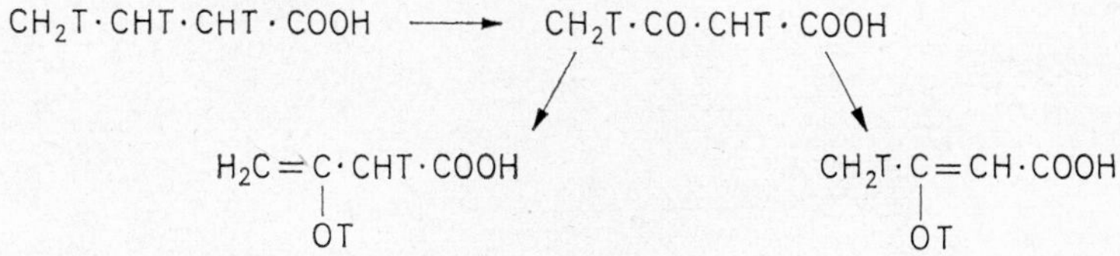

$$CH_2T \cdot CHT \cdot CHT \cdot COOH \longrightarrow CH_2T \cdot CO \cdot CHT \cdot COOH$$

$$H_2C = C \cdot CHT \cdot COOH \qquad\qquad CH_2T \cdot C = CH \cdot COOH$$
$$\underset{OT}{|} \qquad\qquad\qquad\qquad\qquad \underset{OT}{|}$$

$$. \quad . \quad . \quad . \quad (6.51)$$

Loss of tritium from both the methyl group and from the α-position can occur in the beta keto acid under alkaline conditions.

(f) *Stability of tritium atoms in heterocyclic compounds*—The heterocyclic group of organic compounds contains the most widely used classes of tritium-labelled compounds; the purines, pyrimidines, nucleosides and nucleotides.

Tritium atoms attached to carbon atoms in the purines adenine, caffeine, theophylline, hypoxanthine and guanine are stable in acid or alkaline solution[73].

Prolonged boiling with 6N-hydrochloric acid does not remove tritium from the pyrimidine thymine labelled in the 6-position or the 5-methyl group[145]. The 5-halogenated derivatives of uracil-6-T are equally stable[146]. Although tritium atoms in the 6-position or in the 5-methyl group are non-labile under acid or alkaline conditions, tritium attached to the 5-position exchanges with hydrogen ions in N-sulphuric acid with first-order kinetics[147]. Thus tritium in the 5-position of uracil-5,6-T for example (6.52; $R_1 = R_3 = $—OH; $R_2 = H$) is lost under acid conditions. Losses also occur from the 5-position under alkaline conditions but at a slower rate[148]. High-temperature hydrolysis with formic acid tends to cleave tritium from the ring carbons (probably only the 5-position) of deoxycytidine-T, while the methyl tritium atoms of thymidine are quite stable[149].

Nucleosides are hydrolysed by mineral acids into their respective purine or pyrimidine bases and a sugar (ribose or deoxyribose) (6.52). In addition to the loss of tritium by exchange from the 5-position of the pyrimidine bases, losses also occur from the 5-position of nucleo-sides[148], but the rate is slow compared with the pyrimidine bases. Thus in 1N-sulphuric acid at room temperature little or no loss of tritium occurs from uridine-5-T or cytidine-5-T, but at 100° C all the tritium is exchanged after 9 days. Losses also occur in hot alkali but at a slower rate than in acid solution[148].

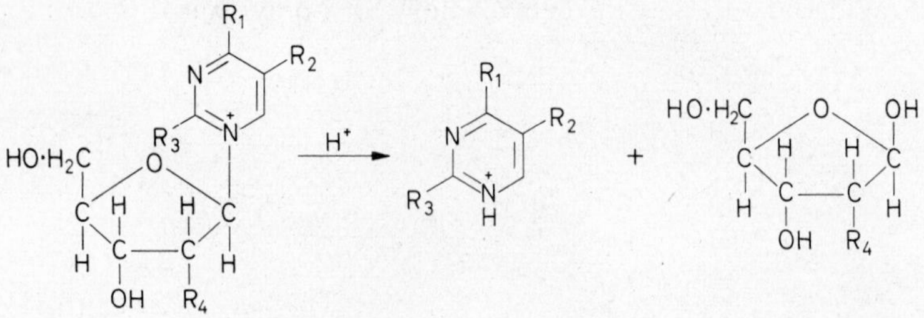

$$\cdots \cdots \quad (6.52)$$

Uracil $(R_1 = R_3 = -OH; \ R_2 = H)$; Thymine $(R_1 = R_3 = -OH; \ R_2 = -CH_3)$

D-Ribose $(R_4 = -OH)$; 2-Deoxy-D-ribose $(R_4 = H)$

Uridine $(R_1 = R_3 = -OH; \ R_2 = H; \ R_4 = -OH)$

Thymidine $(R_1 = R_3 = -OH; \ R_2 = -CH_3; \ R_4 = H)$

These results demonstrate the importance of knowing the position of the tritium atoms within the labelled molecule in order to assess their stability. This is even futher exemplified by consideration of the stability of tritium atoms in nucleosides under biological conditions.

There is no evidence of tritium loss or exchange from the thymine moiety of tritiated thymidine (6-T or 5-*methyl*-T) under biological conditions or after incorporation into the DNA of proliferating cells[150]. Some confusion has arisen concerning the authenticity of the tritium label in thymidine[151]. Three forms of tritium-labelled thymidine have been described and used; thymidine-T(G), thymidine-6-T and thymidine-5-*methyl*-T. All have been employed for labelling DNA and in this process there is no evidence to suggest loss of tritium by exchange, or by enzymatic processes. However, for studying the degradative metabolism of thymidine the actual positions of the tritium atoms in the molecule are of considerable importance. In the presence of thymine oxidase the tritium atom at position-6 is lost due to the formation of 5-methyl barbituric acid[152] (6.53):

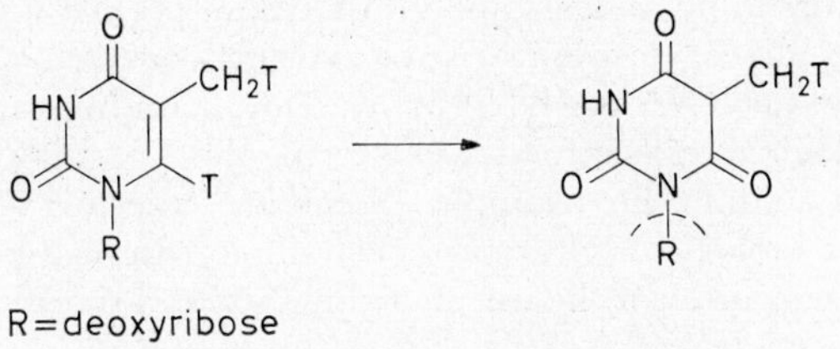

R=deoxyribose

. . . . (6.53)

Metabolic pathways involving the demethylation of thymidine would obviously cause the loss of tritium from this part of the molecule[153]. For example, the results of Takats and Smellie[154] suggested that the thymidine-T they were using for studying the metabolism of thymidine in the root-tips of *Vicia faba*, was not exclusively labelled in the 5-methyl group.

In uridine and cytidine the tritium label can be associated with the 5- and 6-positions of the pyrimidine base moiety. Uridine-C14 (labelled either in the uracil or ribose moiety) is efficiently converted into 5-ribosyluracil in yeast[155]. However, when uracil or uridine labelled in the 5- and 6-positions with tritium are converted into 5-ribosyl uracil (6.54):

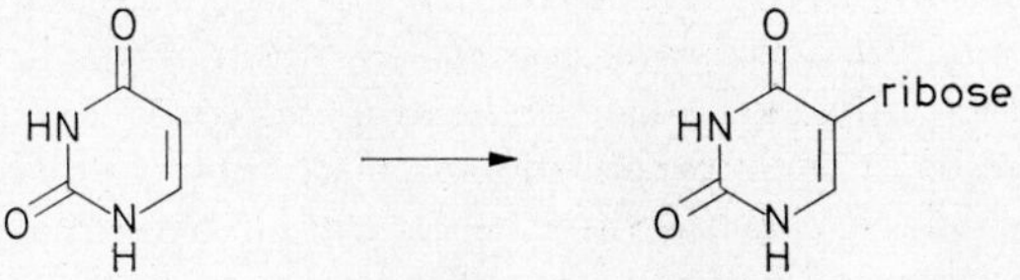

. . . . (6.54)

in *Neurospora* there is complete loss of tritium attached to the 5-position, and little loss of tritium from the 6-position as would be expected. The partial loss of tritium from the 5-position of uracil when incorporated into nucleic acid, uridine, cytidine and deoxycytidine is explained by a reversible conversion to the 5-ribosyl derivatives[156].

The incorporation of cytidine-2-C14 labelled with tritium in the ribosyl group into DNA without loss of tritium provided proof that reduction does not involve loss of hydrogen atoms from the 2'-position[157]. Loss of tritium has been reported during the incorporation

371

of tritiated cytidine and uridine into DNA of proliferating cells[158]. These losses almost certainly arise by exchange occurring during the extraction of the RNA and DNA under acidic conditions and possibly during biological transformations involving the 5-position, 5-methylation to thymidine, for example. Sometimes the loss of a tritium label under biological (enzymatic) conditions can be used advantageously. An example is the use of uridine-5-T as a specific precursor of RNA (see page 43).

Interest in the 5-halogenated nucleosides, particularly 5-iodo-nucleosides[188], prompted a number of workers to prepare these derivatives from commercially available nucleosides, for which the position and distribution of the tritium atoms was unknown. Reports of tritium losses of 70 per cent or more are recorded[159,160]. Tritiated nucleosides, especially those at high specific activity are often prepared by the dehalogenation of the 5-iodo- or 5-bromo-derivatives (see Chapter 4) with tritium gas. It is not surprising therefore that some tritium is lost when the process is reversed.

(g) *Stability of tritium atoms in organometallic compounds*—There is little known about the stability of tritium atoms in organometallic compounds. Trialkylboranes containing tritium attached to the carbon atoms appear to be quite stable under alkaline conditions (see Chapter 4). Tritium atoms attached to silicon atoms would be expected to be stable under acid or alkaline conditions in view of the results obtained with deuterium exchange reactions[161]. No other work appears to have been reported.

(h) *Stability of tritiated metal hydrides*—Tritium atoms in the metal hydrides are readily exchanged on heating in hydrogen, a fact which is made use of in their preparation (see Chapter 4). Those metal hydrides which react with water can lose their tritium as hydrogen tritide or as tritiated hydroxyl ions (6.55):

$$\text{metal-T} + H_2O \rightarrow \text{metal-OH} + \text{metal-OT} + HT$$

$$\cdots \quad (6.55)$$

Mixed metal hydrides behave quite differently. Lithium borohydride and sodium borohydride exchange their hydrogen atoms much less readily than the corresponding metal hydrides and lithium aluminium hydride hardly at all, when heated in tritium gas. Sodium borotritide does not exchange its tritium on dissolving in water or alkali[162] and the reduction of ketones and aldehydes with either sodium- or lithium-borohydrides can be carried out in hydroxylic solvents.

Concluding Remarks

In concluding this chapter two additional points should be remembered; firstly, that a much more complex picture is presented when tritium compounds are metabolized. If tritiated water is produced as one of the metabolic products, it may label many other compounds by exchange or synthesis. The water will be extensively diluted by the aqueous medium, so that although some of the tritium is likely to be incorporated into non-labile positions by enzyme–co-enzyme hydrogen transfer and other reactions[166], the specific activity of the products from such tritium transfer processes is likely to be a different order of magnitude from the normal metabolic products. Caution must nevertheless be exercised when interpreting data.

The second point is the importance of working with truly physiological concentrations of labelled compounds, which is illustrated by an effect observed by Painter and Rasmussen[163]. They were studying the effect of x-irradiation on DNA synthesis in cultures of mammalian cells, using tritiated thymidine to follow the DNA synthesis. Using thymidine at high specific activity (low chemical concentration) the inhibitory effect of the x-irradiation on DNA synthesis was smaller than when using thymidine at low specific activity (high chemical concentration). Upon further investigation, it was found that thymidine itself, in excessive concentrations, inhibits DNA synthesis; an effect quite independent, of course, of radioactivity. Similar results have been reported by Bootsma, Budke and Vos[164].

The effective specific activity of a tracer compound added to a biological system depends (obviously) on the existing 'pool' of the unlabelled compound. It may be less obvious that the conditions of the experiment may alter the pool size without being immediately recognized. Anomalous results in the incorporation of labelled amino acids into serum proteins, in irradiated mice (for example) were traced to augmentation of the normal 'amino acid pool' as a result of irradiation[165].

This brief discussion and some examples of errors which can arise in using tritium as a tracer may at first sight appear to be discouraging, but this would be a short-sighted view. Tritium has great, indeed unique, merits as a radioactive tracer, which have been amply demonstrated in a mass of published work. The debt which modern biochemistry (and to a lesser extent, physical chemistry) owes to another hydrogen tracer–deuterium–should not be forgotten.

Even more fruitful use will be made of tritium, as knowledge accumulates about some of the unknowns discussed in this chapter.

REFERENCES

[1] Rutherford, E. *Nature, Lond.* 140 (1937) 303
[2] Crane, E. J. *Report of Committee on Nomenclature, Spelling and Pronunciation* (Am. Chem. Soc.); Nomenclature of the Hydrogen Isotopes and their compounds. *Ind. Engng Chem. News Edn,* 13 (1935) 200
[3] Hodnett, E. M. and Gallagher, R. *J. org. Chem.* 24 (1959) 564
[4] Murray, A. and Williams, D. L. *Organic Syntheses with Isotopes* 1958. New York; Interscience
[5] Catch, J. R. *Carbon-14 Compounds* 1961. London; Butterworths
[6] *Handbook for Chemical Society Authors* 1960. London; Chem. Soc.
[7] Cacace, F. *Proc. Conf. Methods Preparing Storing Marked Molecules,* Brussels, Belg. Nov. 13–16 (1963). European Atomic Energy Community, Euratom EUR 1625e (May, 1964) p. 1339
[8] Schulze, P. E. and Wenzel, M. (as ref. 7. p. 1271); *Z. analyt. Chem.* 201 (1964) 349
[9] Verly, W. G., Rachele, J. R., Du Vigneaud, V., Eidinoff, M. L. and Knoll, J. E. *J. Am. chem. Soc.* 74 (1952) 5941
[10] Collins, C. J. *Adv. phys. org. Chem.* 2 (1964) 63. Ed. Gold, V. London and New York; Academic Press
[11] Zollinger, H. *Adv. phys. org. Chem.* 2 (1964) 163. Ed. Gold. V. London and New York; Academic Press
[12] Bigeleisen, J. and Wolfsberg, M. Theoretical and Experimental Aspects of Isotope Effects in Chemical Kinetics in *Adv. chem. Phys.* 1 (1958) 15. New York; Interscience
[13] Melander, L. *Isotope Effects on Reaction Rates* 1960. New York; Ronald Press
[14] Brown, L. M. *Nat. Bur. Stand. Rep.* NBS–4611 (May, 1956); NBS–4712 (July, 1956); NBS–4877 (Nov. 1956)
[15] Evans, E. A. and Crowter, D. G. Radiochemical Centre.
[16] Weldon, L. H. P. and Wilson, C. L. *J. chem. Soc.* (1946) 235
[17] Assarsson, L. O. *Acta chem. scand.* 9 (1955) 1399
[18] Melander, L. *Ark. Kemi.* 2 (1950) 260
[19] Kresge, A. J. and Brennan, J. F. *Proc. chem. Soc.* (1963) 215
[20] Melander, L. *Ark. Kemi.* 2 (1950) 211
[21] Bergmann, W. and Meyers, M. B. *Justus Liebigs Annln Chem.* 620 (1959) 46
[22] Chaudhuri, A. C., Harada, Y., Shimizu, K., Gut. M. and Dorfman, R. I. *J. biol. Chem.* 237 (1962) 703
[23] Hodnett, E. M., Taylor, E. D., Tormo, J. V. and Lewis, R. E. *J. Am. chem. Soc.* 81 (1959) 4528
[24] Isbell, H. S., Sniegoski, L. T. and Frush, H. F. *Analyt. Chem.* 38 (1962) 982
[25] Isbell, H. S. and Sniegoski, L. T. *J. Res. Nat. Bur. Stand.* 68A (1964) 145, 301
[26] Gold, V. *Proc. chem. Soc.* (1963) 141
[27] Heinzinger, K. and Weston, R. E. *J. phys. Chem.* 68 (1964) 744
[28] Sepall, O. and Mason, S. G. *Can. J. Chem.* 38 (1960) 2024
[29] Smith, H. A. and Fitch, K. R. *J. phys. Chem.* 67 (1963) 920
[30] Moore, R. and Buskirk, E. R. *Nature, Lond.* 189 (1961) 149
[31] Riley, C. J. and Brooks, H. *Talanta* 11 (1964) 897
[32] Simon, H. and Heubach, G. *Z. Naturf.* 18b (1963) 160

REFERENCES

[33] Root, J. W. and Rowland, F. S. *J. Am. chem. Soc.* 85 (1963) 1021

[34] Isbell, H. S. and Sniegoski, L. T. *J. Res. Nat. Bur. Stand.* 67A (1963) 569

[35] Sniegoski, L. T., Frush, H. L. and Isbell, H. S. *J. Res. Nat. Bur. Stand.* 65A (1961) 441

[36] Sniegoski, L. J. T. *Diss. Abstr.* 22 (1961) 1832

[37] Simon, H. and Müllhofer, G. *Chem. Ber.* 96 (1963) 3167

[38] Hodnett, E. M. and Flynn, J. J. *J. Am. chem. Soc.* 79 (1957) 2300

[39] Gottschling, H. and Freese, E. *Nature, Lond.* 196 (1962) 829

[40] Klein, P. D. *Atomlight* (41) (1964) 1; *Adv. Tracer Methodol.* 2 (1965) 145.

[41] Wilzbach, K. E. and Riesz, P. *Science, N.Y.* 126 (1957) 748

[42] Liberti, A., Cartoni, C. P. and Bruner, F. *J. Chromat.* 12 (1963) 8

[43] Carter, E. H. and Smith, H. A. *J. phys. Chem.* 67 (1963) 1512

[44] Weygand, F., Simon, H. and Keil, K. D. *Chem. Ber.* 92 (1959) 1635

[45] Klein, P. D., Simborg, D. W. and Szczepanik, P. A. *Proc. Symp. Isotope Mass Effects Chem. Biol.*, Vienna (December 1963) p. 357; (1964) London; Butterworths

[46] Isbell, H. S., Frush, H. L. and Holt, N. B. *Analyt. Chem.* 33 (1961) 225

[47] Weygand, F., Simon, H., Keil, K. D., Isbell, H. S. and Sniegoski, L. T. *Analyt. Chem.* 34 (1962) 1753

[48] Rabe, J. G., Guarino, A., Rabe, B. *Int. J. appl. Radiat. Isotopes* 14 (1963) 571

[49] Burr, J. G. *Proc. Symp. Tritium Phys. Biol. Sci.*, I.A.E.A., Vienna 1 (1962) 137

[50] Verly, W. G. *Archs int. Physiol. Biochem.* 64 (1956) 365

[51] Tsuk, G., Castro, Th., Laufer, L. and Schwarz, D. R. *Proc. Conf. Methods Preparing Storing Marked Molecules*, European Atomic Energy Community, Euratom, EUR 1625e (May, 1964) p. 497

[52] Rachele, J. R., Kuchinskas, E. J., Knoll, J. E. and Eidinoff, M. L. *Archs Biochem. Biophys.* 81 (1959) 55

[53] Siri, W. and Evers, J. *Proc. Symp. Tritium Phys. Biol. Sci.*, I.A.E.A., Vienna 2 (1962) 71

[54] Oppenheim, I. and Friedman, A. S. *J. chem. Phys.* 35 (1961) 35

[55] Mislow, K., Graeve, R., Gordon, A. J. and Wahl, G. H. *J. Am. chem. Soc.* 85 (1963) 1199

[56] Melander, L. and Carter, R. E. *Acta chem. scand.* 18 (1964) 1138

[57] Hodnett, E. M. *J. chem. Phys.* 31 (1959) 275

[58] Collins, C. J. *J. Am. chem. Soc.* 77 (1955) 5517

[59] Silver, M. S. *J. Am. chem. Soc.* 83 (1961) 3487

[60] Isbell, H. S., Frush, H. L. and Sniegoski, L. T. *Proc. Symp. Tritium Phys. Biol. Sci.*, I.A.E.A., Vienna 2 (1962) 93

[61] Träger, L., Kornhauser, A. and Wacker, A. (ref. 51, p. 1217)

[62] Swallow, A. J. *Radiation Chemistry of Organic Compounds* 1960. Oxford; Pergamon Press

[63] Bayly, R. J. and Weigel, H. *Nature, Lond.* 188 (1960) 384

[63a] Goodier, I. W. and Pritchard, D. H. *Int. J. appl. Radiat. Isotopes* 17 (1966) 121

[64] Manning, P. G. and Monk, C. B. *J. chem. Soc.* (1962) 2573

[65] Snell, A. H., Pleasonton, F., Leming, H. E. *J. inorg. nucl. Chem.* 5 (1957) 112

[66] Snell, A. H. and Pleasonton, F. *J. phys. Chem.* 62 (1958) 1377

[67] Wexler, S. and Hess, D. C. *J. phys. Chem.* 62 (1958) 1382

[67a] Kandel, R. J. *J. phys. Chem.* 39 (1963) 2581

[68] Evans, E. A. and Stanford, F. G. *Nature, Lond.* 197 (1963) 551

375

[69] Wolfgang, R. L., Anderson, R. C. and Dodson, R. W. *J. chem. Phys.* 24 (1956) 16
[70] Nefedov, V. D., Skorobogatov, G. A., Novak, K., Pluchennik, G. and Gusev, Yu. K. *Zh. obshch. Khim.* 33 (1963) 339
[71] Person, S. *Biophys. J.* 3 (1963) 183
[71a] Person, S. and Brockrath, R. C. *J. molec. Biol.* 13 (1965) 600
[72] Tolbert, B. M. *Atomlight* (11) (1960) 1; *Adv. Tracer Methodol.* 1 (1963) 64
[73] Radiochemical Centre—Unpublished results
[74] Lemmon, R. M., Gordon, P. K., Parsons, M. A. and Mazzetti, F. *J. Am. chem. Soc.* 80 (1958) 2730
[75] Manno, P. J. and Johnston, W. H. *J. Am. chem. Soc.* 79 (1957) 807
[76] Conway, D. and Libby, W. F. *J. Am. chem. Soc.* 80 (1958) 1077
[77] Lemmon, R. M., Parsons, M. A. and Chin, D. M. *J. Am. chem. Soc.* 77 (1955) 4139
[78] Evans, E. A. and Stanford, F. G. *Nature, Lond.* 199 (1963) 762
[79] Osinski, P. A. and Deconinck, J. M. *Proc. Conf. Methods Preparing Storing Marked Molecules*, Brussels (Nov. 1963). European Atomic Energy Community, Euratom, EUR 1625e (May, 1964) p. 931
[80] Apelgot, S., Ekert, B. and Tisne, M. R. (as ref. 79, p. 939)
[81] Hempel, K. (as ref. 79, p. 1009)
[81a] Nouvertne, W. and Hempel, K. *Euratom Rep.*, EUR 1828d (1964)
[82] Guarino, A. (as ref. 79, p. 1059)
[83] Roche, J., Nunez, J., Jacquemin, C. and Pommier, J. (as ref. 79, p. 813)
[84] Collison, E. and Swallow, A. J. *Q. Rev. chem. Soc.* (Lond.) 9 (1955) 311
[85] Brown, D. W., Florin, R. E. and Wall, L. A. *J. phys. Chem.* 66 (1962) 2602
[86] Henriksen, T. *Radiat. Res.* 17 (1962) 158
[87] Henriksen, T. *J. chem. Phys.* 38 (1963) 1926
[88] Henriksen, T., Sanner, T. and Pihl, A. *Radiat. Res.* 18 (1963) 163
[89] Pihl, A., Sanner, T. and Henriksen, T. *Acta chem. scand.* 17 (1963) 2124
[90] Pearlman, W. H. *J. biol. Chem.* 236 (1961) 700
[91] Ghormley, J. A. and Allen, A. O. *Oak Ridge Natn Lab. Rep.* ORNL–128 (Sept. 1948)
[92] Whittemore, I. M. and Lehman, R. L. *Univ. Calif. U.S.A. Rep.* UCRL–8056 (Nov. 1957)
[93] Goldblatt, M. *J. phys. Chem.* 68 (1964) 147
[94] Collinson, E., Dainton, F. S. and Kroh, J. *Roczn. Chem.* 36 (1962) 313
[95] Brustad, A. T. *Tidsskr. Kjemi. Bergv. Metall.* 23 (1963) 27
[96] Apelgot, S., Ekert, B. and Bouyat, A. *J. Chim. phys.* 60 (1963) 505
[97] Beukers, R. and Berends, W. *Biochim. biophys. Acta* 41 (1960) 550
[98] Murray, A., Petersen, D. F., Hayes, F. N. and Magee, M. *Los Alamos Biol. Med. Res. Group Hlth Div., Semiannual Rep.* LAMS–2627 (Jan.–June, 1961) 51
[99] Brodskii, A. I. and Sulima, L. V. *Dokl. Akad. Nauk. SSSR* 74 (1950) 513
[100] Kaplan, L. and Wilzbach, K. E. *J. Am. chem. Soc.* 76 (1954) 2593
[101] Shatenshtein, A. I. *Isotopic Exchange and the Replacement of Hydrogen in Organic Compounds* 1962. New York; Consultants Bureau
[102] Geller, L. E. *Atomlight* (19) (1961) 11
[103] Achor, L. B. *J. Pharm. exp. Ther.* 122 (1958) 1A
[104] Okita, G. T., Kabara, J. J., Richardson, F. and Leroy, G. V. *Nucleonics* 15 (6) (1957) 111
[105] LaBrosse, E. H. *Adv. Tracer Methodol.* 1 (1963) 247

REFERENCES

[106] Levy, H. R., Talalay, P. and Vennesland, B. *Progress in Stereochemistry* 3 (1962) 299. Ed. de la Mare, P.B.D. and Klyne, W. 1962. London; Butterworths

[107] Spratt, J. L., Okita, T. and Geiling, E. M. K. *Int. J. appl. Radiat. Isotopes* 2 (1957) 167

[108] Cooke, A. M., Rogers, A.W. and Thomas, G. H. *J. Endocrin.* 27 (1963) 299

[109] Moss, A. R. and Schoenheimer, R. *J. biol. Chem.* 135 (1940) 421

[110] Gurin, S. and Delluva, A. M. *J. biol. Chem.* 170 (1947) 545

[111] Sykes, P. *A Guidebook to Mechanism in Organic Chemistry* 1961. London; Longmans

[112] Kay, J. G. and Rowland, F. S. *J. org. Chem.* 24 (1959) 1800

[113] Nagatsu, T., Levitt, M. and Udenfriend, S. *Biochem. biophys. Res. Commun.* 14 (1964) 543; *Analyt. biochem.* 9 (1964) 122

[114] Crawhall, J. C. and Smyth, D. G. *Biochem. J.* 69 (1958) 280

[115] Clark, I. and Rittenberg, D. *J. biol. Chem.* 189 (1951) 521

[116] Sprinson, D. B. and Rittenberg, D. *J. biol. Chem.* 184 (1950) 405

[117] Evans, E. A., Green, R. H., Spanner, J. A. and Waterfield, W. R. *Nature, Lond.* 198 (1963) 1301

[118] Evans, E. A. and Green, R. H. Radiochemical Centre.

[119] Parikh, J. R., Greenstein, J. P., Winitz, M. and Birnbaum, S. M. *J. Am. chem. Soc.* 80 (1958) 953

[120] Konikova, A. S., Doebert, N. N. and Braunstein, A. E. *Nature, Lond.* 159 (1947) 67

[121] Samal, B. A., Frazier, L. E., Monto, G., Slesers, A., Hruban, Z. and Wissler, R. W. *Proc. Soc. exp. Biol. Med.* 112 (1963) 442

[122] Gut, M. and Hayano, M. *Atomlight* (23) (1962) 1

[123] Ayres, P. J. *Proc. Symp. Tritium Phys. Biol. Sci.*, I.A.E.A., Vienna 2 (1962) 131

[124] Osinski, P. *Proc. Symp. Tritium Phys. Biol. Sci.*, I.A.E.A., Vienna 2 (1962) 113

[125] Fieser, L. F. and Fieser, M. *Experientia* 4 (1948) 285

[126] Hayano, M., Ringold, H. J., Stefanovic, V., Gut, M. and Dorfman, R. I. *Biochem. biophys. Res. Commun.* 4 (1961) 454

[127] Hayano, M., Gut, M., Dorfman, R. I., Sebek, O. K. and Peterson, D. H. *J. Am. chem. Soc.* 80 (1958) 2336

[128] Corey, E. J., Gregoriou, G. A. and Peterson, D. H. *J. Am. chem. Soc.* 80 (1958) 2338

[129] Corey, E. J. and Gregoriou, G. A. *J. Am. Chem. Soc.* 81 (1961) 3127

[130] Bergstrom, S., Lindstredt, S., Samuelson, B., Corey, E. J. and Gregoriou, G. A. *J. Am. chem. Soc.* 80 (1958) 2337

[131] Samuelsson, B. *J. biol. Chem.* 234 (1959) 2852

[132] Osinski, P. A. *Nature, Lond.* 187 (1960) 777

[133] Gut, M. and Uskokovic, M. *J. org. Chem.* 25 (1960) 792

[134] Hayano, M., Gut, M., Dorfman, R. I., Schubert, A. and Siebert, R. *Biochim. biophys. Acta* 32 (1959) 269

[135] Isbell, H. S., Frush, H. L. and Holt, N. B. *Analyt. Chem.* 33 (1961) 225

[136] Lowenstein, J. M. *J. biol. Chem.* 236 (1961) 1213

[137] Rittenberg, D., Schoenheimer, R. and Evans, E. A. (Jr.) *J. biol. Chem.* 120 (1937) 503

[137a] Dunn, A. and Strahs, S. *Nature, Lond.* 205 (1965) 705

[137b] Katz, J., Rognstad, R. and Kemp, R. G. *J. biol. Chem.* 240 (1965) PC 1484

[138] Baker, R., Eaborn, C. and Sperry, J. A. *J. chem. Soc.* (1962) 2382 and earlier papers (see also Chapter 2)

[139] Thomas, R. J. and Long, F. A. *J. Am. chem. Soc.* 86 (1964) 4770

[140] Melander, L. and Olsson, S. *Acta chem. scand.* 10 (1956) 879

[141] Andrews, K. J. M., Bultitude, F., Evans, E. A., Gronow, M., Lambert, R. W. and Marrian, D. H. *J. chem. Soc.* (1963) 3440

[142] Senoh, S., Creveling, C. R., Udenfriend, S. and Witkop, B. *J. Am. chem. Soc.* 81 (1959) 6236

[143] Lapidot, A., Reuben, J. and Samuel, D. *J. chem. Educ.* 41 (1964) 570

[144] Condon, F. E. *J. Am. chem. Soc.* 73 (1951) 4675

[145] Crowter, D. G., Evans, E. A. and Lambert, R. W. *Chemy Ind.* (1960) 899

[146] Moravek, J. and Filip, J. *Coll. Czech. chem. Commun. Engl. edn.* 25 (1960) 2697

[147] Fink, R. M. *Fedn. Proc. Fedn Am. Socs exp. Biol.* 22 (2, Pt. 1) (1963) 471

[148] Fink, R. M. *Archs Biochem. Biophys.* 107 (1964) 493

[149] Main, R. K. and Walwick, E. R. U.S. NRDL–TR–452 (July, 1960)

[150] Johnson, H. A., Rubini, J. R., Cronkite, E. P. and Bond, V. P. *Lab. Invest.* 9 (1960) 460

[151] Friedkin, M. *Fedn. Proc. Fedn Am. Socs exp. Biol.* 19 (1960) 312 (Abstract)

[152] Pastore, E. J. and Friedkin, M. *J. biol. Chem.* 237 (1962) 3802

[153] Fink, R. M. and Fink, K. *J. biol. Chem.* 237 (1962) 2889

[154] Takats, S. T. and Smellie, R. M. S. *J. Cell Biol.* 17 (1963) 59

[155] Robbins, P. W. and Hammond, J. B. *J. biol. Chem.* 237 (1962) PC 1379

[156] Fink, R. M. *J. biol. Chem.* 238 (1963) 1764

[157] Thompson, R. Y., Scotto, G. T. and Brown, G. B. *J. biol. Chem.* 237 (1962) 3510

[158] Baserga, R. *J. Cell Biol.* 19 (1963) 6A

[159] Chang, P. K. and Welch, A. D. *Biochem. Pharmac.* 8 (1961) 327

[160] Smith, H. H., Kugelman, B. H., Commerford, S. L. and Szybalski, W. *Proc. Natn. Acad. Sci. Wash. U.S.A.* 49 (1963) 451

[161] Brodskii, A. I. and Khaskin, I. G. *Dokl. Akad. Nauk SSSR* 74 (1950) 299

[162] Girardot, P. R. and Parry, R. W. *J. Am. chem. Soc.* 73 (1951) 2368

[163] Painter, R. B. and Rasmussen, R. E. *Nature, Lond.* 201 (1964) 409

[164] Bootsma, D., Budke, L. and Vos, O. *Expl Cell Res.* 33 (1964) 301

[165] Sassen, A., Reuter, A., Kennes, F. and Franssen, J. *Preparation Bio-Medical Applications of Labelled Molecules*, European Atomic Energy Community. Euratom, EUR 2200e (Dec. 1964) p. 175

[166] Pastore, E. J., Friedkin, M. and Jardetzky, O. *J. Am. chem. Soc.* 85 (1963) 3058

[167] Fujita, Y., Gottlieb, A., Peterkofsky, B., Udenfriend, S. and Witkop, B. *J. Am. chem. Soc.* 86 (1964) 4709

[168] Ebert, P. S. and Prockop, D. J. *Biochem. biophys. Res. Commun.* 8 (1962) 305

[169] Prockop, D. J., Ebert, P. S. and Shaoiro, B. M. *Archs Biochem. Biophys.* 106 (1964) 112

[170] Hayano, M. *Oxygenases*. Ed. O. Hayaishi, p. 182, 1962. New York and London; Academic Press

[171] Irreverre, F., Morita, K., Robertson, A. V. and Witkop, B. *J. Am. chem. Soc.* 85 (1963) 2824

[172] Kaplan, A., Witkop, B. and Udenfriend, S. *J. biol. Chem.* 239 (1964) 2559

REFERENCES

173 Lamport, D. T. A. *Nature, Lond.* 202 (1964) 293

174 Gant, P. L. and Yang, K. *J. Am. chem. Soc.* 86 (1964) 5063

175 West, D. L. and Marston, A. L. *J. Am. chem. Soc.* 86 (1964) 4731

176 Carter, E. H. and Smith, H. A. *J. phys. Chem.* 67 (1963) 1512

177 Lee, E. K. C. and Rowland, F. S. *Analyt. Chem.* 36 (1964) 2181

178 Staats, P. A., Morgan, H. W. and Goldstein, J. H. *J. phys. Chem.* 25 (1956) 582

179 Rao, K. N., Brim, W. W. and Hoffman, J. M. *J. molec. Spectrosc.* 7 (1961) 362

180 Pichat, L. *Proc. Conf. Methods Preparing Storing Marked Molecules.* European Atomic Energy Community, Euratom, EUR 1625e (May, 1964) p. 763

181 Apelgot, S., Ekert, B., Tham, G. and Tordjman-Bouyat, A. *J. chim. phys.* 62 (1965) 845

182 Apelgot, S., Frilley, M. and Defaux, A. *J. Chim. phys.* 62 (1965) 838

183 Evans, E. A. and Stanford, F. G. Radiochemical Centre.

184 Tanovka, H. *Radiat. Res.* 21 (1964) 26

185 Apelgot, S., Ekert, B. and Frilley, M. *Biochim. biophys. Acta* 103 (1965) 563

186 Winand, M., Bricteux-Gregoire, S. and Verly, W. G. *Prep. and Bio-Med. Applications of Labelled Molecules.* European Atomic Energy Community, Euratom, EUR 2200e (Dec. 1964) p. 17

187 Kowarski, A., Finkelstein, J., Loras, B. and Migeon, C. T. *Steroids* 3 (1964) 95

188 O'Sullivan, D. G. *Viruses and the Chemotherapy of Viral Diseases. R. Inst. Chem.* Lecture Series (1965) No. 2

189 Ford, H. C. and Bailey, R. E. *Steroids* 7 (1966) 30

APPENDIX

The flood of publications relating to investigations using radioactive isotopically labelled compounds has prompted the addition of this appendix as a 'stop-press' review in which some interesting recent developments concerning tritium and its compounds, in the various fields of study, are discussed.

The subject matter is considered under the chapter headings used previously, and the bibliography of tritium measurement is extended to cover publications to March 1966.

Notable general publications include a new journal *The Journal of Labelled Compounds* which is produced quarterly[1], and a bibliography of tritium measurement and preparation of labelled molecules by Mantescu and Genunche[2] containing some 588 references.

Chapter 1—PRODUCTION AND PROPERTIES

While nothing has been published that would invalidate the properties stated for tritium, there has been some argument as to the existence of the isotopes hydrogen-4 and hydrogen-5. Rogers and Stokes[3] suggest that the failure to find ^4H protons from the $^3H(n,p)$ reaction lends support to any argument for the non-existence of particle stable hydrogen-4. Goldanskii[4] points out that the results and calculation of the decay energy and the discovery of a beta active helium isotope of mass 8, cast some doubt upon the existence of hydrogen-5.

Isotopic composition of hydrogen–tritium mixtures has been determined by emission-spectral analysis[5], and some expected vibrational energies of tritium have been computed by Kolos and Wolniewicz[6] in connection with other spectral properties of the isotope. Balling and Pipkin[7] record measurements of the gyromagnetic ratio of hydrogen, tritium, free electrons and rubidium-85.

Diffusion coefficients of the hydrogen isotopes[8, 9] and of the systems He-T_2 and He-TH[10], in the temperature range 195–374° K have been reported, and Kochurikhin and Zel'Venskii[11] have determined their separation factor and adsorption isotherms in the low-temperature adsorption on synthetic zeolites.

Calculation of some physico-chemical parameters such as heat capacity at constant pressure, entropy and free energy function, have been made for tritiated phosphine, arsine and ammonia[12].

Chapter 2—USES

Applications of tritium and its compounds continue to increase very rapidly indeed. In this appendix, the uses of tritium and its compounds are discussed under two main headings only, namely non-biological and biological uses.

1. Non-biological Uses

1.1. *Analytical*

An alternative to the carboxylation method for determining the number of carbon–lithium bonds present in lithium-terminated polymers (for example, in polybutadienyl lithium) is proposed by Campbell and Warner[13]. The method consists essentially of reacting the carbon–lithium bond with an alcohol labelled with tritium on the hydroxyl group, followed by a determination of the specific activity of the resulting tritiated polymer. Suitable alcohols-(*hydroxyl*-T) include methanol, ethanol, n-propanol and n-butanol. The method has the advantage of being applicable to polymers containing (as impurities), n-butyl lithium, phenyl lithium, lithium alkoxides and phenoxides, lithium hydride and lithium metal, which react with the tritiated alcohol to give mainly volatile products.

This analytical application provides another of the few examples[13a] of the use of tritium compounds having tritium atoms in readily labile positions.

1.2 *Hydrogen Tracer*

Detritiation reactions for studying aromatic reactivity have been extended to include 1-tritionaphthalenes[14] and the substituent effects in the acid-catalysed hydration of phenylacetylenes[15]. 1-Tritio-2-phenylacetylene hydrated in a mixture of acetic acid and aqueous sulphuric acid, does not *exchange* any of its tritium during the hydration of the triple bond[15]. The mechanism of the hydration is the same as that for the hydration of alkynyl alkyl ethers and sulphides in aqueous acids, namely, a rate-determining proton transfer being followed by a rapid reaction of the formed carbonium ion with the solvent to give a hydroxy-ethylene which subsequently rearranges to a ketone (A.1):

$$Ar \cdot C \equiv CH + H_3O^+ \rightarrow Ar \cdot \overset{+}{C} = CH_2 + H_2O$$

$$Ar \cdot \overset{+}{C} = CH_2 + H_2O \rightarrow Ar \cdot \overset{+}{C}(OH_2) = CH_2$$

$$Ar \cdot C(OH_2^+) = CH_2 + H_2O \rightarrow Ar \cdot C(OH) = CH_2 + H_3O^+$$

$$Ar \cdot C(OH) = CH_2 \rightarrow Ar \cdot CO \cdot CH_3$$

(Ar = Aryl)   . . . . (A.1)

Tritiated dimethylsulphoxide has been used to investigate the mechanism of the base-catalysed β-elimination reactions of sulphones[16].

The work of Akhtar and Gibbons[17] concerning the mechanism of the pre-vitamin-$D_3 \rightleftharpoons$ vitamin-D_3 conversion, is an interesting illustration of the use of tritium as a tracer for hydrogen in hydrogen transfer reactions.

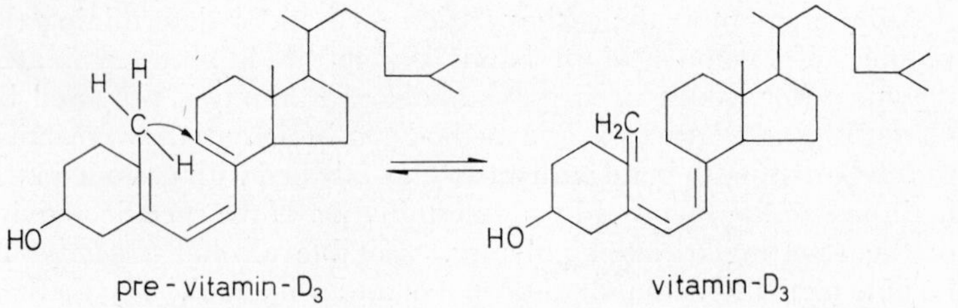

pre - vitamin - D_3 vitamin-D_3

$$\cdots \cdots \quad (A.2)$$

Ozonolysis of tritiated vitamin-D_3, prepared from pre-vitamin-D_3, labelled in the 19-methyl group (see page 400), gave formaldehyde-T containing nearly half (48 per cent) of the radioactivity of the vitamin. This result clearly demonstrated that the known[18-20] intramolecular hydrogen transfer from the 19-methyl group to the 9-position (A.2) is a non-stereospecific transfer in which the 9α and 9β-hydrogen atoms are equivalent.

Other recent uses of tritium as a tracer for hydrogen include the determination of the reactivity of surface (nickel) adsorbed hydrogen[21] and for investigating the reaction of tritium atoms with films of solid ethylene[22]. At this low temperature $(63^\circ K)$ the reaction involves the disproportionation and combination of ethyl radicals.

1.3. *Hydrology*

Hydrological applications of tritium (mainly as tritiated water) continue to provide useful information to the geophysicists[23-28]. One interesting application is the use of tritiated water to examine the depths to which trees will extend their roots in efforts to get water[29]. Woods and O'Neal[30] conducted similar investigations to study the withdrawal of water from the soil by small trees. The transpired water was collected by surrounding the leaves with a polythene bag and the tritium activity measured. The experiments were carried out with only 5 c of tritiated water at an initial specific activity of 10 mc/mM.

One can foresee the results of such investigations being of importance in agriculture.

2. Biological Uses

The applications of tritium compounds in biological investigations continue to preponderate over their other uses. Some of the many recent examples are considered here.

2.1. *Analysis of Body Fluids*

The determination of organic compounds in body fluids continues to be vigorously pursued in the hope that more sensitive and rapid methods can be found for the early detection of pathological disorders. The availability of tritium compounds particularly those at very high specific activity (curies per millimole), has spurred the development of radioactive procedures for the analysis of compounds in body fluids based on the principle of competitive inhibition of a reaction involving the labelled compound by its unlabelled counterpart. An excellent example demonstrating this principle is provided by Rothenberg[31] who used tritiated folic acid at a very high specific activity (4·45 c/mM) for the determination of picogram (10^{-12}) quantities of folic acid in human serum.

Unlabelled folic acid will competitively inhibit the enzymatic reduction of tritiated folic acid and hence enables the determination of minute quantities of folic acid (A.3):

$$\text{Folate} + \text{NADPH}_2 \xrightleftharpoons{\text{folic acid reductase}} \text{Tetrahydrofolate} + \text{NADP}$$

$$\text{.} \quad \text{.} \quad \text{.} \quad \text{.} \quad \text{(A.3)}$$

The technique generally offers a useful approach to the analysis of any substrate for which any enzymatic reaction has been defined and provided an efficient method exists for the separation of the labelled reactant and product. It is of course very important for investigations of this kind that the tracer compound should be of high radiochemical and chemical purity.

Tritiated digitonin has been used to measure the tissue levels of 3β-hydroxysterols[32]. Digitonin complexes specifically with the β-isomer of 3-hydroxy sterols such as cholesterol. Thus by using cholesterol-C14 and tritiated digitonin the double isotope derivative analysis procedure (see page 16) can be adopted.

The use of labelled acetic anhydride in the analysis of body fluids for steroids is now routine in many institutions and hospitals [33-38, 38a]. Acetylations are usually carried out with benzene solutions of tritium (or carbon-14) labelled acetic anhydride and to achieve accurate and meaningful results it is normally necessary to use the freshly distilled reagent (see page 410). A suitable apparatus for re-distillation of the labelled anhydride in benzene solution has been described [39].

Sulphur-35-labelled thiosemicarbazide is used to form the thio-semicarbazones of tritium (or carbon-14) labelled androstenedione, testosterone or progesterone, for their double isotope derivative analysis [40]. A gas–liquid chromatographic method [41] for the estim-ation of testosterone in human peripheral blood has been stated to be simpler and quicker than the double isotope derivative method. However, it remains to be demonstrated whether such a method matches the general applicability and accuracy of the double isotope derivative analysis technique.

Other investigations include the use of high specific activity oestrone-6,7-T for determining millimicrogramme amounts of urinary oestrone [42], and cholesterol-7α-T for estimating plasma cholesterol esterifying activity (plasma fatty acid transferase activity) [43].

2.2. *Biosynthesis*

Just how complex molecules, such as the alkaloids for example, arise in plants is always a fascinating subject for investigation, and tritium tracers continue to play an important role in such studies [44, 45, 45a]. Barton, Kirby and Kirby [45] have mapped the biosynthetic pathway of the alkaloid sinomenine in *Sinomenium acutum*, as indicated (A.4), by the use of tritiated reticuline and sinoacutine. The reticuline was readily labelled in the positions shown (A.4) by exchange in alkaline tritiated water.

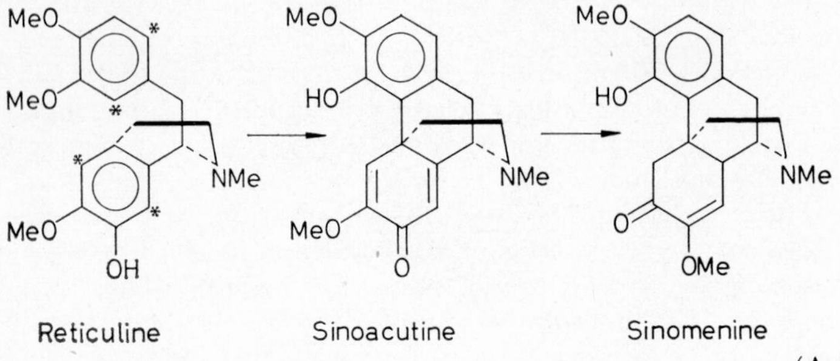

Reticuline   Sinoacutine   Sinomenine

. . . . (A.4)

Position of the tritium atoms.

384

The use of mevalonic acid stereospecifically labelled with tritium in the 4R and 4S positions to demonstrate that the 4S-hydrogen atom is the one eliminated in the biosynthesis of squalene, provides an excellent example of the use of tritium as a hydrogen tracer[46]. The investigations have been extended to study the stereospecificity of carotenoid biosynthesis[47], cholesterol biosynthesis[48], and the incorporation of tritiated mevalonate into squalene, ubiquinone and ergosterol of *Aspergillus fumigatus* Fresenius[49].

Other investigations include the use of acetate-2-T, succinic acid-2,3-T and tyrosine-T(G) for studying the biogenesis of furocoumarins[50], such as bergatene (A.5a) and psoralene (A.5b) which are found in the leaves of *Ficus carica*, and the furanic terpenes (marrubine) and phytosterols (22,23-dihydrostigmasterol) in cultures of *Marrubium vulgare* plants and *Wistaria sinesis* flowers respectively[51].

(a)   (b)

. . . . (A.5)

2-Hydroxypalmitic acid-9,10-T has been used to study the formation of sphingolipid bases in the yeast *Hansenula ciferri*[52]. Prostaglandins are biosynthesized from (tritiated) arachidonic acid by homogenates of guinea pig lung[52a].

2.3. *Diagnostic Medicine*

Nearly all the present uses of isotopes in diagnosis are extensions of pre-isotopic methods using radioisotopes only to improve the sensitivity of measurement[53].

The uptake of tritiated noradrenaline serves to measure the extent of sympathetic innervation in peripheral tissues[54] and has been used to demonstrate an abnormality in the dynamics of noradrenaline metabolism in patients with essential hypertension[55]. Noradrenaline clearances become exponential at rates uniformly more rapid in the hypertensive than in the normal subjects.

Hyperglycinemia, a disorder of amino acid metabolism characterized by abnormal concentrations of glycine in the blood, urine and cerebrospinal fluid, has been studied in a 4½-year-old child using glycine-2-T at 44 mc/mM[56]. Following an intravenous dose of 30 μc/kg the size of the glycine pool in the patient was found to be approximately twice that of the control subjects. Among the excreted amino acids only serine (other than glycine) was labelled and the formation of serine from glycine was markedly less efficient in the patient. The data were suggested to indicate that hyperglycinemia is marked by a fundamental abnormality in the conversion of glycine to serine.

Biochemical disorders in inherited metabolic diseases have been reviewed by Crawhall[57].

The adaptation of such known biochemical abnormalities, often established by the use of labelled compounds, to routine diagnostic procedures using such compounds, is regrettably very slow.

2.4. *Metabolism*

Research workers continue to be cautious (and rightly so) in the use of tritiated compounds for metabolic studies. Results are normally confirmed using double labelling with carbon-14 or sulphur-35. When available, specifically labelled tritium compounds are nearly always used.

Pearlman[58] reviews work on the metabolism and localization of tritium-labelled steroid in tissues, with particular reference to the *in vivo* use of progesterone-7α-T, oestrone-6,7-T and Δ^4-androstene-3,17-dione-7α-T in humans with breast cancer. The metabolism of 11-deoxycorticosterone-1,2-T suggests that the preferred pathway for aldosterone formation in human adrenal tumour tissue is progesterone → 11-deoxycorticosterone → corticosterone → 18-hydroxycorticosterone → aldosterone[59].

Dehydroepiandrosterone-7α-T and testosterone-1,2-T were used to demonstrate that the human foetus (of both sexes) can aromatize androstenedione and testosterone but not dehydroepiandrosterone[60].

Further support for the concept that sulphated intermediates such as cholesterol or pregnenolone sulphates for example, are involved in the metabolic pathway of the steroid hormones, is provided by Roberts and colleagues[61]. The proposed pathway is as shown in the reaction scheme (A.6).

'Doubly labelled' cholesterol-7α-T sulphate-S35 injected into the left splenic artery of a female patient with inoperable carcinoma, was converted into dehydroepiandrosterone-7α-T sulphate-S35 (a major secretory product of the adrenal gland). The ratio of T to S35 in the isolated dehydroepiandrosterone sulphate was the same as that in the administered cholesterol sulphate.

Cholesterol-7α-T sulphate is used as a tracer for the isolation of cholesterol sulphate from human blood and gallstones[62].

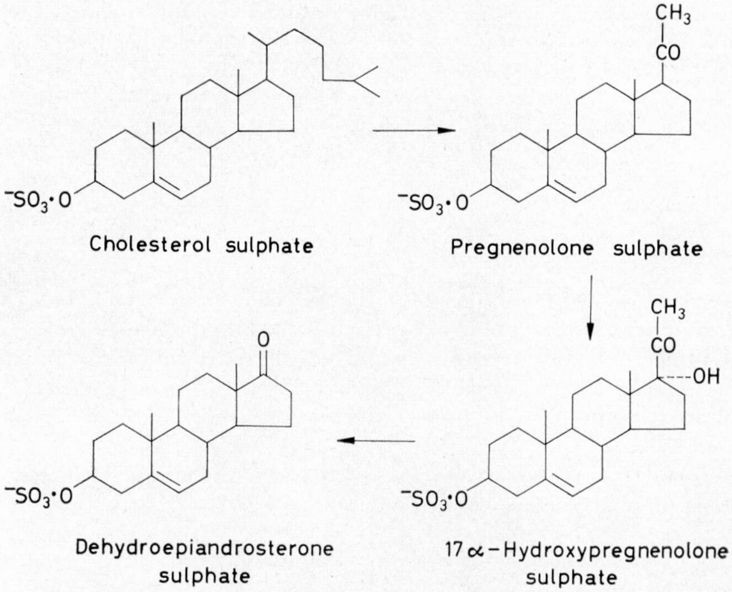

Cholesterol sulphate

Pregnenolone sulphate

Dehydroepiandrosterone
sulphate

17α−Hydroxypregnenolone
sulphate

. . . . (A.6)

Other investigations with tritiated steroids include the metabolism of cholest-5-ene-3β,20α-diol-7α-T and cholest-5-ene-3β,17,20α-triol-7α-T by human adrenal tissue[63]; 3α,6β-dihydroxy-5β-cholanoic acid-24-C14-6α-T[64], cholest-4-ene-7α,12α-diol-3-one-T(G) and 5β-cholestane-7α,12α-diol-3-one-T(G)[65] in the rat; a study of the transfer of tritium from cholesterol-7α-T to the fatty acids of tissue lipids in male baboons[66] and the tritium concentration in dog brain tissues following an intravenous dose of cortisol-1,2-T[67].

Tritiated vitamin-D_3 has been used in attempts to achieve a better understanding of the mechanism by which calcium absorption in the body is regulated[68, 69, 69a]. Results show that the metabolism of vitamin-D_3-T is abnormal in patients with sarcoidosis[68].

Tritiated inulin and mannitol, two compounds thought not to penetrate the cell membrane, were used to investigate their diffusion into heart muscle[70].

Samuelsson and colleagues[71] using 9α,11α,15-trihydroxyprost-13-enoic acid-9-T (prostaglandin $F_1α$), demonstrated that the main urinary metabolite of this substance in the rat is 2,3-dinorprostaglandin $F_1α$ which is two carbon atoms shorter in the chain (A.7).

Khan and Wilson make use of tritiated water for studies of turnover in mammalian subcellular particles, brain nuclei, mitochondria and microsomes, in the rat[72], while D-sorbitol-1-T has been used to

OH   OH   OH   OH

11   15   11   15

10   →   10

9   CO_2H 9 CO_2H

OH   OH

. . . . (A.7)

demonstrate certain aspects of the mechanism by which insulin stimulates glucose uptake in rat epididymal adipose tissue *in vitro*[73].

Other metabolic investigations include the use of tritiated vitamin-A[74], β-carotene[74], digoxin[75], diethylstilboestrol[76], myoinositol[223] 'butter yellow' (*NN*-dimethylaminoazobenzene)[224] and reserpine[224a].

Graul[77] discusses 10 years' experience in the use of (tritiated) drugs in pharmacological investigations.

2.5 *Molecular Biology* (Cytology and Autoradiography)

Applications of tritium compounds in cytological investigations continue to account for at least 50 per cent of their uses. The results of this vigorous and intensive research must ultimately play a major role in elucidating the mechanism by which cancer arises and perhaps also to improvements in the treatment and prevention of the disease.

The search for the mechanism which triggers cell division (see page 41) continues; results obtained by Laurence and Butler[78] using generally labelled tritiated lysine, led them to suggest that histones which are found in cells *only* in association with DNA can certainly be regarded as part of the mechanism controlling the replication and function of chromosomes. Akai and Kobayashi[79] use tritiated thymidine to demonstrate that in the nucleus of the silk gland (of the silk worm), DNA is synthesized on chromatin bodies.

Although Roll and Killman[80] observed no diurnal variation in the (thymidine) labelling index of human leukaemic blast cells, Bruce and Meeker[81], in their experiments comparing the sensitivity of normal haematopoietic and transplanted lymphoma colony-forming cells of mice to high specific activity tritiated thymidine *in vivo*, found that a large fraction of normal cells do not pass through DNA synthesis in 24 h but most lymphoma cells do and consequently may incorporate tritiated thymidine and die (from the intracellular radiation) during this period. A dose of 6 mc of tritiated thymidine (labelled in the 5-methyl group at specific activity above 10 c/mM) is sufficient to reduce to 20 per cent the number of normal colony-forming cells, while lymphoma colony-forming cells are reduced to less than 0·1 per cent. These results were advanced as explaining the action of chemotherapeutic agents that kill cells which pass through the cell cycle.

Research workers are becoming more aware[82, 82a] of the possible effects during experiments of the intracellular radiation produced by tritiated compounds at high specific activity. The effect of the actual dose given on the incorporation of tritiated thymidine in nuclei of the liver capsule cells in the newt (*Triturus viridescens*)[83] showed that the labelled thymidine was available for labelling the cells in the system for a much longer period of time than has been reported for other cell systems, and also a definite dose dependency of availability time of the tritiated thymidine. 1 μc, 0·1 μc, 0·05 μc and 0·01 μc/g weight of newt for example, gave maximum uptake times in the liver capsule cells of 24–48 h, 10–30 h, 12–18 h and 4–12 h respectively, which is much longer than Rubini's results (see page 30).

Pachler, Koch and Schaechter[84], using thymine-(*methyl*-T) provide further evidence that bacterial cells, under certain conditions, appear to synthesize DNA throughout their entire cycle of cell division, in contrast to plant and animal cells (see page 43).

Considerable interest is attached to the mode of action of actinomycin-D, which is known[85] to inhibit DNA-dependent RNA synthesis without affecting DNA replication. At the cytological level this results in an inhibition of nucleolar RNA synthesis with the concomitant failure to form ribosomal RNA[86]. Leukocyte RNA (labelled with uridine-T) synthesis for example, is almost totally suppressed by the action of this antibiotic[87]. It was during such investigations that Kasten, Strasser and Turner[88] discovered that nucleolar and cytoplasmic RNA synthesis was also inhibited by high (chemical) concentrations of thymidine, which is similar to the thymidine inhibition of DNA synthesis observed by other investigators (see page 373). The mechanism and specificity of actinomycin binding to DNA has been investigated by Gellert and colleagues[89] using tritiated actinomycin prepared biosynthetically (see page 191).

Tritiated methotrexate has been suggested as a granulocyte label[90]; it has the potential advantages over tritiated thymidine in that (*a*) methotrexate-T is localized in the cytoplasm rather than in the nucleus, thus obviating to some extent, localized radiation to the nucleus that may lead to cytological modifications; (*b*) methotrexate-T can be displaced from the body with unlabelled methotrexate or with

pharmacological doses of folate or dihydrofolate and (c) methotrexate-T is not diluted by endogenous synthesis, as is tritiated
thymidine. A minor disadvantage of methotrexate-T, in normal
subjects, is the necessity for 'inducing' the methotrexate-binding
enzyme, dihydrofolate reductase, with a prior dose of unlabelled
methotrexate.

An autoradiographic study of the distribution of tritiated folic acid
in the mouse gut by Creamer and Shiner [91], indicated that bile is not
the only pathway by which folic acid reaches the intestinal lumen.
The folic acid is concentrated in the adult (mouse) epithelial cells of
the upper gastrointestinal tract and then passes out into the lumen.
In certain circumstances folic acid may possibly reach the gut-lumen
by passage through the mucosa of the stomach, duodenum and
jejunum as well as by the bile.

The important connection between folic acid deficiency and
anaemia which occurs in pregnancy will no doubt stimulate further
interest in the use of tritiated folic acid and related compounds.

Tritiated thymidine (as a DNA label) has shown that cell proliferation in *Hydra littoralis* is distributed along the body column and
that there is no localized growth zone unless there is rapid cell
migration from a growth region [92]. This result supports the earlier
work on growth in the Hydra carried out over 30 years ago [93] but
disagrees with the more recent work by Burnett [94] and by Brien and
Reniers-Decoen [95]. The relative impermeability of Hydra to organic
molecules in the external milieu has hindered previous attempts to
label its nuclei. Campbell [92] overcomes this difficulty by injecting the
tritiated thymidine solution into the Hydra's gastric cavity immediately after the animal had been fed *Artemia nauplii*; autoradiographic
analysis showed the incorporation of the label into cell nuclei.

The application of special autoradiographic techniques for visualizing water-soluble tritiated compounds in various tissues draws
particular attention to facts which can easily be missed [95a] unless such
techniques are applied. Using tritiated thymidine Pelc and Appleton [96] demonstrated for example, that the cell contents of water-
soluble material is 'turned over' once every 3–5 min, and also the
importance of the permeability of the cell membrane; thymidine-T
which is not phosphorylated by thymidine kinase passes into the cell
and out again. Other recent advances concerning autoradiographic
techniques are discussed on page 404.

It has been shown autoradiographically that testosterone-1,2-T is
physically attracted and becomes attached to the sites of active RNA
synthesis; the attachment appears to be to the histone portion of the

chromosomes[97]. Other investigations include that of Goldfeder[98] on the radiosensitivity of tumours and that of Lipkin and colleagues[99] concerning the replication of epithelial cells in atrophic gastric mucosa (in cases of pernicious anaemia). Tritiated thymidine was used for both these examples.

2.6. *Miscellaneous Uses*

Other uses of tritium compounds include that of tritiated naphthalene in a chemical dosimeter for low radiation doses (below 10 rads)[100]. Hydrophilic compounds (probably naphthols) are produced when aqueous solutions of naphthalene are irradiated. The use of tritiated naphthalene enables the yield of these compounds to be measured accurately. With a concentration of 0·065 mM an internal dose of 0·3 rad/day can be measured. The method assumes that tritium is not exchanged or displaced from the radiation-produced products.

Tritiated water can be used for studying the desorption of tritiated bound-water from the passive film formed on stainless steels[101].

Chapter 3—SAFE HANDLING

Publication[102] of papers presented at a seminar on the protection against the dangers of tritium, provide an interesting collection of information which does not add significantly to what has been written in Chapter 3. A number of the papers deal with the hazards of tritium from heavy water moderated reactors and others discuss the measurement of tritium contamination in air, but much of the information is really of little relevance to the *tracer* user of tritium compounds. The conclusions reached may be summarized in the statement by Dr. Morgan[103] that 'tritium is not one of the most dangerous radionuclides but it can present very serious radiation problems *if it is not handled properly*'.

3.1. *Handling*

An apparatus for handling volatile radioactive materials without a vacuum manifold system is described by Farber[104].

Scharpenseel[105] describes the construction of a combined high-vacuum line for chemical syntheses, degradation, Wilzbach tritiations, gas-phase counting of carbon-14 after Pregl-combustion and for gas-phase measurement of tritium after Wilzbach combustion with zinc and nickel oxide. Such an 'all purposes' vacuum manifold system is satisfactory *only* if the levels of activity for the various uses are of the same order of magnitude. In the author's experience at the Radiochemical Centre, any vacuum system used for filling measurement tubes should be quite separate from one used in labelling procedures, and especially Wilzbach labelling.

3.2. *Monitoring*

Sims[106] has suggested the possibility of detecting and dating the accidental exposure of laboratory staff to the ingestion of small amounts of labelled amino acids, by an autoradiographic examination of their hair. The concentration of radioactivity along the length of hair allows the date of the ingestion to be estimated. This is an interesting idea but it would take far too long to be routinely useful for the control of personal uptake.

3.3. *Toxicity of Tritium Compounds*

Little more need be added to the interesting review by Wimber[107] of the effects of intracellular irradiation with tritium, which adequately reviews recent work concerning radiation damage occurring during the use of tritium compounds (mainly thymidine). In studies of cell population growth, intranuclear radiation from tritium may considerably alter the kinetics of the system. Wimber also draws attention to the lack of information concerning similar effects with compounds other than thymidine.

Chapter 4—PREPARATION OF TRITIUM COMPOUNDS

The methods available for labelling compounds with tritium are very briefly reviewed by Jones[108], and by Wang and Willis[109] in their excellent book on *Tracer Methodology in Biological Science*. No fundamentally new procedures have been described recently, although some interesting innovations to existing methods have been published.

Exchange Techniques

Wilzbach labelling—Fewer publications are appearing specifically dealing with the preparation of tritium compounds by exposure to tritium gas, which is only to be expected (see Chapter 4). Tritium compounds prepared by this procedure or modifications of it, which have been recently described include polyvinylpyrrolidone (Tesladischarge)[110], phenylacetic acid[111], the insecticide 'DDT'[112], hydrocarbons[113] ($Co/Mo/S$ on Al_2O_3 as catalyst at $400°$ C), DL- and L-valine[114], dehydrocholesterol and vitamin-D_3 (exposed at $-196°$ C)[115], cebroside[184], dimethylamine hydrochloride[225] wood components[225a], bretylium[225b] and methane[116]. In all these examples, the tritiated products required extensive purification in order to achieve a specific activity in the μc/mg range for the pure compound. It is interesting to note that racemization occurred during the exposure of L-valine to tritium gas at room temperature[114], although only about 4 per cent of the D-isomer was formed (compare the results obtained with other amino acids, on page 121); 80 per cent racemization is observed with octan-2-ol[114].

Digitonin labelled by the Wilzbach method is successfully purified by complexing with cholesterol[32].

Cardinaud and colleagues[117] tritiated an anti-γ-globulin by a high-frequency discharge modification of the Wilzbach technique, and their results suggest that this method is better than the normal procedure. A higher specific activity was obtained without a concomitant increase in decomposition.

Makari[118] labelled 'tumour polysaccharide substance' (TPS) by exposure to tritium gas. The crude product has a specific activity of 0·073 mc/mg which retained only 1·47 per cent of its activity on dialysis. TPS is a cancer antigen with characteristics of glycoprotein, but just how one establishes radiochemical purity and the integrity of the tritium label for such a substance whose structure is even unknown, is still a problem. One is therefore cautious in interpreting the results obtained using tritiated macromolecules labelled in this manner, or in fact by any *exchange* procedure. One cannot be at all certain that the biological activity is associated with the labelled molecules or that biologically active labelled molecules behave in a similar manner to the unlabelled molecules, especially in biological systems.

Cardinaud and Bouchet[119] studied the labelling of carbohydrates, benzoic and maleic acids supported on glass fibre, 'Norite' and active charcoal, exposed to tritium gas. Their results show that the nature of the support has a marked influence on the degree of labelling and on the products obtained. Cardiac glycosides (digitoxin at 590 mc/mM) have been supported on silica gel for labelling[120].

Ethane, ethylene and butane are the only products isolated by the reaction of tritium atoms with films of frozen ethylene at 63° K[23] Solid propene at 77° K yields tritiated propene, propane and 2,3-dimethylbutane[122]. These products result essentially from the disproportionation and combination of ethyl and isopropyl radicals in the case of ethylene and propene respectively. The tritium atoms are produced by atomization at a hot filament and the method has been tried also for labelling starch granules at 77° K[123]. Like the Wilzbach method, a high degree of decomposition occurred and purification of the crude starch proved difficult and tedious.

A palladium (10 per cent on alumina) catalysed modified (electric discharge) Wilzbach labelling was found to yield the best results in attempts to prepare high specific activity actinomycin-D[124]. Exposure of 2·5 mg on 10 per cent Pd/Al_2O_3 (10 mg) to tritium gas (0·9 c) while an electric discharge was passed for 20 min yielded actinomycin at 93·6 mc/mM after purification as a DNA-actinomycin complex.

Perhaps the most interesting recent investigation is a further study of the mechanism of Wilzbach labelling. Garnett, Law and Till[125] labelled anthranilic acid (A.8a), isopropanol (A.8b) and phenyl allyl ether (A.8c) by exposing the compounds (1 g) to tritium gas (1 c) for 10 days and then they examined the distribution of tritium in the rigorously purified products.

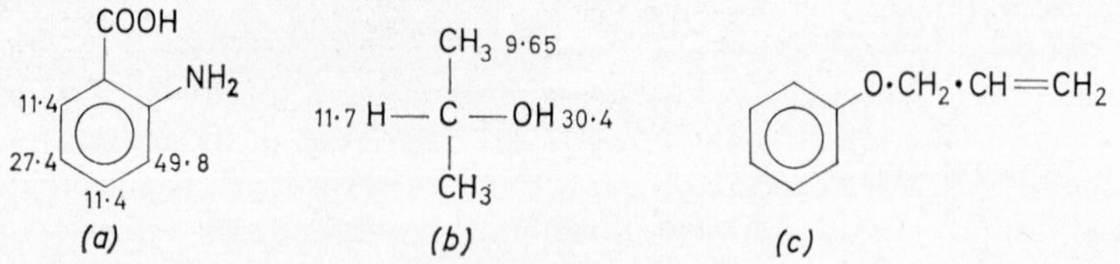

COOH
NH₂
11·4
27·4   49·8
11·4

CH₃ 9·65
11·7 H — C — OH 30·4
CH₃

O·CH₂·CH=CH₂

(a)   (b)   (c)

. . . . (A.8)

In anthranilic acid the highest tritium concentration was found at the most electronegative position in the ring, namely ortho to the amino group. In isopropanol three times as much tritium was associated with the hydroxyl group as with other hydrogen positions, while exchange at the secondary C—H bond was slightly more efficient than at the primary C—H bonds of the methyl group. Phenyl allyl ether yielded only polymeric material, no Claisen rearrangement or even addition to the allyl group was detected.

Garnett, Law and Till[125] proposed a free radical mechanism involving the initiation of organic radicals by either the β-particles or $(HeT)^+$ produced by the decay of tritium molecules, followed by abstraction of tritium by these radicals to form tritiated products. Thus the high tritium incorporation into the ortho-amino position in anthranilic acid can be explained by reactions analogous to the following type shown (A.9):

The possibility of bond rupture is essentially a function of (a) its bond dissociation energy and (b) shielding through possible steric effects. N—H bonds are known[126] to be sensitive to rupture by ionizing radiation and this lends further support to this type of mechanism. In isopropanol the lower bond dissociation energy for the secondary C—H (94 kcal/mole) than the primary C—H (97 kcal/mole)[127], is suggested[125] to account for the higher labelling in the secondary C—H position, the higher steric hindrance at this position being insufficient to cancel out the difference in the bond dissociation energies.

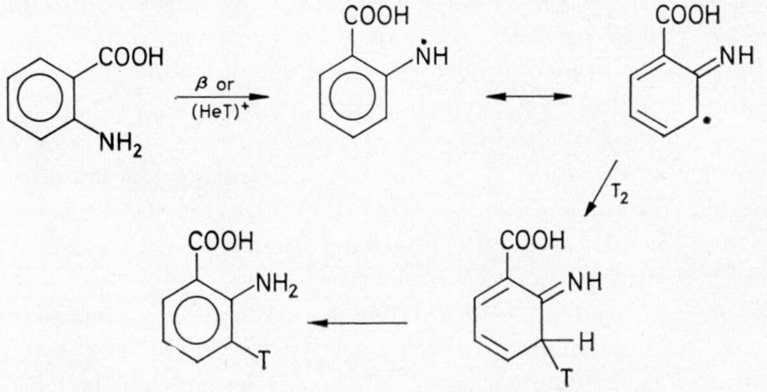

. . . . (A.9)

Other workers[128] have also proposed radical processes in Wilzbach labelling (see page 108).

Other investigations include the tritium β-radiation-induced exchange with water vapour[129] and a study of the kinetics of the exchange between methane and tritium[130].

Catalytic Exchange in Solution

Acid-catalysed exchange was used to label 3-hydroxy-L-kynurenine[131]. This compound (0·2 g) on heating at 90° C for 2 h in 1-N hydrochloric acid (1 ml containing 1 c), gave after purification 3-hydroxy-L-kynurenine-T(G) at 8·1 mc/mM. ε-Dinitrophenyl-L-lysine-T(G) was prepared by a platinum-catalysed exchange in tritiated glacial acetic acid, but no details were recorded[132].

A modification of the Yavorsky–Gorin reagent (see page 124), borontrifluoride–acetic acid-(*carboxyl*-T) $CH_3 \cdot COOTBF_3^+ \cdot CH_3 \cdot COO^-$ prepared by saturating tritiated acetic acid with boron trifluoride, has been used in the acid-catalysed exchange labelling of lipoprotein, amino acids and cholesterol[132a]. The exchange is carried out at room temperature (24° C) for 20 h with about a tenfold excess of the reagent. Specific activities in the range 1–3 μc/mg are obtained using the reagent at 133 μc/mg. The advantages and disadvantages previously discussed for the Yavorsky–Gorin reagent would equally apply to the use of this reagent.

LePage and Junga[133] have reported a mercuric chloride-catalysed exchange between tritiated aromatic hydrocarbons, such as toluene or benzene, and nucleosides on heating under reflux for several hours. The efficiency of the exchange was very low, the specific activity of the nucleosides being two orders of magnitude lower than that of the tritiated hydrocarbons. Although possibly offering advantages over Wilzbach labelling for such radiation-sensitive compounds, the method would appear much less effective than platinum-catalysed exchange in tritiated aqueous solvents (see page 127).

For platinum-catalysed exchange reactions in solution, the preparation of the catalyst by reduction of platinum metal salts with sodium borohydride has not been found to provide a more active catalyst than by reduction of PtO_2 with hydrogen[134], although known to do so for hydrogenation reactions[135].

Keto (oxo) steroids can be labelled by adsorption chromatography on basic alumina treated with tritiated water[136, 136a]. The position of labelling is as one might expect, on the carbon atom adjacent to the keto group. Such tritiated steroids have limited application since at least 95 per cent of the tritium can be re-exchanged from the molecule under strongly basic conditions. It is interesting to note however, that reduction of the tritiated keto-steroids to the corresponding sterols with lithium aluminium hydride occurs without loss of tritium and does provide a simple method for specifically labelling sterols. Phenols and phenolic amino acids are labelled by exchange in tritiated water under alkaline or acidic conditions[121].

Chemical Synthesis

The use of a palladium–barium sulphate catalyst was found to give specific labelling in the halogen–tritium exchange reactions of bromo-terphenyls[137]. The tritiations were carried out using ethyl cellosolve containing potassium acetate, as solvent. Provided the starting bromo-compound is pure, over 99 per cent of the tritium is found in the expected position. This result is very encouraging since most catalytic labelling procedures normally give some degree of non-specific labelling (see page 265).

(*a*) *Acids and esters*—Bardou and Crastes de Paulet[138] adopted the Mahadevan and Lundberg[139] method of heating cholesteryl acetate and the fatty acid methyl ester, for the preparation of cholesteryl-7α-T esters of linolenate and arachidonate on the 1–10 μM scale.

Four stereospecifically labelled monotritiated stearic acids have been prepared from the optically active methyl-9-hydroxyocta-decanoate (A.10 $n = 8$; $m = 7$) or 10-hydroxyoctadecanoate (A.10 $n = 7$; $m = 8$)[140].

Two stereospecifically tritiated mevalonic acids labelled in the 4R-and 4S-positions have been prepared[141] and these have been used

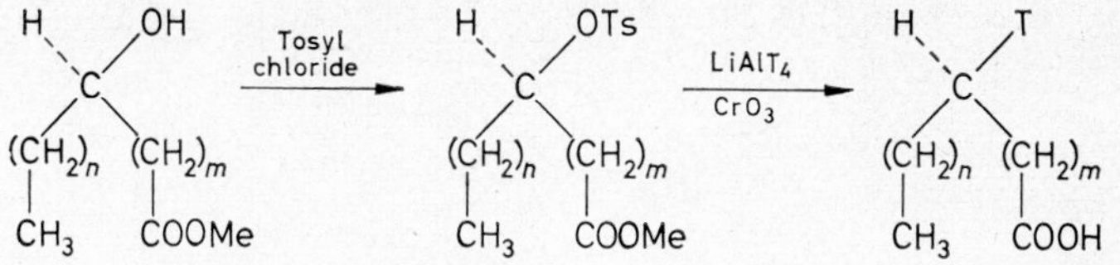

$$. . . . \text{(A.10)}$$

for studying the mechanism of β-carotene formation[142] and similar hydrogen elimination reactions[142a-c] (see also page 385).

Stoffel[143] briefly discusses the chemical synthesis of tritiated (and carbon-14-labelled) polyunsaturated fatty acids.

'Doubly' labelled lecithin was prepared[228] by catalytic hydrogenation of 1-oleoyl-glycero-3-phosphoryl choline with tritium followed by acylation with stearoyl chloride-1-C14. The specificity of labelling was determined by biochemical degradation using an enzyme (phospholipase *A*) from *Crotalus adamanteus* (snake venom); 92 per cent of the tritium was found attached to the 1-position fatty acid and 96 per cent of the C14 at position -2.

A series of acids, *p*-methoxyphenyl acetic acid, *p*-hydroxyphenyl-acetic acid, β-alanine, γ-aminobutyric acid and δ-aminovaleric acid, all labelled at the α-carbon atom, were synthesized by rearrangement of diazo-ketones with tritiated water–dioxan in the presence of silver oxide (A.11)[144].

$$. . . . \text{(A.11)}$$

α-Alanine at 100 mc/mM can also be prepared by the hydrogenation of *N*-acetyldehydroalanine (prepared from pyruvic acid and acetamide) with tritium gas in the presence of 10 per cent palladium–charcoal catalyst[145].

L-Phenylalanine labelled with tritium in the 2,3-positions of the side-chain at high specific activity, is prepared by the catalytic hydrogenation of α-acetamino-cinnamoyl-L-glutamic acid[146].

(*b*) *Aromatic compounds*—A convenient synthesis of 1-fluoro-2,4-dinitrobenzene-3-T, a reagent used in protein and peptide analysis

397

(see page 15), at very high specific activity, has been described by Hesselbo[147].

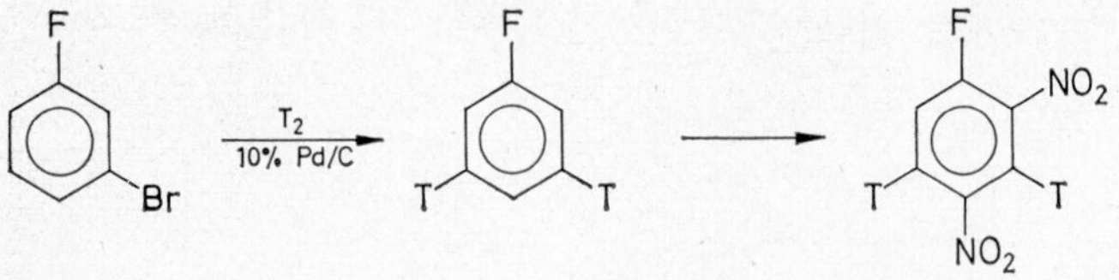

. . . . (A.12)

The method involves catalytic halogen–tritium exchange between *m*-bromofluorobenzene and tritium gas in 3 per cent methanolic potash (A.12). The reaction stops in this solvent when the bromine atom is replaced by tritium and the reaction provides an interesting example of selective halogen–tritium exchange. The tritiated fluorobenzene-3(5)-T is nitrated in carbon tetrachloride with a mixture of nitric and sulphuric acids. The overall yield is about 65 per cent and specific activities above 15 c/mM are readily obtained.

(*c*) *Peptides and proteins*—These still remain difficult groups of compounds to label. Agishi and Dingman[148] have published details for the preparation of tritiated oxytocin by catalytic halogen-exchange. Iodinated oxytocin is reduced with tritium gas in dilute acetic acid solution using a palladium–charcoal catalyst. After extensive purification oxytocin-T labelled on the tyrosyl residues, was obtained at a specific activity of 228 μc/mg. However, solid-phase peptide synthesis as described by Merrifield[149] for the synthesis of bradykinin, probably offers one of the best synthetic approaches to the preparation of radioactive peptides with the added advantages that labelling can be in selected amino acid residues and the process automated[150,150a].

Trifluoroacetic acid-(*carboxyl*-T) has been used in the synthesis of tritiated amino acids and peptides via the 2-trifluoromethyl-pseudo-5-oxazolones.[151] Exchange of tritium into oxazolones is used in a recently described[151a] method for the determination of C-terminal groups of peptides.

Tritiated ethyl methane sulphonate (prepared from ethanol-2-T) has been used to label proteins, such as globulin for example, with which it reacts via ionized amino groups, sulphydryl and carboxyl groups[152]. High specific activity acetic anhydride (3,570 mc/mM) has been used to label human growth hormone (275 μc/mg; 3·2), bovine growth hormone (570 μc/mg; 12) and pork insulin (127 μc/mg; 0·5)[153]. The specific activities attained and the degree of acetylation (acetyls/mole) are shown in parentheses. It has previously been shown[154] that human and bovine growth hormone acetylated to the extent indicated behave in a comparable manner with the unlabelled hormones, both biologically and antigenically. However, a word of caution; the validity of labelled derivatives as tracers of macromolecules must be thoroughly investigated both *in vivo* and *in vitro;* differential behaviour between the macromolecule and its derivative may be observed, as found for example with the labelled derivatives of inulin[155].

At present proteins are probably best labelled *in vivo* using tritiated amino acids[156a-c] (see also page 31).

(*d*) *Heterocyclic compounds*—O'Brien[157] makes use of the acid lability of tritium in the 5-position of uracil-5,6-T and uridine-5,6-T for the preparation of these compounds specifically labelled in the 6-position. Tritiated indole labelled in the 2-position is prepared by reduction of indoxyl[158].

(*e*) *Steroids*—Levitz and Katz[159] describe the synthesis of oestriol-15-T by the reaction of the 3-benzyl ester of dimethyl marrianolate with triphenylmethyl sodium. The tritiated marrianolate which forms when the sodio-derivative is reacted with tritiated water, undergoes an acyloin condensation with sodium in liquid ammonia to give 16-keto-oestradiol-15-T. This keto steroid is an intermediate in the metabolism of oestriol[160], and is reduced to oestriol by sodium amalgam (A.13). An attempt to exchange tritium from the 15-position of oestriol by heating with acid or with alkali failed to remove more than 5 per cent of the tritium, demonstrating the chemical stability of the label.

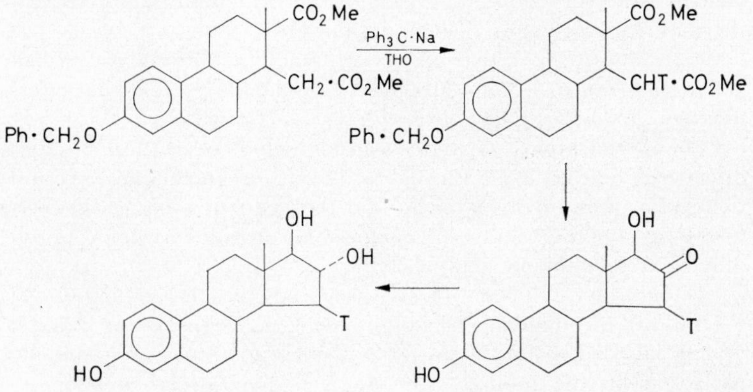

. . . . (A.13)

Akhtar and Gibbons[17] have prepared tritiated vitamin-D_3 labelled in the 9 and 19-positions (A.14):

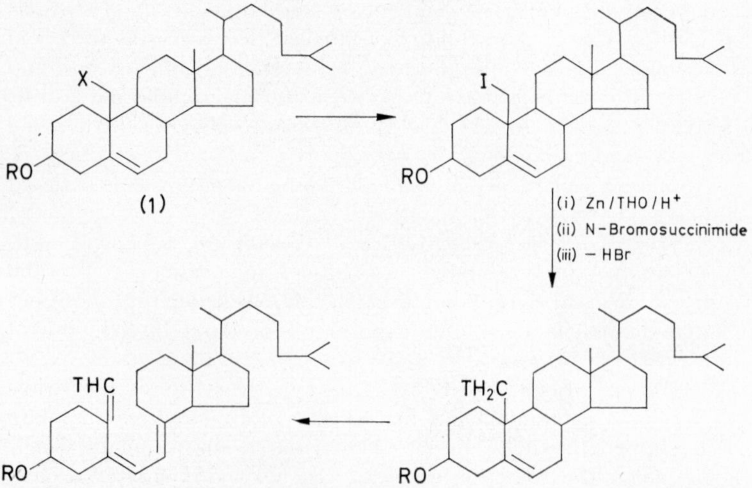

. . . . (A.14)

19-Tosyl cholesteryl acetate (A.14(1) R$=$Ac; X$=$—$OSO_2 \cdot C_6H_4 \cdot CH_3$) was converted into the 19-iodide by sodium iodide in boiling ethyl methyl ketone. Reduction of the iodide with zinc in tritiated water containing a trace of acid gave cholesteryl acetate-19-T. Bromination and dehydrobromination of the cholesteryl acetate yielded 7-dehydrocholesteryl acetate-19-T which on photolysis and thermal rearrangement yielded vitamin-D_3-9,19-T.

Oestradiol-6,7-T at 51·6 c/mM is obtained by the catalytic hydrogenation of oestra-,1,3,5,6-tetraene-3,17β-diol diacetate with carrier-free tritium gas[161].

Other preparations of tritiated steroids include for example 17,20α-dihydroxycholesterol-7α-T from 17α-hydroxypregnenolone-7α-T and isohexylmagnesium bromide[63], and the reduction of 3α-acetoxy-6-keto-5β-cholanic acid with sodium borotritide to yield 3α,6β-dihydroxy-5β-cholanic acid-6α-T[64].

(f) Sugars—D-Glucose-3-T is prepared by the reduction of 1,2,5,6-di-isopropylidene-3-keto-glucose with lithium borotritide[199]. Xylose labelled in the 5-position with tritium can be prepared by reduction of the methyl ester if 1,2-mono-O-cyclohexylidene-L-xyluronic acid with tritiated sodium borohydride[162] (A.15):

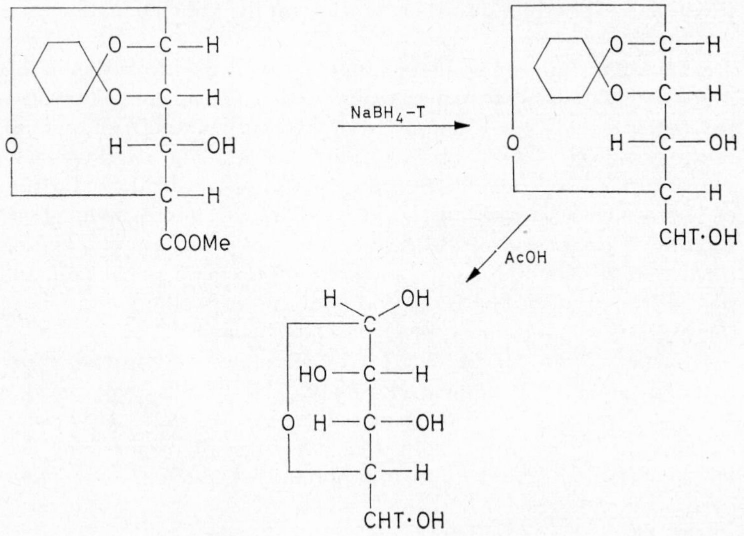

$$
\begin{array}{c}
\text{O}-\text{C}-\text{H} \\
\text{O}-\text{C}-\text{H} \\
\text{H}-\text{C}-\text{OH} \\
\text{C}-\text{H} \\
\text{COOMe}
\end{array}
\quad \xrightarrow{\text{NaBH}_4-\text{T}} \quad
\begin{array}{c}
\text{O}-\text{C}-\text{H} \\
\text{O}-\text{C}-\text{H} \\
\text{H}-\text{C}-\text{OH} \\
\text{C}-\text{H} \\
\text{CHT}\cdot\text{OH}
\end{array}
$$

AcOH

$$
\begin{array}{c}
\text{H} \quad \text{OH} \\
\text{C} \\
\text{HO}-\text{C}-\text{H} \\
\text{O} \quad \text{H}-\text{C}-\text{OH} \\
\text{C}-\text{H} \\
\text{CHT}\cdot\text{OH}
\end{array}
$$

. . . . (A.15)

Hydrolysis of the protecting groups with acetic acid yielded xylose-5-T.

α-Methyl-D-glucoside-5-T and α-methyl-L-iodside-5-T are prepared by the hydroboration (using tritiated diborane) of substituted methylglucosenides[162a].

The nucleotide sugars, uridine diphosphate glucose (UDPG) and uridine diphosphate galactose (UDPGal) are prepared labelled in the 4-position of the sugar moiety by the reaction of the corresponding sugar-1-phosphate bis-(tri-n-octylammonium) salt with uridine-5′-phosphoromorpholidate in anhydrous pyridine[163].

Biosynthesis

Increasing use is being made of biochemical methods for the preparation of tritium compounds, a pattern in publications observed by Mantescu and Genunche[2].

DNA labelled with tritium in the thymine base at a specific activity of about 0·02 mc/mg, is prepared by cultivating E. coli in a medium containing tritiated thymine-methyl-T. After a culture time corresponding to some 20 generations, the homogeneity of labelling is guaranteed[164].

Tritiated thymidine can be converted into thymidylic acid and thymidine triphosphate by regenerating rat liver homogenate on the 200 μmole scale[165].

Thymidine diphosphoglucose (TDPG) labelled with tritium in the 3-position of the glucose moiety is obtained in 95 per cent yield by the reaction of α-D-glucose-1-phosphate-3-T with thymidine triphosphate in the presence of TDPG pyrophosphorylase[166]. The α-D-glucose-1-phosphate-3-T is prepared[166a] almost quantitatively by the reduction of 3-keto-sucrose with sodium borotritide followed by treatment of the mixture of α-D-allosyl-β-D-fructofuranoside-3-T and α-D-glucosyl-β-D-fructofuranoside-3-T with sucrosephosphorylase. The 3-keto-sucrose required for the reduction is obtained by the oxidation of sucrose with a culture of *Agrobacterium tumefaciens*[166a].

Glucose-4-T and glucose-3-T can be prepared enzymatically from tritiated dihydroxyacetone-3-phosphate (DHAP)[167]. Glyceraldehyde-3-phosphate-1-T was prepared by incubating DHAP and aldolase in tritiated water and then enzymatically isomerizing the DHAP-1-T to glyceraldehyde-3-phosphate-1-T (A.16):

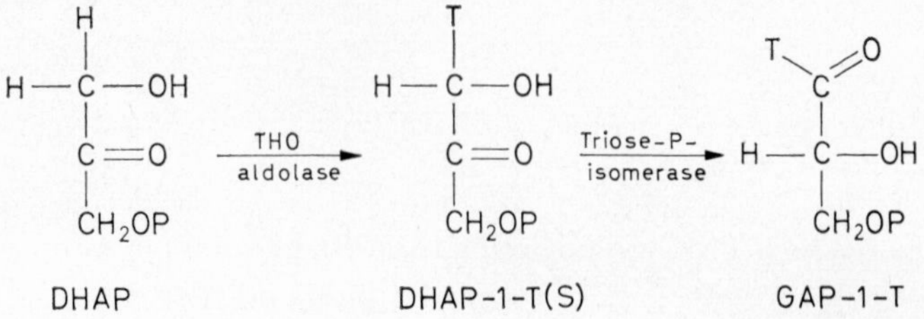

$$\ldots \ldots (A.16)$$

DHAP-1-T(R) was prepared by incubating GAP with triose phosphate isomerase in THO (A.17):

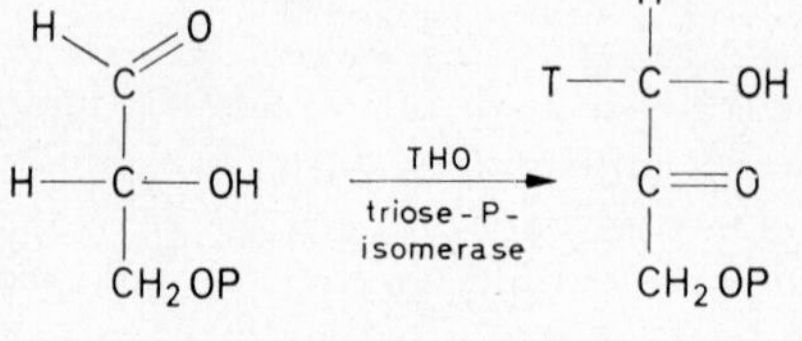

$$\ldots \ldots (A.17)$$

GAP-1-T and unlabelled DHAP, and DHAP-1-T(R) and unlabelled GAP, were condensed by means of aldolase to fructose-1,6-diphosphate-4-T and FDP-3-T respectively. The diphosphates were hydrolysed to the 6-monophosphates and then isomerized to glucose-6-phosphate enzymatically. Dephosphorylation with phosphatase yielded glucose-4-T and glucose-3-T in overall yields of less than 1 per cent and with a specific activity of only 5 mc/mM. The specific activity could undoubtedly be increased by using tritiated water at higher specific activity.

The (S) and (R) refer to the stereospecificity of the tritium atoms in DHAP according to Cahn, Ingold and Prelog[168].

DL-Lysine-4,5-T and DL-leucine-4,5-T were used for labelling milk proteins (β-lactoglobulin and α-lactalbumin) using bovine mammary cell cultures, *in vitro*[169]. The percentage incorporation of the amino acids was quite low being 1·82 for lysine and 0·96 for leucine. A very poor incorporation of tritiated amino acids (glycine and phenylalanine-T(G) compared with carbon-14-labelled amino acids) into proteins has been observed by McFarlane[170] which may be partly explained by the lability of the tritium in the α-position under biological conditions (see page 358); such losses of tritium should not occur when the tritium atoms are situated away from the asymmetric centre as in lysine-4,5-T and leucine-4,5-T.

S-Adenosyl-L-methionine-*methyl*-T is prepared in 10–15 per cent yield[199] from L-methionine-*methyl*-T using methionine-activating enzyme from rabbit liver, essentially as described by Cantoni[226].

Recoil Labelling

Numerous papers have appeared dealing further with the theoretical implications of tritium recoil reactions[171–180a–i]. However, recent papers describes the preparation of 16-dehydroprogesterone generally labelled by tritium recoil from the $^6Li(n,\alpha)^3H$ reaction, but no yields or specific activity were recorded[221] and arabinose[180j].

Chapter 5—MEASUREMENT AND ANALYSIS

More than 80 per cent of publications relating to tritium measurement are concerned with β-liquid scintillation methods. An excellent book on the theory and practice of scintillation counting has been written by Birks[232] for those who wish to delve more deeply into the scintillation processes occurring in organic molecules.

Houtman[241–242] describes a useful technique for liquid scintillation counting of blood by extracting the blood with a solvent such as 'polyether 611', dioxan or ethanol. Blood samples containing from 0·01 nc (nanocuries) of tritium or 0·003 nc of carbon-14 per millilitre can be measured.

403

Apelgot[229] describes the use of a membrane support for liquid scintillation measurement of suspensions. However, care must be taken in counting paper discs (for example) containing tritium compounds since the actual size of the molecules adsorbed on the paper has a pronounced effect on the scintillation efficiency. Furlong, Williams and Willis[237] found that tritiated DNA is counted with an efficiency six times greater than tritiated thymidine triphosphate on paper discs, in scintillation solvents. These observations were explained by assuming that the smaller tritiated molecules are able to penetrate deeper into the paper fibrils, resulting in a decrease in the efficiency of photon formation (and detection) by self-absorption and energy transfer factors. Hence small molecular tritiated compounds should not be used as reference standards for macromolecular structures in efficiency calibrations of this kind.

A new solute for liquid scintillation counting 'BBOT', 2,5-bis[5'-t.butylbenzoxazolyl(2')]-thiophene is commercially available (Ciba Ltd.).

Autoradiography

Many investigations with tritium compounds, particularly in cytological investigations[161a-c], rely on autoradiographic techniques for visualizing the experimental results (see Chapters 2 and 5).

No fundamentally new techniques have been reported recently. For light microscopy/autoradiography with water-soluble tritium (or other labelled) compounds, Hammarström, Appelgren and Ullberg[181] describe a technique similar to that of André (see page 248). Sections of 3–5 μ are cut from fresh-frozen preparations in a cryostat, or from freeze-dried embedded material and then attached to cellophane tape for autoradiography. Kalberer[162b] describes a technique for sectioning whole animals for autoradiography.

Caro and Schnös[182] have investigated the sensitivity of Ilford L-4 nuclear emulsion for β-particles from tritium and phosphorus-32 and generally concluded that all β-emitters give a sensitivity of 2·5–20 grains/100β-particles and a resolution of 0·1 μ (for tritium) to 0·3 μ (for phosphorus-32) depending on the energy of the emitted particle. The relatively poor resolution (compared with tritium) using ^{32}P is seen from an autoradiographic study of orthophosphate-P32 incorporation into tumour cells[227].

The efficiency of autoradiographic detection of tritium on stripping film has been measured by Tykva and Vesely[183]. Avian plasma myeloblasts were labelled with tritiated cytidine and autoradiographed using Kodak AR.10 stripping film. After grain counting the samples of cells were burnt to tritiated water, converted into acetylene and the activity measured in a gas proportional counter. The mean number of disintegrations required to develop one grain was 45·8 (compare figures on page 247) and the efficiency of detection was 2·2 per cent which dropped over 28 days to 1·6 per cent, due to such factors as latent image fading, self-adsorption, techniques used for developing etc. Tykva and Vesely point out that the quantitative evaluation of such factors which influence the detection efficiency would be without any significance because the values determined can only be related to the model and procedure used at the time.

Tritiated polymethylmethacrylate reference sources are available commercially[199] and should prove useful for studying the variants in autoradiography. These infinitely thick sources are prepared by polymerizing monomeric methyl-T methacrylate which ensures a uniform distribution of tritium. Tritiated polymethylmethacrylate in gelatine or polythene capsules can be cut with a microtome to provide very thin tritiated reference sources for use in electron-microscopy autoradiography for example[185].

Analysis

Verly and Gerday[186] describe a method for investigating the optical purity of a tritiated L- (or D-) amino acid. The procedure consists of adding to the radioactive optically active compound (for example, L-phenylalanine-T), inactive DL-acid (DL-phenylalanine) and condensing the mixture with L-glutamic acid. The diastereoisomers of the resulting dipeptide are resolved chromatographically on Dowex 50 resin and the radioactivity associated with each isomer measured. which gives a value for the radiochemical purity of the optically active amino acid. This method provides a useful alternative to reverse dilution analysis (see page 257), especially when the optically active amino acid is at a very low specific activity and large additions of carrier acids cannot be tolerated.

A computer programme for the statistical analysis of radio-chemical purity, particularly the analysis of countercurrent distribution data, has been designed[187].

It is interesting to note that the optical isomers of DL-tryptophan, 5-hydroxy-DL-tryptophan and 6-hydroxy-DL-tryptophan have been resolved by paper and thin-layer chromatography on cellulose powder 'CC41'[188]. The solvent required for the separation of the D- and L-isomers is n-butanol:pyridine:water (1:1:1). The D-isomers have the greater R_f in this solvent.

One must be on guard for isotope effects during chromatography

405

of tritium compounds. Cejka and Venneman[189] found small differences in the chromatographic behaviour of aldosterone and aldosterone-1,2-T. Isotope fractionation in steroid chromatography is of course not new being first mentioned by Ulick and Tait[190] and subsequently by Klein and colleagues[191,192] who found a progressive rise in the isotopic ratio across the chromatographic peak when aldosterone-T and tetrahydroaldosterone-T as their carbon-14-labelled acetates were chromatographed on partition columns, and when aldosterone-T acetate-C14 was chromatographed on paper.

Wilson and Spedding[193] review the techniques for the detection of tritium on paper and thin-layer chromatograms. They point out particularly the advantages of spraying chromatograms with anthracene in benzene which doubles the sensitivity of detection for tritium. Silica gel (G) used for thin-layer chromatography, is itself a scintillator and gives off light when bombarded with ionizing radiation including the weak β-particles from tritium. Thus, using Kodak 'Royal Blue' film, $0\cdot01$ μc/3 mm^2 in a thickness of $0\cdot2$ mm was detected in 7 days. Wilson and Spedding have called this process 'scintillation autoradiography', but one must remember that this is a photographic (light) process and is subject to reciprocity failure.

Luthi and Waser[194] have investigated scintillation autoradiography (which they have called 'fluorography') in more detail. Anthracene was ground in a ball mill with an equal amount of silica gel G (gypsum content 13 per cent) to a crystal size of 1–5 μ. The ground mixture (30 g) was added to 96 per cent alcohol (80 ml) and spread on a plate 20×10 cm to give a 250 μ thick layer. After drying at room temperature, chromatograms of tritiated diallyl-nor-toxiferine ('Alloferine') were developed using acetic acid:hexane:diethylamine $(77\cdot5:17\cdot5:5)$ as the solvent. The tritiated compound was applied as a spot of 7 mm diameter or of 3 mm diameter[195] and the radioactivity detected by x-ray film ('Kodirex') exposed over 'dry ice' at $-70°$ C. The maximum range of the tritium β-particles in a layer of silica gel of 250 μ thickness is calculated from its surface density:

$$250 \times 0\cdot28/5\cdot7 = 12\cdot2 \ \mu$$

A tritium activity of $0\cdot08$ μc was detected after an exposure time of one day, and the presence of anthracene was found to be essential although it does not need to be especially pure. A low temperature for the exposure is also essential; a tritium-induced 'fluorograph' is twice as intense when exposed at $-30°$ C than at $4°$ C and 30 times as intense at $-70°$ C. No further increase in sensitivity is observed in going to lower temperatures $(-196°$ C). Luthi and Waser explained this temperature dependence of the scintillator response in terms of the vibrational freedom of the molecules. At low temperatures vibration is 'frozen-in' and less energy is lost for radiationless transitions.

Although the technique offers no advantage for the analysis of carbon-14 compounds[194], it should prove very useful for the detection and analysis of low activities of tritium compounds.

Lambiotte[196] describes a new method for the separation and detection of tritiated compounds by autoradiography of electrophoretograms on photographic gelatin. The separations are sharp, the diffusion is slight, and provided the specific activities are not very high, the radioactive ions do not have time to leave any track as they move in the photographic gelatin. A suitable supporting medium for the electrophoresis is a strip of 'Kodirex' x-ray film immersed for a few minutes in a saturated buffer, then quickly dried between filter paper. After the electrophoresis, the film strip is dried and stored in the dark until its development. The method allows the detection of 0·001 μc of tritium in 6 days exposure.

Cholesterol-7α-T is sometimes used as a reference steroid in the quantitative isolation and gas–liquid chromatographic analysis of total dietary and faecal neutral steroids[197].

One cannot have too many methods available for the analysis of tritium compounds, and as Craig[198] has pointed out 'absolute proof of the purity or the identity of a substance is unattainable although this desirable goal may be approached as the number of independent criteria satisfied increases'.

Specificity of Tritium Labelling

Labelling of phenol, by the platinum-catalysed exchange in tritiated water, is uniform in the ring positions[199]. The π-complexing of the compound with the metal catalyst appears to modify the mesomeric effects of the hydroxyl group in its ortho- and para-directing properties.

Inositol-T, labelled by the Wilzbach method, has 36 per cent tritium at the C_1 and C_6 positions, 30 per cent at C_2 and C_5 and 34 per cent at C_3 and C_4[200]. The results show that the equatorial hydrogen atoms at C_1 and C_6 are more readily exchanged than the axial hydrogen atoms. If hexa-O-methyl-$(-)$-inositol is exposed to tritium gas, the labelling pattern is only slightly different, the distribution being 39 per cent at C_1 and C_6, 30 per cent at C_2 and C_5 and 31 per cent at C_3 and C_4[200].

Ciranni, Ciranni and Guarino[201] have studied the distribution of tritium in aromatic hydrocarbons by the recoil reaction $^6Li(n,\alpha)^3H$.

The results (A.18) showed that the tritium distribution does not change with the lithium salt concentration or with the irradiation

$$\begin{array}{ccc} \textbf{Me} \ 25 \cdot 9 & C_2H_5 \ 38 \cdot 1 & C_3H_7 \ 38 \cdot 2 \\ \end{array}$$

Me 25·9
26·3
32·1
15·7

C₂H₅ 38·1
39·6
8·9
13·0

C₃H₇ 38·2
44·4
0·5
19·3

. . . . (A.18)

conditions, but it is interesting to observe the marked decrease in the incorporation of tritium in the meta position as the length of the side-chain is increased. The reason for this effect is not clear but it may be due to steric effects.

It is encouraging to find that some catalytic hydrogenations of ethylenic bonds with tritium gas do give specific labelling. Popenoe, Aronson and van Slyke[202] have degraded DL-lysine-4,5-T, prepared by the catalytic hydrogenation of acetamido-(4-amino-Δ^2-butenyl)-malonic acid diethyl ester hydrochloride with tritium, to glutaric and succinic acids (A.19) without loss of tritium; the specific activity of both the glutaric acid and succinic acid was the same as the starting lysine-4,5-T.

$$\overset{6}{NH_2} \cdot \overset{5}{CH_2} \cdot \overset{4}{CH_2} \cdot \overset{3}{CH_2} \cdot \overset{2}{CH_2} \cdot \overset{1}{CH} \cdot COOH \xrightarrow{KMnO_4}$$
$$\underset{NH_2}{|}$$

$$\overset{6}{HO_2C} \cdot \overset{5}{CH_2} \cdot \overset{4}{CH_2} \cdot \overset{3}{CH_2} \cdot \overset{2}{CO_2H}$$

(i) hydrazoic acid
(ii) KMnO₄

$$\overset{6}{HOOC} \cdot \overset{5}{CH_2} \cdot \overset{4}{CH_2} \cdot \overset{3}{COOH}$$

. . . . (A.19)

The investigations of Cornforth, Popjak and colleagues[46, 48, 141] (and others[47, 49, 140, 142]) draws particular attention to the growing importance of knowing the stereospecificity of tritium labelling, as well as the position of the tritium atoms in the molecule.

Chapter 6—PECULIAR PROPERTIES

A better understanding of the difference in the behaviour of tritium-labelled compounds from their unlabelled counterpart is gradually being achieved as experience accumulates with the preparation and use of these compounds.

Isotope effects are obvious peculiarities to be observed and some of these have already been mentioned (see page 406). Kinetic isotope effects are observed in tritium exchange reactions between hydrocarbons and bases[203], and in the gas–liquid chromatography of acetylated steroids. Kirschner and Lipsett[204] found that on GLC of testosterone-C14 acetate-T and dehydroepiandrosterone-C14 acetate-T, although there is no change in the tritium to carbon-14 ratio when the whole effluent peak is measured, if the peak is split the ratio is higher in the earlier fractions, i.e. the tritiated molecules 'lag behind' the other molecules.

Compounds labelled with tritium at the active centres of unsaturation show a higher retention time on silver-nitrate impregnated silica gel columns than the corresponding carbon-14 (*carboxyl*) labelled compound[205]. Some examples include, methyl linoleate-T, oleic acid-9,10-T and linoleic acid-T. It has been suggested[205] that isotope effects occur during the formation and breaking of the silver ion double-bond complexes which comprise the transition structure during sorption and desorption.

Goutier[206, 206a] has reported isotope effects during the *in vitro* enzymatic phosphorylation of thymidine.

Large isotope effects were observed in the tritium–hydrogen exchange between keratins and tritiated water[207].

Decomposition of tritium compounds by self-irradiation is a growing problem as increasing use is made of these compounds at very high specific activities. Better methods for reducing the rates of decomposition to a tolerable level are still needed. The use of additives (free radical scavengers) to control decomposition promises to be a most useful, practical and convenient method for minimizing the decomposition of tritium compounds stored in aqueous solution. The preliminary results with a few tritiated nucleosides and amino acids, using benzyl alcohol, ethanol and sodium formate as scavengers, has been published[208]. It is interesting to note that the addition of ethyl alcohol or sodium formate to γ-irradiated solutions of cytosine actually increases the decomposition of this pyrimidine[209]. One must be cautious in correlating observed effects with γ-irradiation to expected effects with tritium compounds.

Ciranni, Guarino and colleagues[210] have published their results on the storage of methyl stearate-T as clathrates using desoxycholic acid, cycloveratryl, tri-*o*-thymotide and β-cyclodextrin as the 'host' compounds. Although offering only a marginal improvement (less than 30 per cent), clathrate formation may prove of some practical interest for storing compounds at high specific activity. However, there are two major difficulties; (*1*) it is difficult to get the active molecules completely inside the host molecules; crystallization procedures tend to leave some 20 per cent or so of the labelled compound adsorbed (and unprotected) on the surface of the adduct and (2) a simple technique must be available for *quantitative* recovery of the labelled compound free of chemical contamination by the host molecule.

Other investigations include an analysis of the decomposition products of chimyl alcohol-T (1-*O*-hexadecylglycerol[211a]) stored in benzene at $-20°C$[211]. Hydrocarbons were identified as the major decomposition products. A comprehensive study of the decomposition of tritiated fatty acids and esters has been carried out by Guarino and colleagues[212, 213].

Retention of biological activity and less than 5 per cent decomposition is observed when the tritiated peptide oxytocin (see page 398) is stored at $+4°$ C in aqueous acetic acid for 12 weeks[148]. L-Tyrosine-3,5-T at high specific activity (above 10 c/mM) stored in aqueous solution at $+2°$ C is observed to racemize completely in a few months even in the presence of sodium formate as a radical scavenger[208]. It is interesting to note however, that L-amino acids uniformly labelled with carbon-14 have not yet been observed to racemize when stored under similar conditions[199].

Storage of acetic anhydride-T (at 100 mc/mM) as a 17–20 per cent solution in benzene at room temperature, produces a radioactive nonvolatile polymeric material which may interfere with steroid analyses for example (see page 16). The rate of formation of this polymer is about 1 per cent/month at room temperature and is slightly less when the solutions are stored at $-40°$ C[199]. No acetic acid is observed to form as a product of radiation decomposition.

Although not a β-radiation decomposition problem, Smith[214] gives a very illuminating account of factors (such as oxidation, hydrolysis, biological reactions etc.) which influence the chemical decomposition of medical preparations. The contribution from these factors must be *added* to the decomposition of labelled medical preparations by self-irradiation.

The possible use of the primary decay of tritium to helium-3 for the preparation of helium fluoride has been suggested by Moody and Thomas[215]; tritium fluoride for example, may give rise to helium fluoride.

Bayly and Evans[228a] have recently reviewed the stability of radioactive compounds on storage.

Stability of the tritium label remains the most important consideration to be given in selecting tritium compounds for tracer investigations. Sgoutas, Kim and Kummerow[216] have established the stability *in vivo* (rat) of linoleic acid-9,10,12,13-T, which one might have predicted from earlier observations with palmitic acid-T by Ono and Fredrickson[217]. Evans[218] found that loss of tritium (by exchange) from the photo-oxidation products of succinic acid-2,3-T by chromatophores of *Rhodospirillum rubrum*, made it impossible to interpret the mechanism of hydrogen transfer reactions in this system.

The formation of collagen hydroxylysine in rat biopsy connective tissue (*in vitro*) and in chick embryos (*in vivo*), results in the loss of only one hydrogen (tritium) atom from lysine-4,5-T used as a precursor. This result eliminated either the formation of 5-keto-lysine or a 4,5-unsaturated intermediate, in the mechanism for the hydroxylation reaction[202].

When stereospecifically labelled stearic acid-T (see page 396) is incubated with growing cultures of a strain of *Corynebacterium diphtheriae*, it is converted into oleic acid with loss of tritium from the molecule if the 9-D- or 10-D-tritio stearic acid is used, but not if the 9-L- or 10-L-tritio compound is used. This clearly demonstrates stereospecific removal of hydrogen atoms at C_9 and C_{10}. Isotope effects observed in the formation of the oleic acid suggested that hydrogen removal from the stearic acid at C_9 preceded hydrogen removal at C_{10}[140].

Incubation of thymidine diphosphoglucose-3-T (TDPG-3-T) with an enzyme preparation from *Pseudomonas aeruginose* quantitatively yields TDP-4-keto-6-deoxyglucose, but the conversion is accompanied by complete loss of tritium from the compound. However, if an enzyme preparation from *Xanthomonas campestris* is used, the tritium label is retained in the formation of TDP-4-keto-6-deoxyglucose. If the tritiated TDP-4-keto-6-deoxyglucose-3-T is now incubated with the *Pseudomonas* enzyme, tritium is again lost from the molecule[166]. These results suggest that two different mechanisms are operative; the loss of tritium may be due to stereospecific binding of the compound at position-3 to the enzyme from *Pseudomonas* but not to the enzyme from *Xanthomonas*.

Leng and Leonard[219] have reported the loss of tritium from the methyl group when sodium acetate-T is metabolized in merino ewes. The ratio of tritium to carbon-14 in acetate isolated from the rumen fell with time when a mixture of either acetate-1-C14 or -2-C14 and acetate-T were infused into the animals.

Contractor[220] found that almost all of the tritium can be exchanged from DL-5-hydroxytryptophan-T(G) during the metabolism *in vivo* (rat) to 5-hydroxytryptamine.

411

Cholest-4-ene-3α,7α-diol-3β-T-4-C14 is converted into cholic acid by the rat, with only partial retention of the tritium label[222].

Under the alkaline conditions required for the preparation of the tertiary-butyloxycarbonyl derivatives of amino acids[149], more than 90 per cent of the tritium is lost from L-proline-T(G) by exchange[199].

Further experiments at the Radiochemical Centre[199] and by Floss, Mothes and Günther[222a] suggest that a tritium atom in the α-position (that is, attached to the asymmetric carbon-atom) in heterocyclic tritiated amino acids, for example tryptophan-(*alanine*-2-T) and proline-T(G), is not labilized by the action of biological oxidases. This is in contrast to what has been observed with other tritiated amino acids (see page 359).

In these few examples, the loss of tritium from the compounds under the biological conditions could not have been predicted, and this emphasizes the importance of carefully checking the stability of the tritium label under the experimental conditions.

REFERENCES

[1] *J. Labelled Compounds.* Ed. Sirchis, J., Publ. Presses Académiques Européennes, Brussels

[2] Mantescu, C. and Genunche, A. Institute of Atomic Physics, Bucharest, Rumania. I.F.A./CO/29 (1965)

[3] Rogers, P. C. and Stokes, R. H. *Phys. Lett.* 8 (1964) 320

[4] Goldanskii, V. I. *Phys. Lett.* 9 (1964) 184

[5] Mosichev, V. I., L'Vov, B. V. and Khartsizov, A. D. *Zh. prikl. Spektrosk.* 2 (1965) 9

[6] Kolos, W. and Wolniewicz, L. *J. chem. Phys.* 41 (1964) 3674

[7] Balling, L. C. and Pipkin, F. M. *Phys. Rev.* 139 (1965) A19

[8] Amdur, I. and Beatty, J. W. *J. chem. Phys.* 42 (1965) 3361

[9] Mason, E. A., Annis, B. K. and Islam, M. *J. chem. Phys.* 42 (1965) 3364

[10] Amdur, I. and Malinauskas, A. P. *J. chem. Phys.* 42 (1965) 3355

[11] Kochurikhin, V. E. and Zel'Venskii, Ya. D. *Zh. fiz. Khim.* 38 (1964) 2594

[12] Antonov, A. A. *Russ. J. phys. Chem.* 38 (1964) 935

[13] Campbell, D. R. and Warner, W. C. *Analyt. Chem.* 37 (1965) 276

[13a] Koch, G. K. and Jurriens, G. *Nature, Lond.* 208 (1965) 1321

[14] Bott, R. W., Spillet, R. W. and Eaborn, C. *Chem. Communs* 8 (1965) 147

[15] Bott, R. W., Eaborn, C. and Walton, D. R. M. *J. chem. Soc.* (1965) 384

[16] Hofmann, J. E., Wallace, T. J. and Schriesheim, A. *J. Am. chem. Soc.* 86 (1964) 1561

[17] Akhtar, M. and Gibbons, C. J. *Tetrahedron Lett.* 9 (1965) 509

[18] Autrey, R. L., Barton, D. H. R., Ganguly, A. K. and Reusch, W. H. *J. chem. Soc.* (1961) 3313

[19] Havinga, E. and Schlatmann, J. L. M. A. *Tetrahedron* 16 (1961) 146; *Recl. Trav. chim. Pays-Bas Belg.* 80 (1961) 1101

[20] Velluz, L. and Amiard, G. *Bull. Soc. chim. Fr.* 22 (1955) 205

[21] Miyatani, D. and Takeuchi, T. *Radio-Isotopes (Tokyo)* 13 (1964) 439

[22] Watkins, K. W. and Moser, H. C. *J. phys. Chem.* 69 (1965) 1040

REFERENCES

[23] Nir, A. *J. geophys. Res.* 69 (1964) 2589
[24] 'Radioisotopes in Hydrology'. *Proc. Symp. Applic. Radioisotopes Hydrol.*, Tokyo, 5–9 March, 1963. Vienna; I.A.E.A.
[25] Taylor, C. B., Polach, H. A. and Rafter, T. A. *Inst. Nucl. Sci.*, *D.S.I.R.*, *N.Z.*, *Rep.* I.N.S.–R-24 (July, 1963)
[26] Mawson, C. A. Papers presented by Canada to the *3rd Int. Conf. peaceful Uses Atom. Energy*, Geneva, 31 Aug.–9 Sept. (1964). *Atom. Energy Canada Ltd. Rep.* AECL–2005
[27] Reader, H. O. 'Tritium Used as a Ground-Water Tracer Between Lake McMillan and Major Johnson Springs, Eddy County, New Mexico'. *Geological Survey, Rep.* TEI–839 (June, 1963) Washington D.C.
[28] Bibron, R. (Thesis Presented to the Faculty of Science, Univ. of Paris, 29 June, 1964) *Centre D'Etudes Nucleaires De Saclay, Rep.* CEA–2629 (1965)
[29] Lewis, D. C. and Burgy, R. H. *J. geophys. Res.* 69 (1964) 2579
[30] Woods, F. W. and O'Neal, D. *Science, N.Y.* 147 (1965) 148
[31] Rothenberg, S. P. *Nature, Lond.* 206 (1965) 1154; *Analyt. biochem.* 13 (1965) 530
[32] Morris, M. D. *Analyt. Biochem.* 11 (1965) 402
[33] Biglieri, E. G. *Adv. Tracer Methodol.*, 2 (1965) 221. Plenum Press N.Y. (Ed. Rothchild, S.)
[34] Kliman, B. *Adv. Tracer Methodol.* 2 (1965) 213
[35] Bryan, G. T., Kliman, B., Bartter, F. C. and Diller, E. *J. clin. Invest.* 44 (1965) 957
[36] Peterson, R. E. and Eilers, E. A. *Proc. 2nd Int. Congr. Endocrinology*, London 17–22 Aug. 1964. *Int. Congr. Ser. 83* Ed. Taylor, S. Excepta Medica Foundation, London (1965), page 267
[37] Coghlan, J. P., Hudson, B., Wintour, M. and Dulmanis, A., as ref. 36, page 275
[38] Tait, J. F., Little, B., Tait, S. A. S., Riondel, A., Flood, C., Joachim, E. and Gut, M., as ref. 33, page 227
[38a] Solomon, S., Watanabe, M., Dominguez, O. V., Gray, M. J., Meeker, C. I. and Sims, E. A. H. *Biol. Clin. Aspects Placental Steroidogenesis*, Meeting Milan 1962; p. 32 (Publ. Karger, Basel/N.Y. 1964)
[39] Henderson, H. H., Crowley, F. and Gaudette, L. E., as ref. 33, page 83
[40] Horton, R. and Tait, J. F., as ref. 36, page 262
[41] Brownie, A. C., Van der Molen, H. J., Nishizawa, E. E. and Eik-Nes, K. B., (as ref. 36), page 279
[42] Exley, D. and Corker, C. S. *Biochem. J.* 96 (1965) 818
[43] Glomset, J. A. and Wright, J. L. *Biochim. biophys. Acta* 89 (1964) 266
[44] Barton, D. H. R., Kirby, G. W., Steglich, W., Thomas, G. M., Battersby, A. R., Dobson, T. A. and Ramuz, H. *J. chem. Soc.* (1965) 2423
[45] Barton, D. H. R., Kirby, A. J., Kirby, G. W. *Chem. Communs* (3) (1965) 52
[45a] Kirby, G. W. and Tiwari, H. P. *J. chem. Soc.* 7c (1966) 676
[46] Popjak, G. *Biochem. J.* 96 (1965) 1P
[47] Goodwin, T. W. *Biochem. J.* 96 (1965) 2P
[48] Cornforth, J. W., Cornforth, R. H., Donninger, C., Popjak, G., Shimizu, Y., Ichii, S., Forchielli, E. and Caspi, E. *J. Am. chem. Soc.* 87 (1965) 3224
[49] Stone, K. J. and Hemming, F. W. *Biochem. J.* 96 (1965) 14C
[50] Caporale, G., Breccia, A. and Rodighiero, G. *Prep. Bio-Medical Applic. Labelled Molecules*, European Atomic Energy Community, Euratom EUR 2200e (1964) page 103

413

APPENDIX

[51] Abbondanza, A., Breccia, A. and Crespi, A. (as ref. 50), page 95

[52] Greene, M. L., Kaneshiro, T. and Law, J. H. *Biochim. biophys. Acta* 98 (1965) 582

[52a] Änggärd, E. and Samuelsson, B. *J. biol. Chem.* 240 (1965) 3518

[53] Catch, J. R. (as ref. 50), page 303

[54] Iversen, L. L., Glowinski, J. and Axelrod, J. *Nature, Lond.* 206 (1965) 1222

[55] Gitlow, S. E., Mendlowitz, M., Wilk, E. K., Wilk, S., Wolf, R. L. and Naftchi, N. E. *J. clin. Invest.* 43 (1964) 2009

[56] Nyhan, W. L. and Childs, B. *J. clin. Invest.* 43 (1964) 2404

[57] Crawhall, J. C. *Chem. Soc. Ann. Reports* LXI (1964) 476

[58] Pearlman, W. H., in Hormonal Steroids I—Biochemistry, Pharmacology and Therapeutics. *Proc. 1st Int. Congr. Hormonal Steroids.* Ed. Martini, L and Pecile, A. 1964. N.Y. and London; Academic Press

[59] Raman, P. B., Sharma, D. C., Dorfman, R. I. and Gabrilove, J. L. *Biochemistry* 4 (1965) 1376

[60] Mancuso, S., Dell'Acqua, S., Eriksson, G., Wiqvist, N. and Diczfalusy, E. *Steroids* 5 (1965) 183

[61] Roberts, K. D., Bandi, L., Calvin, H. I., Drucker, W. D. and Lieberman, S. *J. Am. chem. Soc.* 86 (1964) 958; *cf.* Wu, H. L. C. and Mason, M. *Steroids* 5 (1965) 45

[62] Drayer, N. M. and Lieberman, S. *Biochem. biophys. Res. Commun* 18 (1965) 126

[63] Shimizu, K. *J. biol. Chem.* 240 (1965) 1941

[64] Thomas, P. J., Hsia, S. L., Matschiner, J. T., Thayer, S. A., Elliott, W. H., Doisy, E. A. (Jr.) and Doisy, E. A. *J. biol. Chem.* 240 (1965) 1059

[65] Berséus, O., Danielsson, H. and Kallner, A. *J. biol. Chem.* 240 (1965) 2396

[66] Kritchevsky, D., Werthessen, N. T., Shapiro, I. L., Nair, P. P. and Turner, D. A. *Nature, Lond.* 207 (1965) 194

[67] Eik-Nes, K. B. and Brizzee, K. R. *Biochem. biophys. Acta* 97 (1965) 320

[68] Avioli, L. V., McDonald, J. E., Lund, J. and Deluca, H. *J. clin. Invest.* 44 (1965) 1026 (Abstract only)

[69] Thompson, G. R., Lewis, B. and Booth, C. C. *J. clin. Invest.* 45 (1966) 94

[69a] Thompson, G. R., Lewis, B. and Booth, C. C. *Lancet* (7435) (1966) 457

[70] Page, E. (as ref. 33), page 179

[71] Granström, E., Ingar, U. and Samuelsson, B. *J. biol. Chem.* 240 (1965) 457

[72] Khan, A. A. and Wilson, J. E. *J. Neurochem.* 12 (1965) 81

[73] Crofford, O. B. and Renold, A. E. *J. biol. Chem.* 240 (1965) 14

[74] Goodman, D. S., Blomstrand, R., Werner, B., Huang, H. S. and Shiratori, T. *J. clin. Invest.* 44 (1965) 1054

[75] Nelp, W. B. and Bloom, P. M. *J. clin. Invest.* 44 (1965) 1080

[76] Hinds, F. C., Draper, H. H., Mitchell, G. E. and Neumann, A. L. *J. agric. Fd Chem.* 13 (1965) 256

[77] Graul, E. H. (as ref. 50), page 217

[78] Laurence, D. J. R. and Butler, J. A. V. *Biochem. J.* 96 (1965) 53

[79] Akai, H. and Kobayashi, M. *Nature, Lond.* 206 (1965) 847

[80] Roll, K. and Killmann, S. A. *Nature, Lond.* 205 (1965) 1235

[81] Bruce, W. R. and Meeker, B. E. *J. Can. Cancer Ass.* (In the press) Dept. of Biophys., Univ. of Toronto and Ontario Cancer Res. Inst. Toronto

[82] Koch, A. L. *Radiat. Res.* 24 (1965) 398

[82a] Sarkar, S. K. and Poddar, R. K. *Nature, Lond.* 207 (1965) 550

[83] Grillo, R. S., Urso, P. and O'Brian, D. M. *Expl Cell Res.* 37 (1965) 662

REFERENCES

84 Pachler, P. F., Koch, A. L., Schaechter, M. *J. molec. Biol.* 11 (1965) 650
85 Reich, E., Franklin, R. M., Shatkin, A. J. and Tatum, E. L. *Science, N.Y.* 134 (1961) 556
86 Perry, R. P. *Expl. Cell Res.* 29 (1963) 400
87 Cline, M. J. *J. clin. Invest.* 44 (1965) 1036
88 Kasten, F. H., Strasser, F. F. and Turner, M. *Nature, Lond.* 207 (1965) 161
89 Gellert, M., Smith, C. E., Neville, D. and Felsenfeld, G. *J. molec. Biol.* 11 (1965) 445
90 Bertino, J. R., Johns, D. G., Almquist, P., Hollingsworth, J. W. and Evans, E. A. *Nature, Lond.* 206 (1965) 1052
91 Creamer, B. and Shiner, M. *Lancet* (7391) (1965) 913
92 Campbell, R. D. *Science, N.Y.* 148 (1965) 1231
93 McConnell, C. H. *Science, N.Y.* 72 (1930) 170: *Biol. Bull. mar. biol. Lab.* 64 (1933) 86, 96; Schneider, K. C. *Arch. mikrosk. Anat. EntwMech.* 35 (1890) 321
94 Burnett, A. L. *J. exp. Zool.* 146 (1961) 21
95 Brien, P. and Reniers-Decoen, M. *Bull. biol. Fr. Belg.* 83 (1949) 293
95a Bond, V. P. and Feinendegen, L. E. *Fed. Proc. Fedn. Am. Socs. exp. Biol.* 23 (3, Pt. 1) (1964) 634
96 Pelc, S. R. and Appleton, T. C. *Nature, Lond.* 205 (1965) 1287
97 Wilson, J. D. and Loeb, P. M. *J. clin. Invest.* 44 (1965) 1111 (Abstract only)
98 Goldfeder, A. *Nature, Lond.* 207 (1965) 612
99 Lipkin, M., Bell, B., Sherlock, P. and Kim, Y. S. *J. clin. Invest.* 44 (1965) 1070 (Abstract only)
100 Ahnström, G. and Rosen, C.-G. *Acta chem. scand.* 19 (1965) 263
101 Okamoto, G. and Shibata, T. *Nature, Lond.* 206 (1965) 1350
102 Seminar on the Protection Against the Dangers of Tritium. French Section Health Physics Society, Central Service for the Protection against Ionizing Radiation, European Society for Protection against Radiation. Le Vesinet 16–18 April 1964 Ed. SCPRI
103 Dr. K. Z. Morgan, Director, Health Physics Division, Oak Ridge, Tennessee, U.S.A. (as ref. 102), page 1
104 Farber, T. M. *Analyt. Biochem.* 9 (1964) 483
105 Scharpenseel, H. W. *Atompraxis* 11 (1965) 147
106 Sims, R. T. *J. cell Biol.* 22 (1964) 403
107 Wimber, D. E., in *Adv. Radiat. Biol.* 1 (1964) 85. Ed. L. G. Augenstein, R. Mason and H. Quastler. N.Y. and London; Academic Press
108 Jones, J. R. *Lab. Pract.* 14 (1965) 433
109 Wang, C. H. and Willis, D. L. *Radiotracer Methodology in Biological Science* 1965. U.S.A.; Prentice-Hall Inc.
110 Koch, H., Seige, K., Löbe, H. and Hartmann, H. *Kernenergie* 7 (1964) 507
111 Uhlenhut, G. J. and Koch, H. *Kernenergie* 7 (1964) 504
112 Mercer, W. A. (Ed.) *U.S. A.E.C. Rep.* SAN-1023 (1964)
113 Gordon, B. E. and Madison, J. J. (as ref. 33), page 21
114 Parmentier, J. H. *J. Labelled Compounds* 1 (1965) 93
114a Crawford, B. R. and Garnett, L. *Aust. J. Chem.* 18 (1965) 1951
115 Parekh, C. K. and Wasserman, R. H. *J. Chromat.* 17 (1965) 261
116 Nash, J. B. *Univ. Calif. Radiat. Lab. Rep.* UCRL-16009 (April 1965)
117 Cardinaud, R., Takashima, K., Dausset, J. and Fromageot, P. *Int. J. appl. Radiat. Isotopes* 15 (1964) 1

415

[118] Makari, J. G. *Nature, Lond.* 205 (1965) 1178
[119] Cardinaud, R. and Bouchet, J.-C. *Bull. Soc. chim. France* (1965) 834
[120] Rabitzsch, G., Herzmann, H. *Justus Liebig's Annln Chem.* 685 (1965) 261
[121] Kirby, G. W. and Ogunkoya, L. *J. chem. Soc.* (1965) 6914
[122] Yun, H. B. and Moser, H. C. *J. phys. Chem.* 69 (1965) 1059
[123] Nordin, P., Moser, H. C. and Senne, J. K. *Biochem. J.* 96 (1965) 336
[124] Cardinaud, R., Grosse, N. and Fromageot, P. (as ref. 50), page 23
[125] Garnett, J. L., Law, S. W. and Till, A. R. *Aust. J. Chem.* 18 (1965) 297
[126] Swallow, A. J. *Radiation Chemistry of Organic Compounds* 1960. Oxford; Pergamon Press
[127] Trotman-Dickenson, A. F. *Disc. Faraday Soc.* 10 (1951) 111
[128] Dutton, H. J. and Nystrom, R. F. *Adv. Tracer Methodol.* 1 (1963) 18. Ed. S. Rothchild. New York; Plenum Press
[129] Yang, J. Y. and Gevantman, L. H. *J. phys. Chem.* 68 (1964) 3115
[130] Kandel, R. J. *J. chem. Phys.* 41 (1964) 2435
[131] Ishiguro, I. and Linzen, B. *Hoppe-Seyler's Z. physiol. Chem.* 340 (1965) 285
[132] Eisen, H. N. and Siskind, G. W. *Biochemistry*, 3 (1964) 996
[132a] Gosztonyi, T., Marton, J. and Kovacs, A. *Nature, Lond.* 208 (1965) 381
[133] LePage, G. A. and Junga, I. G. *Can. J. Chem.* 43 (1965) 1279
[134] Calf, G. E. and Garnett, J. L. *J. phys. Chem.* 68 (1964) 3887)
[135] Brown, H. C. and Brown, C. A. *J. Am. chem. Soc.* 84 (1962) 2827
[136] Klein, P. D. and Knight, J. C. *J. Am. chem. Soc.* 87 (1965) 2657
[136a] Klein, P. D. and Erenrich, E. H. *Analyt. chem.* 38 (1966) 480
[137] Otto, P. Ph. H. L. and Juppe, G. *J. Labelled Compounds* 1 (1965) 115
[138] Bardou, L. and Crastes de Paulet, A. *J. Labelled Compounds* 1 (1965) 54
[139] Mahadevan, V. and Lundberg, W. O. *J. Lipid Res.* 3 (1962) 106
[140] Schroepfer, G. J. and Bloch, K. *J. biol. Chem.* 240 (1965) 54
[141] Cornforth, J. W., Cornforth, R. H., Donninger, C. and Popjak, G. *Proc. Roy. Soc.* 163B (1966) 492
[142] Goodwin, T. W. and Williams, R. J. H. *Biochem. J.* 94 (1965) 5c
[142a] Goodwin, T. W. and Williams, R. J. H. *Proc. Roy. Soc.* 163B (1966) 515
[142b] Arigoni, D., Lynen, F. and Retey, J. *Helv. chim. Acta* 49 (1966) 311
[142c] Archer, B. L., Barnard, D., Cockbain, E. G., Cornforth, J. W., Cornforth, R. H. and Popjak, G. *Proc. Roy. Soc.* 163B (1966) 519
[143] Stoffel, W. *J. Am. Oil Chem. Soc.* 42 (1965) 569
[144] Birkofer, L., Hempel, K., Nouvertne, W. *J. Labelled Compounds* 1 (1965) 20
[145] Neta, P., Anbar, M. and Sela, M. *Israel Atom. Energy Comm. Rep.* IA–822 May 1963) 104
[146] Winand, M., Bricteux-Gregoire, S. and Verly, W. G., as ref. 50, page 17
[147] Hesselbo, T. *Int. J. appl. Radiat. Isotopes* 16 (1965) 329
[148] Agishi, Y., Dingman, J. F. *Biochem. biophys. Res. Commun* 18 (1965) 92
[149] Merrifield, R. B. *J. Am. chem. Soc.* 86 (1964) 304
[150] Merrifield, R. B. and Stewart, J. M. *Nature, Lond.* 207 (1965) 522
[150a] Merrifield, R. B. *Science N.Y.* 150 (1965) 178
[151] Weygand, F., Mayer, D. and Steglich, W. (as ref. 50), page 57
[151a] Matsuo, H. Fujimoto Y. and Tatsuno, T. *Tetrahedron Lett.* (1965) 3465
[152] Rosen, C.-G., Ehrenberg, L., Ahnström, G. *Nature, Lond.* 204 (1964) 796
[153] Collipp, P. J., Kaplan, S. A., Boyle, D. G., Shimizu, C. S. N. and Ling, S. M. *Nature, Lond.* 207 (1965) 876
[154] Collipp, P. J., Kaplan, S. A., Boyle, D. C. and Shimizu, C. S. N. *Metabolism* 13 (1964) 532; *J. biol. Chem.* 240 (1965) 143

REFERENCES

[155] Chen, P. S., Terepka, A. R. and Lane, K. *Proc. Soc. exp. Biol. Med.* 113 (1963) 584

[156] Gottschling, H. and Zachau, H. G. *Biochim. biophys. Acta* 103 (1965) 418

[156a] Leonis, J. European At. En. Community, *Euratom Rep.* EUR 1845f (1965)

[156b] Nunez, J., Mauchamp, J., Macchia, V., Jerusalmi, A. and Roche, J. *Biochem. biophys. Res. Commun.* 20 (1965) 71

[156c] Sassen, A., Gerber, G. B., Kennes, F. and Remy-Defraigne, *J. Radiat. Res.* 25 (1965) 158

[157] O'Brien, R. E. *Atomlight* (44) (1965) 10

[158] Kirby, G. W. and Shah, S. W. *Chem. Communs.* (16) (1965) 381

[159] Levitz, M. and Katz, J. *Steroids* 5 (1965) 11

[160] Levitz, M., Spitzer, J. R., Twombly, G. H. *J. biol. Chem.* 231 (1958) 787

[161] King, R. J. B., Gordon, J. and Inman, D. R. *J. Endocrin.* 32 (1965) 9

[161a] Dewey, W. C. and Humphrey, R. M. *Radiat. Res.* 26 (1965) 538

[161b] Schwarzacher, H. G. and Schnedl, W. *Nature, Lond.* 209 (1966) 108

[161c] Sharma, A. K. and Sharma, A. p. 214 *Chromosome Techniques-Theory and Practice*, 1965, London; Butterworths

[162] Von Schuching, S. and Frye, G. H. *J. org. Chem.* 30 (1965) 1288

[162a] Lehmann, J. *Angew. Chem.* 77 (1965) 863

[162b] Kalberer, F. *Atomlight* (51) (1966) 1

[163] Bevill, R. D., Hill, E. A., Smith, F. and Kirkwood, S. *Can. J. Chem.* 43 (1965) 1577

[164] *Labelled Compounds Bull.* L.C.4 June, 1965 European Atom. Energy Community, Euratom. [cf. Paoletti, C. and Lamonthezie, N. EUR 1625e (1964) 855]

[165] Behki, R. M. and Morgan, W. S. *Archs Biochem. Biophys.* 107 (1964) 427

[166] Gabrill, O. and Ashwell, G. *Fed. Proc. Fedn Am. Socs exp. Biol.* 23 (1964) 380 (Abstract only)

[166a] Marzluf, G. A. and Metzenberg, R. L. *Analyt. biochem.* 13 (1965) 168

[167] Rognstad, R., Kemp, R. G., Katz, J. *Archs Biochem. Biophys.* 109 (1965) 372

[168] Cahn, R. S., Ingold, C. K. and Prelog, V. *Experientia* 12 (1956) 81

[169] Groves, T. D. D. and Larson, B. L. *Biochim. biophys. Acta* 104 (1965) 462

[170] McFarlane, A. S., M.R.C. National Institute for Medical Research, Mill Hill, London. Personal communication

[171] Lee, E. K. C., Miller, G., Rowland, F. S. *J. Am. chem. Soc.* 87 (1965) 190

[172] Nesmeyanov, An. N., Tszyan, Tai-Van and Filatov, E. S. *Vest. mosk. gos. Univ.* No. 6 (1964) 27

[173] Nesmeyanov, An. N., Tai-Wang, C. and Filatov, E. S. *Soviet Radiochem.* 5 (1963) 476

[174] Urch, D. S. and Welch, M. J. *Chem. Communs.* (7) (1965) 126; *Trans. Faraday Soc.* 61 (1965) 1411

[175] Garland, J. K. and Rowland, F. S. *Radiochem. Acta* 4 (1965) 115

[176] Garland, J. K. *Diss. Abstr.* 25 (1964) 1598

[177] Avdonina, E. N. and Nesmeyanov, An. N. *Soviet Radiochem.* 5 (1963) 475

[178] Posdeev, V. V., Nesmeyanov, An. N. and Dzantiev, B. G. *Soviet Radiochem.* 5 (1963) 364

[179] Tang, Y-N. and Rowland, F. S. *J. Am. chem. Soc.* 87 (1965) 3304

[180] Dzantiev, B. G. and Shvedchikov, A. P. *Radiokhimiya* 7 (1965) 370

[180a] Avdonia, F. N., Nezmeyanov, An. N. and Wung, H-M. *Soviet Radiochemistry*, 6 (1964) 312

[180b] Tang, Y-N. *Diss. Abstr.* 26 (1965) 121

[180c] Wolfgang, R. *A. Rev. phys. Chem.* 16 (1965) 15

[180d] Root, J. W. *Diss. Abstr.* 26 (1965) 119

[180e] Tang, Y.-N. and Rowland, F. S. *J. phys. Chem.*, Ithaca 69 (1965) 4297

[180f] Root, J.W., Breckenridge, W. and Rowland, F. S. *J. chem. Phys.* 43 (1965) 3694

[180g] Schmidt-Bleek, F. and Rowland, F. S. *Angew. Chem.* 76 (1964) 901

[180h] Dzantiev, B. G. and Shvetchikov, A. P. *Soviet Radiochemistry* 6 (1964) 359

[180i] Avdonina, E. N. and Karasev, B. V. *Soviet Radiochemistry* 6 (1964) 613

[180j] Rodriguez Pasques, R. H. Argentine At. En. Commission, *Inform.* No. 153 (1965)

[181] Hammarström, L., Appelgren, L.-E. and Ullberg, S. *Expl Cell Res.* 37 (1965) 608

[182] Caro, L. G. and Schnös, M. *Science, N.Y.* 149 (1965) 60

[183] Tykva, R. and Vesely, J. *Coll. Czech. chem. Commun. Engl. edn* 30 (1965) 898

[184] Brady, R. O., Bradley, R. M., Young, O. M. and Kaller, H. *J. biol. Chem.* 240 (1965) PC3693

[185] Leblond, C. P. and Kopriwa, B. McGill University, Montreal, Canada (Personal communication)

[186] Verly, W. G. and Gerday, C. *J. Labelled Compounds* 1 (1965) 27

[187] Purdy, R. H., Goldman, N. L. and Richardson, G. S. *J. biol. Chem.* 240 (1965) 1573

[188] Contractor, S. F. and Wragg, J. *Nature, Lond.* 208 (1965) 71

[189] Cejka, V. and Venneman, E. M. *Clinica Chim. Acta* 11 (1965) 188

[190] Ulick, S. and Tait, J. F., in *Aldosterone* Ed. Baulieu, E.-E. and Robel, P. p. 6 *et seq.* 1964. Oxford; Blackwell

[191] Klein, P. D., Simborg, D. W. and Szczepanik, P. A. *Pure appl. Chem.* 8 (1964) 357

[192] Laragh, J. H. Sealey, J. E. and Klein, P. D. *I.A.E.A. Symp. on Radiochemical Methods of Analysis* Salzburg, Oct. 19–23 (1964) I.A.E.A. 2 (1965) 353

[193] Wilson, A. T. and Spedding, D. J. *J. Chromat.* 18 (1965) 76

[194] Luthi, U. and Waser, P. G. *Nature, Lond.* 205 (1965) 1190

[195] Luthi, U. Dr. Pharmakologisches Institut, University of Zurich, Switz. (Personal communication)

[196] Lambiotte, M. *C.r. hebd. Séanc. Acad. Sci.*, Paris 260 (1965) 1799; *Nature, Lond.* 207 (1965) 516

[197] Miettinen, T. A., Ahrens, E. H., Grundy, S. M. *J. Lipid Res.* 6 (1965) 411

[198] Craig, L. C. and Craig, D., in *Technique of Organic Chemistry* Vol. III (1) 2nd ed, p. 268 (149) 1956. New York; Interscience

[199] Radiochemical Centre—Unpublished results

[200] Angyal, S. J., Fernandez, C. M., Garnett, J. L. *Aust. J. Chem.* 18 (1965) 39

[201] Ciranni, E., Ciranni, G. and Guarino, A. *Gazz. chim. ital.* 95 (1965) 52

[202] Popenoe, E. A., Aronson, R. B. and van Slyke, D. D. *J. biol. Chem.* 240 (1965) 3089

[203] Shatenshtein, A. I., Yakushin, F. S., Arshinova, M. I. and Yakovleva, E. A. *Kinet. Katal.* 5 (1964) 1000 (Russian)

[204] Kirschner, M. A. and Lipsett, M. B. *J. Lipid Res.* 6 (1965) 7

[205] Sgoutas, D. S. and Kummerow, F. A. *J. Chromat.* 16 (1964) 448

[206] Goutier, R. Paper Presented at the 'Colloquium on Chemical Stability and Biological Uses of Tritiated Pyrimidine Nucleosides', European Atomic Energy Community, Euratom, Mol (Belgium) 16–18 March, 1965.

[206a] Baugnet-Mahieu, L., Goutier, R. and Semal, M. *Arch. Intern. physiol. Biochem.* 72 (1964) 312

[207] Leach, S. J., Hill, J. and Holt, L. A. *Biochemistry* 3 (1964) 737

[208] Evans, E. A. *Nature, Lond.* 209 (1966) 169, 196

[209] Kamal, A. and Garrison, W. M. *Nature, Lond.* 206 (1965) 1315

[210] Ciranni, G., Guarino, A., Pizzella, R. and Possagno, E. *J. Labelled Compounds* 1 (1965) 1

[211] Haigh, W. G. and Hanahan, D. J. *Biochim. biophys. Acta* 98 (1965) 640

[211a] Thompson, G. A. *J. biol. Chem.* 240 (1965) 1912

[212] Guarino, A., Pizzella, R., Possagno, E. *J. Labelled Compounds* 1 (1965) 10

[213] Ciranni, G., Guarino, A., Pizzella, R., Possagno, E., Rabe, B. and Rabe, G. European atomic Energy Community—*Euratom Rep.* EUR 2452e (1965)

[214] Smith, G. *Pharm. J.* 194 (1965) 219

[215] Moody, G. J. and Thomas, D. R. *Nature, Lond.* 206 (1965) 613

[216] Sgoutas, D., Kim, M. J. and Kummerow, F. A. *J. Lipid Res.* 6 (1965) 383

[217] Ono, K. and Fredrickson, D. S. *J. biol. Chem.* 239 (1964) 2482

[218] Evans, M. C. W. *Biochem. J.* 95 (1965) 661

[219] Leng, R. A. and Leonard, G. J. *Nature, Lond.* 207 (1965) 760

[220] Dr. S. F. Contractor, Queen Charlotte's Maternity Hospital, London. (Personal communication)

[221] Kadis, B. *Steroids* 5 (1965) 319

[222] Björkhem, I., Dannielsson, H., Issidorides, C. and Kallner, A., Unpublished results, see ref. 65

[222a] Floss, H. G., Mothes, U. and Günther, H. *Z. Naturf.* 196 (1964) 784

[223] Margolis, R. U. and Heller, A. *Biochim. biophys. Acta* 98 (1965) 438

[224] Roberts, J. J. and Warwick, G. P. *Biochem. J.* 93 (1964) 18P

[224a] Mirolli, M. *Science, N.Y.* 149 (1965) 1503

[225] Lee, K. Y., Lijinsky, W., Magee, P. N. *J. natn. Cancer Inst.* 32 (1964) 65

[225a] Stone, J. E. and Clayton, D. W. *Pulp. Paper. Mag. Can.* 65 (1964) 3531

[225b] Fischer, J. E., Weise, V. K. and Kopin, I. J. *Nature, Lond.* 209 (1966) 778

[226] Cantoni, G. L. *Biochem. Prep.* 5 (1957) 58. New York; Wiley

[227] Bastos, A. L., Nunes, J. F. M., Terrinha, A. M. and Baptista, A. M. *Acta cytol.* 9 (1965) 234

[228] Van den Bosch, H., Postema, N. M., De Haas, G. H. and Van Deenen, L. L. M. *Biochim. biophys. Acta* 98 (1965) 657

[228a] Bayly, R. J. and Evans, E. A. *J. Labelled Compounds* 2 (1966) 1

TRITIUM MEASUREMENT BIBLIOGRAPHY

A. Beta Liquid Scintillation Measurement

[229] Apelgot, S. European Atomic Energy Community, *Euratom Rep.* EUR 2459. f (1965). 'Measurement of Radioactivity by Scintillation in a Liquid Medium: Biological Uses'

[230] Baggett, B., Presson, T. L., Presson, J. B. and Coffey, J. C. *Analyt. Biochem.* 10 (1965) 367. 'Correction for Quenching of Samples from Oxygen Flask Combustion Method for Tritium Analysis'

[231] Bibron, R. Centre D'Etudes Nucleaires De Saclay *CEA*–2629 (1965). 'Detection of Atmospheric Tritium by Scintillation. Variations in its Concentration in France'

[232] Birks, J. B. *Theory and Practice of Scintillation Counting* 1964. Oxford; Pergamon Press

APPENDIX

[233] Brown, B. L. and Reith, W. S. *Biochim. Biophys. Acta* 97 (1965) 378. 'Determination of ^{3}H in Substances Containing a Large Amount of ^{131}I-activity'

[233a] Carr, R. J. and Gordon, B. E. *J. polymer Sci.* Pt. C8 (1965) 71. 'Determination of Polyacrolein Labelled with Tritium or Carbon-14'

[233b] Christman, D. R. *Nucleonics* 23 (12) (1965) 39. 'Measuring Radio-isotopes in Organic Compounds.' (A review)

[233c] Corti, F. *Istituto Superiore Di Sanita Rep.* ISS 65/8 Pt. I and ISS 65/9 Pt. II (March 24, 1965). 'Determination of Tritium Content in Samples.' (A review)

[233d] Cramer, W. A., Houtman, J. P. W., Koch, R. O. and Piet, G. J. *Int. J. appl. Radiat. Isotopes* 17 (1966) 97. 'Measurement of Radioactivity in Effluents of a Gas Chromatograph.'

[234] Daruschy, P. *Atompraxis* 11 (1965) 273. 'A Rapid and Simple Method for the Detection of Tritium in Biological Material'

[234a] Davies, J. W. and Cocking, E. C. *Biochim. biophys. Acta* 115 (1966) 511. 'Liquid Scintillation Counting of ^{14}C and ^{3}H samples using Glass-fibre or Filter-paper Discs'

[235] Dobbs, H. E. *A.E.R.E., Harwell Rep.* AERE-M 1574 (1965); 'Dispensing Solutions for Liquid Scintillation Counting'

[236] Fallot, P., Girgis, A., Laine-Böszörmenyi, M. and Vieuchange, J. *Int. J. appl. Radiat. Isotopes* 16 (1965) 349. 'Use of a Liquid Scintillation Spectrometer for the Direct Measurement of the Radioactivity of Tritium Incorporated in the Cells of Mammals Cultivated *in vitro*.'

[236a] Franc, Z., Svobodova, J., Francova, V., Lipovska, M. and Horesovsky, C. *Coll. Czech. chem. Commun.* 30 (1965) 2875. 'Measurement of Soft β-radiation in Biological Material with the Aid of Liquid Scintillators Part 2. Determination of ^{14}C and ^{3}H by Oxidation in Oxygen Atmosphere'

[237] Furlong, N. B., Williams, N. L. and Willis, D. P. *Biochim. biophys. Acta* 103 (1965) 341. 'Enhancement of Tritium-counting Efficiency on Paper Discs after Incorporation into (^{3}H) DNA'

[238] Garfinkel, S. B., Mann, W. B., Medlock, R. W. and Yura, O. *Int. J. appl. Radiat. Isotopes* 16 (1965) 27. The Calibration of the National Bureau of Standards 'Tritiated-toluene Standard of Radioactivity'

[239] Hattori, T., Aoki, H., Matsuzaki, I., Maruo, B. and Takahashi, H. *Analyt. Chem.* 37 (1965) 159. 'Liquid Scintillation Counting of ^{3}H-nucleic Acids'

[240] Hattori, T., Aoki, H., Matsuzaki, I., Takahashi, H. and Maruo, B. *Radio-Isotopes, Tokyo* 14 (1965) 148. 'Selection of the Effective Detergent for the Decontamination of Vials of the Liquid Scintillation Spectrometer'

[240a] Hoffmann, W. *Radiochim. Acta* 4 (1965) 222. 'Measuring Low-energetic β-rays in Heterogenous Phase with Liquid Scintillators' (In German)

[241] Houtman, A. C. *Int. J. appl. Radiat. Isotopes* 16 (1965) 65. 'Liquid Scintillation Counting of Blood'

[242] Houtman, A. C. *Preparation and Bio-Medical Applications of Labelled Molecules*, European Atomic Energy Community, Euratom EUR 2200. e (1964) page 297. 'Determination of ^{3}H and ^{14}C in Blood'

[243] Iwakura, T., Kasida, Y. and Morisaki, N. *Radio-Isotopes, Tokyo* 14 (1965) 132. '^{14}C and ^{3}H Measurement by the Use of a Liquid Scintillation

Spectrometer. Determination of the Counting Efficiency by the Discriminator Ratio Method'

[244] Kasida, Y. and Iwakura, T. *Radio-Isotopes, Tokyo* 14 (1965) 152. 'Recent Advances in Liquid Scintillation Counting'

[245] Knoche, H. W. and Bell, R. M. *Analyt. Biochem.* 12 (1965) 49. 'Tritium Assay by Combustion with Novel Oxygen Train and Liquid Scintillation Techniques'

[246] Kusama, K. *Radio-Isotopes, Tokyo* 14 (1965) 142. 'An Improved Method for Liquid Scintillation Counting of Biological Compounds in Aqueous Solution'

[246a] Le Pape, M. and Emmanuel, H. At. En. Commission (Fr.) *Ser. Bibliog.* No. 38 (1963). 'Techniques for the Detection and Measurement of Tritium and its Compounds'

[246b] Mahin, D. T. *Int. J. appl. Radiat. Isotopes* 17 (1966) 185, 'A New Way to Reduce Oxygen Quenching in Liquid Scintillation Samples'

[247] Mattijsen, C. and Goldzieher, J. W. *Analyt. Biochem.* 10 (1965) 401. 'Precision and Reliability in Liquid Scintillation Counting'

[247a] Mercer, N. J. H. and Henderson, J. F. *Analyt. biochem.* 13 (1965) 559. 'Selective Elution of Scintillating Phosphors from Chromatography Paper following Radioactivity Measurements'

[248] Miwa, H., Morita, I., Kasai, T., Yamamoto, Y., Horio, H., Hino, N. and Asayama, Y. *Radio-Isotopes, Tokyo* 14 (1965) 126. '200 Sample-changer Liquid Scintillation Counter with Channel Ratio Computer'

[249] Nagai, T. *Radio-Isotopes, Tokyo* 14 (1965) 166. 'Large Volume Liquid Scintillation Counter'

[250] Nakshbandi, M. M. *Int. J. appl. Radiat. Isotopes* 16 (1965) 157. 'Plastic Scintillator Method for Radioassay of ^{3}H- and ^{14}C-Labelled Compounds on filter Paper'

[251] Patterson, M. S. and Greene, R. C. *Analyt. Chem.* 37 (1965) 854. 'Measurement of Low Energy Beta-emitters in Aqueous Solution by Liquid Scintillation Counting of Emulsions'

[252] Peng, C. T. *Atomlight* No. 44 (1965) 1. 'Quenching Correction in Liquid Scintillation Counting'

[252a] Petroff, C. P., Patt, H. H. and Nair, P. P. *Int. J. appl. Radiat. Isotopes* 16 (1965) 599. 'A Rapid Method for Dissolving Tissue for Liquid Scintillation Counting'

[252b] Perry, S. and Moxley, J. H. *Nature, Lond.* 209 (1966) 882. 'Investigations of Leucocyte Kinetics in Normal and Leukaemic Individuals by means of Scintillation Counting'

[253] Scharpenseel, H. W. and Pietig, F. *Atompraxis* 11 (1965) 98. 'Inorganic Scintillators for ^{14}C and ^{3}H-measurement in Radiocolumn Chromatography Flow Cell'

[254] Spratt, J. L. *Int. J. appl. Radiat. Isotopes* 16 (1965) 439. 'Computer Program for Calculation of Liquid Scintillation Counting Data'

[254a] Thomas, R. C., Judy, R. W. and Harpootlian, H. *Analyt. biochem.* 13 (1965) 358. 'Dispenser for Addition of Internal Standard in Liquid Scintillation Counting'

[255] Tsurufuji, S., Takahashi, A., Uchida, M. and Takagi, K. *Radio-Isotopes Tokyo* 14 (1965) 146. 'A Combustion Method for Liquid Scintillation Counting of ^{3}H-labelled Biological Materials'

[256] Vasvari, G. *Int. J. appl. Radiat. Isotopes* 16 (1965) 327. 'A New Wavelength Shifter for Liquid and Plastic Scintillators'
[256a] Wright, E. and Millar, K. R. *Nature, Lond.* 208 (1965) 889. 'Use of Dimethyl Sulphoxide in Liquid Scintillation Counting'
[256b] Yamazaki, M., Ishihama, H. and Kasida, Y. *Int. J. appl. Radiat. Isotopes* 17 (1966) 134. 'Tritium Measurement with a Liquid Scintillation Counter. The Application of the Oxygen-flask Combustion Method to a Strong Coloured Sample'
[256c] Yang, J. Y. *Polymer Letters* 4 (1966) 21 'Radioassay of Tritium and ^{14}C-Labelled Polymer'

B. Other Methods

[257] Bleecken, S., Kaufmann, G. and Kummer, K. *J. Chromat.* 19 (1965) 105. 'Quantitative Determination of Tritium Labelled Compounds on Thin Layer Chromatograms'
[257a] von Buttlar, H. and Wiik, B. *Science, N. Y.* 149 (1965) 1371. 'Enrichment of Tritium by Thermal Diffusion and Measurement of Dated Antarctic Snow Samples'
[258] Drobinski, J. C., La Gatta, D. P., Goldin, A. S. and Terrill, J. G. *Hlth Phys.* 11 (1965) 385. 'Analyses of Environmental Samples for Carbon-14 and Tritium'
[259] Erbe, H. *Nucl. Instrum. Meth.* 33 (1965) 169. 'A Gas-flow Counter with Variable Sensitive Area for Low-level Beta Counting'
[260] Gabriel, O. *Analyt. Biochem.* 10 (1965) 143. 'Specific Activity Determination of Radioactive Formic Acid'
[261] Jordan, P. and Lykourézos, Ph. A. P. *Helv. chim. Acta* 48 (1965) 581. 'Total Conversion of Organic Compounds into Gaseous Products for Simultaneous Determination of ^3H and ^{14}C in Proportional Counting Tubes'
[261a] Ito, S. *Radio-Isotopes, Tokyo* 14 (1965) 525. 'The Direct Counting Method of Tritium-Tagged Compounds in Blood with 2π-gas Flow Counter'
[262] Jordan, P. *Nucleonics* 23 (11) (1965) 46. 'Simultaneous Gas-Proportional Counting of H^3 and C^{14}'
[263] Jordan, P. and Lykourézos, Ph. A. P. *Int. J. appl. Radiat. Isotopes* 16 (1965) 631. 'Precise Method for the Routine Determination of ^{14}C and H^3 in Proportional Counting Tubes'
[264] Jordan, P., Köberle, P. and Lykourézos, Ph. A. P. *Mikrochim. Ichnoanalyt. Acta* (1965) 660. 'Determination of ^3H and ^{14}C in Organic Compounds with the Aid of Proportional Counting Tubes'
[265] Seimiya, T., Sekine, K. and Sasaki, T. *J. scient. Instrum.* 42 (1965) 906. 'Counting of Tritium with a Thin Windowed Geiger–Müller Counter Tube'
[265a] Sommerville, I. F. and Collins, W. P. *Steroids* (Suppl. 2) (1965) 223. 'Steroid Gas-liquid Radiochromatography: Continuous Monitoring of the Effluent for Carbon-14 and Tritium'
[266] Snyder, F. and Kimble, H. *Analyt. Biochem.* 11 (1965) 510. 'An Automatic Zonal Scraper and Sample Collector for Radioassay of Thin-layer Chromatograms'
[267] Yura, O. and Kimura, M. *Oyo Butsuri* 33 (1964) 342. 'Absolute Determination of Radioactivity of Tritium by Micro-calorimetry'

INDEX OF COMPOUNDS

Compounds are listed alphabetically; those which are recorded in the *Isotope Directory*[1] or the *Isotope Index*[2] as being commercially available labelled with tritium, are marked with an asterisk.

INDEX OF COMPOUNDS

INDEX OF COMPOUNDS

435

REFERENCES

[1] *International Directory of Isotopes* 3rd Edn. (1964). I.A.E.A. Vienna.

[2] *The Isotope Index 1963-1964*. Ed. J. L. Sommerville. Pub. Indianapolis, Indiana, U.S.A., Scientific Equipment Co.

SUBJECT INDEX

SUBJECT INDEX